D1134746

REFRESHER

MATHEMATICS

with PRACTICAL APPLICATIONS

EDWIN I. STEIN

1967

ALLYN AND BACON, INC.

Boston Rockleigh, N. J. Atlanta Dallas Belmont, Calif.

Refresher Mathematics is the new title for
the latest edition of *Refresher Arithmetic*

© Copyright, 1965 by

ALLYN AND BACON, INC.

PREFACE

The publication of *Refresher Mathematics* replaces *Refresher Arithmetic*. However, the new text retains the entire content and all the features of *Refresher Arithmetic* which was originally designed for use in arithmetic classes at any grade level to develop and maintain a high level of proficiency in arithmetic skills.

While the subject of arithmetic still receives considerable emphasis in *Refresher Mathematics,* there is a comprehensive treatment of other branches of mathematics including background, enrichment, and optional material in contemporary mathematics. With the extension of the keying of inventory tests to these other subject areas, this text, just as its title *Refresher Mathematics* implies, is ideal as a refresher or remedial textbook in elementary general mathematics with emphasis on arithmetic. The new inventory tests allow teachers to diagnose pupil difficulties with ease. *Refresher Mathematics* may also be used as a basal textbook featuring individualized assignments according to each student's need.

Refresher Mathematics is divided into five parts. In Part I, Decimal System of Numeration, the exercises are arranged under unit topics. For each exercise the text gives (I) the aim, (II) the procedure to be followed, (III) sample solutions completely worked out, and wherever necessary (IV) the definitions of terms used. Following this developmental material come the diagnostic tests, keyed to the immediately succeeding practice examples.

The examples in the diagnostic tests and the related practice examples are closely calibrated in difficulty. Step by step, because one example is not perceptibly more difficult than the preceding one, the pupil is led to think clearly, to develop a full understanding of mathematical concepts, and to experience the pride of success. The final examples in each exercise provide an automatic end test.

Included in Part I are four inventory tests in arithmetic and one inventory test in contemporary arithmetic, all keyed to the exercises that follow. They are used to diagnose general difficulties. Four keyed achievement tests which serve as mastery tests close this section.

In Part II ancient and modern non-decimal systems of numeration are studied so that pupils may develop a better understanding of the decimal system and lay a foundation for the future study of the computer.

Units of measurement, informal geometry, and numerical trigonometry are studied in Part III. Inventory tests direct each pupil to the topics for which he requires help. Problems follow the practice examples in the exercises of Parts I and III and show the value and uses of the related skills and principles. The applications are functional and interesting. They may be used to introduce topics and to motivate instruction.

In Part IV the number system is extended to include positive and negative numbers. The language of algebra, the solution of equations and inequalities, the graphing on the number line of equations and inequalities in one variable, and ratio and proportion are studied. Statistics include the bar, line, and circle graphs, averages, and the study of probability. An inventory test helps to direct each pupil to the practice he requires.

Part V is a complete unit on everyday problems. It includes applications of all types. This section is very useful in consumer mathematics classes.

Elementary concepts of contemporary arithmetic are studied throughout the text. They include number and numeral, number line, properties of number and operation, number sentences, sets, inequalities, tests for divisibility, scientific notation, repeating decimals, modular arithmetic, number theory, precision and accuracy, significant digits, and approximate numbers, among other topics.

Maintenance tests, called "Refresh Your Skills," and reviews are provided throughout the book.

The carefully planned, flexible organization of *Refresher Mathematics* allows for individual differences and at the same time provides maximum and minimum materials for modern group methods of instruction. Each pupil is directed quickly to his own assignment. Since pupils do not waste time drilling on examples that they can solve without difficulty, this system of individualized assignments accelerates individual achievement. Sufficient practice material for class, home, and optional assignments is included.

The author acknowledges his indebtedness to the *Philadelphia Inquirer* for permitting him to use the picture of the 24-hour clock. He is deeply grateful to his many associates for their valuable suggestions.

EDWIN I. STEIN

CONTENTS

PART I. DECIMAL SYSTEM OF NUMERATION

INTRODUCTION

Counting, 2; Number Symbols, 3; Word Names for Numbers, 3; Decimal System of Numeration, 4; Operations, 5; Properties: Commutative and Associative, 5–6; Distributive, 7; Closure, 7; of Zero, 8; of One, 8

UNIT I. WHOLE NUMBERS

Tests for Divisibility, 60; Averages, 62; Review, 64

ADDITIONAL TOPICS

Odd and Even Numbers, 66; Prime and Composite Numbers, 67; Sets, 69; Subsets, 71; Operations with Sets, 73; Factors and Factoring, 75; Number Multiples, 77; Expanded Notation, 79; Number Sentences, 81; Modular Arithmetic, 82; Miscellaneous Practice Problems, 85

UNIT II. COMMON FRACTIONS

v

UNIT III. DECIMAL FRACTIONS

UNIT IV.   PER CENT

UNIT V.   SQUARES AND SQUARE ROOTS

PART II.   ANCIENT AND NON-DECIMAL MODERN SYSTEMS OF NUMERATION

PART III. BASIC UNITS OF MEASURE, INFORMAL GEOMETRY, NUMERICAL TRIGONOMETRY

PART IV. ALGEBRA, RATIO AND PRO-PORTION, STATISTICS

PART V.   EVERYDAY PROBLEMS

PART I

DECIMAL SYSTEM OF NUMERATION

INTRODUCTION

Counting

The primitive people who lived many, many years ago did not know how to count. They did not write number symbols or speak number names.

These primitive people used to match animals and objects one-by-one with pebbles or with their fingers. Although a primitive shepherd could not name or indicate by some symbol how many sheep he had, he could tell by his corresponding tally of pebbles or fingers whether any sheep were missing upon their return from pasture.

It is interesting to note that the word *calculate* is derived from the Latin word calculus meaning pebble and the word *digit* from digitus meaning finger.

Later number names were developed to represent numbers. Sometimes names of things containing the same quantity were used. The word for two in Tibet is the same as the word meaning wings and in China it is the same as the word meaning ears.

When people began to trade, a system of counting was developed. Counting devices were used. One was a wax- or sand-covered board on which symbols were marked with a stylus. The Romans used a table marked with lines. To count they placed counters between these lines. The Chinese and Japanese still use a counting device, called an abacus, consisting of a frame with moveable beads on wires.

In counting there is exact pairing or matching or one-to-one correspondence between objects that are being counted and the set of counting numbers. See page 18.

Number Symbols

After people learned to count, they developed number symbols so that they could make permanent records. Clay tablets have been found containing "cuneiform" number symbols which were written more than 5,000 years ago by the Babylonians. The British Museum has in its possession an arithmetic manuscript on a roll of papyrus, said to have been written about 4,000 years ago by Ahmes, an Egyptian.

Number symbols were expressed in many ways.

The Babylonians (see page 272) used repeated wedge-shaped symbols; the Egyptians (see page 272) used a different grouping symbol for 1, 10, 100, etc.; the Mayans (see page 273) used combinations of dots and horizontal bars; the Romans (see page 276) used the symbols I, V, X, L, C, D, and M; the Greeks and Hebrews used the letters of their respective alphabets. For the Chinese traditional number symbols see page 273.

We use the number symbols of the Hindu-Arabic System. These symbols were introduced in Europe during the 12th century and are now used generally throughout the world. They were brought to the United States by the colonists. In this system there are ten symbols: 0, 1, 2, 3, 4, 5, 6, 7, 8, and 9. Each of these number symbols is called a digit or figure.

The number symbols we write to represent numbers are not numbers but names for numbers which we call numerals. Number is an abstract idea. We cannot see or write a number. Although it is usually called a number, technically 25 is a numeral or group of number symbols which represent the number named *twenty-five*. A number may be represented by symbols in many ways; it has many names. The number named twenty-five may be represented by 25 or XXV or $13 + 12$ or 5^2, etc. It should be noted however, that number symbols are generally used to denote both numbers and numerals as "Add the numbers 35 and 54" and "Write the numeral 796."

Word Names for Numbers

Most civilized people throughout the world use the same number symbols 0, 1, 2, 3, 4, 5, 6, 7, 8, and 9 but some differ in writing and speaking word names for numbers because of their respective languages.

Here are the word names for whole numbers from one to ten inclusive in several different languages:

	English	French	Spanish	Italian	German
1	one	un	uno	uno	eins
2	two	deux	dos	due	zwei
3	three	trois	tres	tre	drei
4	four	quatre	cuatro	quattro	vier
5	five	cinq	cinco	cinque	fünf
6	six	six	seis	sei	sechs
7	seven	sept	siete	sette	sieben
8	eight	huit	ocho	otto	acht
9	nine	neuf	nueve	nove	neun
10	ten	dix	diez	dieci	zehn

Decimal System of Numeration

A system of numeration is a method of naming numbers by writing numerals.

In our system of numeration, called the decimal system, ten number symbols, 0, 1, 2, 3, 4, 5, 6, 7, 8, and 9, are used to represent all numbers. There is no single number symbol in our notation system for the number ten or for numbers greater than ten. The numerals representing numbers greater than nine are formed by writing two or more number symbols next to each other in different positions or places.

Our system of numeration is built on the base ten. The base of a system of numeration is the number it takes in any one place to make 1 in the next higher place. In the decimal system it takes ten in any one place to make 1 in the next higher place. It takes 10 ones to make 1 ten, 10 tens to make 1 hundred, 10 hundreds to make 1 thousand, and so forth.

The decimal system is a positional system. Instead of a special symbol to represent each power of ten it uses place value. The value of each place in the decimal number scale is ten times the value of the next place to the right. (See page 19.) Thus in a numeral the value of each symbol depends not only on what the symbol is but also on its position in the numeral. The symbol 4 in the decimal numeral 47 means 4 tens but in a decimal numeral 427 it means 4 hundreds.

A numeral may be written as a sum of terms called a polynomial. Each digit is expressed as a product of the digit and a power of ten. (See page 80.)

Some ancient systems of numeration used different grouping symbols instead of place value. See page 272. Other modern systems of numeration each have number symbols uniquely belonging to it. See page 277.

Operations

In arithmetic we use the operations of addition, subtraction, multiplication and division. In each case we are operating with two numbers to get a third number. This is called a binary operation.

Operations that undo each other are called inverse operations· It can be shown that addition and subtraction are inverse operations and that multiplication and division are inverse operations because they undo each other. Addition and multiplication are considered to be principal operations with subtraction the inverse operation of addition and division the inverse operation of multiplication.

Properties

Operations have certain characteristics or properties.

1. Commutative Property of Addition

Adding 5 and 6 gives the same sum as adding 6 and 5.

$$\text{That is, } 5 + 6 = 6 + 5$$

The order we use in adding two numbers does not affect the sum. The commutative property of addition states that when we add one number to a second number we get the same sum as when we add the second number to the first.

2. Associative Property of Addition

Only two addends may be added at any one time. When there are three addends, we must first select two addends, find their sum, and add the third addend to this sum.

$5 + 6 + 4$ may be thought of as either:

$$(5 + 6) + 4 \quad \text{or} \quad 5 + (6 + 4)$$

The associative property of addition permits us to group or associate the first and second numbers and add their sum to the third number or to group or associate the second and third numbers and add their sum to the first number. Either way we get the same final sum.

3. Commutative Property of Multiplication

Multiplying 5 by 6 is the same as multiplying 6 by 5.

$$\text{That is, } 5 \times 6 = 6 \times 5$$

The order we use in multiplying two numbers does not affect the product. The commutative property of multiplication states that when we multiply one number by a second number we get the same product as when we multiply the second number by the first number.

4. Associative Property of Multiplication

Only two factors may be multiplied at any one time. When there are three factors, we must first select two factors, find their product, and then multiply this product by the third factor.

$5 \times 6 \times 4$ may be thought of as either:

$$(5 \times 6) \times 4 \quad \text{or} \quad 5 \times (6 \times 4)$$

The associative property of multiplication permits us to group or associate the first and second numbers and multiply their product by the third number or to group or associate the second and third numbers and multiply their product by the first number. We get the same final product in each case.

5. Distributive Property of Multiplication over Addition

To find the product of $5 \times (3 + 7)$ we may find the sum of 3 and 7 and then multiply this sum (10) by 5.

$$5 \times (3 + 7) = 5 \times 10 = 50$$

Or we may multiply the 3 by 5 and the 7 by 5 and add the products.

$$5 \times (3 + 7) = (5 \times 3) + (5 \times 7) = 15 + 35 = 50$$

Either way we get the same final result.

The distributive property of multiplication over addition states that when we multiply one number by the sum of a second and a third number we get the same result as when we add the product of the first and second numbers to the product of the first and third numbers. Multiplication is being distributed over addition.

We use the distributive property in computation such as 2×23.

$$2 \times 23 = 2 \times (20 + 3) = (2 \times 20) + (2 \times 3) = 40 + 6 = 46$$

or
$$\frac{23}{\times 2} = \frac{20 + 3}{\times 2} = \frac{20}{\times 2} + \frac{3}{\times 2}$$

We also use the distributive property in the following:

$$(9 \times 6) + (9 \times 4) = 9 \times (6 + 4)$$

or
$$(6 \times 9) + (4 \times 9) = (6 + 4) \times 9$$

6. Closure

When we add the whole numbers 5 and 4, the sum is the whole number 9. When we multiply the whole numbers 6 and 7, the product is the whole number 42. However, when we subtract the whole number 8 from the whole number 3, the answer is the integer -5. See page 487. When we divide the whole number 6 by the whole number 4, the answer is the mixed number $1\frac{1}{2}$.

If we, using all numbers in a given set, add any two numbers (or subtract or multiply or divide) and get as our answer in every case one of the numbers described in the given set, we say the set is *closed* under that operation. This property is called closure.

Thus we see above that the set of whole numbers is closed under addition and multiplication but not under subtraction and division.

7. Properties of Zero

(a) When we add zero (0) to any number, the number remains unchanged. The sum of 5 and 0 is 5. A number which, when added to a given number, does not change the given number is called the additive identity (or identity element for addition). Therefore zero (0) is the additive identity.

(b) Zero subtracted from any number is the number. $6 - 0 = 6$

(c) The difference between any number and itself is zero. $9 - 9 = 0$

(d) The product of any number and zero is zero. $3 \times 0 = 0$; $0 \times 8 = 0$; $0 \times 0 = 0$

(e) If the product of two numbers is zero, then one of the factors is zero or both factors are zero.

(f) If zero is divided by any number other than zero, the quotient is zero. $0 \div 2 = 0$

(g) In arithmetic division by zero is excluded.

8. Properties of One

(a) When we multiply any number by one (1), the number remains unchanged. 5 times 1 is 5. A number which, when multiplied by a given number, does not change the given number is called the multiplicative identity (or the identity element for multiplication). Therefore one (1) is the multiplicative identity.

(b) When any number, except zero, is divided by itself, the quotient is one. Thus one may be expressed in symbols as any one of the following:

$$\tfrac{1}{1}, \ \tfrac{2}{2}, \ \tfrac{3}{3}, \ \tfrac{4}{4}, \ \tfrac{5}{5}, \ \tfrac{6}{6}, \text{ etc.}$$

(c) One raised to any power is one. For example:

$$1^5 = 1 \times 1 \times 1 \times 1 \times 1 = 1$$

(d) The multiplicative identity one (1) is used to change the form of fractions to lower terms (page 89), and to higher terms (page 95); to divide fractions and mixed numbers (pages 127 and 128), and to divide by a decimal (page 182).

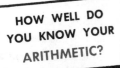

HOW WELL DO YOU KNOW YOUR ARITHMETIC?

TRY THE EXAMPLES IN EACH OF THE INVENTORY TESTS ON THE FOLLOWING PAGES.

IF YOUR DIFFICULTY IS WITH THE SAME KIND OF EXAMPLE IN ALL TESTS, YOU HAVE LOCATED A WEAKNESS.

IF YOU HAVE DIFFICULTY WITH ANY EXAMPLES IN THESE TESTS. YOU NEED HELP.

TO GET THIS HELP

SEE PAGE **17.**

1. Read the numeral 5,374,089 or write it as a word statement.
2. Round off 4,826,678 to the nearest thousand.
3. Add: 279   4. Subtract: 5. Multiply: 5,280 × 97
   3,482   427,534   6. Divide: 13,968 ÷ 144
   68,926   372,895   7. Reduce $\frac{60}{96}$ to lowest terms.
   8,597   8. Change $\frac{25}{12}$ to a mixed number.
   19,308   9. Reduce $3\frac{10}{8}$ to simplest form.

$4\frac{1}{4}$

10. Change $\frac{3}{4}$ to 24ths.
11. Find the lowest common denominator of the following fractions: $\frac{1}{4}, \frac{2}{3}, \frac{5}{6}$
12. Add: $6\frac{1}{2}$ 13. Find the missing numbers:
        $5\frac{3}{8}$ $5\frac{1}{2} = 5\frac{}{8} = 4\frac{}{8}$
        $4\frac{7}{16}$ 14. Subtract: $7\frac{1}{4}$
                                             $6\frac{7}{8}$

15. Which is larger: $\frac{3}{5}$ or $\frac{5}{8}$?
16. Change $3\frac{1}{3}$ to an improper fraction.
17. Multiply: $1\frac{2}{3} \times 2\frac{1}{4}$ 18. Divide: $6\frac{3}{4} \div 1\frac{5}{16}$
19. 60 is what part of 72?   20. $\frac{2}{3}$ of what number is 18?
21. Write as a decimal numeral: Two hundred and seventy-two thousandths.
22. Find correct to nearest hundredth: 6.8352
23. Add: .36   24. Subtract: 2.6 − .14   2.46
          5.2   25. Which is larger: .03 or .029?
          4.   26. Multiply: .06 × 1.35   .081
          1.04   27. Divide: .36)‾18   50

28. Multiply by short method: 1,000 × 34.27
29. Divide by short method: 6.89 ÷ 100
30. Change $\frac{3}{4}$ to a decimal (2 places).   .61
31. Change 1.875 to a mixed number.   32. Add .36 and $\frac{1}{4}$.
33. Multiply 92 by 25, using short method.
34. Write forty-one hundredths as a per cent, decimal, and fraction.   .64
35. Express 64% as a decimal.   36. Express .04$\frac{1}{2}$ as a per cent.
37. Express $83\frac{1}{3}\%$ as a common fraction.
38. Express $\frac{17}{20}$ as a per cent.   39. Find 29% of 67.   19.43
40. What per cent of 80 is 36?   41. 15% of what number is 3?
42. Square 62.   43. Find the square root of 24,336.

85%
45%
3,844

1. Read the numeral 163,000,987 or write it as a word statement.

2. Round off 18,268,395 to the nearest hundred thousand.

3. Find the sum of: 4,132; 375; 81,580; 69; 5,364

4. Subtract 259 from 3,120.   5. Multiply: $736 \times 6,080$

6. Divide: $24 \overline{)7,392}$

7. Reduce $\frac{52}{64}$ to lowest terms. $\frac{13}{16}$

8. Change $\frac{8}{3}$ to a mixed number. $2 \frac{2}{3}$

9. Reduce $10 \frac{18}{24}$ to simplest form.

10. Change $\frac{7}{8}$ to 32nds.

11. Find the lowest common denominator of the following fractions: $\frac{1}{6}$ and $\frac{3}{8}$

12. Add: $2 \frac{3}{4} + 6 \frac{5}{8}$ 13. Find the missing number: $6 = 5 \frac{}{16}$

14. Subtract: 8   15. Which is smaller: $\frac{3}{4}$ or $\frac{7}{10}$?

$\qquad 3 \frac{2}{5}$ 16. Change $1 \frac{5}{6}$ to an improper fraction.

17. Find $\frac{7}{12}$ of 84.   18. Divide: $2 \frac{9}{16} \div 2$

19. What part of 50 is 35?

20. $\frac{3}{8}$ of what number is 27?

21. Write as a decimal numeral: Five hundred twenty-four thousandths.

22. Find correct to nearest cent: $8.3674

23. Add: $6.8 + .24 + 16$ 24. Subtract: $8 - 1.5$

25. Which is smaller: 1.05 or .247?   26. Find .75 of 2.60

27. Divide: $3.6 \overline{)51.12}$ 14.2

28. Multiply by short method: $100 \times .09$

29. Divide by short method: $576.5 \div 1,000$

30. Change $\frac{11}{12}$ to a decimal (2 places).

31. Change .6 to a common fraction.

32. Subtract: $\frac{1}{2} - .12 \frac{1}{2}$

33. Multiply 57 by $33 \frac{1}{3}$, using short method.

34. Write seven hundredths as a per cent, decimal, and fraction.

35. Express 30% as a decimal.

36. Express $1.66 \frac{2}{3}$ as a per cent.

37. Express $12 \frac{1}{2}\%$ as a common fraction.

38. Express $\frac{27}{36}$ as a per cent.

39. Find 8% of $8.27 (nearest cent). $.66$

40. 16 is what per cent of 12?

41. 7% of what number is 42?

42. Square .08   43. Find the square root of .7396

1. Read 71,059,846,375 or write it as a word statement.
2. Round off 246,508,650 to the nearest million.
3. Add: 87,456   4. Subtract: 5. Multiply:
       93,721   8,615,000   24 × 32 × 58
       69,862   989,625
       48,599   6. Divide:
       74,223   4,918,720 ÷ 6,080

7. Reduce $\frac{270}{420}$ to lowest terms. $^{9}/_{14}$
8. Change $\frac{15}{6}$ to a mixed number. $2\frac{1}{2}$
9. Reduce $4\frac{2}{8}$ to simplest form.   10. Change $\frac{1}{2}$ to 18ths.
11. Find the lowest common denominator of the following fractions: $\frac{9}{16}$ and $\frac{4}{5}$ 80
12. Add: $7\frac{1}{3}$ 13. Find the missing number:
       $5\frac{2}{5}$ $4\frac{2}{3} = 3\frac{}{3}$
       $1\frac{3}{4}$

14. Subtract: $9\frac{1}{16} - 7\frac{3}{4}$ $1\frac{21}{16}$ 15. Which is larger: $\frac{1}{4}$ or $\frac{2}{5}$?
16. Change $4\frac{1}{6}$ to an improper fraction. $^{25}/_{6}$
17. Multiply: $\frac{1}{4} \times \frac{5}{8} \times \frac{4}{5}$ $^{1}/_{8}$ 18. Divide: $3\frac{2}{3} \div 5\frac{1}{2}$ $^{2}/_{3}$
19. 16 is what part of 24?   20. $\frac{4}{5}$ of what number is 60?
6.04 21. Write as a decimal numeral: Six and four hundredths.

22. Find correct to nearest thousandth: 4.6147
23. Add: $.03 + $1.95 + $.86 + $12.43 15.27
24. Subtract: $16.00 - $4.25   25. Which is smaller: .6 or .56?
26. Multiply: 144 × $.62   27. Divide $17.40 by 12
28. Multiply by short method: 1,000 × 2.58
29. Divide by short method: 536 ÷ 10
30. Change $\frac{5}{16}$ to a decimal (2 places). $.31\frac{1}{4}$
31. Change 1.352 to a mixed number.   32. Divide: 8 ÷ .66$\frac{2}{3}$
33. Divide 338 by 25, using short method.
34. Write fifty-four hundredths as a per cent, decimal, and fraction. 1.23
35. Express 123% as a decimal.   36. Express .39 as a per cent. 39%
37. Express 36% as a common fraction. $36/100$
38. Express $\frac{15}{8}$ as a per cent. $187\frac{1}{2}\%$
39. Find $6\frac{1}{2}\%$ of $2,000.   40. What per cent of 36 is 36?
41. $37\frac{1}{2}\%$ of what number is 90?
42. Square $\frac{2}{3}$.   43. Find the square root of 253,009.

1. Read the numeral 5,493,268,003,751 or write it as a word statement.

2. Round off 839,599,696 to nearest thousand.

3. Add: 583,289
698,785
835,869
549,397
897,298

4. Subtract:
3,210,050
1,839,096

5. Multiply:
6,905
9,087

6. Divide: 5,022,702 ÷ 5,937

7. Reduce $\frac{48}{108}$ to lowest terms.

8. Change $\frac{29}{9}$ to a mixed number. 3 2/9

9. Reduce $8\frac{15}{5}$ to simplest form. 11   10. Change $\frac{5}{6}$ to 72nds. 60/72

11. Find the lowest common denominator of the following fractions: $\frac{1}{10}$, $\frac{1}{4}$, and $\frac{1}{6}$ 60

12. Add: $1\frac{2}{3} + 5\frac{7}{12} + 3\frac{1}{6}$ 10 5/12

13. Find the missing number: $3\frac{17}{32} = 2\frac{?}{32}$

14. Subtract: $14\frac{1}{3} - 9\frac{11}{16}$ 15. Which is smaller: $\frac{7}{9}$ or $\frac{10}{13}$?

16. Change $6\frac{5}{7}$ to an improper fraction.

17. Multiply: $2\frac{3}{4} \times 8\frac{2}{5}$ 24 1/5 18. Divide: $(6 \div 8\frac{1}{4}) \div 1\frac{3}{5}$

19. 54 is what part of 192? 9/32 20. $\frac{11}{16}$ of what number is 220?

21. Write as a decimal numeral: Sixty and nine ten-thousandths. 60.0009

22. Find correct to the nearest cent: $68.5349

23. Add: $3.24 + 53.7 + .938$ 57.878

24. Subtract: $4.2 - .351$ 3.849   25. Which is greater: 7.5 or .750?

26. Multiply: $.013 \times .07$ .00091 27. Divide: $.05\overline{)6}$ 120

28. Multiply by short method: 100×90.235

29. Divide by short method: $6,340.7 \div 10,000$

30. Change $\frac{21}{32}$ to a decimal (2 places). .65 5/8

31. Change 3.6 to a mixed number. 3 6/10 3 3/5 32. Add: $\frac{5}{6} + .16\frac{2}{3}$

33. Multiply 48 by $8\frac{1}{3}$, using short method.

34. Write one-fourth hundredth as a per cent, decimal, and fraction.

35. Express 500% as a decimal. 5

36. Express .0875 as a per cent. 8.75%

37. Express $233\frac{1}{3}\%$ as a mixed number.

38. Express $\frac{27}{75}$ as a per cent.   39. Find $100\frac{1}{2}\%$ of $9,000.

40. $.56 is what % of $.48?   41. $83\frac{1}{3}\%$ of what number is 30?

42. Square .09   43. Find the square root of .000225

SUPPLEMENTARY INVENTORY TEST

For pupils who have studied a contemporary program in arithmetic. Explanatory material for each of these problems may be found on the page indicated at the end of each problem.

1. Read the numeral 4,285,493,074,619 or write it as a word statement. **19**

2. Expand 43,728,469 as a polynomial. **79**

3. Round off 76,809,713 to the nearest thousand. **22**

4. Add: **24** 5. Subtract: **35** 6. Multiply: **43**

638,259	3,507,010	6,059 × 4,879
876,497	886,939	
58,968		7. Divide: **52**
386,537		23,827,076 ÷ 3,908
739,789		

Semester Exam

8. Which of the following are odd numbers? Which are even numbers? **66**

335   986   512   807   2,060   691

9. Which of the following are prime numbers? Which are composite numbers? **67**

83   57   1   79   91   103

10. If $R = \{$all prime numbers greater than 16 and less than 40$\}$, which of the following statements are true? **69**

(a) $31 \in R$ (c) $35 \notin R$ (e) $23 \in R$
(b) $27 \in R$ (d) $19 \notin R$ (f) $39 \notin R$

11. If $A = \{$all one-digit natural numbers$\}$, $B = \{$all even prime numbers$\}$, $D = \{2,3,5,7\}$, and $E = \{2,4,6,8\}$, which of the following are true? **71**

(a) $D \subset A$ (c) $E \subset D$ (e) $B \subset D$
(b) $B \subset E$ (d) $A \subset B$ (f) $A \subset E$

12. If $U = \{0,1,2,3,4,5,6,7,8\}$, $R = \{1,3,4,6,7,8\}$, $S = \{0,2,4,6,8\}$, and $T = \{0,2,5\}$, find each of the following: **73**

(a) $S \cap R$ (c) $\overline{R}$ (e) $S \cup R$
(b) $T \cup S$ (d) $R \cap T$ (f) $\overline{T}$

13. What is the greatest common factor of 36, 144, and 54? **75**

14. Factor 108 as the product of prime factors. **76**

15. What is the least common multiple of 8, 12, and 16? **77**

14

16. Find the missing numbers: **85**

(a) $(14 \times 9) \div 9 = \square$ (b) $(26 + \square) - 53 = 26$

17. Which of the following statements are true? **81**

(a) $12 + 6 = 6 + 12$ (e) $(24 + 6) + 2 = 24 + (6 + 2)$
(b) $12 - 6 = 6 - 12$ (f) $(24 - 6) - 2 = 24 - (6 - 2)$
(c) $12 \times 6 = 6 \times 12$ (g) $(24 \times 6) \times 2 = 24 \times (6 \times 2)$
(d) $12 \div 6 = 6 \div 12$ (h) $(24 \div 6) \div 2 = 24 \div (6 \div 2)$

18. Is the set $\{5, 10, 15, 20, \cdots\}$ closed under the opera- **85**
tion of addition? Subtraction? Multiplication? Division?

19. Determine the value of each of the following: **85**

(a) 0×0 (c) $9 + 0$ (e) $\dfrac{16 - 16}{8}$ (g) $24 - 24$

(b) $\frac{24}{24}$ (d) $7 \times 0 \times 3$ (f) 1^8 (h) $\dfrac{8 + 6}{7 - 7}$

20. Is 738,000 divisible by 10? by 2? by 4? by 5? by 8? **60**
by 9? by 3? by 6?

21. Do as directed: **82**

(a) Add $11 + 8 \equiv ?$ (mod 3)
(b) Multiply: $7 \times 10 \equiv ?$ (mod 4)

22. Determine which of the following sentences are true **81**
and which are false:

(a) $9 + 7 > 30 - 19$ (c) $30 \div 30 = 30 - 30$
(b) $6 \times 8 < 7^2$ (d) $18 - 3 \nless 45 \div 3$

23. Write (7, 16) as a numeral naming a fraction. **147**
24. Express $\frac{39}{65}$ in lowest terms. $\frac{3}{5}$ **89**
25. Express $\frac{23}{7}$ as a numeral naming a mixed number. **91**
26. Express $8\frac{25}{10}$ in simplest form. **93**
27. Express $\frac{5}{6}$ as 72nds. **95**
28. Find the lowest common denominator of the follow- **97**
ing fractions: $\frac{3}{4}$, $\frac{5}{12}$, and $\frac{11}{16}$.
29. Are $\frac{18}{27}$ and $\frac{30}{45}$ equivalent fractions? **145**
30. Write the set of fractions equivalent to $\frac{6}{11}$. **145**
31. Write the set of equivalent fractions of which $\frac{9}{24}$ is a **145**
member.
32. Write the multiplicative inverse of: (a) 8 (b) $\frac{5}{12}$ **148**

33. Add: **100**   **34.** Find the missing number: **106**
$4\frac{2}{3} + 8\frac{9}{10} + 1\frac{3}{5}$ $7\frac{19}{32} = 6\frac{\square}{32}$

35. Subtract: **108**   **36.** Which is greater: **114**
$3\frac{4}{9} - 1\frac{7}{12}$ $\frac{5}{7}$ or $\frac{8}{11}$?

37. Express $9\frac{13}{16}$ as an improper fraction. **116**

38. Multiply: **118**   39. Divide: **127**

$8\frac{7}{8} \times 5\frac{9}{10}$ $6 \div 3\frac{1}{3}$

40. Which of the following are true statements? **114**

(a) $\frac{27}{63} = \frac{20}{36}$ (b) $\frac{5}{18} > \frac{3}{11}$ (c) $\frac{9}{17} < \frac{5}{9}$ (d) $\frac{7}{12} > \frac{11}{18}$

41. 105 is what part of 140? 42. $\frac{3}{8}$ of what number is 57? **139**

43. Write as a decimal numeral: Four hundred and **150**
seven thousandths.

44. Write 4,936.857 as a polynomial. **215**

45. Find correct to nearest hundredth: 60.8073 **155**

46. Add: $4.96 + 28.3 + .059$ **158** 47. Subtract: $.86 - .2$ **166**

48. Arrange by size, greatest number first: .04 .004 .40 **173**
4.0

49. Multiply: $.005 \times 800.2$ **175** 50. Divide: $.25\overline{)\,.1}$ **182**

51. Which of the following are true statements? **173**

(a) $.0010 < .010$ (c) $.399 > .4$
(b) $23.7 = 2.37$ (d) $1 < .998$

52. Multiply by short method: $10,000 \times 7.58$ **209**

53. Divide by short method: $.003 \div 1,000$ **209**

54. Write by scientific notation: **216**

(a) 84,000,000,000   (b) .00000000128

55. Express $\frac{5}{8}$ as a decimal numeral. **200**

56. Express $\frac{8}{9}$ as a repeating decimal. **218**

57. Express .85 as a numeral naming a common fraction. **203**

58. Express $.\overline{36}$ as a numeral naming a common fraction. **218**

59. Add: $.66\frac{2}{3} + \frac{1}{3}$ **206**

60. Divide 350 by $12\frac{1}{2}$ using short method. **209**

61. Write seventeen hundredths as a numeral naming **221**
a per cent, decimal, and fraction.

62. Express $9\frac{1}{2}\%$ as a decimal numeral. **223**

63. Express .846 as a per cent. **225**

64. Express 65% as a numeral naming a common **227**
fraction.

65. Express $\frac{49}{56}$ as a per cent. **229**

66. Find 5.7% of 854. **232** 67. What per cent of 36 is 42? **240**

68. 8% of what number is 3? **246**   69. Square $1\frac{2}{5}$ **256**

70. (a) Find the square root of 39 by estimation, divi- **258**
sion, and average.

(b) Find the square root of 65,270,241

DO YOU NEED HELP
IN ARITHMETIC? HAVE
INVENTORY TESTS I, II, III, AND
IV SHOWED YOU THE KIND
OF EXAMPLES ON WHICH
YOU NEED HELP?

FOR HELP TURN TO THE
EXERCISES THAT HAVE THE SAME
NUMERALS AS THE EXAMPLES YOU
COULD NOT DO. FOR EXAMPLE:

DID YOU HAVE TROUBLE WITH EXAMPLE
6 (LONG DIVISION) IN EVERY TEST?
IF YOU DID, TURN TO EXERCISE 6, PAGE 52.
MAYBE YOU DID EXAMPLE 17 INCORRECTLY.
THEN TURN TO EXERCISE 17, PAGE 118.

IN EACH EXERCISE, STUDY THE
INSTRUCTIONS and the SAMPLE
SOLUTION. DO THE EXAMPLES
IN THE DIAGNOSTIC TEST.

CONCENTRATE ON THE PRACTICE WORK
YOU NEED MOST. THE PRACTICE EXAMPLES
IN EACH EXERCISE ARE KEYED TO THOSE IN
THE DIAGNOSTIC TEST SO THAT YOU CAN
QUICKLY FIND THE ONES YOU NEED.

UNIT I . . . WHOLE NUMBERS

INTRODUCTION

The numbers 0, 1, 2, 3, 4, 5, 6, 7, 8, 9, 10, 11, 12, 13, 14, 15, etc. are called whole numbers. The whole numbers beginning with 1 that are used in counting are called counting or natural numbers. Natural numbers have order. Every natural number is followed by another natural number. Thus there is no last natural number and no greatest natural number. Zero is generally not considered to be a natural number.

A number that tells how many things are in a group or the size of a group is called a cardinal number. A number that tells the order as first, second, third, fourth, and so forth is called an ordinal number. The same number symbols are used for both the cardinal and ordinal numbers.

A line may be thought of as an endless set of points. A straight line that has its points labeled with numerals so that each point is associated with a number is called a number line. The numerals are arranged in a definite order on the number line so that they correspond one-to-one with the points on the line.

To draw a number line, two points are chosen with the one on the left labeled 0 and the other point labeled 1. With the interval between these points as the unit of measure, points are located to the right of the point marked 1, equally spaced along the line. Each point is assigned a corresponding whole number (*coordinate*) in consecutive order.

Observe that the number corresponding to the point on the line farther to the right is the greater number. Sometimes a point is indicated by a capital letter. The coordinate of the above point A is 3.

In this unit we learn to read numerals, round whole numbers, and compute with whole numbers.

EXERCISE 1

READING NUMERALS NAMING WHOLE NUMBERS

I. Aim: To read numerals naming whole numbers.

II. Procedure

1. Starting from the units' place and going to the left, separate by commas the given numeral, when it contains 4 or more figures, into as many groups or periods of 3 figures each as possible.

2. (*a*) Starting from the left and going to the right, read each group of figures separately, applying the proper name to the comma as it is reached.

(*b*) The first comma from the right is read "thousand," the second comma "million," the third comma "billion," and the fourth comma "trillion."

Ten Trillions	Trillions	Hundred Billions	Ten Billions	Billions	Hundred Millions	Ten Millions	Millions	Hundred Thousands	Ten Thousands	Thousands	Hundreds	Tens	Units or Ones
7	3,	6	2	1,	4	6	8,	3	5	9,	7	8	2

The above numeral is read: Seventy-three trillion, six hundred twenty-one billion, four hundred sixty-eight million, three hundred fifty-nine thousand, seven hundred eighty-two.

3. To write numerals naming whole numbers, write each period of figures and use commas to represent the names of the periods.

4. To write numerals by expanded notation, see page 79.

III. Sample Solutions

1. Read 476,923.

Answer: Four hundred seventy-six thousand, nine hundred twenty-three.

2. Read 34,008,290.

  Answer: Thirty-four million, eight thousand, two hundred ninety.

3. Read 2,540,250,000.

  Answer: Two billion, five hundred forty million, two hundred fifty thousand.

DIAGNOSTIC TEST

Read the following numerals (or write them as word statements):

1. 68	**4.** 5,003	**7.** 4,900,000	**10.** 18,467,125
2. 582	**5.** 10,500	**8.** 7,847,000	**11.** 195,048,000
3. 4,975	**6.** 823,659	**9.** 3,582,942	**12.** 3,480,000,000

RELATED PRACTICE EXAMPLES

Read the following numerals (or write them as word statements):

SET 1	SET 2	SET 3
1. 96	**1.** 426	**1.** 8,278
2. 47	**2.** 784	**2.** 3,926
3. 53	**3.** 269	**3.** 2,474
4. 84	**4.** 905	**4.** 4,206
5. 79	**5.** 380	**5.** 7,959

SET 4	SET 5	SET 6
1. 6,004	**1.** 27,432	**1.** 150,000
2. 4,045	**2.** 59,117	**2.** 291,429
3. 9,080	**3.** 20,730	**3.** 723,805
4. 7,032	**4.** 45,063	**4.** 900,281
5. 3,007	**5.** 81,896	**5.** 674,364

SET 7	SET 8	SET 9
1. 3,000,000	**1.** 9,250,000	**1.** 1,596,271
2. 8,000,000	**2.** 3,746,000	**2.** 7,122,843
3. 2,500,000	**3.** 4,891,000	**3.** 8,900,527
4. 7,600,000	**4.** 2,006,000	**4.** 5,416,084
5. 4,200,000	**5.** 5,670,000	**5.** 6,004,009

Set 10	Set 11	Set 12
1. 32,429,784	1. 700,000,000	1. 5,000,000,000
2. 57,105,933	2. 241,849,000	2. 6,450,000,000
3. 28,246,219	3. 928,376,500	3. 9,207,800,000,000
4. 96,863,848	4. 406,923,685	4. 52,825,463,928,000
5. 25,000,975	5. 843,297,861	5. 147,194,652,805

MISCELLANEOUS EXAMPLES

Write the numeral naming each of the following numbers:

1. Six thousand, eight hundred forty-three.
2. Seventy-four thousand, nine hundred four.
3. Three hundred seventeen thousand, fifty-two.
4. Two million, seven hundred twenty-five thousand, two hundred thirty-five.
5. Forty-nine million, six hundred fifty thousand.

PRACTICAL APPLICATIONS

Read the numerals in the following facts or write them as word statements:

1. The total area of the first 48 states of the United States is 3,022,387 square miles. Alaska adds 586,400 square miles and Hawaii 6,454 square miles.

2. A government study reveals that 10,933,379 males and 3,642,313 females were employed in the manufacturing industries, 6,998,784 males and 3,548,785 females in the wholesale and retail trades, and 1,956,967 males and 2,717,581 females in the professional and related fields.

3. The United States Mints manufactured during the year 243,500,503 dimes, 194,437,910 nickels, and 419,615,850 pennies.

4. A United States Treasury report shows that its cash position is: Balance, $3,176,689,943; deposits for the fiscal year, $33,789,916,198; withdrawals for the year, $41,378,897,750; total debt, $280,350,866,129; gold assets, $21,692,706,238.

5. The Pacific Ocean has an area of 63,801,668 square miles, Atlantic Ocean 31,830,718 square miles, Indian Ocean 28,356,276 square miles, and Arctic Ocean 5,440,197 square miles.

EXERCISE 2

ROUNDING OFF WHOLE NUMBERS

I. Aim: To round off whole numbers.

II. Procedure

1. Rewrite as many figures as are needed and write zeros in place of the other figures. (See sample solutions 2, 4, and 6.)

2. If the first figure dropped is 5 or more, increase the preceding figure by 1. (See sample solutions 1, 3, and 5.)

III. Sample Solutions

Round off:

1. 287 to nearest ten. *Answer:* 290

2. 5,249 to nearest hundred. *Answer:* 5,200

3. 48,628 to nearest thousand. *Answer:* 49,000

4. 283,175 to nearest ten thousand. *Answer:* 280,000

5. 654,927 to nearest hundred thousand. *Answer:* 700,000

6. 26,385,000 to nearest million. *Answer:* 26,000,000

DIAGNOSTIC TEST

Round off the given numbers to

1. Nearest ten:

(*a*) 57
(*b*) 394

2. Nearest hundred:

(*a*) 5,626
(*b*) 890

3. Nearest thousand:

(*a*) 4,501
(*b*) 63,289

4. Nearest ten thousand:

(*a*) 71,989
(*b*) 149,000

5. Nearest hundred thousand:

(*a*) 243,762
(*b*) 1,650,059

6. Nearest million:

(*a*) 3,728,409
(*b*) 41,371,000

RELATED PRACTICE EXAMPLES

Round off the given numbers to

Nearest ten: Nearest hundred:

Set 1(a)	Set 1(b)	Set 2(a)	Set 2(b)
1. 28	1. 31	1. 230	1. 389
2. 45	2. 84	2. 947	2. 551
3. 97	3. 152	3. 2,529	3. 7,863
4. 416	4. 683	4. 3,814	4. 9,092
5. 2,539	5. 3,844	5. 5,408	5. 15,654

Nearest thousand: Nearest ten thousand:

Set 3(a)	Set 3(b)	Set 4(a)	Set 4(b)
1. 8,726	1. 9,485	1. 23,400	1. 56,000
2. 3,867	2. 5,094	2. 94,872	2. 37,160
3. 24,539	3. 36,320	3. 80,056	3. 295,928
4. 57,603	4. 40,159	4. 142,625	4. 528,050
5. 10,954	5. 878,208	5. 6,531,009	5. 7,849,323

Nearest hundred thousand: Nearest million:

Set 5(a)	Set 5(b)	Set 6(a)	Set 6(b)
1. 120,000	1. 560,500	1. 4,500,000	1. 2,450,000
2. 345,946	2. 283,475	2. 9,742,820	2. 7,398,250
3. 1,510,214	3. 2,375,908	3. 8,906,437	3. 14,487,095
4. 3,835,837	4. 5,481,481	4. 32,671,352	4. 462,264,128
5. 22,403,541	5. 19,792,624	5. 84,827,466	5. 8,250,175,000

PRACTICAL APPLICATIONS

1. Round off the numbers in the following news item to the nearest thousand: United States car factories will build 141,914 cars this week against 135,663 last week and 164,265 in the same week last year.

2. Round off to the nearest hundred thousand the numbers in the following census report showing the 1960 population of the ten leading cities: New York, 7,710,346; Chicago, 3,492,945; Los Angeles, 2,448,018; Philadelphia, 1,959,966; Detroit, 1,672,574; Houston, 932,680; Baltimore, 921,363; Cleveland, 869,867; Washington, 746,958; St. Louis, 740,424.

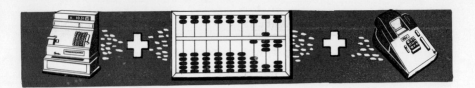

EXERCISE 3

ADDITION OF WHOLE NUMBERS

I. Aim: To add whole numbers.

II. Procedure

1. If it is necessary to write the example, place units under units, tens under tens, etc.

2. When there are two or more columns of numerals, add each column, starting from the units' column. If the sum of any column is ten or more, write the last figure of the sum in the answer and carry the other figures to the next column.

3. Check by adding the columns in the opposite direction or by adding the sum of each column as shown in the sample solution.

Note: See page 5 for the commutative and associative properties.

III. Sample Solution

Add as indicated: $984 + 1,292 + 2,484 + 337 + 4,069$

Solution: *Check:*

984	26	sum of units' column
1,292	34	sum of tens' column
2,484 ← addends	18	sum of hundreds' column
337	7	sum of thousands' column
4,069	9,166	
9,166 ← sum		

Answer: 9,166

IV. Definitions

1. The sum is the answer in an addition.
2. The addends are the numbers that are added.
3. A plus (+) sign indicates addition.

PRELIMINARY EXAMPLES

Basic Addition Combinations

Add:

1.	2	3	7	1	0	5	4	6	8	9
	1	5	6	8	3	2	4	9	0	7

2.	4	7	5	6	9	3	0	8	1	2
	6	1	0	7	9	4	2	5	3	8

3.	5	2	9	0	6	7	3	1	4	8
	3	0	2	4	5	7	9	1	8	6

4.	0	6	3	9	1	2	8	7	4	5
	1	8	0	3	4	6	7	2	9	5

5.	3	4	8	2	0	7	5	9	6	1
	8	5	2	7	9	3	6	1	4	0

6.	6	0	2	5	4	8	3	1	9	7
	6	0	9	8	3	1	2	7	5	4

7.	1	8	4	7	2	9	6	0	3	5
	5	4	0	8	2	6	3	7	1	9

8.	9	5	1	8	3	4	2	7	0	6
	0	7	9	3	6	1	4	5	8	2

9.	4	1	0	7	8	6	9	2	5	3
	2	6	5	9	8	0	4	3	1	7

10.	8	4	6	3	5	1	7	0	2	9
	9	7	1	3	4	2	0	6	5	8

DIAGNOSTIC TEST

Add and check:

1. 32
  45
	7. 25
	  94
	  84
	  39
		11. 3,592
		    2,738
			17. 3,962
			    6,109
			    2,854
			    6,875

2. 56
  17
		12. 86,056
		    44,598	

3. 67
  59
	8. 5
	  7
	  6
	  8
	  9
		13. 435
		  599
		  796
			18. 79,459
			    68,417
			    75,388
			    91,754

4. 9
  5
  8
		14. 3,598
		    6,487
		    5,739
			19. 258
			  584
			  845
			  207
			  396

5. 15
  26
  87
	9. 34
	  90
	  23
	  65
	  57
		15. 24,673
		    12,762
		    37,857	

6. 6
  2
  4
  9
	10. 389
	    459
		16. 556
		  479
		  628
		  493
			20. 4,973
			    9,282
			    3,970
			    2,639
			    9,789

21. 83,625 94,774 87,146 32,753 64,838	**22.** 9,651 78 83,795 206 5,184 16,745	**23.** 1,483,297 3,915,485 20,500 372,173 5,283,094 7,848 608,556

24. 3,845 + 928 + 63,847 + 795 + 1,356

25. Find the sum of: 2,381; 967; 29; 8,406; 750

RELATED PRACTICE EXAMPLES

Add and check:

SET 1

34	67	20	42	63
25	32	58	44	26

SET 2

59	36	37	59	28
8	45	57	24	62

Set 3

48	24	83	56	95
94	76	60	58	99

Set 4   Set 5

7	8	9	4	9	42	25	86	65	34
5	6	7	6	8	27	50	92	7	79
8	8	7	9	9	19	83	58	94	88

Set 6   Set 7

3	8	9	4	7	82	45	94	28	86
5	4	7	0	6	43	79	36	8	59
7	9	7	9	2	92	63	49	7	97
4	6	8	8	9	30	42	78	14	95

Set 8   Set 9

5	8	2	8	9	12	82	73	91	76
1	6	5	9	9	26	64	9	30	89
3	9	9	4	6	21	37	24	54	97
9	4	7	7	8	13	56	8	79	88
2	7	4	8	9	22	28	87	68	53

Set 10

231	573	267	974	608
457	119	385	566	96

Set 11

6142	2,358	6,834	5,705	7,478
3756	4,135	8,879	986	9,757

Set 12

37454	75,633	946	35,878	21,973
41345	83,698	30,306	89,646	92,027

Set 13

582	861	779	926	639
143	495	698	15	852
214	827	579	658	543

Set 14

4214	2,616	4,043	8,588	6,957
1152	3,942	3,285	765	9,799
3403	4,585	9,772	89	7,186

Set 15

13581	62,583	45,496	68,432	73,858
61132	17,914	27,383	257	59,576
15273	28,619	31,576	9,746	38,643

Set 16

637	458	682	39	787
131	173	745	896	957
528	649	384	9	236
300	326	973	372	598

Set 17

2105	2,374	4,966	7,581	6,479
3216	4,834	3,859	470	8,642
1143	1,496	5,573	28	9,736
2319	3,587	8,426	6	6,857

Set 18

34832	56,834	42,763	6,445	76,542
11913	67,509	96,833	95,214	81,276
22741	31,915	47,485	87	998
10420	47,628	92,739	1,756	5,823

Set 19

129	289	646	7	688
325	769	53	226	734
356	427	8	589	597
218	892	24	36	905
497	976	593	328	799

Set 20

1673	2,765	46	7,328	6,494
2191	4,497	315	478	3,849
1814	2,086	2	9,663	8,589
1271	2,199	1,597	98	6,355
2353	7,385	221	8,976	2,914

Set 21

15924	54,683	45,618	75	96,545
24872	82,759	4,973	5,491	32,678
29644	38,742	87	67,987	49,924
18873	81,599	564	446	85,397
15692	76,847	9	51,743	26,785

Set 22(a)

6	16	387	529	6,583
5	8	596	63	3,476
2	29	347	784	4,285
8	9	482	8	3,842
4	65	574	29	5,273
2	22	108	685	2,646

Set 22(b)

95329	82,541	4,953	362,474	642,566
458	31,796	58,275	67,580	255,887
7509	28,865	87	85,030	974,464
26	49,496	893,574	250,545	850,952
84531	22,738	64,705	414,650	527,327
727	57,633	9,268	2,647	741,969

Set 23(a)

8	48	653	4,591	46,398
3	36	28	8,216	127
9	53	3	9,137	3,874
7	29	792	1,615	58,462
4	74	89	2,293	95
2	83	246	3,748	4,267
6	98	36	5,157	67,839

Set 23(b)

167450	698,523	487,944	2,459,630	4,369,565
32184	34,769	921,593	25,400	7,436,859
500863	178	678,105	580,575	3,050,762
200	9,874	637,050	243,125	4,598,083
89157	968,452	986,967	8,549	6,452,136
8	789,347	369,725	9,783,484	7,587,327
38524	59,791	917,862	15,338	3,967,009

Add as indicated:

SET 24(a)

1. $6 + 2 + 7$
2. $8 + 5 + 6 + 4 + 9$
3. $72 + 37 + 84$
4. $69 + 75 + 29 + 82 + 51$
5. $24 + 33 + 49 + 53 + 38 + 84 + 70$
6. $18 + 3 + 5 + 26$
7. $89 + 7 + 16 + 8 + 19$
8. $47 + 4 + 19 + 72 + 5 + 27$
9. $6 + 21 + 78 + 7 + 36 + 81$
10. $85 + 15 + 3 + 30 + 9 + 28 + 6$

SET 24(b)

1. $903 + 412$
2. $328 + 139 + 426$
3. $475 + 189 + 88 + 423$
4. $264 + 593 + 34 + 766 + 872$
5. $502 + 74 + 365 + 82 + 171$
6. $97 + 227 + 56 + 5 + 764$
7. $639 + 422 + 91 + 587 + 36 + 58$
8. $597 + 329 + 649 + 864 + 975 + 800$
9. $278 + 42 + 764 + 95 + 556 + 476$
10. $886 + 529 + 793 + 438 + 927 + 572 + 106$

SET 24(c)

1. $6,545 + 7,182$
2. $92,114 + 345 + 21,533$
3. $69,483 + 24,752 + 80,599 + 2,843$
4. $9,787 + 1,578 + 463 + 9,242 + 89$
5. $50,422 + 1,525 + 396 + 85 + 4,152$
6. $253 + 9,052 + 59,628 + 4 + 786$
7. $20,500 + 2,483 + 15,814 + 350 + 9,453 + 87$
8. $14,208 + 932 + 5,919 + 28 + 36,545 + 15,970$
9. $29,751 + 34,462 + 45,432 + 382 + 2,456 + 3,084$
10. $37,442 + 42,596 + 807 + 6,638 + 52,800 + 51 + 9,046$

SET 25

Find the sum of:
1. 86; 153; 128; 249
2. 425; 836; 595; 26; 84
3. 762; 158; 32; 17; 4; 365
4. 200; 175; 335; 95; 480; 45
5. 731; 453; 846; 924; 877; 382; 502
6. 1,469; 8,355; 2,076; 3,416; 123; 4,125
7. 8,500; 250; 960; 63,075; 407; 2,155
8. 24,057; 6,799; 4,276; 9,341; 8,223; 37,165
9. 83; 9; 472; 1,857; 343; 8,158; 48,494
10. 53,196; 9,324; 4,197; 3,283; 44,915; 6,258; 1,970

MISCELLANEOUS EXAMPLES

Find the missing numbers, adding horizontally and vertically:

1. $8 + 7 + 4 =$
    $3 + 5 + 9 =$
    $6 + 3 + 7 =$
    $9 + 8 + 6 =$
    $\underline{++=}$

2. $62 + 25 + 32 =$
    $13 + 7 + 15 =$
    $6 + 18 + 48 =$
    $35 + 9 + 4 =$
    $\underline{++=}$

3. $153 + 42 + 29 =$
    $35 + 51 + 7 =$
    $24 + 143 + 62 =$
    $109 + 84 + 46 =$
    $\underline{++=}$

4. $16 + 95 + 84 + 7 =$
    $8 + 23 + 2 + 91 =$
    $27 + 8 + 30 + 25 =$
    $70 + 16 + 53 + 6 =$
    $\underline{+++=}$

5. $5 + 8 + 6 =$
    $9 + 7 + 8 =$
    $3 + 9 + 9 =$
    $4 + 5 + 9 =$
    $7 + 8 + 4 =$
    $\underline{++=}$

6. $9 + 5 + 7 + 8 =$
    $4 + 9 + 8 + 4 =$
    $7 + 9 + 4 + 9 =$
    $2 + 8 + 2 + 5 =$
    $8 + 9 + 5 + 8 =$
    $\underline{+++=}$

7. $15 + 58 + 97 =$
    $28 + 9 + 34 =$
    $14 + 73 + 81 =$
    $55 + 61 + 48 =$
    $74 + 26 + 64 =$
    $\underline{++=}$

8. $38 + 49 + 2 =$
    $57 + 27 + 95 =$
    $21 + 54 + 7 =$
    $68 + 15 + 38 =$
    $95 + 6 + 14 =$
    $\underline{++=}$

9. 152 + 69 + 200 =
827 + 143 + 92 =
507 + 258 + 181 =
26 + 400 + 6 =
242 + 75 + 47 =
_____
+ + =

10. 1,500 + 938 + 4,926 =
284 + 29 + 1,385 =
65 + 300 + 50 =
146 + 8 + 267 =
3,650 + 1,825 + 928 =
_____
+ + =

PRACTICAL APPLICATIONS

1. The Washington High School presented this year three performances of their dramatic show. 1,058 persons saw the opening performance. On the succeeding two nights 993 and 1,196 persons respectively attended. What was the total attendance at the school show?

2. In the election for president of the student body at the Fernwood High School 146 freshmen, 198 sophomores, 127 juniors, and 208 seniors voted for Jack and 179, 124, 218, and 134 respectively voted for Tom. Who received the greater number of votes?

3. Find the total enrollment at the Central Junior High School if in grade 7A there are 225 pupils; 7B, 193 pupils; 8A, 249 pupils; 8B, 216 pupils; 9A, 368 pupils; and 9B, 257 pupils.

4. What was the total attendance at the 4 school league football games played by Greenville High School if the first game was witnessed by 2,973 spectators, the second by 2,684, the third by 3,189, and the last game by 2,708 spectators?

5. There are 135 boys and 146 girls in the freshman class at the Carson High School, 118 boys and 139 girls in the sophomore class, 169 boys and 129 girls in the junior class, and 107 boys and 158 girls in the senior class. How many boys are enrolled at the school? How many girls? What is the total enrollment?

6. Find the final scores of the following high school games:

Football

Washington	7	14	0	13 =	Carson	6	19	7	14 =
Fernwood	13	9	16	6 =	Greenville	0	13	12	6 =

Baseball

Carson	0	3	0	2	4	0	2	1	0 =
Springdale	1	2	1	0	2	1	0	3	0 =

Basketball

Greenville 12 21 14 19 =   Washington 15   8 24 16 =
Jefferson 17 15   9 26 =   Hilton   13 18 17 10 =

7. Find the winner of a 9-hole golf match (the smaller number of strokes wins):

Jones, Carson H. S.   4   4   5   6   3   4   5   4   5 =
Williams, Dalton H. S. 3   5   4   5   4   5   6   5   4 =

8. Bowling—3-game match—Find (*a*) which player scored the most points, (*b*) which team won the most games, and (*c*) which team had the greater total match score.

Washington High				Kingston High		
Benson	152	217	169	Richards	154	131	176
Allen	163	150	178	Carter	159	182	198
Young	148	176	214	Turner	165	157	188

9. How many calories are contained in the following meal: vegetable soup, 86; roast lamb, 175; fresh peas, 66; boiled potato, 117; 2 slices of white bread, 134; apple, 81; glass of milk, 170?

10. During the year Mr. Johnson bought the following amounts of fuel oil to heat his house: 175 gallons, 208 gallons, 246 gallons, 239 gallons, 195 gallons, and 250 gallons. How many gallons of fuel oil did he buy in all?

11. A 2-story factory building with office and showroom is available for rent. The office has 540 square feet of floor space; showroom, 975 square feet; first floor, 8,350 square feet; and second floor, 4,960 square feet. What is the total floor space of the building?

12. A streamlined passenger train goes from Miami to Jacksonville, a distance of 405 miles; from Jacksonville to Savannah, 140 miles; from Savannah to Raleigh, 343 miles; from Raleigh to Richmond, 157 miles; from Richmond to Washington, 116 miles; and from Washington to New York City, 227 miles. What is the total distance by train from Miami to New York City?

13. What is the total area of the Great Lakes if the area of each lake is as follows: Lake Superior, 31,820 square miles; Lake Erie, 9,940 square miles; Lake Michigan, 22,400 square miles; Lake Ontario, 7,540 square miles; and Lake Huron, 23,010 square miles?

14. What is the total seating capacity at the county baseball stadium if there are 978 box seats, 8,496 reserved seats, 19,564 general admission seats, and 3,825 bleacher seats?

15. The township public library has 2,309 fiction books, 1,894 non-fiction books, 195 reference books, and 275 magazines. What is the total number of books and magazines?

16. What is the population of New England if Maine has a population of 913,774; New Hampshire, 533,242; Vermont, 377,747; Massachusetts, 4,690,514; Rhode Island, 791,896; and Connecticut, 2,007,280?

17. Find the total area of the Pacific States if the area of California is 158,693 square miles; Oregon, 96,981 square miles; and Washington, 68,192 square miles.

18. There are 30,673,800 pupils enrolled in the public schools of the United States, 4,281,000 in private and parochial schools, 76,100 in residential schools, 78,800 in model and practice schools, and 50,300 in Federal schools. Find the total school enrollment.

19. How many farms are in the East North Central States (Ohio, Indiana, Illinois, Michigan, Wisconsin) if there are 199,359 farms in Ohio, 166,627 in Indiana, 195,268 in Illinois, 155,589 in Michigan, and 168,561 in Wisconsin?

20. What was the total attendance at the recent San Francisco-New York 7-game World Series if 43,852 persons saw the first game, 43,910 the second, 71,434 the third, 66,607 the fourth, 63,165 the fifth, 43,948 the sixth, and 43,948 the seventh game?

REFRESH YOUR SKILLS

1. Write 6,862,925 as a word statement.

2. Round off 129,484,056 to the nearest million.

3. Add:
16834
32605
57428
45887
84065

4. Add:
92,153
8,449
376
9,849
75,698

5. Add:
38,669
81,767
63,898
89,948
56,877

SUBTRACTION OF WHOLE NUMBERS

I. Aim: To subtract whole numbers.

II. Procedure

1. If it is necessary to write the example, place units under units, tens under tens, etc.

2. Subtract the figures in the subtrahend from the corresponding figures in the minuend. Start from the units' place and work to the left. If any figure in the subtrahend is greater than the corresponding figure in the minuend, increase the figure in the minuend by 10 by taking 1 from the preceding figure in the next higher place.

3. Check by adding the remainder to the subtrahend. Their sum should equal the minuend.

III. Sample Solutions

Subtract in the following examples:

1. 7,485 − 2,648

Solution:	*Check:*
7,485 ← minuend	2,648
2,648 ← subtrahend	4,837
4,837 ← remainder	7,485
or difference	

Answer: 4,837

2. 94,500 − 93,264

Solution:	*Check:*
94,500	93,264
93,264	1,236
1,236	94,500

Answer: 1,236

3. From 8,337 subtract 6,828.

Solution:	*Check:*
8,337	6,828
6,828	1,509
1,509	8,337

Answer: 1,509

4. Take 279 from 3,456.

Solution:	*Check:*
3,456	279
279	3,177
3,177	3,456

Answer: 3,177

IV. Definitions

1. The minuend is the number from which you subtract.
2. The subtrahend is the number you subtract.
3. The remainder *or* difference is the answer in subtraction.
4. The minus (−) sign indicates subtraction.

PRELIMINARY EXAMPLES

Basic Subtraction Combinations

Subtract:

1.	5	7	2	6	17	16	11	9	8	7
	2	7	0	4	8	9	6	5	1	3
2.	7	10	13	5	9	3	8	6	10	11
	4	5	9	0	1	2	8	3	6	7
3.	6	11	9	10	5	15	3	12	8	6
	5	9	6	1	4	8	3	7	0	2
4.	1	5	6	7	16	9	11	7	9	14
	0	3	1	6	7	4	5	2	9	8
5.	10	11	15	12	8	4	17	3	8	10
	3	8	7	5	6	1	9	0	2	4
6.	6	4	13	8	10	14	7	16	5	4
	6	2	4	3	9	7	1	8	5	0
7.	5	12	2	15	11	8	0	12	10	9
	1	4	2	6	3	5	0	9	7	8
8.	15	3	4	10	8	14	7	4	13	7
	9	1	3	2	7	6	0	4	8	5
9.	13	9	12	18	14	12	9	13	11	1
	7	0	8	9	5	3	2	6	4	1
10.	10	12	13	9	11	6	14	2	9	8
	8	6	5	7	2	0	9	1	3	4

DIAGNOSTIC TEST

Subtract and check:

1. 28
  5
	6. 59
	  51
		11. 465
		   359
			16. 6,841
			   2,327
				21. 85,924
				   23,713

2. 31
  6
	7. 50
	  29
		12. 800
		   698
			17. 7,653
			   4,725
				22. 92,045
				   21,924

3. 76
  14
	8. 496
	  263
		13. 604
		   589
			18. 3,962
			   1,487
				23. 68,247
				   44,395

4. 87
  68
	9. 562
	  228
		14. 255
		    37
			19. 5,000
			   3,792
				24. 89,463
				   15,684

5. 32
  12
	10. 643
	  367
		15. 4,965
		   1,842
			20. 8,429
			     64
				25. 70,571
				   39,782

26. 35,823
   19,341
      27. 45,936
       798
      28. 845,094
    384,276
      29. 4,575,000
   1,395,463

30. 98,370 − 84,697.
31. From 8,463 subtract 579.
32. Take 3,582 from 9,348.
33. Find the difference between 17;947 and 13,799.

RELATED PRACTICE EXAMPLES

Subtract and check:

Set 1

59 4	84 2	96 3	77 6	69 5

Set 2

23 8	86 7	94 6	47 9	52 3

Set 3

85 61	66 35	98 26	49 15	57 23

Set 4

36 19	71 23	64 25	93 58	85 37

Set 5

78 48	53 23	95 35	29 9	87 17

Set 6

26 23	37 34	86 82	98 90	79 72

SET 7

40	60	30	40	90
17	36	23	8	65

SET 8

475	978	362	549	853
132	642	150	325	721

SET 9

891	582	439	918	647
379	166	284	627	493

SET 10

842	516	975	482	923
358	179	587	295	476

SET 11

428	785	972	964	545
218	380	672	357	138

SET 12

609	750	500	300	600
392	273	307	160	485

SET 13

538	972	784	901	735
453	965	697	838	686

SET 14

253	467	526	884	573
26	58	72	9	83

SET 15

8654	4,296	6,582	9,728	7,849
2431	3,003	4,172	6,215	3,812

SET 16

9642	8,657	2,938	3,463	9,185
6425	5,846	1,682	2,702	6,345

SET 17

7194	5,371	8,362	5,774	3,680
3457	2,925	4,554	2,968	2,962

SET 18

9426	8,335	4,900	5,371	8,796
3258	6,452	3,825	4,691	6,099

SET 19

8324	6,153	8,050	6,000	9,000
5975	2,896	4,584	2,505	8,427

SET 20

4823	6,752	3,058	1,971	3,000
8	127	65	986	479

SET 21

38762	93,596	55,706	45,383	79,648
26521	61,593	52,304	32,162	36,136

SET 22

45962	79,614	83,253	90,349	52,767
12535	48,532	52,028	70,281	28,343

SET 23

37424	56,382	80,545	76,200	38,509
15258	42,491	39,644	41,350	32,754

SET 24

61847	97,325	54,000	18,508	79,406
25952	83,459	23,475	10,809	25,837

SET 25

97437	42,662	50,583	62,471	90,000
28769	25,896	48,794	42,587	82,575

SET 26

24593	57,924	67,500	29,070	82,957
10638	39,819	59,045	14,924	53,498

SET 27

65925	46,000	21,507	86,500	95,374
386	897	4,742	95	8,298

SET 28

645987	705,961	658,235	450,000	532,654
314265	536,809	621,791	328,542	2,867

SET 29

8935299	2,963,475	7,694,251	2,500,000	4,000,000
3411274	1,724,133	86,206	1,758,625	2,950,966

Subtract as indicated:

SET 30(*a*)

1. 25 − 18
2. 645 − 382
3. 476 − 387
4. 500 − 298
5. 4,563 − 3,275
6. 5,694 − 4,987
7. 78,000 − 54,092
8. 95,375 − 92,186
9. 636,059 − 278,770
10. 3,540,000 − 3,269,145

SET 30(*b*)

1. 63 − 8
2. 427 − 76
3. 300 − 84
4. 4,517 − 28
5. 3,788 − 909
6. 1,500 − 6
7. 58,625 − 9,775
8. 32,743 − 814
9. 545,611 − 39,768
10. 750,000 − 7,050

SET 31

1. From 300 subtract 152.
2. From 798 subtract 476.
3. From 237 subtract 95.
4. From 4,583 subtract 3,178.
5. From 3,489 subtract 2,183.
6. From 2,000 take 504.
7. From 9,153 take 2,846.
8. From 15,000 take 3,825.
9. From 37,450 take 15,968.
10. From 84,073 take 28,536.

SET 32

1. Take 63 from 324.
2. Take 574 from 1,582.
3. Take 497 from 520.
4. Take 38 from 1,000.
5. Take 7,352 from 9,514.
6. Subtract 633 from 1,981.
7. Subtract 200 from 1,582.
8. Subtract 4,156 from 8,915.
9. Subtract 347 from 59,784.
10. Subtract 2,059 from 37,685.

SET 33

Find the difference between:

1. 942 and 368.
2. 450 and 199.
3. 8,256 and 8,147.
4. 3,794 and 900.
5. 45,836 and 21,862.
6. 68,593 and 40,500.
7. 300,000 and 171,938.
8. 821,575 and 390,695.
9. 761,350 and 385,025.
10. 5,000,000 and 2,750,000.

PRACTICAL APPLICATIONS

1. During the football season Southwest High School scored 219 points against their opponents' 136 points and gained 1,246 yards against 891 yards in running plays, and 932 yards against 798 yards in passing. How many more points did Southwest score? How many more yards did they gain running? Passing?

2. The seating capacity at the new Jackson High School athletic field is 4,120. The stands at the old field held only 1,584 persons. How many more spectators can now be seated?

3. In the election for secretary of the student association at the Rowell Junior High School, Mary received 1,206 votes and Joan, 978 votes. How many more votes did Mary receive?

4. The present enrollment at the Township Junior High School is 849 pupils. There are 675 pupils registered at the senior high school. What is the difference in their enrollments?

5. The total attendance at all athletic events at the Nelson High School for the school year was 48,547. The attendance for the previous year was 39,498. Find the amount of increase in attendance.

6. Tom's father is interested in buying a new house. He likes two houses, one priced at $19,600 and the other at $20,575. How much more does the second house cost? If he expects to make a down payment of $6,850, what would be the amount of the mortgage (balance) in each case?

7. Mother asked John to check the electric and gas bills. If the previous month's reading of the electric meter was 7,095 kw. hr. and the present reading is 7,264 kw. hr., how many kilowatt hours of electricity were used during the month? He found the present reading of the gas meter to be 5,105 hundred cubic feet and the previous reading 4,937 hundred cubic feet. How many hundred cubic feet of gas were used?

8. Mr. Warren paid $17,450 for his house 4 years ago. If the house depreciated in the amount of $1,396, what would its present value be?

9. A salesman's automobile mileage for the past year was 25,642 miles. If 6,954 miles represents pleasure driving, how many miles was the car driven for business purposes?

10. A poultry farmer handled 29,344 chickens during the year. His sales totaled 27,872 chickens. Find the number of chickens that remained unsold.

11. The deepest place thus far discovered in the world is 35,640 feet in the Marianas Trench near the island of Guam. The greatest depth in the Atlantic Ocean is 30,246 feet, located near Puerto Rico. Find the difference in these depths.

12. The highest point in Asia is Mount Everest with an elevation of 29,028 feet. Mount McKinley in Alaska with an elevation of 20,300 feet is the highest point in North America. What is the difference in their altitudes?

13. Just off the coast of California is a submarine mountain called San Juan Seamount. How far below the surface of the water is the top of the mountain if the ocean floor depth is 12,000 feet and the mountain rises 10,188 feet?

14. How much larger is the state of Texas with an area of 265,896 square miles than the state of Rhode Island with an area of 1,248 square miles?

15. The area of the earth is 196,950,000 square miles. If there are 139,440,000 square miles of water, how many square miles of land are on the earth?

16. The seating capacity of the Rose Bowl in Pasadena, California, is 100,188. How many more people can be seated in the Philadelphia municipal stadium if its seating capacity is 105,000?

17. The distance from the moon to the earth is 238,857 miles and from the sun to the earth is 92,897,416 miles. How much farther away is the sun from the earth than the moon?

18. How many farms less are there in the United States if the number of farms decreased from 5,859,169 to 5,382,162?

19. How many more square miles of territory did the United States acquire by the Louisiana Purchase of 827,192 square miles than by the purchase of Alaska with 586,400 square miles?

REFRESH YOUR SKILLS

1. Write 208,070,009 as a word statement.

2. Round off 7,583,284 to the nearest thousand.

3. Add:

45,836
29,797
75,086
18,925
56,498

4. Subtract:

21673
4689

5. Subtract:

965,425
829,517

EXERCISE 5

MULTIPLICATION OF WHOLE NUMBERS

I. Aim: To multiply whole numbers.

II. Procedure

1. If it is necessary to write the example, place units under units, tens under tens, etc.

2. If the multiplier has only one figure, multiply each and every figure in the multiplicand by this figure. Start from the right and work in order to the left. (See sample solution 1.)

3. If the multiplier has more than one figure, find the partial products by multiplying all the figures in the multiplicand by each figure in the multiplier, starting from the right. Write the partial products under each other, placing the numbers so that the right-hand figure of each partial product is directly under its corresponding figure in the multiplier. Then add the partial products. (See sample solutions 2 and 3.)

4. Check by interchanging the multiplier and multiplicand and multiplying again (see sample solution 2), or by dividing the product by either the multiplier or the multiplicand. (See sample solutions 1 and 3.)

Note: See pages 6 and 7 for the commutative, associative, and distributive properties.

III. Sample Solutions

1. Multiply 647 by 8.

Solution:	Check:
647	647
8	8)5,176
5,176	

2. Multiply 36 by 45.

Solution:

36 ← multiplicand
45 ← multiplier
180 ← partial
144 ← products
1,620 ← product

Check:

45
36
270
135
1,620

Answer: 5,176

Answer: 1,620

43

3. Multiply 54 by 29.

	Solution:	*Check:*	
	54	29	54
	29	54)1,566	29)1,566
	486	108	145
	108	486	116
	1,566	486	116
		...	...

Answer: 1,566

IV. Definitions

1. The multiplicand is the number you multiply.
2. The multiplier is the number by which you multiply.
3. The product is the answer in multiplication.
4. A partial product is the product obtained by multiplying the multiplicand by any figure in the multiplier.
5. The symbol × (times sign) indicates multiplication.
6. A factor is any one of the numbers used in multiplication to form a product.

PRELIMINARY EXAMPLES

Basic Multiplication Combinations

Multiply:

1.
5	8	2	9	7	1	6	3	4	0
3	1	5	6	9	2	7	0	4	8

2.
1	7	4	5	8	6	0	9	2	3
7	6	3	8	2	4	5	9	0	1

3.
0	2	7	9	4	3	6	5	1	8
2	9	7	3	0	5	8	6	1	4

4.
4	8	6	7	9	5	0	1	3	2
8	7	9	0	5	1	4	3	6	2

5.
7	3	2	8	6	9	1	4	0	5
4	3	1	9	0	8	6	5	7	2

6.
6	2	0	3	7	9	5	8	4	1
1	4	6	2	3	7	0	8	9	5

7.	5	7	6	1	0	8	2	3	9	4
	4	2	5	9	1	3	8	7	0	6

8.	8	3	9	6	5	1	0	4	7	2
	6	9	4	2	5	0	3	1	8	7

9.	0	8	1	6	2	4	7	9	3	5
	0	5	8	6	3	7	1	2	4	9

10.	7	3	4	8	2	0	9	6	5	1
	5	8	2	0	6	9	1	3	7	4

DIAGNOSTIC TEST A

Multiply and check:

1. 23	5. 231	9. 34,267	13. 302
3	2	6	2

2. 72	6. 319	10. 8	14. 5,208
4	3	2,532	8

3. 24	7. 874	11. 60	15. 3,000
3	6	3	5

4. 39	8. 1,728	12. 400	16. 4,006
7	9	5	7

17. 50,800
    4

18. 6 × 985

19. Multiply 48 by 9.

20. Find the product of 314 and 8.

RELATED PRACTICE EXAMPLES

Multiply and check:

SET 1

32	11	43	22	21
2	8	2	4	3

SET 2

63	94	52	82	71
3	2	3	2	6

SET 3

23	28	19	15	46
4	3	5	6	2

SET 4

48	65	36	64	59
6	8	7	4	9

SET 5

321	144	542	823	912
3	2	2	3	4

SET 6

217	928	816	191	649
4	3	5	6	2

SET 7

376	593	842	938	697
2	7	5	9	8

SET 8

2143	1,728	5,914	7,896	4,789
2	4	5	7	9

SET 9

24239	69,382	49,663	39,145	84,574
4	9	7	6	8

SET 10

7	8	9	3	6
13	36	537	2182	72,589

SET 11

20	60	4	5	50
8	5	70	80	9

SET 12

700	9	200	100	6
3	900	5	8	800

SET 13

104	203	2	3,012	34,032
2	3	304	3	2

SET 14

208	405	1,806	8	46,084
3	4	7	9,072	5

SET 15

5280	1,760	9,500	82,000	6
8	4	7	5	30,000

SET 16

2004	4,008	30,049	80,005	90,026
2	7	3	6	9

SET 17

3040	4,070	6,080	50,700	40,030
7	6	5	9	8

SET 18

1. 8×21
2. 4×923
3. 6×709
4. $3 \times 5,762$
5. $7 \times 13,758$
6. 5×700
7. $8 \times 5,030$
8. 351×9
9. 605×4
10. $5 \times 2,006$

SET 19

Multiply:

1. 26 by 4
2. 752 by 7
3. 6 by 401
4. 3,600 by 5

5. 5,975 by 8
6. 5,000 by 3
7. 3,002 by 9
8. 1,728 by 4

9. 5,280 by 7
10. 16,000 by 5

SET 20

Find the product of:

1. 144 and 9
2. 6 and 231
3. 640 and 8
4. 5 and 320

5. 4 and 1,000
6. 5,175 and 3
7. 9 and 2,446
8. 6,080 and 7

9. 25,050 and 6
10. 81,041 and 2

DIAGNOSTIC TEST B

Multiply and check:

1. 37
   24

2. 78
   56

3. 485
   92

4. 6,948
   89

5. 45,847
   65

6.   36
   9,967

7. 592
   231

8. 6,342
   358

9. 16,959
   786

10. 4,574
   1,728

11. 74,686
   9,743

12. 38,457
   75,962

13. 8,500
   54

14. 700
   500

15. 208
   144

16. 693
   907

17. 5,009
   69

18. 40,603
   28

19. 8,001
   306

20. 6,080
   705

21. 384 × 597
22. 36 × 407 × 743
23. Multiply 75 by 49.

24. Find the product of 144 and 24.

RELATED PRACTICE EXAMPLES

Multiply and check:

SET 1

23	28	42	19	53
12	25	21	37	14

SET 2

72	93	35	57	74
18	27	49	68	96

SET 3

144	526	967	231	897
23	42	36	47	88

SET 4

4113	6,374	8,439	1,728	6,582
21	35	78	93	46

SET 5

93153	38,642	68,459	84,696	54,587
24	85	47	63	72

SET 6

24	53	32	25	48
312	659	2,978	68,426	76,383

SET 7

144	975	347	583	886
324	638	231	963	697

SET 8

9645	2,786	149	8,327	4,784
529	231	9,687	524	379

SET 9

21462	78,356	65,815	764	15,647
344	492	873	34,687	989

SET 10

2467	6,374	8,622	9,675	4,569
1236	2,462	7,393	8,326	6,271

SET 11

12345	64,632	56,397	3,846	96,749
1728	4,436	8,457	86,798	8,795

SET 12

23814	49,279	57,625	91,352	42,387
16523	82,536	34,719	73,858	29,998

SET 13

50	300	6,000	2,240	3,600
62	27	24	38	375

SET 14

59	8,963	365	640	5,280
30	40	200	3,000	15,000

SET 15

501	409	603	803	3,205
26	32	59	144	475

SET 16

529	69	2,534	59,735	3,842
706	608	109	203	8,067

SET 17

3006	4,009	6,008	9,005	80,006
34	87	365	2,183	176

SET 18

2050	6,080	60,506	40,702	329
16	53	125	6,713	7,070

SET 19

4003	3,009	7,006	20,058	80,002
205	6,082	7,006	1,009	74,004

SET 20

6080	50,306	73,050	46,050	50,903
203	504	8,007	2,500	60,704

SET 21

1. 24×35
2. 87×832
3. $56 \times 4,973$
4. $68 \times 13,764$
5. 156×849

6. $523 \times 6,942$
7. $709 \times 52,723$
8. $408 \times 2,050$
9. 200×503
10. $4,520 \times 3,006$

SET 22

1. $42 \times 37 \times 23$
2. $63 \times 524 \times 201$
3. $30 \times 605 \times 178$
4. $264 \times 671 \times 9$
5. $829 \times 72 \times 485$

6. $273 \times 100 \times 126$
7. $3,000 \times 20 \times 50$
8. $10 \times 6,020 \times 200$
9. $845 \times 172 \times 674$
10. $3,568 \times 4,123 \times 9,035$

SET 23

Multiply:

1. 32 by 16
2. 50 by 29
3. 18 by 45
4. 296 by 83
5. 144 by 97

6. 314 by 52
7. 400 by 125
8. 871 by 408
9. 693 by 834
10. 1,265 by 200

SET 24

Find the product of:

1. 56 and 17
2. 48 and 70
3. 253 and 85
4. 72 and 481
5. 953 and 249

6. 405 and 840
7. 9,700 and 82
8. 762 and 300
9. 649 and 206
10. 5,280 and 487

PRACTICAL APPLICATIONS

1. The auditorium of Franklin High School has 26 rows of 24 seats each. In the lunch room there are 32 tables each accommodating 17 pupils. What is the seating capacity of the auditorium? Of the lunch room? Which is greater? How much greater?

2. Find the leading scorer in the school football league. Thomas made 13 touchdowns, 2 field goals, and 5 points after touchdown. Wilson made 14 touchdowns and 4 points after touchdown. Harrison made 12 touchdowns, 3 field goals, and 9 points after touchdown.

3. In the Forrest High School there are 8 classes with 40 pupils on roll, 15 classes with 41 pupils, and 13 classes with 39 pupils. What is the total enrollment of the school?

4. Charlotte's father saves $85 every month out of his monthly salary of $592. What is his annual salary? How much does he save in a year?

5. David's brother wants to buy an automobile costing $1,250. If he pays $640 in cash, he could pay off the balance in 18 monthly installments of $37 each. How much could he save by paying the entire sum at the time of purchase?

6. How far can a car go on a tankful of gasoline if it averages 16 miles on a gallon and the tank holds 19 gallons?

7. A merchant bought 48 radios at $59 each. He sold them at $76 each. How much profit did he make all together?

8. If 1 inch represents 64 nautical miles, how many nautical miles apart are two cities 13 inches apart on the chart?

9. Find the total number of books needed to make 29 class sets of 36 books each?

10. At an average ground speed of 325 miles per hour, how far can an airplane fly in 14 hours?

11. Each of the 16 major baseball teams has 25 players on its team roster. How many major league players are there in all?

12. If a box contains 144 envelopes, how many envelopes will there be in 26 boxes?

13. How many sheets of writing paper are in 19 packages, each containing 500 sheets?

14. A farmer has 39 rows of pear trees each containing 26 trees. He expects each tree to produce on an average of 29 bushels of pears. How many bushels of pears does the farmer expect from his trees?

15. A merchant purchased 18 dozen shirts at $27 per dozen, 16 dozen ties at $14 per dozen, 30 dozen pairs of socks at $5 per dozen, and 9 dozen belts at $11 per dozen. Find the total cost of the merchandise.

16. (*a*) If sound travels at a speed of 1,088 feet per second, how far does it travel in 1 hour?

(*b*) At a speed of 186,324 miles per second, how far does light travel in 1 hour?

17. Tom's average reading rate is 205 words per minute. How many words can he read in half an hour?

18. Peggy can type an average of 48 words per minute. Her term report contains 2,136 words. Will she be able to type it in 45 minutes?

19. If there are 179 days in the average school year, what is the total number of days one attends the elementary and secondary schools (12 years) when his attendance is perfect?

REFRESH YOUR SKILLS

1. Round off 5,963,499,716 to the nearest million.

2. Add:	**3.** Subtract:	**4.** Multiply:	**5.** Multiply:
9,832	105,000	807	1,728
17,496	98,634	609	853
50,957			
8,268			
594			

EXERCISE 6

DIVISION OF WHOLE NUMBERS
(See "Tests for Divisibility" page 60)

I. Aim: To divide whole numbers.

II. Procedure

1. Find the quotient figure by dividing the one-figure divisor or the trial divisor, when it contains more than one figure, into the first figure or, if necessary, into the first two figures of the dividend. When the divisor contains two or more figures, use as the trial divisor the first figure of the divisor if the next figure on the right is 0, 1, 2, 3, 4, or 5, and increase the first figure of the divisor by one (1) if the next figure on the right is 6, 7, 8, or 9. The largest trial quotient figure that can be used at any one time is 9. (See step 1 of sample solution 2.)

2. Multiply the whole divisor by this quotient figure. Write this product under the corresponding figures in the dividend. If this product is greater than the partial dividend, then use as the trial quotient a figure one less than the figure first tried. (See step 2 of sample solution 2.)

3. Subtract this product from the corresponding numbers in the dividend. If the remainder is greater than the whole divisor, then use as the trial quotient figure one more than the figure tried. (See step 3 of sample solution 2.)

4. Bring down the next figure of the dividend and annex it to the remainder, if any. (See step 4 of sample solution 2.)

5. Using the remainder and the annexed numbers as partial dividends, repeat steps 1 to 4 until the remainder is no longer divisible.

6. Check by multiplying the quotient by the divisor and adding the remainder, if any, to the product. The result should equal the dividend. (See sample solutions 3 and 4.)

III. Sample Solutions

1. Divide 42,574 by 7.

Solution:

$$6,082 \leftarrow \text{quotient}$$
$$\text{divisor} \rightarrow 7\overline{)42,574} \leftarrow \text{dividend}$$

Answer: 6,082

Check:

$$6,082$$
$$\times 7$$
$$\overline{42,574}$$

2. Divide 986 by 29.

Step 1	*Step 2*	*Step 3*	*Step 4*	
3	3	3	3	
$29\overline{)986}$	$29\overline{)986}$	$29\overline{)986}$	$29\overline{)986}$	
	87	87	87	partial
		11	116 $\leftarrow$	dividend

Repeat Step 1.	*Repeat Step 2.*	*Repeat Step 3.*	*Check:*
34	34	34	34
$29\overline{)986}$	$29\overline{)986}$	$29\overline{)986}$	$\times 29$
87	87	87	306
‚116	116	116	68
	116	116	986
Answer: 34		. . .	

3. Divide 45,034 by 89.

Solution:

$$506$$
$$89\overline{)45,034}$$
$$44\ 5$$
$$\overline{534}$$
$$534$$
$$. . .$$

Answer: 506

Check:

$$506$$
$$89$$
$$\overline{4\ 554}$$
$$40\ 48$$
$$\overline{45,034}$$

4. Divide 70,861 by 165.

Solution:

$$429$$
$$165\overline{)70,861}$$
$$66\ 0$$
$$\overline{4\ 86}$$
$$3\ 30$$
$$\overline{1\ 561}$$
$$1\ 485$$
$$\text{Remainder} \rightarrow 76$$

Check:

$$429$$
$$165$$
$$\overline{2\ 145}$$
$$25\ 74$$
$$42\ 9$$
$$\overline{70,785}$$
$$76$$
$$\overline{70,861}$$

Answer: 429 R76 or $429\frac{76}{165}$

IV. Definitions

1. The dividend is the number you divide.

2. The divisor is the number by which you divide.

3. The quotient is the answer in division.

4. When the division is not exact, the number left is the remainder.

5. The partial dividend is part of the dividend annexed to the remainder.

6. The symbols ÷ and $\overline{)}$ indicate division.

PRELIMINARY EXAMPLES

Basic Division Facts

Divide:

1. 3)6   4)28   8)8   2)18   9)0   5)20   1)1   6)24   7)42

2. 2)14   3)15   7)35   1)9   5)10   4)32   6)0   8)32   9)63

3. 5)35   2)2   9)45   6)36   7)21   1)0   3)21   4)12   8)24

4. 6)48   9)18   3)0   5)45   1)7   2)4   8)16   7)63   4)4

5. 4)0   6)18   5)5   8)72   2)6   3)27   9)81   1)5   7)14

6. 1)3   8)48   4)24   7)7   6)42   9)54   3)9   2)16   5)0

7. 9)36   5)40   1)2   8)0   3)3   4)20   2)10   7)28   6)54

8. 7)56   1)4   4)16   9)72   8)64   6)6   5)15   2)12   3)18

9. 8)40   4)36   6)30   3)12   5)25   1)8   7)0   9)27   2)8

10. 4)8   2)0   7)49   5)30   6)12   9)9   3)24   8)56   1)6

DIAGNOSTIC TEST A

Divide and check:

1. 2)68   6. 7)427   11. 8)3,928   15. 4)804

2. 3)78   7. 6)552   12. 4)96,852   16. 6)642

3. 2)846   8. 4)8,448   13. 7)36,533   17. 2)6,008

4. 4)928   9. 3)8,526   14. 3)6,900   18. 5)5,030

5. 6)834   10. 6)9,852

Write quotient and remainder (**19** and **20**).

19. 7)156   **20.** 4)6,923

Write remainder as fraction in lowest terms (**21, 22, 23**).

21. 6)935   **22.** 8)4,668   **23.** 7)843

24. 8,795 ÷ 5   **25.** Divide 3,870 by 9.

RELATED PRACTICE EXAMPLES

Divide and check:

SET 1

3)93   2)46   3)66   4)84   2)28

SET 2

2)34   3)87   5)85   6)96   4)64

SET 3

3)693   2)682   4)488   2)646   3)366

SET 4

6)846   4)496   3)819   7)798   8)968

SET 5

4)944   5)745   6)918   3)861   7)882

SET 6

6)246   9)729   2)128   3)216   4)368

SET 7

7)504   4)348   6)468   5)315   8)608

SET 8

2)6448   4)8,484   3)9,636   2)2,486   3)6,993

SET 9

5)8255   8)9,928   6)6,894   3)9,738   4)9,568

SET 10

3)7491   4)9,156   6)8,748   2)9,574   5)7,490

SET 11

7)5243   6)2,154   8)6,792   4)3,392   6)4,584

SET 12

3)69876   7)96,544   4)95,860   2)76,952   6)85,794

SET 13

8)72976   5)37,460   7)40,992   3)14,595   4)29,984

SET 14

$4\overline{)840}$ $2\overline{)9,680}$ $3\overline{)3,600}$ $5\overline{)2,000}$ $6\overline{)90,000}$

SET 15

$2\overline{)608}$ $3\overline{)903}$ $2\overline{)4,082}$ $4\overline{)8,408}$ $3\overline{)9,060}$

SET 16

$5\overline{)525}$ $4\overline{)836}$ $8\overline{)8,416}$ $6\overline{)67,218}$ $2\overline{)81,106}$

SET 17

$3\overline{)9003}$ $2\overline{)8,004}$ $2\overline{)60,024}$ $4\overline{)40,008}$ $5\overline{)50,005}$

SET 18

$3\overline{)6012}$ $6\overline{)24,036}$ $4\overline{)80,032}$ $2\overline{)10,010}$ $2\overline{)60,180}$

SET 19

Write quotient and remainder:

$5\overline{)14}$ $3\overline{)553}$ $6\overline{)4,583}$ $7\overline{)27,645}$ $4\overline{)98,622}$

SET 20

Write quotient and remainder:

$6\overline{)65}$ $8\overline{)243}$ $3\overline{)8,582}$ $5\overline{)38,403}$ $6\overline{)98,405}$

SET 21

Write remainder as a fraction in lowest terms:

$9\overline{)35}$ $5\overline{)74}$ $4\overline{)685}$ $6\overline{)4,657}$ $8\overline{)89,749}$

SET 22

Write remainder as a fraction in lowest terms:

$4\overline{)78}$ $6\overline{)940}$ $8\overline{)7,534}$ $8\overline{)37,580}$ $6\overline{)59,374}$

SET 23

Write remainder as a fraction in lowest terms:

$6\overline{)365}$ $8\overline{)644}$ $3\overline{)812}$ $9\overline{)9,815}$ $7\overline{)85,264}$

SET 24

1. $438 \div 3$
2. $8,694 \div 2$
3. $69,376 \div 9$
4. $42,965 \div 6$
5. $94,500 \div 4$

6. $37,624 \div 8$
7. $23,583 \div 7$
8. $84,215 \div 5$
9. $72,708 \div 9$
10. $91,862 \div 6$

SET 25

1. Divide 932 by 4.
2. Divide 5,795 by 8.
3. Divide 3,482 by 9.
4. Divide 83,007 by 3.
5. Divide 94,075 by 2.

6. Divide 42,840 by 5.
7. Divide 51,382 by 6.
8. Divide 65,424 by 8.
9. Divide 38,971 by 9.
10. Divide 70,056 by 7.

DIAGNOSTIC TEST B

Divide and check:

1. $24\overline{)96}$
2. $38\overline{)228}$
3. $27\overline{)567}$
4. $14\overline{)1,022}$
5. $26\overline{)8,164}$
6. $85\overline{)71,995}$
7. $48\overline{)61,584}$
8. $54\overline{)349,272}$
9. $60\overline{)28,980}$
10. $57\overline{)34,656}$
11. $36\overline{)230,400}$

12. $42\overline{)126,252}$
13. $63\overline{)27,044}$

Write remainder as fraction in Ex. 14:

14. $72\overline{)45,018}$
15. $144\overline{)864}$
16. $174\overline{)7,482}$
17. $298\overline{)11,026}$
18. $357\overline{)44,982}$
19. $946\overline{)810,722}$
20. $907\overline{)61,676}$

21. $506\overline{)405,306}$
22. $843\overline{)522,660}$
23. $400\overline{)338,000}$
24. $391\overline{)185,805}$

Write remainder as fraction in Ex. 25:

25. $144\overline{)75,984}$
26. $1,760\overline{)14,080}$
27. $1,728\overline{)101,952}$
28. $8,526\overline{)3,939,012}$

29. $5,280\overline{)23,876,160}$
30. $8,005\overline{)4,306,690}$

31. $21,714 \div 231$
32. Divide 300,960 by 5,280.

RELATED PRACTICE EXAMPLES

Divide and check:

SET 1

$16\overline{)80}$ $23\overline{)92}$ $27\overline{)81}$ $24\overline{)72}$ $19\overline{)76}$

SET 2

$54\overline{)378}$ $43\overline{)301}$ $48\overline{)432}$ $83\overline{)332}$ $67\overline{)536}$

SET 3

$32\overline{)896}$ $48\overline{)672}$ $29\overline{)667}$ $12\overline{)324}$ $24\overline{)984}$

SET 4

48)3120   24)1,824   72)2,664   95)6,935   41)1,845

SET 5

37)4551   26)8,918   34)7,344   17)3,366   52)9,672

SET 6

72)39456   85)41,820   94)73,508   46)30,038   77)64,603

SET 7

29)70035   32)49,984   17)48,892   25)81,325   48)74,976

SET 8

43)224417   54)526,932   64)212,416   71)138,947   89)61,365

SET 9

30)5670   50)37,450   70)61,040   80)41,840   40)37,040

SET 10

36)25380   69)41,607   37)29,933   55)22,330   83)25,232

SET 11

15)3300   57)51,300   30)144,000   46)358,800   66)574,200

SET 12

12)24048   24)120,168   69)276,207   56)392,448   35)105,140

SET 13

56)48297   75)19,366   82)37,981   48)36,923   64)24,869

SET 14

Write remainder as a fraction:

14)2412   38)17,993   52)47,639   24)58,819   78)651,092

SET 15

213)693   128)896   427)3,416   640)1,920   569)3,414

SET 16

173)8996   144)6,768   321)8,025   234)5,382   285)9,690

SET 17

229)10992   231)13,398   929)52,024   745)51,405   144)10,800

Set 18

152)95608   289)42,194   223)66,008   475)75,525   337)95,708

Set 19

863)650702   629)367,336   847)337,953   768)433,920   487)363,302

Set 20

208)7696   706)55,068   302)28,086   405)25,110   504)49,392

Set 21

106)31906   204)124,032   903)367,521   502)355,416   805)329,245

Set 22

478)152960   640)524,800   372)219,480   679)549,990   725)304,500

Set 23

200)85200   300)290,100   700)408,800   500)304,500   600)492,000

Set 24

692)365489   375)323,467   927)429,227   589)433,704   866)583,759

Set 25

Write remainder as a fraction:

320)149520   231)188,518   144)41,088   625)294,625   258)191,049

Set 26

5280)42240   2,774)22,192   2,240)20,160   8,304)74,736   4,568)22,840

Set 27

6080)255360   1,728)115,776   9,286)529,302
        3,974)337,790   5,280)153,120

Set 28

8366)3906922   5,280)2,481,600   5,863)2,872,870
        1,728)1,627,776   6,080)1,824,000

Set 29

2240)12286400   8,267)31,050,852   1,760)17,321,920
        2,794)12,802,108   3,246)24,377,460

Set 30

7006)4581924   6,080)4,572,160   3,600)2,109,600

9,004)1,854,824   3,007)1,202,800

Set 31	Set 32
1. $408 \div 24$	1. Divide 5,616 by 144.
2. $93,940 \div 35$	2. Divide 13,398 by 231.
3. $287,246 \div 41$	3. Divide 153,600 by 320.
4. $173,712 \div 231$	4. Divide 342,720 by 2,240.
5. $401,280 \div 5,280$	5. Divide 1,487,200 by 1,760.

TESTS FOR DIVISIBILITY

The following tests may be used to determine whether a given number is divisible (can be divided exactly so that there is no remainder) by 2, 3, 4, 5, 6, 8, 9, or 10.

(*a*) A number is divisible by 2 only if it ends in 0, 2, 4, 6, or 8.

All even numbers are divisible by 2.

(*b*) A number is divisible by 3 only if the sum of its digits is divisible by 3.

To test whether 4,971 is divisible by 3, first find the sum of the digits of 4,971 ($4 + 9 + 7 + 1$). This sum is 21, which is divisible by 3. Therefore, 4,971 is divisible by 3.

(*c*) A number is divisible by 4 only if it is an even number* and the number represented by the last two digits (tens and units digits) is divisible by 4. Numbers ending in two zeros are divisible by 4.

To test whether the even number 92,136 is divisible by 4, check whether the number formed by the last two digits (36) is divisible by 4. Since 36 is divisible by 4, therefore 92,136 is divisible by 4.

(*d*) A number is divisible by 5 only if it ends in 5 or 0.

The number 3,645 ends in a 5; therefore it is divisible by 5. The number 430 ends in a 0; therefore it is divisible by 5.

(*e*) A number is divisible by 6 only if it is an even number and the sum of its digits is divisible by 3.

To test whether 9,558 is divisible by 6, first check whether 9,558 is an even number. Then check whether the sum of the digits of 9,558 ($9 + 5 + 5 + 8$) is divisible by 3. The sum of the digits is 27 which is divisible by 3. Therefore 9,558 is divisible by 6.

*See p. 66.

(*f*) A number is divisible by 8 only if it is an even number and the number represented by the last three digits (hundreds, tens, and units digits) is divisible by 8. Numbers ending in three zeros are divisible by 8. Use this test only when the number is 1,000 or larger.

> The even number 39,712 is divisible by 8. Observe that the number formed by the last three digits (712) is divisible by 8.

(*g*) A number is divisible by 9 only if the sum of its digits is divisible by 9.

> 50,382 is divisible by 9. Observe that the sum of the digits of 50,382 (5 + 0 + 3 + 8 + 2) is 18 and 18 is divisible by 9.

(*h*) A number is divisible by 10 only if it ends in 0.

> 9,670 is divisible by 10 because it ends in 0.

PRACTICE PROBLEMS

1. (*a*) Is 68,532 divisible by 2?   by 3?   by 9?   by 6?
   (*b*) Is 384,670 divisible by 4?   by 2?   by 5?   by 10?
   (*c*) Is 165,501 divisible by 6?   by 9?   by 3?   by 2?
   (*d*) Is 483,000 divisible by 10?   by 5?   by 8?   by 3?
   (*e*) Is 759,258 divisible by 3?   by 8?   by 4?   by 6?

2. Determine whether the following numbers are divisible:

(*a*) By 3:	417	2,853	7,415	29,538	593,618
(*b*) By 5:	251	8,970	1,565	38,006	686,400
(*c*) By 8:	4,794	1,352	86,727	75,000	827,223
(*d*) By 2:	518	6,359	4,506	83,000	179,244
(*e*) By 9:	837	5,706	89,784	40,389	779,895
(*f*) By 4:	536	9,252	1,874	92,425	954,768
(*g*) By 6:	914	8,349	6,858	27,291	906,702
(*h*) By 10:	470	3,000	20,105	90,790	813,060

PRACTICAL APPLICATIONS

1. Mr. Watson earns an annual salary of $6,468. What is his monthly salary?

2. Joan's mother bought a washing machine costing $285. If she paid $45 in cash and arranged to pay off the balance in 8 equal monthly payments, what is the amount of each payment?

3. How long will it take a man driving at a speed of 40 miles per hour to travel from Los Angeles to San Francisco, a distance of 420 miles? If the car averages 15 miles on a gallon of gasoline, how many gallons are required to make the trip?

4. Two cities, 350 miles apart, are to be plotted on a chart with the scale 1 inch = 25 miles. How many inches apart should they be plotted?

5. A ship reached port after steaming for a distance of 1,121 nautical miles at a speed of 19 knots (1 knot = 1 nautical mile per hour). How many hours did it take?

Averages

1. In the last football game of the season the Hartville High School team gained 168 yards from scrimmage in 28 tries. How many yards gained did they average per try?

2. The total attendance at the Bartram Junior High School for the 21 school days in March was 19,467. What was the average daily attendance?

3. An airplane left airport A at 1 P.M. and reached airport B, 1,176 miles away, at 4 P.M. Find the average speed of the airplane.

4. In 16 basketball games, Ted Harris scored 83 field goals (2 points each) and 26 foul goals (1 point each). What is his average in points per game?

5. When Mr. Conroy had the tank of his car filled with gasoline, he noticed that the speedometer read 29,853. The next time he stopped for gasoline, it required 13 gallons to fill the tank. If the speedometer then read 30,074, how many miles was the car averaging on a gallon of gasoline?

To find the average of 2 or more numbers, add the given numbers, then divide the sum by the number of given numbers. If there are 2 numbers given, divide their sum by 2, if there are 3 numbers given, divide their sum by 3, etc.

6. Find the average of the following numbers:

(a) 1,389 men and 2,563 men.
(b) 46 pupils, 35 pupils, 38 pupils, 41 pupils, and 45 pupils.
(c) 225 miles, 199 miles, and 206 miles.
(d) 8 inches, 15 inches, 9 inches, and 17 inches.
(e) $28, $19, $23, $34, $20, and $44.

7. What is a student's average in arithmetic if he receives the following marks: 87, 94, 72, 65, 81, 100, 75, and 90?

8. A class with an enrollment of 43 pupils had 1 absentee on Monday, 2 on Tuesday, 3 on Wednesday, 1 on Thursday, and 3 on Friday. Find the average daily attendance for the week.

9. What was the average daily temperature for a week in a western city if the temperatures were as follows: Monday, 58°; Tuesday, 62°; Wednesday, 59°; Thursday, 56°; Friday, 53°; Saturday, 57°; and Sunday, 61°.

10. The weights of the seven linemen on the State College football team starting with the left end are 170, 195, 185, 188, 174, 215, and 182 pounds respectively. The weights of the backfield men are 168, 182, 175, and 179 pounds. What is the average weight per man in the line? In the backfield? Of the entire team?

11. In the championship football game the four backs of the Springdale High School team played as follows: Johnson in 9 tries gained 108 yards, Bell in 13 tries gained 104 yards, Leonard in 4 tries gained 20 yards, and Tompkins in 3 tries gained 36 yards. Find each player's average gain per try. Find the team's average gain per try.

12. The total enrollment in the 5 freshman sections at the Fairmount High School is 185 pupils; in 4 sophomore sections, 152 pupils; in 4 junior sections, 164 pupils; and in 3 senior sections, 123 pupils. What is the average pupil enrollment per section for each grade? For the entire school?

REFRESH YOUR SKILLS

1. Round off 409,261 to the nearest hundred.

2. Add: **3.** Subtract: **4.** Multiply: **5.** Divide:

2. Add:	3. Subtract:	4. Multiply:	5. Divide:
916	483,251	6,080	875)619,500
3,827	479,628	905	
54,296			
8,689			
26,778			

REVIEW

1. Write each of the following numerals as a word statement:
(*a*) 4,998,281   (*b*) 67,050,003   (*c*) 703,428,986
(*d*) 2,000,083,000   (*e*) 401,575,700,000

2. Round off: (*a*) 275,648 to the nearest hundred; (*b*) 19,841,007 to the nearest million; (*c*) 386,248,500 to the nearest hundred thousand; (*d*) 7,009,989 to the nearest thousand; (*e*) 4,952,426 to the nearest ten thousand.

3. Add:

(*a*)	(*b*)	(*c*)	(*d*)
5894	68,299	82,625	659,693
7579	85,067	49,836	429,774
6658	3,188	76,257	787,309
8784	59,083	34,967	169,497
9679	4,348	25,814	858,935
			589,788

(*e*) Find the sum of: 462; 8,395; 1,984; 26; 3,572

4. Subtract:

(*a*)	(*b*)	(*c*)	(*d*)
8392	25,703	610,324	7,800,000
5487	9,698	280,719	5,975,008

(*e*) Subtract 438,794 from 647,600.

5. Multiply:

(*a*)	(*b*)	(*c*)	(*d*)
48	207	896	1,509
93	900	759	3,084

(*e*) Multiply 685 by 45.

6. Divide:
(*a*) 67)3953   (*b*) 75)29,850   (*c*) 905)8,913,345

(*d*) 5,280)4,609,440   (*e*) Divide 561,660 by 138.

7. The Amazon River is 3,900 miles long and the St. Lawrence is 1,945 miles long. How many miles longer is the Amazon River?

8. Last year Joan's father received $5,350 salary, $1,785 commission, and $495 bonus. Find the total amount of his earnings for the year.

9. A boat sailed from Panama to Jacksonville, a distance of 1,560 miles in 78 hours. What speed did it average for the trip?

10. An electric appliance dealer during the last month purchased 15 refrigerators at $298 each, 36 electric irons at $13 each, 20 washing machines at $195 each, 12 clothes dryers at $179 each, 24 television sets at $207 each, and 48 radios at $34 each. What was the total cost of the merchandise?

11. Find the increase in population in the Northeast region of the United States if in 1950 the population was 39,477,986 and in 1960 it was 44,667,819.

12. Alaska has a land area of 591,065 square miles and an inland water area of 15,335 square miles while Hawaii has a land area of 6,415 square miles and an inland water area of 9 square miles. Find the total area of each state and the difference in their total areas.

KEYED ACHIEVEMENT TEST

For additional practice turn to the exercise indicated by the numerals in the circles.

1. Write 4,010,001 as a word statement.   ①

2. Round off 1,290,075,986 to the nearest million.   ②

3. Add:
68,426
99,587
42,686   ③
87,967
95,989

4. Subtract:
724,005
296,486   ④

5. Multiply:
8,004
 609   ⑤

6. Divide:
869)7,873,140   ⑥

REFRESH YOUR SKILLS

1. Write 34,522,010,427,895 as a word statement.

2. Round off 657,493,056 to the nearest hundred thousand.

3. Add:
684,527
527,839
399,785
687,596
748,695

4. Subtract:
4,328,053
 857,949

5. Multiply:
7,096 × 8,967

6. Divide:
7,386)37,646,442

ADDITIONAL TOPICS

Odd and Even Numbers

Whole numbers may be separated into even and odd numbers. An even number is a whole number that is divisible by two (2). An odd number is a whole number that is not divisible by two (2). Zero is considered an even whole number.

PRACTICE PROBLEMS

1. Which of the following numbers are odd numbers? Which are even numbers?

   9   4   76   31   800   965   3,648   9,027

2. Write the numerals of all one-digit even natural numbers.

3. Write the numerals of all the odd numbers greater than 10 and less than 20.

4. Choose any two odd numbers. Is their sum an odd number or an even number? Is their product an odd number or an even number?

5. Choose any two even numbers. Is their sum an odd number or an even number? Is their product an odd number or an even number?

6. Choose any odd number and any even number. Is their sum an odd number or an even number? Is their product an odd number or an even number?

7. Is one more than any whole number an even number? Is two more than any whole number an even number?

8. Is one more than any even number an odd number? Is one more than any odd number an even number? Is two more than any even number an odd number or an even number? Is there an odd number between every pair of even numbers? Is there an even number between every pair of odd numbers?

9. Is two times any natural number an odd number or an even number? Is the square* of any odd number an even number or an odd number? Is the square of any even number an odd number or an even number?

* See page 256.

10. Given the set of odd numbers: 1, 3, 5, 7, 9, 11, 13, 15, etc., find the sum of the first two odd numbers, first three odd numbers, first four odd numbers. What is the relation between the number of addends and their sum. What is the sum of the first 6 consecutive odd numbers beginning with 1 without using addition? First 8 consecutive odd numbers? First 15 consecutive odd numbers? First 40 consecutive odd numbers? First 100 consecutive odd numbers?

Prime and Composite Numbers

Whole numbers other than 0 and 1 may be separated into prime and composite numbers.

A prime number is a whole number other than 0 and 1 which is divisible only by itself and by 1 and by no other whole number.

A composite number is a whole number other than 0 and 1 which is not a prime number but can be expressed as a product of two or more smaller whole numbers. On page 75 we shall see how a composite number can be expressed as a product of prime numbers.

A method called the Sieve of Eratosthenes may be used to find prime numbers less than a given number. To find prime numbers less than 30 by this method, we write the numerals 2 to 29 inclusive (1 is excluded; it is not a prime number) as follows:

2 3 ~~4~~ 5 ~~6~~ 7 ~~8~~ ~~9~~ ~~10~~ 11 ~~12~~ 13 ~~14~~ ~~15~~
~~16~~ 17 ~~18~~ 19 ~~20~~ ~~21~~ ~~22~~ 23 ~~24~~ ~~25~~ ~~26~~ ~~27~~ ~~28~~ 29

We cross out numerals representing numbers which are not primes by the following procedure:

(1) 2 is a prime number. We retain numeral 2 but we cross out every second numeral after 2. These numerals represent multiples of 2. See page 77.

(2) 3 is a prime number. We retain numeral 3 but we cross out every third numeral after 3. These numerals represent multiples of 3. Some of the numerals are already crossed out but they are included in the count.

(3) Numeral 4 is already crossed out.

(4) 5 is a prime number. We retain numeral 5 but we cross out every fifth numeral after 5. These numerals represent multiples of 5.

(5) We continue this process until all numerals for numbers other than prime numbers are crossed out.

The prime numbers less than 30 are: 2, 3, 5, 7, 11, 13, 17, 19, 23, 29.

Two prime numbers are called twin primes if one number is two more than the other number. 17 and 19 are a pair of twin primes.

PRACTICE PROBLEMS

1. Which of the following numbers are prime numbers?

14   23   79   51   85   97   69   117

2. Which of the following numbers are composite numbers?

81   18   49   2   91   39   53   119

3. Write the numerals naming:

(a) Any four composite numbers greater than 17 and less than 35.

(b) All the one-digit prime numbers.

(c) All the one-digit even prime numbers.

(d) All the one-digit odd prime numbers.

4. Use the Sieve of Eratosthenes to find all the prime numbers less than 100.

5. What twin primes may be found among numbers less than 75?

6. Are all even numbers composite numbers? If not, name an even prime number.

7. Are all odd numbers prime numbers? If not, name an odd composite number.

8. Find two prime numbers (factors*) which when multiplied give the product of:

(a) 15   (b) 26   (c) 143   (d) 58   (e) 178   (f) 85

9. Find two prime numbers which when added give the sum of:

(a) 8   (b) 14   (c) 32   (d) 76   (e) 98   (f) 110

Goldbach, a mathematician, guessed that "Any even number greater than 4 can be expressed as the sum of two odd prime numbers." Is this true for each of the above given numbers?

10. (a) Choose any other even number and show that it is the sum of two odd prime numbers. Can you find an even number greater than 4 that is not the sum of two odd prime numbers?

*See page 75.

(b) Choose an odd number that is the sum of two prime numbers. Illustrate this.

(c) Choose an odd number that is the sum of two odd prime numbers. Illustrate this.

Sets

In mathematics a set is a well-defined collection of objects. The symbol consisting of a pair of braces { } is used to designate a set with the objects (called either members or elements of the set) listed or written inside the braces. The set of one-digit odd natural numbers may be expressed as: {1, 3, 5, 7, 9}. A set of this type consisting of a limited number of elements is called a finite set. It is unnecessary to repeat an element when listing the elements of a set.

When the set contains an unlimited number of elements (called an infinite set) like the set of all natural numbers, it may be expressed as:

$$\{all\ natural\ numbers\} \quad or \quad \{1,\ 2,\ 3,\ 4,\ 5,\ \cdots\}$$

The three dots at the end of 1, 2, 3, 4, 5, mean "and so on endlessly." In the set {1, 2, 3, $\cdots$, 12} the three dots mean "and so on up to and including."

A set containing no members is called a null set or empty set and is designated either by ϕ or { }. {0} is not an empty set. It contains one element which is zero (0).

Sets which contain exactly the same elements are called equal sets. {1, 2, 3, 4} and {2, 4, 1, 3} are equal sets. The elements may be listed or written in any order. Sets which contain the same number of elements are called equivalent sets. {0, 1, 2, 3, 4}, {5, 6, 7, 8, 9}, and {1, 3, 4, 7, 9} are equivalent sets.

Capital letters are used to designate sets like: $A = \{0, 1, 2, 3, 4\}$. The braces mean "the set of" or "the set whose members are." Thus $A = \{0, 1, 2, 3, 4\}$ is read "A is the set whose members are zero, one, two, three, four."

The epsilon symbol "ϵ" or the "$\in$" is used to indicate that an object is a member of the set whereas the symbol "$\notin$" indicates that the object is not a member of the set. In the above set $3 \in A$ but $6 \notin A$. Small letters may be used as names for members of sets.

PRACTICE PROBLEMS

1. For each of the following write the set that lists within braces:

 (a) Elements 1, 4, 9, 16, 25, and 36.

 (b) The first eight letters of our alphabet.

 (c) The names of the seven days of the week.

 (d) The names of all the oceans of the world.

 (e) The one-digit odd prime numbers.

 (f) All whole numbers greater than 5 and less than 11.

 (g) All natural numbers less than 9.

 (h) The two-digit odd numbers between 18 and 30.

 (i) All the two-digit numbers that are divisible by 7.

 (j) All composite numbers greater than 47 and less than 59.

2. Read each of the following:

 (a) {21, 23, 25, 27, 29}

 (b) {u, v, w, x, y, z}

 (c) {0, 3, 6, 9, 12, 15, 18}

 (d) {Truman, Eisenhower, Kennedy, Johnson}

 (e) {New York, California, Pennsylvania, Illinois, Ohio, Texas}

3. Read, or write in words, each of the following:

 (a) $T = $ {all odd numbers}

 (b) $D = $ {0, 6, 12, 18, 24, 30}

 (c) $R = $ {3, 7, 11, 15, 19, 23, 27, 31, 35}

 (d) $N = $ {Seattle, Boston, Miami, Dallas, Kansas City}

4. Write using the proper symbols:

 (a) 6 is an element of set G

 (b) p is not an element of set S

 (c) 17 is not a member of set J

 (d) m is a member of set H

5. Which of the following sets are pairs of equal sets?

 $A = $ {4, 8, 12, 16} $D = $ {4, 8, 10, 16}

 $B = $ {2, 3, 5, 7, 11} $E = $ {7, 3, 11, 2, 5}

 $C = $ {2, 3, 7, 11, 9} $F = $ {12, 4, 16, 8}

6. Which of the following sets are pairs of equivalent sets?

 $A = $ {3, 9, 16, 22} $D = $ {11, 9, 15, 4, 6}

 $B = $ {2, 11, 15, 9, 3, 7} $E = $ {8, 4, 9, 7}

 $C = $ {0, 1, 2, 3, 4, 5, 6, 7} $F = $ {20, 21, 22, 23, 24, 25}

7. If $L = \{$all whole numbers that are divisible by 8$\}$, which of the following are members of set L?

    16   42   56   84   108   140   176   288   300   1,000

8. If $N = \{$all even numbers greater than 15 and less than 33$\}$, which of the following are *not* members of set N?

    36   18   24   53   31   16   27   14   19   30

9. If $R = \{9, 10, 12, 13, 16, 17, 18, 20\}$, which of the following statements are true?

(a) $13 \in R$ (c) $18 \notin R$ (e) $\;8 \in R$
(b) $15 \in R$ (d) $11 \notin R$ (f) $14 \notin R$

10. If $B = \{$all two-digit prime numbers$\}$, which of the following statements are false?

(a) $93 \in B$ (c) $\;7 \notin B$ (e) $81 \in B$
(b) $47 \in B$ (d) $29 \notin B$ (f) $57 \notin B$

11. Which of the following are infinite sets? Which are finite sets?

(a) $\{0, 1, 2, 3, 4, 5, 6, 7, 8, 9\}$
(b) $\{0, 1, 2, 3, 4, \cdots\}$
(c) $\{$all even numbers$\}$
(d) $\{$entire population of the United States$\}$
(e) $\{$all whole numbers greater than 4 and less than 25$\}$
(f) $\{$all whole numbers less than 4 and greater than 25$\}$

12. Which of the following is a null set?

(a) The set of all even numbers that are divisible by 3.
(b) The set of all prime numbers that are divisible by 5.
(c) The set of all odd numbers that are divisible by 2.

Subsets

If every member of one set is also a member of a second set, then the first set is said to be a subset of the second set. Any subset of a set that is not the whole set is called a proper subset. Since any set is considered to be a subset of itself and the null or empty set is considered to be a subset of every set, the subsets of any set include: all the proper subsets, the null set, and the whole set itself.

When a particular set in a discussion has one or more subsets, this overall set, usually designated U, is called the universal set or universe.

A subset may be represented by either the same capital letter that is used for the whole set but with a subscript or by any other capital letter.

The subsets of $M = \{1, 2, 3\}$ are:

$M_1 = \{1, 2, 3\}$, $M_2 = \{1, 2\}$, $M_3 = \{1, 3\}$, $M_4 = \{2, 3\}$,
$M_5 = \{1\}$, $M_6 = \{2\}$, $M_7 = \{3\}$, $M_8 = \phi$

The symbols $\subset$, $\supset$, $\subseteq$ and $\supseteq$ are used to indicate that one set is a subset of another, with symbols $\subset$ and $\supset$ used with proper subsets only and $\subseteq$ and $\supseteq$ used with all sets.

$B \subset D$ or $D \supset B$ indicates that B is a proper subset of D and is read "B is properly contained in D."

$B \subseteq D$ or $D \supseteq B$ is read "B is contained in D."

PRACTICE PROBLEMS

1. Read, or write in words, each of the following:

    (a) $M \subset A$ (c) $B \subseteq T$

    (b) $K \supset S$ (d) $\{3, 5, 7\} \subset \{2, 3, 4, 5, 6, 7, 8\}$

2. If $D = \{1, 2, 4, 5, 6, 8, 9, 10\}$, $E = \{2, 6, 8, 9\}$,   and $F = \{1, 2, 4, 5, 6, 8, 9\}$, is

    (a) E a subset of D?   (c) F a subset of E?

    (b) F a subset of D?   (d) D a subset of F?

3. (a) Is $\{1, 3, 8, 12\}$ a subset of $\{0, 1, 2, 3, 7, 8, 10, 11, 12\}$?

    (b) Is {Florida, Ohio, Utah} a subset of {all the states of the United States}?

    (c) Is $\{4, 5, 8, 9, 12, 17\}$ a subset of $\{3, 4, 5, 6, 7, 8, 9, 13, 14, 17, 18\}$?

    (d) Is {all odd numbers} a subset of {all whole numbers}?

    (e) Is {all prime numbers} a subset of {all odd numbers}?

4. If $R = \{$all natural numbers$\}$, $S = \{$all even whole numbers$\}$, $T = \{$all whole numbers divisible by 4$\}$, and $Z = \{8, 16, 20, 36, 42\}$, which of the following statements are true?

    (a) $S \subset R$ (c) $T \subset R$ (e) $T \subset S$

    (b) $Z \subset T$ (d) $Z \subset S$ (f) $R \subset Z$

5. If $M = \{$all even prime numbers$\}$, $N = \{1, 2, 3, 4, 5, 6, 7, 9,$ $11, 13\}$, $P = \{$all one-digit odd whole numbers$\}$, and $Q = \{$all one-digit even whole numbers$\}$, which of the following statements are false?

(a) $M \subset N$ (c) $N \subset P$ (e) $P \subset N$
(b) $Q \subset N$ (d) $M \subset Q$ (f) $Q \subset P$

6. Write all the possible subsets of:

(a) $\{0, 1\}$ (c) $\{a, b, c, d\}$
(b) $\{1\}$ (d) $\{0, 1, 2, 3, 4\}$
(e) $\{$all odd natural numbers less than 10$\}$
(f) $\{$all two-digit prime numbers greater than 70$\}$

7. How many subsets does a set have if it contains:

(a) 2 members?   (b) 3 members?   (c) 4 members?   (d) 5 members?   (e) n members?

Operations with Sets

The operation of intersection, indicated by the symbol $\cap$, is used with two sets to find the set composed of the common elements that belong to both sets. $B \cap D$ is read "B intersection D" or "the intersection of B and D" or "B cap D."

The operation of union, indicated by the symbol $\cup$, is used with two sets to find the set composed of those elements which are in either of the two given sets or in both sets. $B \cup D$ is read "B union D" or "the union of B and D" or "B cup D."

If $E = \{5, 6, 7, 8, 9\}$ and $F = \{1, 3, 5, 7, 9\}$, then

$E \cap F = \{5, 7, 9\}$ $E \cup F = \{1, 3, 5, 6, 7, 8, 9\}$

Only elements 5, 7, 9 appear   The common elements are
   in both sets   only written once

A third operation is the operation used to find the complement of a set with respect to a given universe. Here we find the set of elements in the universe which are not in the given set. The symbol for the complement is a bar over the letter like $\overline{B}$, or the symbol $'$ on the upper right of the letter like B', or the symbol $\sim$ preceding the letter like $\sim B$. $\overline{B}$ is read "B bar."

If $U = \{0, 1, 2, 3, 4, 5, 6, 7, 8, 9\}$ and $R = \{0, 2, 4, 6, 8\}$ then $\overline{R} = \{1, 3, 5, 7, 9\}$

Two sets are said to be disjoint if they have no elements in common. Their intersection is the null set.

$M = \{2, 4, 6, 8, 10\}$ and $N = \{1, 3, 5, 7, 9\}$ are disjoint sets because there is no common element. Thus, $M \cap N = \phi$.

PRACTICE PROBLEMS

1. If $C = \{1, 3, 4, 9, 10\}$, $D = \{2, 5, 6, 7, 8, 9\}$, and $E = \{1, 4, 6, 8, 10\}$, list in braces the elements of the resulting set for each of the following:

(a) $C \cap D$ (c) $E \cap C$ (e) $E \cup D$
(b) $D \cap E$ (d) $D \cup C$ (f) $C \cup E$

2. If $U = \{0, 1, 2, 3, 4, 5, 6, 7, 8, 9\}$ and $T = \{2, 4, 5, 7, 8\}$ what is $\overline{T}$?

3. Which of the following pairs of sets are disjoint sets?

(a) $A = \{0, 2, 5, 7, 9\}$ (c) $E = \{$all prime numbers$\}$
    $B = \{1, 3, 4, 6, 8\}$ $F = \{$all even whole numbers$\}$
(b) $C = \{$all odd natural numbers$\}$
    $D = \{$all even natural numbers$\}$

4. If $U = \{0, 1, 2, 3, 4, 5, 6, 7, 8, 9, 10, 11, 12\}$, $M = \{0, 2, 4, 6, 8, 10, 12\}$, $N = \{1, 3, 7, 9\}$, $D = \{2, 6, 7, 10, 11\}$, and $S = \{0, 3, 6, 9, 12\}$, find each of the following:

(a) $\overline{D}$ (e) $D \cup N$ (i) $S \cap D$ (m) $\overline{M}$
(b) $M \cap N$ (f) $\overline{N}$ (j) $M \cup S$ (n) $M \cup D$
(c) $D \cup S$ (g) $S \cap N$ (k) $\overline{S}$ (o) $D \cap N$
(d) $S \cap M$ (h) $N \cup M$ (l) $D \cap M$ (p) $N \cup S$

5. If $B = \{0, 1, 2, 4, 6, 7\}$, $R = \{1, 3, 5, 7\}$, and $T = \{0, 2, 4, 5\}$,

(a) Does $B \cap R = R \cap B$?
(b) Does $R \cup T = T \cup R$?
(c) Does $(B \cap R) \cap T = B \cap (R \cap T)$?
(d) Does $(B \cup R) \cup T = B \cup (R \cup T)$?
(e) Does $B \cap (R \cup T) = (B \cap R) \cup (B \cap T)$?
(f) Does $B \cup (R \cap T) = (B \cup R) \cap (B \cup T)$?

Factors and Factoring

A factor is any one of the numbers used in multiplication to form a product. To find whether a whole number is a factor, test whether it divides a number exactly with a zero remainder.

Any number that is a factor of each of two or more given whole numbers is called a common factor of the numbers. Sometimes it is called the common divisor of the numbers.

The greatest common factor of two or more whole numbers is the greatest whole number that will divide all the given numbers exactly.

The factors of 16 are: 1, 2, 4, 8, 16

The factors of 24 are: 1, 2, 3, 4, 6, 8, 12, 24

The common factors of 16 and 24 are: 1, 2, 4, 8

The greatest common factor of 16 and 24 is 8.

To factor a natural number means to replace the number by its whole-number factors expressed as an indicated product. There may be two or more whole-number factors in the indicated product.

To factor 18 means to replace 18 by any one of the following:

1×18, 2×9, 3×6, 6×3, 9×2, 18×1, $2 \times 3 \times 3$, $3 \times 2 \times 3, 3 \times 3 \times 2$

The factor 1 is excluded when there are more than two whole-number factors.

Observe that in the indicated products $2 \times 3 \times 3$, $3 \times 2 \times 3$, and $3 \times 3 \times 2$ the factors are the same: 2, 3, and 3, but they appear in different orders. Here the factors are all prime numbers in which case they are called proper factors. Thus a composite number may be expressed as a product of prime numbers and from the above we see that it has only one set of prime factors which may be arranged in different orders.

A composite number is said to be completely factored only if the factors are all prime numbers. To factor completely, find two factors of the given number by inspection and continue to factor any of the resulting factors which are composite numbers until only prime factors result.

Or divide the given number and the resulting quotients successively by prime numbers that divide these numbers exactly until
a quotient of 1 is obtained. The divisors are
the desired prime factors.

$$
\begin{array}{r}
2)\overline{18} \\
3)\overline{9} \\
3)\overline{3} \\
\overline{1}
\end{array}
$$

$$18 = 2 \times 3 \times 3$$

PRACTICE PROBLEMS

1. Is 6 a factor of 24? Is 5 a factor of 40? Is 18 a factor of 90?

2. What is the second factor of the pair of factors when:

(a) 7 is one factor of 21?   (d) 14 is one factor of 98?

(b) 8 is one factor of 56?   (e) 25 is one factor of 1,000?

(c) 18 is one factor of 144?   (f) 10 is one factor of 100,000?

3. Write the whole set of factors of each of the following numbers:

(a) 26	(c) 17	(e) 54	(g) 48	(i) 250	(k) 400
(b) 18	(d) 45	(f) 70	(h) 84	(j) 72	(l) 132

4. What are the factors of 12? What are the factors of 16? What are the common factors of 12 and 16?

5. What are the factors of 36? What are the factors of 108? What are the factors of 81? What are the common factors of 36, 108, and 81?

6. For each of the following sets of numbers, first find the factors of each number, then find their common factors:

(a) 8 and 12	(d) 54 and 72	(g) 24, 60, and 96
(b) 4 and 5	(e) 63 and 84	(h) 56, 140, and 168
(c) 48 and 56	(f) 225 and 150	(i) 84, 144, and 360

7. For each of the following sets of numbers write the set of common factors:

(a) 16 and 18	(d) 45 and 135	(g) 39, 65, and 91
(b) 21 and 9	(e) 8, 10, and 12	(h) 252, 588, and 420
(c) 32 and 104	(f) 36, 108, and 156	(i) 225, 375, and 825

8. What are the factors of 126? What are the factors of 162? What are the common factors of 126 and 162? What is the greatest common factor of 126 and 162?

9. What are the factors of 48? What are the factors of 80? What are the factors of 112? What are the common factors of 48,

80, and 112? What is the greatest common factor of 48, 80, and 112?

10. Find the greatest common factor of each of the following sets of numbers:

(*a*) 16 and 20	(*d*) 35 and 63	(*g*) 18, 54, and 198
(*b*) 3 and 2	(*e*) 150 and 200	(*h*) 34, 85, and 102
(*c*) 54 and 144	(*f*) 120 and 216	(*i*) 250, 375, and 625

11. Factor each of the following numbers as the product of two whole-number factors in as many ways as possible:

(*a*) 24	(*c*) 56	(*e*) 48	(*g*) 144	(*i*) 400
(*b*) 19	(*d*) 42	(*f*) 220	(*h*) 108	(*j*) 360

12. Factor each of the following numbers as the product of prime numbers:

(*a*) 14	(*c*) 54	(*e*) 100	(*g*) 168	(*i*) 960
(*b*) 36	(*d*) 72	(*f*) 135	(*h*) 600	(*j*) 1,000

Number Multiples

A multiple of a given whole number is a product of the given number and another whole number factor. The multiples of 4 are: 0, 4, 8, 12, · · ·. A multiple of a given number is divisible by the given number.

Any number which is a multiple of two or more numbers is called the common multiple of the numbers. Numbers may have many common multiples.

The least common multiple (L.C.M.) of two or more numbers is the smallest natural number which is a multiple of all of them. It is the smallest possible natural number that can be divided exactly by all the given numbers. Although zero (0) is a common multiple of any two or more natural numbers, it is excluded when determining the least common multiple.

The multiples of 4 are: 0, 4, 8, 12, 16, 20, 24, · · ·
The multiples of 6 are: 0, 6, 12, 18, 24, 30, 36, · · ·
The first three common multiples of 4 and 6 are 0, 12, 24.
The least common multiple of 4 and 6 is 12 since 0 is excluded.

The L.C.M. may be determined by factoring each given number as primes and forming a product of these primes using each the greatest number of times it appears in the factored form of any one number.

Since $4 = 2 \cdot 2$
and $6 = 2 \cdot 3$,   therefore L.C.M. $= \overset{4}{\overbrace{2 \cdot 2 \cdot 3}}_{6}$
                                                                L.C.M. $= 12$

PRACTICE PROBLEMS

1. Which of the following numbers are multiples of 4?

28   34   52   78   60   90   106   132   148   302

2. Name five different multiples of each of the following numbers:

(a) 3	(ℓ) 5	(e) 11	(g) 27	(i) 100
(b) 2	(d) 7	(f) 14	(h) 59	(j) 225

3. What are the factors of 24? Is 24 a multiple of each of its factors?

4. Write the set of all multiples of each of the following numbers, listing the first four members:

(a) 8	(c) 10	(e) 40	(g) 75	(i) 120
(b) 9	(d) 32	(f) 17	(h) 96	(j) 275

5. Are all even whole numbers multiples of 2? Are all whole numbers multiples of 1?

6. Is 18 a multiple of 6? Is 18 a multiple of 9? Is 18 a common multiple of 6 and 9?

7. What are the first twenty multiples of 8? Of 12? What are the first six common multiples of 8 and 12?

8. Write the set of common multiples of each of the following, listing the first five members:

(a) 3 and 5	(d) 16 and 18	(g) 4, 8 and 16
(b) 8 and 4	(e) 20 and 25	(h) 12, 18 and 30
(c) 10 and 12	(f) 2, 5 and 8	(i) 14, 21, and 35

9. Is the product of 4 and 10 a common multiple of 4 and 10? Is it the smallest common multiple? If not, what is the smallest natural number that can be divided exactly by both 4 and 10?

10. Find the least common multiple of each of the following sets of numbers:

(a) 3 and 8   (e) 25 and 100   (i) 105 and 150
(b) 6 and 12   (f) 42 and 56   (j) 2, 3 and 4
(c) 15 and 20   (g) 84 and 96   (k) 8, 10 and 12
(d) 16 and 24   (h) 75 and 100   (l) 15, 40 and 75

Expanded Notation

When two equal factors are used in multiplication like 5×5, it may be written in exponential form as 5^2; three equal factors like $7 \times 7 \times 7$ may be written as 7^3; four equal factors like $10 \times 10 \times 10 \times 10$ may be written as 10^4; five equal factors like $2 \times 2 \times 2 \times 2 \times 2$ may be written as 2^5; etc. The small numeral written to the upper right (superscript) of the repeated factor is called an exponent. Here it tells us how many times the factor is being used. The factor that is being repeated is called the *base*.

5^2 is read "five to the second power" or "the second power of five" or "five squared" or "the square of five." 7^3 is read "seven to the third power" or "seven cubed" or "the cube of seven." 10^4 is read "ten to the fourth power." 2^5 is read "two to the fifth power."

Numbers like 10^1, 10^2, 10^3, 10^4, 10^5, 10^6, etc. are called *powers* of 10 and are described in the following table:

$$
\begin{aligned}
10 &= 10 & &= 10^1 \\
100 &= 10 \times 10 & &= 10^2 \\
1{,}000 &= 10 \times 10 \times 10 & &= 10^3 \\
10{,}000 &= 10 \times 10 \times 10 \times 10 & &= 10^4 \\
100{,}000 &= 10 \times 10 \times 10 \times 10 \times 10 & &= 10^5 \\
1{,}000{,}000 &= 10 \times 10 \times 10 \times 10 \times 10 \times 10 & &= 10^6
\end{aligned}
$$

Note in the table that 10 used one time as a factor may be written with the exponent 1; and that the number of zeros found after each digit in the product (first column above) corresponds in each case to the exponent of 10 (third column above).

The complete value of each digit in a decimal numeral is equal to the value of the digit itself times its place value. $800 = 8 \times 100$; $7{,}000 = 7 \times 1{,}000$; etc.

We may write a decimal numeral as a sum of the products of each digit in the numeral and its place value expressed as a power of ten. This method of writing numerals as an indicated sum or polynomial is sometimes called expanded notation

---

The decimal numeral 4,963

$= 4$ thousands $+ 9$ hundreds $+ 6$ tens $\quad + 3$ ones

$= (4 \times 1,000) + (9 \times 100) + (6 \times 10) + (3 \times 1)$

$= (4 \times 10^3) \quad + (9 \times 10^2) \quad + (6 \times 10^1) + (3 \times 1)$

PRACTICE PROBLEMS

1. Read, or write in words, each of the following:
   - (a) 3^4
   - (c) 2^{11}
   - (e) 6^1
   - (g) 5^3
   - (i) 16^7
   - (k) 30^{14}
   - (b) 7^8
   - (d) 10^5
   - (f) 11^9
   - (h) 20^2
   - (j) 35^{10}
   - (l) 1^{25}

2. Write as a numeral:
   - (a) Two to the eighth power
   - (d) Nine cubed
   - (b) Eight to the twelfth power
   - (e) Fifty squared
   - (c) Five to the seventh power
   - (f) Fourteen to the sixth power

3. What is the exponent in: (a) 4^7 (b) 5^1 (c) 10^9 (d) 3^{12}? How many times is the base being used as a factor in each case?

4. Use the exponential form to write:
   - (a) $2 \times 2 \times 2 \times 2$
   - (b) 9×9
   - (c) $5 \times 5 \times 5 \times 5 \times 5$
   - (d) $3 \times 3 \times 3 \times 3 \times 3 \times 3 \times 3 \times 3$
   - (e) $6 \times 6 \times 6 \times 6 \times 6 \times 6 \times 6 \times 6 \times 6 \times 6$
   - (f) $4 \times 4 \times 4 \times 4 \times 4 \times 4 \times 4 \times 4 \times 4 \times 4 \times 4$

5. First express each of the following as a product of a repeated factor, then in exponential form:
   - (a) 16 as a power of 2
   - (c) 49
   - (e) 125
   - (b) 27 as a power of 3
   - (d) 32
   - (f) 64

6. Find the value of each of the following:
   - (a) 16^2
   - (b) 4^4
   - (c) 2^8
   - (d) 3^7
   - (e) 8^3
   - (f) 5^6

7. Express each of the following as a power of ten:
   - (a) 1,000,000
   - (c) 10,000,000,000
   - (b) 100,000,000
   - (d) 1,000,000,000,000

8. Express each of the following as a product of a digit and a power of ten:

(a) 50   (e) 4,000,000   (i) 700,000,000,000
(b) 700   (f) 200,000   (j) 90,000,000,000
(c) 80,000   (g) 50,000,000   (k) 6,000,000,000,000
(d) 6,000   (h) 3,000,000,000   (l) 400,000,000,000,000

9. Express each of the following polynomials as a decimal numeral:

(a) $(6 \times 10^4) + (7 \times 10^3) + (2 \times 10^2) + (9 \times 10^1) + (4 \times 1)$
(b) $(3 \times 10^5) + (5 \times 10^4) + (6 \times 10^3) + (8 \times 10^2) +$
   $(2 \times 10^1) + (7 \times 1)$

10. Write each of the following numerals in expanded form as a polynomial:

(a) 58   (e) 37,026   (i) 46,212,597
(b) 492   (f) 29,142,358   (j) 25,384,569,703
(c) 3,564   (g) 5,688,241   (k) 6,739,158,245
(d) 892,187   (h) 823,917,084   (l) 937,175,486,298

NUMBER SENTENCES

When two numbers are compared by subtraction there are three possibilities. One number may be (a) equal to the other, (b) greater than the other, or (c) less than the other. In any specific case only one of these is true. For example, when the numbers are 6 and 4, it is true that 6 is greater than 4 and it is false that 6 is equal to 4 or 6 is less than 4.

Sentences that deal with numbers are called number sentences. The equality $8 + 9 = 20 - 3$ is a number sentence. It is read "Eight plus nine is equal to twenty minus three." The symbol $=$ is the equality sign. The expressions on both sides of the equality sign designate the same number.

When one number is greater than or less than a second number, an inequality exists. Symbols of inequality include $>$, $<$, $\neq$, $\not>$, and $\not<$. Both inequalities and equalities are number sentences. A sentence that is either true or false is called a statement.

The symbol $=$ means *is equal to*. $9 = 9$ is read "Nine is equal to nine."

The symbol $>$ means *is greater than*. $9 > 5$ is read "Nine is greater than five."

The symbol $<$ means *is less than*. $9 < 12$ is read "Nine is less than twelve."

The symbol $\neq$ means *is not equal to*, $\not>$ means *is not greater than*, and $\not<$ means *is not less than*.

PRACTICE PROBLEMS

1. Read, or write in words, each of the following:

(a) $8 < 20$ (e) $2 + 3 \not< 3 + 2$ (i) $9 \times 7 \not> 12 \times 6$

(b) $6 + 5 = 11$ (f) $13 - 8 \neq 10 + 5$ (j) $11 - 4 > 2 \times 3$

(c) $32 > 41 - 9$ (g) $7 + 1 = 16 \div 2$ (k) $41 - 18 \not< 15 - 15$

(d) $14 \not> 23$ (h) $9 \times 6 < 8 \times 7$ (l) $8 + 5 \neq 8 - 5$

2. Write each of the following sentences symbolically:

(a) Five is equal to three plus two.

(b) Eight is greater than four.

(c) Ten is less than forty-two.

(d) Twenty-one is not equal to eight times five.

(e) The sum of six and nine is not less than the difference between nineteen and eight.

3. Determine which of the following sentences are true and which are false:

(a) $6 + 7 = 7 + 6$ (g) $12 - 3 \neq 3 + 12$

(b) $15 \times 8 = 8 \times 15$ (h) $18 \div 18 \not> 18 - 18$

(c) $25 > 31 - 19$ (i) $4 + 8 \not< 0$

(d) $60 \div 5 < 3^2$ (j) $2 + 5 + 9 < 9 + 5 + 2$

(e) $61 > 9 \times 8$ (k) $5^2 > 2^5$

(f) $0 < 10 - 4$ (l) $6 \times (3 + 7) \neq (6 \times 3) + (3 \times 7)$

Modular Arithmetic

Modular arithmetic is sometimes called clock arithmetic or remainder arithmetic.

Suppose on a five-minute clock which contains the symbols 0, 1, 2, 3, and 4 we add 4 minutes and 3 minutes by counting clockwise beginning at the numeral 0. We reach the numeral 2. Suppose we add 4 minutes and 8 minutes, we again reach the numeral 2.

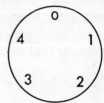

When we add 4 minutes and 13 minutes, again we reach the numeral 2.

Instead of writing $4 + 3 = 2$; $4 + 8 = 2$; $4 + 13 = 2$; in modular arithmetic we write $4 + 3 \equiv 2$ (mod 5); $4 + 8 \equiv 2$ (mod 5); $4 + 13 \equiv 2$ (mod 5).

The sentence $4 + 3 \equiv 2$ (mod 5) is read "Four plus three is congruent to two, modulo five." Mod 5, the abbreviation of modulo five, indicates that 5 numerals are used and is called the modulus number.

Another way to determine the answer to $4 + 3 \equiv$? (mod 5) is the remainder method. Here divide the sum of 4 and 3 by the modulus number 5. Discard the quotient and use the remainder as the answer.

$$4 + 3 = 7; \ 7 \div 5 = 1, \text{ remainder } 2. \qquad \textit{Answer:} \ \mathbf{2}$$

In the case of $4 + 8 \equiv$? (mod 5),
$4 + 8 = 12$; $12 \div 5 = 2$, remainder 2.   *Answer:* **2**

In the case of $4 + 13 \equiv$? (mod 5),
$4 + 13 = 17$; $17 \div 5 = 3$, remainder 2.   *Answer:* **2**

When two numbers, divided by the same modulus number, result in the same remainder although the quotient differ, they are called congruent. In mod 5 the above sums 7, 12, and 17 are congruent numbers because each, when divided by the modulus number 5, gives the remainder 2.

To express a number that is equal to or greater than the modulus number as a congruent number less than the modulus number, divide the given number by the modulus number and use the remainder as the answer.

To add two numbers in modular arithmetic, find the sum of the numbers, then divide this sum by the given modulus number and use the remainder as the answer.

$9 + 7 \equiv$? (mod 4)
$9 + 7 = 16$; $16 \div 4 = 4 \, \text{R} \, 0$
$9 + 7 \equiv 0$ (mod 4)

To multiply two numbers in modular arithmetic, find the product of the numbers, then divide this product by the given modulus number and use the remainder as the answer.

$8 \times 6 \equiv$? (mod 9)
$8 \times 6 = 48$; $48 \div 9 = 5 \, \text{R} \, 3$
$8 \times 6 \equiv 3$ (mod 9)

PRACTICE PROBLEMS

1. Read, or write in words, each of the following:
   - (a) $18 \equiv 2 \pmod 4$
   - (b) $39 \equiv 4 \pmod 7$
   - (c) $9 + 6 \equiv 0 \pmod 5$
   - (d) $12 \times 9 \equiv 4 \pmod 8$
   - (e) $26 + 11 \equiv 1 \pmod{12}$
   - (f) $5 \times 6 \equiv 3 \pmod 9$

2. Write the digits and symbols for:
   - (a) Five is congruent to one, modulo two
   - (b) Sixteen plus nineteen is congruent to zero, modulo seven
   - (c) Eight times seven is congruent to two, modulo six

3. Find each of the following:
   - (a) $7 \equiv ? \pmod 3$
   - (b) $19 \equiv ? \pmod 4$
   - (c) $23 \equiv ? \pmod 9$
   - (d) $49 \equiv ? \pmod{12}$
   - (e) $88 \equiv ? \pmod 6$
   - (f) $61 \equiv ? \pmod 5$
   - (g) $96 \equiv ? \pmod 8$
   - (h) $57 \equiv ? \pmod 2$
   - (i) $101 \equiv ? \pmod 4$
   - (j) $114 \equiv ? \pmod 7$

4. Add in each of the following using the remainder method of modular arithmetic:
   - (a) $3 + 5 \equiv ? \pmod 6$
   - (b) $9 + 13 \equiv ? \pmod 7$
   - (c) $4 + 6 \equiv ? \pmod{12}$
   - (d) $23 + 22 \equiv ? \pmod 9$
   - (e) $12 + 35 \equiv ? \pmod 5$
   - (f) $25 + 18 \equiv ? \pmod 2$
   - (g) $43 + 28 \equiv ? \pmod 4$
   - (h) $57 + 5 \equiv ? \pmod 3$
   - (i) $39 + 19 \equiv ? \pmod 8$
   - (j) $64 + 26 \equiv ? \pmod 9$

5. (a) Are 24 and 18 congruent in mod 6? in mod 3? in mod 4?
   (b) Are 16 and 14 congruent in mod 2? in mod 5? in mod 8?
   (c) Are 36 and 48 congruent in mod 12? in mod 9? in mod 3?
   (d) Are 21 and 49 congruent in mod 4? in mod 7? in mod 9?

6. Multiply in each of the following using the remainder method of modular arithmetic:
   - (a) $2 \times 3 \equiv ? \pmod 9$
   - (b) $8 \times 8 \equiv ? \pmod 5$
   - (c) $7 \times 9 \equiv ? \pmod 8$
   - (d) $12 \times 6 \equiv ? \pmod 2$
   - (e) $5 \times 8 \equiv ? \pmod 3$
   - (f) $9 \times 3 \equiv ? \pmod 7$
   - (g) $18 \times 7 \equiv ? \pmod 4$
   - (h) $11 \times 14 \equiv ? \pmod 5$
   - (i) $20 \times 15 \equiv ? \pmod{12}$
   - (j) $18 \times 25 \equiv ? \pmod 6$

7. Compute as indicated:
   - (a) $15 + 23 \equiv ? \pmod 6$
   - (b) $11 \times 5 \equiv ? \pmod 3$
   - (c) $9 \times 17 \equiv ? \pmod 8$
   - (d) $34 + 59 \equiv ? \pmod{12}$
   - (e) $12 \times 21 \equiv ? \pmod 5$
   - (f) $46 + 75 \equiv ? \pmod 7$

MISCELLANEOUS PRACTICE PROBLEMS

For explanatory material see pages 3, 5, 6, 7, 8, 18.

1. (*a*) Write a 3-digit numeral containing the digits 8, 2, and 5.

(*b*) Write the numeral that names the greatest number possible using the digits 5, 1, 4, and 7.

2. Write five different number names for each of the following numbers:

(*a*) seven (*b*) sixteen (*c*) forty (*d*) twelve (*e*) twenty-seven

3. (*a*) What is the cardinal number in the following sentence? Scott ranked number 2 in his class of 125 pupils.

(*b*) What is the ordinal number in the following sentence?

In the baseball line-up containing 9 players, Steve batted number 3.

4. What number corresponds to the point marked:

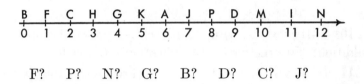

F?   P?   N?   G?   B?   D?   C?   J?

5. What letter labels the point corresponding to each of the following numbers:

3?   6?   11?   2?   0?   5?   10?   4?

6. Which corresponding point is farther to the right on the number line:

(*a*) 5 or 8?   (*b*) 6 or 12?   (*c*) 11 or 1?   (*d*) 9 or 7?

7. Find the missing numbers:

(*a*) $(6 \times 8) \div 8 = \square$ (*c*) $(18 \div \square) \times 6 = 18$

(*b*) $(40 + 5) - 5 = \square$ (*d*) $(\square - 12) + 12 = 20$

8. Which of the following statements are true?

(*a*) $27 + 9 = 9 + 27$ (*c*) $27 \times 9 = 9 \times 27$

(*b*) $27 - 9 = 9 - 27$ (*d*) $27 \div 9 = 9 \div 27$

(*e*) $(60 + 10) + 2 = 60 + (10 + 2)$

(*f*) $(60 - 10) - 2 = 60 - (10 - 2)$

(*g*) $(60 \times 10) \times 2 = 60 \times (10 \times 2)$

(*h*) $(60 \div 10) \div 2 = 60 \div (10 \div 2)$

(i) $8 \times (4 + 2) = (8 \times 4) + (8 \times 2)$

(j) $8 + (4 \times 2) = (8 + 4) \times (8 + 2)$

(k) $8 - (4 \div 2) = (8 - 4) \div (8 - 2)$

(l) $8 \div (4 + 2) = (8 \div 4) + (8 \div 2)$

(m) $8 \times (4 - 2) = (8 \times 4) - (8 \times 2)$

(n) $8 - (4 \times 2) = (8 - 4) \times (8 - 2)$

(o) $8 + (4 \div 2) = (8 + 4) \div (8 + 2)$

(p) $8 \div (4 - 2) = (8 \div 4) - (8 \div 2)$

(q) $8 + (4 - 2) = (8 + 4) - (8 + 2)$

(r) $8 - (4 + 2) = (8 - 4) + (8 - 2)$

9. Find the numbers that will make the following statements true:

(a) $(4 + 7) + 10 = 4 + (7 + ?)$

(b) $16 \times 9 = ? \times 16$

(c) $25 \times (8 \times 12) = (25 \times ?) \times 12$

(d) $32 + ? = 18 + 32$

(e) $10 \times (9 + 6) = (? \times 9) + (? \times 6)$

10. Is the set $\{2, 4, 6, 8, 10\}$ closed under the operation of addition? Subtraction? Multiplication? Division?

11. Is the set $\{3, 6, 9, 12, 15, \cdots\}$ closed under the operation of addition? Subtraction? Multiplication? Division?

12. Is the set {all odd numbers} closed under the operation of addition? Subtraction? Multiplication? Division?

13. Is the set $\{10, 100, 1000, \cdots\}$ closed under the operation of addition? Subtraction? Multiplication? Division?

14. Determine the value of each of the following:

(a) $8 - 0$ (d) 24×0 (g) 0×0 (i) $5 \times 3 \times 0 \times 2 \times 9$

(b) $23 - 23$ (e) $61 + 0$ (h) $\dfrac{6 - 6}{8 + 4}$ (j) $\dfrac{8 + 4}{6 - 6}$

(c) $0 + 19$ (f) $0 \div 15$

15. Determine the value of each of the following:

(a) $\frac{9}{9}$ (f) 6×1^{14}

(b) 1^8 (g) $1^{17} \times 1^9$

(c) 1×57 (h) $1 \times 1 \times 1 \times 1 \times 1 \times 3 \times 1 \times 1 \times 1$

(d) 96×1 (i) $\dfrac{13 + 7}{25 - 5}$

(e) $80 \times 1 \times 1 \times 1 \times 1$

UNIT II . . . COMMON FRACTIONS

INTRODUCTION

When a thing or unit is divided into equal parts, the number expressing the relation of one or more of the equal parts to the total number of equal parts is called a fraction. The symbol for a fraction consists of a pair of numerals, one written above the other, with a horizontal bar between them. The number represented below the fraction bar cannot be zero. Fractions expressed this way are called common fractions. The fraction $\frac{5}{8}$, means 5 parts of 8 equal parts.

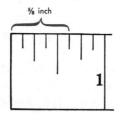

$\frac{5}{8}$ inch

An inch may be divided into 8 equal parts, called eighths. 5 of the 8 equal parts represent $\frac{5}{8}$ of an inch.

When a group of things is divided into equal parts, the number expressing the relation of one or more of the equal parts of the group to the total number of the equal parts is also considered to be a fraction.

The number above the fraction bar is called the numerator and the number below the fraction bar is called the denominator. The denominator tells you the number of equal parts into which the object or group is divided. The numerator tells you how many equal parts are being used. In the fraction $\frac{5}{8}$, 5 is the numerator and 8 is the denominator.

A fraction may be used to indicate division. The fraction $\frac{5}{8}$, sometimes written 5/8, means 5 divided by 8 representing $5 \div 8$ or $8\overline{)5}$. The whole number 2 may be thought of as $\frac{2}{1}$, 3 as $\frac{3}{1}$, 4 as $\frac{4}{1}$, 5 as $\frac{5}{1}$, etc. When a fraction is an indicated division, the numerator is the number that is divided and the denominator is the number by which you divide. Some mathematicians call these fractional numbers rational numbers.

A fraction may also be used to compare two things or two groups of things as a pint is $\frac{1}{2}$ of a quart.

Fractions that name the same number are called equivalent fractions. The fractions $\frac{3}{4}$ and $\frac{6}{8}$ are equivalent fractions. They name the same number which in simplest form is $\frac{3}{4}$.

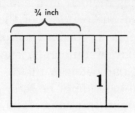

We shall see that when the numerator and denominator of any fraction are each divided by (see page 89) or multiplied by (see page 95) the same number, except by zero, the result is an equivalent fraction.

Observe the drawing on page 89 that the *larger* the denominator, the *smaller* the *size* of the part.

Also we shall see on page 470 that the *smaller* the size of the part (subdivision of the unit), the more *precise* is the measurement.

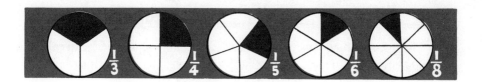

REDUCING FRACTIONS TO LOWEST TERMS

I. Aim: To reduce fractions to lowest terms.

II. Procedure

Divide the numerator and denominator of the fraction by the largest number that can be divided exactly into both or factor (see page 75) and use the multiplicative identity (see page 8).

III. Sample Solution

Reduce $\frac{63}{72}$ to lowest terms.

$$\frac{63}{72} = \frac{63 \div 9}{72 \div 9} = \frac{7}{8} \quad \text{or} \quad \frac{63}{72} = \frac{7 \cdot 9}{8 \cdot 9} = \frac{7}{8} \times 1 = \frac{7}{8}$$

Answer: $\frac{7}{8}$

IV. Definition

A fraction is in its lowest terms or in simplest form when its numerator and denominator cannot be divided exactly by the same number, except by 1.

DIAGNOSTIC TEST

Reduce the following fractions to lowest terms:

1. $\frac{3}{27} =$ 3. $\frac{6}{9} =$ 5. $\frac{26}{39} =$ 7. $\frac{250}{1000} =$

2. $\frac{18}{36} =$ 4. $\frac{48}{64} =$ 6. $\frac{648}{852} =$

RELATED PRACTICE EXAMPLES

Reduce the following fractions to lowest terms:

SET 1

1. $\frac{2}{4} =$ 6. $\frac{3}{18} =$
2. $\frac{5}{15} =$ 7. $\frac{2}{12} =$
3. $\frac{7}{21} =$ 8. $\frac{11}{88} =$
4. $\frac{3}{12} =$ 9. $\frac{23}{46} =$
5. $\frac{7}{35} =$ 10. $\frac{31}{93} =$

SET 2

1. $\frac{8}{16} =$ 6. $\frac{12}{36} =$
2. $\frac{4}{20} =$ 7. $\frac{15}{45} =$
3. $\frac{8}{48} =$ 8. $\frac{32}{96} =$
4. $\frac{6}{42} =$ 9. $\frac{21}{84} =$
5. $\frac{9}{54} =$ 10. $\frac{27}{81} =$

SET 3

1. $\frac{8}{10} =$ 6. $\frac{6}{15} =$
2. $\frac{4}{6} =$ 7. $\frac{10}{16} =$
3. $\frac{6}{20} =$ 8. $\frac{14}{18} =$
4. $\frac{10}{25} =$ 9. $\frac{21}{28} =$
5. $\frac{9}{12} =$ 10. $\frac{18}{32} =$

SET 4

1. $\frac{36}{60} =$ 6. $\frac{20}{36} =$
2. $\frac{12}{16} =$ 7. $\frac{32}{48} =$
3. $\frac{8}{20} =$ 8. $\frac{50}{75} =$
4. $\frac{18}{24} =$ 9. $\frac{42}{60} =$
5. $\frac{24}{32} =$ 10. $\frac{56}{64} =$

SET 5

1. $\frac{38}{57} =$
2. $\frac{68}{85} =$
3. $\frac{58}{87} =$
4. $\frac{57}{76} =$
5. $\frac{69}{92} =$
6. $\frac{52}{91} =$
7. $\frac{62}{93} =$
8. $\frac{34}{119} =$
9. $\frac{91}{104} =$
10. $\frac{85}{102} =$

SET 6

1. $\frac{70}{112} =$
2. $\frac{28}{400} =$
3. $\frac{84}{192} =$
4. $\frac{135}{144} =$
5. $\frac{180}{216} =$
6. $\frac{256}{352} =$
7. $\frac{420}{756} =$
8. $\frac{405}{567} =$
9. $\frac{680}{765} =$
10. $\frac{360}{456} =$

SET 7

1. $\frac{10}{40} =$
2. $\frac{20}{60} =$
3. $\frac{80}{100} =$
4. $\frac{40}{200} =$
5. $\frac{150}{600} =$
6. $\frac{300}{1000} =$
7. $\frac{1200}{2000} =$
8. $\frac{750}{2500} =$
9. $\frac{3500}{5000} =$
10. $\frac{2000}{3600} =$

MISCELLANEOUS EXAMPLES

1. Reduce the following measurements to lowest terms:

SET 1

(a) $\frac{2}{4}$ inch
(b) $\frac{14}{16}$ inch
(c) $\frac{6}{8}$ inch
(d) $\frac{20}{32}$ inch
(e) $\frac{36}{64}$ inch

SET 2

(a) $\frac{8}{12}$ foot
(b) $\frac{3}{12}$ foot
(c) $\frac{30}{36}$ yard
(d) $\frac{220}{1760}$ mile
(e) $\frac{3960}{5280}$ mile

SET 3

(a) $\frac{10}{16}$ pound
(b) $\frac{600}{2000}$ ton
(c) $\frac{840}{2240}$ ton
(d) $\frac{24}{32}$ quart
(e) $\frac{4}{8}$ peck

SET 4

(a) $\frac{24}{60}$ hour
(b) $\frac{45}{60}$ minute
(c) $\frac{9}{24}$ day
(d) $\frac{10}{12}$ year
(e) $\frac{73}{365}$ year

2. Which is greater: (a) $\frac{9}{16}$ inch or $\frac{28}{64}$ inch? (b) $\frac{12}{16}$ inch or $\frac{7}{8}$ inch?

3. Which is smaller: (a) $\frac{26}{32}$ inch or $\frac{15}{16}$ inch? (b) $\frac{3}{8}$ inch or $\frac{40}{64}$ inch?

4. A student read the length of a metal block as $\frac{56}{64}$ of an inch. What other way could he have expressed this measurement?

5. Select the fractions which are not in lowest terms:

(a) $\frac{7}{10}$ $\frac{16}{21}$ $\frac{18}{81}$ (b) $\frac{21}{25}$ $\frac{63}{72}$ $\frac{27}{58}$

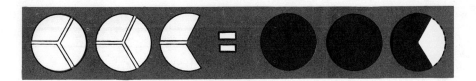

CHANGING IMPROPER FRACTIONS

I. Aim: To change an improper fraction to a whole number or a mixed number.

II. Procedure

1. Divide the numerator by the denominator.

2. Write the remainder, if any, as a fraction reduced to the lowest terms.

III. Sample Solutions

1. Change $\frac{6}{3}$ to a whole number.

$$\frac{6}{3} = 2$$

Answer: 2

2. Change $\frac{8}{5}$ to a mixed number.

$$\frac{8}{5} = 1\frac{3}{5}$$

Answer: $1\frac{3}{5}$

3. Change $\frac{14}{6}$ to a mixed number.

$$\frac{14}{6} = 2\frac{2}{6} = 2\frac{1}{3}$$

Answer: $2\frac{1}{3}$

IV. Definitions

1. A proper fraction is a fraction whose numerator is smaller than its denominator as the fraction $\frac{3}{8}$. The value of a proper fraction is always less than one.

2. An improper fraction is a fraction whose numerator is equal to or larger than its denominator as $\frac{3}{3}$ or $\frac{8}{3}$. The value of an improper fraction is one or more than one.

3. A mixed number is a number containing a whole number and a fraction as $2\frac{3}{8}$.

PRELIMINARY EXAMPLES

1. Select the mixed numbers in the following:

$\frac{13}{16}$ 16 $8\frac{1}{4}$ $\frac{5}{6}$ $3\frac{11}{12}$ 25 $1\frac{4}{5}$ $\frac{7}{8}$

2. Select the proper fractions in the following:

$\frac{3}{4}$ $\frac{9}{8}$ $\frac{7}{16}$ $\frac{5}{5}$ $\frac{19}{20}$ $\frac{11}{6}$ $\frac{8}{12}$ $\frac{21}{32}$

3. Select the improper fractions in the following:

$\frac{1}{8}$ $\frac{7}{6}$ $\frac{4}{4}$ $\frac{3}{16}$ $\frac{5}{2}$ $\frac{18}{20}$ $\frac{8}{8}$ $\frac{45}{24}$

DIAGNOSTIC TEST

Change each of the following improper fractions to a whole number or a mixed number:

1. $\frac{18}{6} =$ **2.** $\frac{5}{3} =$ **3.** $\frac{12}{8} =$ **4.** $\frac{19}{4} =$ **5.** $\frac{35}{10} =$

RELATED PRACTICE EXAMPLES

Change each of the following improper fractions to a whole number or a mixed number:

Set 1	Set 2	Set 3	Set 4	Set 5
1. $\frac{8}{8} =$	**1.** $\frac{3}{2} =$	**1.** $\frac{6}{4} =$	**1.** $\frac{9}{2} =$	**1.** $\frac{10}{4} =$
2. $\frac{5}{5} =$	**2.** $\frac{7}{5} =$	**2.** $\frac{10}{6} =$	**2.** $\frac{7}{3} =$	**2.** $\frac{28}{8} =$
3. $\frac{12}{4} =$	**3.** $\frac{4}{3} =$	**3.** $\frac{12}{9} =$	**3.** $\frac{12}{5} =$	**3.** $\frac{34}{6} =$
4. $\frac{4}{2} =$	**4.** $\frac{13}{8} =$	**4.** $\frac{14}{8} =$	**4.** $\frac{13}{4} =$	**4.** $\frac{60}{16} =$
5. $\frac{15}{5} =$	**5.** $\frac{11}{6} =$	**5.** $\frac{28}{16} =$	**5.** $\frac{25}{8} =$	**5.** $\frac{45}{20} =$
6. $\frac{12}{3} =$	**6.** $\frac{25}{16} =$	**6.** $\frac{18}{10} =$	**6.** $\frac{22}{7} =$	**6.** $\frac{46}{16} =$
7. $\frac{6}{2} =$	**7.** $\frac{14}{9} =$	**7.** $\frac{18}{12} =$	**7.** $\frac{41}{6} =$	**7.** $\frac{33}{9} =$
8. $\frac{18}{3} =$	**8.** $\frac{19}{12} =$	**8.** $\frac{38}{24} =$	**8.** $\frac{32}{9} =$	**8.** $\frac{100}{32} =$
9. $\frac{16}{2} =$	**9.** $\frac{7}{4} =$	**9.** $\frac{52}{32} =$	**9.** $\frac{55}{16} =$	**9.** $\frac{50}{12} =$
10. $\frac{36}{9} =$	**10.** $\frac{13}{10} =$	**10.** $\frac{120}{64} =$	**10.** $\frac{67}{12} =$	**10.** $\frac{80}{24} =$

MISCELLANEOUS EXAMPLES

1. Express each of the following measurements as a mixed number:

Set 1	Set 2	Set 3	Set 4
(a) $\frac{10}{8}$ inches	(a) $\frac{27}{12}$ feet	(a) $\frac{23}{16}$ pounds	(a) $\frac{75}{60}$ hours
(b) $\frac{9}{4}$ inches	(b) $\frac{35}{12}$ feet	(b) $\frac{3500}{2000}$ tons	(b) $\frac{108}{60}$ minutes
(c) $\frac{20}{16}$ inches	(c) $\frac{43}{36}$ yards	(c) $\frac{5040}{2240}$ tons	(c) $\frac{42}{24}$ days
(d) $\frac{7}{2}$ inches	(d) $\frac{3080}{1760}$ miles	(d) $\frac{17}{8}$ gallons	(d) $\frac{15}{12}$ years
(e) $\frac{41}{32}$ inches	(e) $\frac{7920}{5280}$ miles	(e) $\frac{14}{4}$ bushels	(e) $\frac{91}{52}$ years

2. Which is larger: $6\frac{3}{8}$ inches or $\frac{100}{16}$ inches?

3. Which is smaller: $\frac{72}{32}$ inches or $2\frac{3}{4}$ inches?

4. A girl wrote $\frac{28}{15}$ as her answer to a multiplication example. How should it have been expressed?

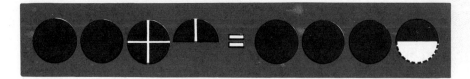

EXERCISE 9

CHANGING MIXED NUMBERS TO SIMPLEST FORM

I. Aim: To change mixed numbers to simplest form.

II. Procedure

1. Simplify the fraction of the given mixed number.
2. Add the result to the given whole number wherever possible.

III. Sample Solutions

1. Simplify $4\frac{8}{8}$.

$4\frac{8}{8} = 5$

since $\frac{8}{8} = 1$ and $4 + 1 = 5$

Answer: 5

2. Simplify $7\frac{4}{6}$.

$7\frac{4}{6} = 7\frac{2}{3}$

since $\frac{4}{6} = \frac{2}{3}$

Answer: $7\frac{2}{3}$

3. Simplify $6\frac{14}{9}$.

$6\frac{14}{9} = 7\frac{5}{9}$

since $\frac{14}{9} = 1\frac{5}{9}$ and $6 + 1\frac{5}{9} = 7\frac{5}{9}$

Answer: $7\frac{5}{9}$

4. Simplify $3\frac{6}{4}$.

$3\frac{6}{4} = 4\frac{1}{2}$

since $\frac{6}{4} = 1\frac{2}{4} = 1\frac{1}{2}$
and $3 + 1\frac{1}{2} = 4\frac{1}{2}$

Answer: $4\frac{1}{2}$

DIAGNOSTIC TEST

Change the following mixed numbers to simplest form:

1. $5\frac{6}{6} =$ **2.** $6\frac{4}{2} =$ **3.** $3\frac{12}{16} =$ **4.** $9\frac{13}{10} =$ **5.** $7\frac{14}{8} =$

RELATED PRACTICE EXAMPLES

Change the following mixed numbers to simplest form:

SET 1	SET 2	SET 3(a)	SET 3(b)
1. $2\frac{3}{3}$	**1.** $3\frac{12}{3}$	**1.** $4\frac{6}{9}$	**1.** $28\frac{8}{12}$
2. $7\frac{2}{2}$	**2.** $9\frac{6}{2}$	**2.** $9\frac{10}{16}$	**2.** $11\frac{16}{30}$
3. $5\frac{7}{7}$	**3.** $8\frac{18}{9}$	**3.** $3\frac{5}{20}$	**3.** $25\frac{24}{32}$
4. $9\frac{12}{12}$	**4.** $12\frac{32}{4}$	**4.** $6\frac{21}{24}$	**4.** $14\frac{25}{40}$
5. $6\frac{16}{16}$	**5.** $15\frac{30}{5}$	**5.** $7\frac{35}{42}$	**5.** $18\frac{28}{49}$

93

Set 4(a)	Set 4(b)	Set 5(a)	Set 5(b)
1. $6\frac{8}{5}$	1. $11\frac{7}{6}$	1. $4\frac{10}{4}$	1. $12\frac{10}{8}$
2. $5\frac{7}{4}$	2. $23\frac{19}{10}$	2. $3\frac{12}{8}$	2. $16\frac{15}{6}$
3. $9\frac{5}{2}$	3. $40\frac{16}{9}$	3. $7\frac{8}{6}$	3. $13\frac{40}{12}$
4. $8\frac{8}{3}$	4. $17\frac{35}{16}$	4. $9\frac{32}{12}$	4. $21\frac{26}{6}$
5. $2\frac{13}{8}$	5. $35\frac{29}{12}$	5. $6\frac{15}{10}$	5. $45\frac{52}{24}$

MISCELLANEOUS EXAMPLES

Express each of the following measurements in simplest form:

Set 1	Set 2	Set 3	Set 4
1. $5\frac{2}{8}$ inches	1. $6\frac{4}{12}$ feet	1. $4\frac{8}{16}$ pounds	1. $2\frac{18}{60}$ hours
2. $3\frac{6}{16}$ inches	2. $1\frac{17}{12}$ feet	2. $5\frac{1400}{2000}$ tons	2. $9\frac{72}{60}$ minutes
3. $1\frac{14}{32}$ inches	3. $4\frac{30}{36}$ yards	3. $2\frac{1960}{2240}$ tons	3. $5\frac{16}{24}$ days
4. $6\frac{5}{4}$ inches	4. $2\frac{440}{1760}$ miles	4. $8\frac{11}{4}$ gallons	4. $3\frac{4}{12}$ years
5. $9\frac{2}{2}$ inches	5. $3\frac{1980}{5280}$ miles	5. $7\frac{6}{32}$ bushels	5. $1\frac{13}{52}$ years

PRACTICAL APPLICATIONS

1. In a letter to his cousin Richard wrote that the fuselage of his model plane was $23\frac{10}{16}$ inches in length. Reading the letter before mailing it, Richard found he could express this measurement in a simpler way. What was it?

2. An answer to an addition example was written as $3\frac{11}{8}$. It was marked incorrect because it was not in simplest form. How should it have been written?

3. Tom measured a window frame and wrote the dimensions as 2 feet $6\frac{14}{16}$ inches by 5 feet $9\frac{2}{8}$ inches. Could these measurements be expressed more simply? If so, how?

4. Is John correct when he says that $6\frac{28}{16}$ is the same as $7\frac{3}{4}$? Prove it.

5. A length of pipe is measured and found to be $14\frac{20}{32}$ inches. Express this length in a simpler form.

6. The dimensions of a box were given as $11\frac{14}{16}$ inches long, $9\frac{6}{8}$ inches wide, and $10\frac{4}{4}$ inches high. What are the dimensions of the box if each were expressed in simplest form?

EXERCISE 10

CHANGING A FRACTION TO HIGHER TERMS

I. Aim: To change a fraction to higher terms.

II. Procedure

1. Divide the new denominator by the denominator of the given fraction.

2. Then multiply both the numerator and denominator of the given fraction by the quotient. This is the same as multiplying the fraction by the multiplicative identity one (1). See page 8.

III. Sample Solutions

Change the following fractions to equivalent fractions having denominators as specified:

1. $\frac{9}{25} = \frac{}{100}$

100 divided by 25 equals 4

$$\frac{9}{25} = \frac{9 \times 4}{25 \times 4} = \frac{36}{100} \quad \text{or} \quad \frac{9}{25} = \frac{9}{25} \times 1 = \frac{9 \times 4}{25 \times 4} = \frac{36}{100}$$

Answer: $\frac{36}{100}$

2. Change $\frac{1}{6}$ to 24ths.

24 divided by 6 equals 4

$$\frac{1}{6} = \frac{1 \times 4}{6 \times 4} = \frac{4}{24}$$

Answer: $\frac{4}{24}$

3. Change $\frac{7}{8}$ to 16ths.

16 divided by 8 equals 2

$$\frac{7}{8} = \frac{7 \times 2}{8 \times 2} = \frac{14}{16}$$

Answer: $\frac{14}{16}$

DIAGNOSTIC TEST

Change the following fractions to equivalent fractions having denominators as specified:

1. $\frac{1}{4} = \frac{}{12}$ 2. $\frac{5}{8} = \frac{}{32}$ 3. $\frac{9}{10} = \frac{}{100}$

RELATED PRACTICE EXAMPLES

Change the following fractions to equivalent fractions having denominators as specified:

SET 1	SET 2(a)	SET 2(b)	SET 3
1. $\frac{1}{2} = \frac{}{8}$	1. $\frac{2}{3} = \frac{}{12}$	1. $\frac{5}{8} = \frac{}{24}$	1. $\frac{7}{10} = \frac{}{100}$
2. $\frac{1}{3} = \frac{}{15}$	2. $\frac{3}{4} = \frac{}{24}$	2. $\frac{7}{9} = \frac{}{45}$	2. $\frac{3}{4} = \frac{}{100}$
3. $\frac{1}{5} = \frac{}{20}$	3. $\frac{7}{8} = \frac{}{32}$	3. $\frac{13}{16} = \frac{}{32}$	3. $\frac{2}{5} = \frac{}{100}$
4. $\frac{1}{4} = \frac{}{28}$	4. $\frac{5}{6} = \frac{}{12}$	4. $\frac{7}{12} = \frac{}{48}$	4. $\frac{9}{20} = \frac{}{100}$
5. $\frac{1}{2} = \frac{}{18}$	5. $\frac{3}{16} = \frac{}{48}$	5. $\frac{3}{4} = \frac{}{16}$	5. $\frac{2}{25} = \frac{}{100}$
6. $\frac{1}{8} = \frac{}{48}$	6. $\frac{5}{12} = \frac{}{60}$	6. $\frac{9}{32} = \frac{}{96}$	6. $\frac{43}{50} = \frac{}{100}$
7. $\frac{1}{12} = \frac{}{72}$	7. $\frac{17}{32} = \frac{}{64}$	7. $\frac{17}{24} = \frac{}{48}$	7. $\frac{21}{25} = \frac{}{100}$
8. $\frac{1}{6} = \frac{}{42}$	8. $\frac{3}{8} = \frac{}{40}$	8. $\frac{11}{16} = \frac{}{80}$	8. $\frac{3}{8} = \frac{}{100}$
9. $\frac{1}{16} = \frac{}{64}$	9. $\frac{5}{9} = \frac{}{72}$	9. $\frac{7}{12} = \frac{}{36}$	9. $\frac{2}{3} = \frac{}{100}$
10. $\frac{1}{10} = \frac{}{70}$	10. $\frac{5}{7} = \frac{}{21}$	10. $\frac{15}{16} = \frac{}{64}$	10. $\frac{17}{50} = \frac{}{100}$

MISCELLANEOUS EXAMPLES

Change:

SET 1

1. $\frac{1}{8}$ to 64ths
2. $\frac{1}{4}$ to 32nds
3. $\frac{1}{2}$ to 12ths
4. $\frac{11}{16}$ to 64ths
5. $\frac{2}{3}$ to 24ths
6. $\frac{4}{5}$ to 100ths
7. $\frac{5}{8}$ to 16ths
8. $\frac{19}{32}$ to 64ths
9. $\frac{5}{6}$ to 30ths
10. $\frac{7}{9}$ to 36ths

SET 2

1. $\frac{3}{8}$ to 32nds
2. $\frac{9}{10}$ to 40ths
3. $\frac{2}{3}$ to 18ths
4. $\frac{3}{5}$ to 20ths
5. $\frac{1}{6}$ to 48ths
6. $\frac{11}{12}$ to 24ths
7. $\frac{3}{4}$ to 64ths
8. $\frac{15}{16}$ to 32nds
9. $\frac{19}{24}$ to 96ths
10. $\frac{23}{25}$ to 100ths

SET 3

Use a ruler to find the answer to each of the following:

1. $\frac{1}{8}'' = \frac{}{16}''$
2. $\frac{5}{8}'' = \frac{}{16}''$
3. $\frac{1}{4}'' = \frac{}{8}'' = \frac{}{16}''$
4. $\frac{3}{4}'' = \frac{}{8}'' = \frac{}{16}''$
5. $\frac{1}{2}'' = \frac{}{4}'' = \frac{}{8}'' = \frac{}{16}''$

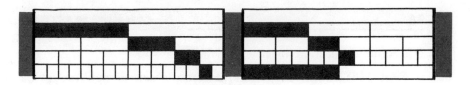

FINDING THE LOWEST COMMON DENOMINATOR
AND
CHANGING FRACTIONS TO EQUIVALENT FRACTIONS

I. Aim: Given fractions with unlike denominators, (1) to find their lowest common denominator and (2) to change the given fractions to equivalent fractions with the lowest common denominator as their denominator.

II. Procedure

1. Find the smallest natural number that can be divided exactly by the denominators of all the given fractions. This number is the lowest common denominator (L.C.D.).

Usually the L.C.D. can be found by inspection when the L.C.D. is the denominator of one of the given fractions (see sample solution 1) or when it is the product of the denominators of the given fractions. (See sample solution 2.)

When the L.C.D. is greater than any given denominator but smaller than the product of all the denominators (see sample solutions 3 and 4) use either the following method when inspection fails or the method used to find the least common multiple (page 77).

(*a*) Arrange the denominators in a row. Divide by the smallest number that will divide exactly into two or more of the denominators. Bring down to the next row the quotients and any denominator not exactly divisible.

(*b*) Continue this process until no two of the remaining numbers can be divided exactly by any number other than by one (1).

(*c*) Multiply together all the divisors and numbers remaining in the last row. The product, thus found, is the lowest common denominator.

2. To change each given fraction to an equivalent fraction having the lowest common denominator as its denominator, use the procedure in changing fractions to higher terms.

III. Sample Solutions

Find L.C.D. of the given fractions, then change the given fractions to equivalent fractions having L.C.D. as their denominators.

1. $\frac{1}{3}$ and $\frac{5}{6}$
  L.C.D. = 6

(6 is the smallest number that can be divided exactly by 3 and 6.)

$$\frac{1}{3} = \frac{1 \times 2}{3 \times 2} = \frac{2}{6}$$

$$\frac{5}{6} = \frac{5}{6}$$

Answer: 6;
  $\frac{2}{6}$ and $\frac{5}{6}$

2. $\frac{1}{2}$ and $\frac{3}{5}$
  L.C.D. = 10

(10 is the smallest number that can be divided exactly by 2 and 5.)

$$\frac{1}{2} = \frac{1 \times 5}{2 \times 5} = \frac{5}{10}$$

$$\frac{3}{5} = \frac{3 \times 2}{5 \times 2} = \frac{6}{10}$$

Answer: 10;
  $\frac{5}{10}$ and $\frac{6}{10}$

3. $\frac{5}{12}$ and $\frac{7}{16}$
  L.C.D. = 48

(48 is the smallest number that can be divided exactly by 12 and 16.)

$$\frac{5}{12} = \frac{5 \times 4}{12 \times 4} = \frac{20}{48}$$

$$\frac{7}{16} = \frac{7 \times 3}{16 \times 3} = \frac{21}{48}$$

Answer: 48;
  $\frac{20}{48}$ and $\frac{21}{48}$

4. $\frac{2}{3}$, $\frac{7}{8}$ and $\frac{1}{6}$

```
3) 3  8  6
   _____
2) 1  8  2
   _____
   1  4  1
```

L.C.D. = $3 \times 2 \times 1 \times 4 \times 1 = 24$

$$\frac{2}{3} = \frac{2 \times 8}{3 \times 8} = \frac{16}{24}$$

$$\frac{7}{8} = \frac{7 \times 3}{8 \times 3} = \frac{21}{24}$$

$$\frac{1}{6} = \frac{1 \times 4}{6 \times 4} = \frac{4}{24}$$

Answer: 24; $\frac{16}{24}$, $\frac{21}{24}$, and $\frac{4}{24}$

IV. Definition

The lowest common denominator is the smallest natural number that can be divided exactly by the denominators of all the given fractions.

DIAGNOSTIC TEST

Find the lowest common denominator (L.C.D.) of the given fractions, then change the given fractions to equivalent fractions having the lowest common denominator (L.C.D.) as their denominators:

1. $\frac{1}{2}$ and $\frac{3}{8}$ **2.** $\frac{3}{4}$ and $\frac{2}{3}$ **3.** $\frac{7}{10}$ and $\frac{9}{16}$ **4.** $\frac{5}{6}$, $\frac{4}{5}$, and $\frac{1}{3}$

RELATED PRACTICE EXAMPLES

Find the lowest common denominator (L.C.D.) of the given fractions, then change the given fractions to equivalent fractions having the lowest common denominator (L.C.D.) as their denominators:

SET 1	SET 2	SET 3
1. $\frac{1}{2}$ and $\frac{1}{4}$	1. $\frac{1}{3}$ and $\frac{1}{2}$	1. $\frac{1}{4}$ and $\frac{1}{6}$
2. $\frac{3}{5}$ and $\frac{9}{10}$	2. $\frac{2}{3}$ and $\frac{5}{6}$	2. $\frac{7}{8}$ and $\frac{9}{10}$
3. $\frac{1}{4}$ and $\frac{9}{16}$	3. $\frac{2}{3}$ and $\frac{1}{4}$	3. $\frac{5}{6}$ and $\frac{3}{8}$
4. $\frac{17}{20}$ and $\frac{4}{5}$	4. $\frac{7}{8}$ and $\frac{3}{5}$	4. $\frac{3}{4}$ and $\frac{7}{10}$
5. $\frac{2}{3}$ and $\frac{1}{6}$	5. $\frac{1}{3}$ and $\frac{5}{8}$	5. $\frac{1}{6}$ and $\frac{15}{16}$
6. $\frac{1}{2}$ and $\frac{13}{16}$	6. $\frac{4}{5}$ and $\frac{3}{4}$	6. $\frac{1}{10}$ and $\frac{9}{32}$
7. $\frac{7}{8}$ and $\frac{3}{4}$	7. $\frac{13}{15}$ and $\frac{1}{4}$	7. $\frac{5}{14}$ and $\frac{1}{4}$
8. $\frac{11}{24}$ and $\frac{5}{8}$	8. $\frac{3}{5}$ and $\frac{5}{12}$	8. $\frac{13}{20}$ and $\frac{7}{12}$
9. $\frac{1}{4}$ and $\frac{21}{32}$	9. $\frac{8}{9}$ and $\frac{3}{4}$	9. $\frac{19}{24}$ and $\frac{13}{18}$
10. $\frac{5}{6}$ and $\frac{7}{18}$	10. $\frac{1}{6}$ and $\frac{4}{7}$	10. $\frac{11}{12}$ and $\frac{27}{32}$

SET 4

1. $\frac{1}{2}$, $\frac{1}{3}$, and $\frac{1}{4}$	5. $\frac{5}{6}$, $\frac{3}{4}$, and $\frac{11}{12}$	9. $\frac{7}{8}$, $\frac{9}{10}$, and $\frac{1}{12}$
2. $\frac{3}{4}$, $\frac{1}{2}$, and $\frac{5}{8}$	6. $\frac{3}{10}$, $\frac{5}{8}$, and $\frac{7}{16}$	10. $\frac{3}{5}$, $\frac{5}{16}$, and $\frac{9}{20}$
3. $\frac{2}{3}$, $\frac{7}{12}$, and $\frac{5}{6}$	7. $\frac{7}{8}$, $\frac{5}{6}$, and $\frac{3}{4}$	
4. $\frac{4}{5}$, $\frac{1}{4}$, and $\frac{2}{3}$	8. $\frac{9}{16}$, $\frac{3}{8}$, and $\frac{13}{24}$	

MISCELLANEOUS EXAMPLES

1. Of which group of fractions is 24 the L.C.D.?

(a) $\frac{3}{4}$ and $\frac{5}{6}$ (b) $\frac{5}{8}$ and $\frac{2}{3}$ (c) $\frac{1}{2}$, $\frac{11}{12}$, and $\frac{1}{3}$

2. Of which group of fractions is 18 the L.C.D.?

(a) $\frac{1}{6}$ and $\frac{2}{3}$ (b) $\frac{7}{9}$ and $\frac{1}{2}$ (c) $\frac{7}{12}$, $\frac{5}{6}$, and $\frac{2}{9}$

3. Of which group of fractions is 12 the L.C.D.?

(a) $\frac{5}{9}$ and $\frac{3}{4}$ (b) $\frac{1}{2}$ and $\frac{5}{6}$ (c) $\frac{2}{3}$, $\frac{3}{4}$, and $\frac{1}{6}$

4. Of which group of fractions is 32 the L.C.D.?

(a) $\frac{11}{16}$ and $\frac{7}{8}$ (b) $\frac{3}{4}$ and $\frac{15}{32}$ (c) $\frac{3}{8}$, $\frac{1}{2}$, and $\frac{3}{4}$

5. Of which group of fractions is 48 the L.C.D.?

(a) $\frac{5}{6}$ and $\frac{3}{8}$ (b) $\frac{7}{12}$ and $\frac{3}{4}$ (c) $\frac{11}{16}$, $\frac{1}{6}$, and $\frac{5}{8}$

ADDITION OF FRACTIONS AND MIXED NUMBERS

I. Aim: To add fractions and mixed numbers.

II. Procedure

1. If the fractions have like denominators, add the numerators and write the sum over the common denominator. Change the answer to simplest form. (See sample solutions 1, 2, and 3.)

2. If the fractions have unlike denominators, find their lowest common denominator and change the fractions to equivalent fractions having a common denominator. Then add as explained in step 1. (See sample solution 4 and Exercise 11.)

3. To add mixed numbers, first add the fractions, then add this sum to the sum of the whole numbers. (See sample solutions 5, 7, and 8.)

4. Check by going over the work again.

Concept:

Add $\frac{3}{4}$ inch and $\frac{5}{8}$ inch.
There are $\frac{6}{8}$ in $\frac{3}{4}$ of an inch. Take $\frac{2}{8}$ from the $\frac{5}{8}$, leaving $\frac{3}{8}$ over. Add the $\frac{2}{8}$ to the $\frac{6}{8}$, making $\frac{8}{8}$, or 1 whole inch. Therefore, $\frac{3}{4}$ inch $+ \frac{5}{8}$ inch $= 1\frac{3}{8}$ inches or $\frac{3}{4} + \frac{5}{8} = 1\frac{3}{8}$.

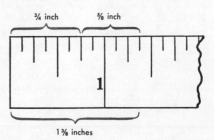

¾ inch   ⅝ inch

1

1 ⅜ inches

III. Sample Solutions

Add in the following examples:

1. $\frac{1}{5}$
$\frac{1}{5}$
$\frac{2}{5}$

Answer: $\frac{2}{5}$

2. $\frac{5}{8}$
$\frac{1}{8}$
$\frac{6}{8} = \frac{3}{4}$

Answer: $\frac{3}{4}$

3. $\frac{11}{16}$
$\frac{8}{16}$
$\frac{19}{16} = 1\frac{3}{16}$

Answer: $1\frac{3}{16}$

4. $\frac{4}{5} = \frac{8}{10}$
$\frac{7}{10} = \frac{7}{10}$
$\frac{15}{10} = 1\frac{5}{10} = 1\frac{1}{2}$

Answer: $1\frac{1}{2}$

5. $2\frac{1}{2} = 2\frac{3}{6}$
$5\frac{2}{3} = 5\frac{4}{6}$
$7\frac{7}{6} = 8\frac{1}{6}$

Answer: $8\frac{1}{6}$

6. 4
$6\frac{5}{8}$
$10\frac{5}{8}$

Answer: $10\frac{5}{8}$

7. $9\frac{7}{8} + \frac{13}{16}$

Solution:

$$9\frac{7}{8} = 9\frac{14}{16}$$
$$\frac{13}{16} = \frac{13}{16}$$
$$9\frac{27}{16} = 10\frac{11}{16}$$

Answer: $10\frac{11}{16}$

8. $13\frac{1}{6} = 13\frac{1}{6}$
$$5\frac{1}{3} = 5\frac{2}{6}$$
$$9\frac{1}{2} = 9\frac{3}{6}$$
$$27\frac{6}{6} = 28$$

Answer: 28

DIAGNOSTIC TEST

Add:

1. $\frac{1}{3}$ $\frac{1}{3}$

6. $\frac{1}{2}$ $\frac{3}{8}$

11. $2\frac{3}{4}$ 5

16. $5\frac{7}{12}$ $6\frac{11}{12}$

21. $15\frac{2}{3}$ $9\frac{5}{6}$

2. $\frac{5}{16}$ $\frac{7}{16}$

7. $\frac{2}{5}$ $\frac{3}{4}$

12. $3\frac{1}{5}$ $4\frac{3}{5}$

17. $8\frac{1}{6}$ $\frac{5}{6}$

22. $6\frac{7}{8}$ $\frac{11}{12}$

3. $\frac{5}{6}$ $\frac{1}{6}$

8. $\frac{7}{8}$ $\frac{5}{6}$

13. $2\frac{3}{10}$ $3\frac{1}{10}$

18. $12\frac{2}{3}$ $5\frac{1}{4}$

23. $\frac{1}{2}$ $3\frac{3}{4}$ $\frac{7}{8}$

4. $\frac{3}{5}$ $\frac{4}{5}$

9. $\frac{3}{10}$ $\frac{1}{2}$ $\frac{4}{5}$

14. $16\frac{5}{8}$ $23\frac{3}{8}$

19. $6\frac{1}{12}$ $8\frac{1}{6}$

24. $4\frac{2}{3}$ $6\frac{1}{2}$ $5\frac{5}{8}$

5. $\frac{3}{4}$ $\frac{3}{4}$

10. 3 $\frac{1}{8}$

15. $7\frac{2}{5}$ $9\frac{4}{5}$

20. $24\frac{9}{10}$ $17\frac{5}{8}$

25. $\frac{7}{8} + \frac{7}{12} + \frac{1}{6}$

26. $2\frac{5}{6} + 3\frac{1}{10} + 4\frac{1}{2}$ **27.** Find the sum of $6\frac{1}{4}$, $3\frac{13}{16}$, and $7\frac{3}{8}$.

RELATED PRACTICE EXAMPLES

Add:

SET 1

$\frac{2}{5}$	$\frac{3}{7}$	$\frac{6}{25}$	$\frac{3}{6}$	$\frac{5}{16}$
$\frac{2}{5}$	$\frac{2}{7}$	$\frac{8}{25}$	$\frac{2}{6}$	$\frac{4}{16}$

SET 2

$\frac{1}{4}$	$\frac{3}{8}$	$\frac{7}{12}$	$\frac{13}{32}$	$\frac{27}{64}$
$\frac{1}{4}$	$\frac{1}{8}$	$\frac{1}{12}$	$\frac{15}{32}$	$\frac{21}{64}$

SET 3

$\frac{1}{2}$	$\frac{1}{3}$	$\frac{5}{8}$	$\frac{27}{32}$	$\frac{11}{20}$
$\frac{1}{2}$	$\frac{2}{3}$	$\frac{3}{8}$	$\frac{5}{32}$	$\frac{9}{20}$

SET 4

$\frac{2}{3}$	$\frac{4}{9}$	$\frac{3}{4}$	$\frac{9}{16}$	$\frac{4}{10}$
$\frac{2}{3}$	$\frac{7}{9}$	$\frac{2}{4}$	$\frac{10}{16}$	$\frac{9}{10}$

Set 5

$\frac{5}{6}$	$\frac{11}{16}$	$\frac{3}{8}$	$\frac{17}{24}$	$\frac{15}{32}$
$\frac{5}{6}$	$\frac{9}{16}$	$\frac{7}{8}$	$\frac{19}{24}$	$\frac{29}{32}$

Set 6

$\frac{1}{2}$	$\frac{5}{8}$	$\frac{5}{6}$	$\frac{1}{10}$	$\frac{13}{32}$
$\frac{1}{4}$	$\frac{3}{64}$	$\frac{5}{12}$	$\frac{2}{5}$	$\frac{3}{4}$

Set 7

$\frac{2}{3}$	$\frac{1}{2}$	$\frac{2}{5}$	$\frac{11}{16}$	$\frac{3}{5}$
$\frac{3}{4}$	$\frac{1}{3}$	$\frac{1}{6}$	$\frac{4}{5}$	$\frac{7}{8}$

Set 8

$\frac{7}{10}$	$\frac{5}{12}$	$\frac{3}{4}$	$\frac{1}{8}$	$\frac{13}{24}$
$\frac{11}{16}$	$\frac{3}{10}$	$\frac{5}{6}$	$\frac{7}{12}$	$\frac{9}{16}$

Set 9

$\frac{3}{8}$	$\frac{2}{3}$	$\frac{3}{16}$	$\frac{7}{24}$	$\frac{5}{6}$
$\frac{4}{8}$	$\frac{3}{4}$	$\frac{1}{8}$	$\frac{3}{16}$	$\frac{3}{10}$
$\frac{1}{8}$	$\frac{5}{6}$	$\frac{1}{4}$	$\frac{5}{12}$	$\frac{7}{16}$

Set 10

4	8	12	$\frac{3}{16}$	$\frac{4}{7}$
$\frac{3}{4}$	$\frac{7}{8}$	$\frac{1}{6}$	7	18

Set 11

$6\frac{3}{5}$	$9\frac{5}{8}$	8	10	23
7	4	$7\frac{1}{2}$	$15\frac{2}{3}$	$8\frac{9}{32}$

Set 12

$4\frac{1}{4}$	$7\frac{2}{9}$	$10\frac{4}{8}$	$15\frac{5}{16}$	$32\frac{3}{10}$
$3\frac{2}{4}$	$2\frac{5}{9}$	$9\frac{3}{8}$	$12\frac{8}{16}$	$14\frac{6}{10}$

Set 13

$5\frac{1}{8}$	$6\frac{7}{32}$	$10\frac{7}{16}$	$17\frac{1}{12}$	$43\frac{9}{64}$
$8\frac{5}{8}$	$3\frac{9}{32}$	$16\frac{7}{16}$	$11\frac{7}{12}$	$18\frac{23}{64}$

Set 14

$6\frac{3}{4}$	$15\frac{1}{2}$	$7\frac{5}{8}$	$13\frac{1}{6}$	$17\frac{3}{16}$
$5\frac{1}{4}$	$9\frac{1}{2}$	$7\frac{3}{8}$	$12\frac{5}{6}$	$22\frac{13}{16}$

Set 15

$1\frac{2}{3}$	$4\frac{3}{5}$	$32\frac{5}{9}$	$16\frac{4}{8}$	$4\frac{7}{16}$
$2\frac{2}{3}$	$7\frac{4}{5}$	$13\frac{8}{9}$	$19\frac{5}{8}$	$5\frac{12}{16}$

Set 16

$8\frac{3}{4}$	$9\frac{8}{10}$	$5\frac{5}{6}$	$28\frac{23}{32}$	$6\frac{3}{8}$
$4\frac{3}{4}$	$8\frac{7}{10}$	$24\frac{5}{6}$	$12\frac{19}{32}$	$16\frac{7}{8}$

Set 17

$6\frac{1}{5}$ $\quad$ $8\frac{5}{8}$ $\quad$ $\frac{1}{4}$ $\quad$ $\frac{7}{12}$ $\quad$ $\frac{9}{16}$

$\frac{1}{5}$ $\quad$ $\frac{7}{8}$ $\quad$ $7\frac{3}{4}$ $\quad$ $1\frac{11}{12}$ $\quad$ $18\frac{5}{16}$

Set 18

$8\frac{1}{8}$ $\quad$ $7\frac{1}{4}$ $\quad$ $6\frac{1}{6}$ $\quad$ $4\frac{3}{10}$ $\quad$ $15\frac{3}{4}$

$2\frac{1}{3}$ $\quad$ $6\frac{2}{5}$ $\quad$ $9\frac{5}{8}$ $\quad$ $8\frac{5}{12}$ $\quad$ $29\frac{3}{16}$

Set 19

$3\frac{1}{3}$ $\quad$ $4\frac{1}{4}$ $\quad$ $5\frac{1}{6}$ $\quad$ $8\frac{1}{5}$ $\quad$ $22\frac{7}{12}$

$3\frac{1}{6}$ $\quad$ $8\frac{5}{12}$ $\quad$ $6\frac{1}{2}$ $\quad$ $6\frac{3}{10}$ $\quad$ $17\frac{1}{6}$

Set 20

$9\frac{1}{2}$ $\quad$ $2\frac{2}{3}$ $\quad$ $8\frac{3}{4}$ $\quad$ $16\frac{11}{12}$ $\quad$ $32\frac{9}{16}$

$5\frac{3}{4}$ $\quad$ $6\frac{4}{5}$ $\quad$ $3\frac{7}{8}$ $\quad$ $14\frac{5}{8}$ $\quad$ $15\frac{7}{12}$

Set 21

$4\frac{4}{5}$ $\quad$ $3\frac{3}{4}$ $\quad$ $4\frac{5}{6}$ $\quad$ $11\frac{17}{24}$ $\quad$ $21\frac{17}{20}$

$6\frac{7}{10}$ $\quad$ $7\frac{5}{12}$ $\quad$ $3\frac{1}{2}$ $\quad$ $4\frac{5}{12}$ $\quad$ $37\frac{2}{5}$

Set 22

$7\frac{1}{4}$ $\quad$ $9\frac{2}{3}$ $\quad$ $5\frac{5}{8}$ $\quad$ $\frac{3}{8}$ $\quad$ $\frac{5}{6}$

$\frac{7}{16}$ $\quad$ $\frac{1}{2}$ $\quad$ $\frac{3}{4}$ $\quad$ $14\frac{9}{10}$ $\quad$ $19\frac{2}{3}$

Set 23

$\frac{5}{6}$ $\quad$ $4\frac{3}{8}$ $\quad$ $7\frac{3}{4}$ $\quad$ $\frac{1}{3}$ $\quad$ $6\frac{7}{12}$

$\frac{2}{3}$ $\quad$ $9\frac{7}{16}$ $\quad$ $\frac{5}{8}$ $\quad$ $8\frac{2}{5}$ $\quad$ $\frac{3}{8}$

$2\frac{1}{2}$ $\quad$ $\frac{5}{8}$ $\quad$ $3\frac{13}{16}$ $\quad$ $\frac{1}{4}$ $\quad$ $5\frac{1}{6}$

Set 24

$5\frac{1}{8}$ $\quad$ $3\frac{2}{3}$ $\quad$ $4\frac{1}{3}$ $\quad$ $15\frac{7}{10}$ $\quad$ $18\frac{5}{8}$

$1\frac{1}{4}$ $\quad$ $2\frac{1}{6}$ $\quad$ $8\frac{3}{8}$ $\quad$ $2\frac{5}{6}$ $\quad$ $13\frac{11}{12}$

$4\frac{1}{2}$ $\quad$ $2\frac{7}{12}$ $\quad$ $2\frac{3}{4}$ $\quad$ $9\frac{1}{4}$ $\quad$ $42\frac{3}{16}$

Set 25

Add as indicated:

1. $\frac{1}{4} + \frac{1}{8}$ 5. $\frac{1}{3} + \frac{1}{12} + \frac{1}{6}$ 9. $\frac{2}{3} + \frac{5}{6} + \frac{5}{8}$

2. $\frac{2}{3} + \frac{1}{6}$ 6. $\frac{3}{4} + \frac{7}{8} + \frac{1}{2}$ 10. $\frac{3}{4} + \frac{1}{6} + \frac{7}{12}$

3. $\frac{5}{16} + \frac{7}{8}$ 7. $\frac{9}{16} + \frac{3}{8} + \frac{3}{4}$

4. $\frac{2}{5} + \frac{3}{5}$ 8. $\frac{1}{2} + \frac{9}{10} + \frac{3}{5}$

SET 26   SET 27

Add as indicated: Find the sum of:

1. $2\frac{3}{8} + 1\frac{1}{4}$ 1. $\frac{2}{3}$ and $\frac{7}{12}$

2. $7 + \frac{5}{16}$ 2. $3\frac{1}{4}$ and $9\frac{3}{4}$

3. $1\frac{2}{5} + \frac{7}{10} + 9$ 3. 9, $\frac{4}{5}$, and $\frac{1}{2}$

4. $6\frac{1}{4} + 3\frac{3}{8} + 1\frac{7}{16}$ 4. $4\frac{1}{3}$, $\frac{2}{3}$, and $6\frac{5}{8}$

5. $4\frac{3}{16} + 2\frac{7}{8} + 5\frac{1}{2}$ 5. $9\frac{1}{5}$, $6\frac{3}{10}$, and $4\frac{1}{2}$

6. $2\frac{1}{2} + 4\frac{9}{16} + 8\frac{1}{2}$ 6. $5\frac{3}{8}$, $8\frac{5}{16}$, and $10\frac{1}{4}$

7. $7\frac{2}{3} + 5\frac{1}{6} + 3\frac{1}{12}$ 7. $3\frac{7}{8}$, $4\frac{3}{4}$, and $2\frac{9}{16}$

8. $8\frac{5}{8} + 6\frac{3}{8} + \frac{5}{6}$ 8. $12\frac{1}{4}$, $5\frac{13}{16}$, and $4\frac{5}{8}$

9. $5\frac{1}{10} + 8\frac{2}{5} + 7\frac{1}{2}$ 9. $8\frac{2}{5}$, $14\frac{7}{10}$, and $9\frac{9}{10}$

10. $23\frac{9}{10} + 12\frac{3}{8} + 9\frac{3}{4}$ 10. $23\frac{5}{8}$, $18\frac{11}{16}$, and $32\frac{3}{4}$

PRACTICAL APPLICATIONS

1. Marilyn made a 2-piece dress, requiring $2\frac{7}{8}$ yards for one part and $1\frac{3}{4}$ yards for the other. How much material did she use?

2. Find the total thickness of two pieces of wood that Donald glued together if one is $\frac{5}{16}$ in. thick and the other $\frac{7}{8}$ in. thick.

3. Tom works after school. During a certain week he worked $3\frac{3}{4}$ hours on Monday, $2\frac{1}{2}$ hours on Wednesday, and 4 hours on Friday. How many hours did he work altogether?

4. Nancy's mother needed $2\frac{1}{4}$ cups of sifted cake flour to make a plain cake and $1\frac{1}{2}$ cups for a pineapple sponge cake. Find the total amount of flour she required.

5. With the last event of the track meet yet to be run, the juniors had 27 points; seniors, $26\frac{1}{2}$ points; sophomores, 26 points; and freshmen, $22\frac{1}{2}$ points. In the last event, the seniors scored $1\frac{1}{2}$ points; juniors, $1\frac{1}{2}$ points; sophomores, 3 points; and freshmen, 5 points. Which class won the meet?

6. The running time of a train from Chicago to San Francisco was changed to $49\frac{1}{3}$ hours. If this schedule saves $13\frac{3}{4}$ hours, how long did the trip take before the change was made?

7. What is the overall length of a certain machine part consisting of 3 joined pieces measuring $2\frac{9}{16}$ inches, $1\frac{27}{32}$ inches, and $\frac{7}{8}$ inch respectively.

8. A heating engineer, in installing an oil burner, finds it necessary to use pieces of pipe measuring $4\frac{11}{16}$ inches, $7\frac{5}{8}$ inches, $3\frac{1}{2}$ inches, and 9 inches. What length of pipe does he need to be able to cut the 4 pieces, disregarding waste?

9. A blueprint calls for 3 separate pieces of wood measuring $8\frac{3}{8}$ inches, $3\frac{5}{16}$ inches, and $5\frac{1}{4}$ inches in length. How long should the piece of wood be in order that the 3 pieces may be cut from it? Allow $\frac{1}{2}$ inch for waste.

10. What is the outside diameter of tubing when the inside diameter is $2\frac{5}{8}$ inches and the wall thickness is $\frac{3}{16}$ inch?

11. What are the outside dimensions of a closed box whose inside dimensions are $4\frac{15}{16}$ inches by $5\frac{5}{8}$ inches by 7 inches if the thickness of material is $\frac{1}{8}$ inch?

12. What is the perimeter (distance around) of a triangle if its three sides measure $6\frac{3}{8}$ in., $4\frac{11}{16}$ in., and $5\frac{3}{4}$ in. respectively?

13. Find the length of the bolt that should be used to go through a piece of tubing $\frac{1}{2}$ inch in diameter, a second piece of tubing $\frac{3}{4}$ inch in diameter, a washer $\frac{1}{16}$ inch thick, and a nut $\frac{1}{8}$ inch thick.

REFRESH YOUR SKILLS

1. Round off 6,280,501 to the nearest thousand.

2. Add:
```
    483
 98,276
  1,584
 67,791
  4,928
```

3. Subtract:
```
 61,074
 38,294
```

4. Multiply:
```
  8,567
    473
```

5. Divide:
```
144)143,424
```

6. Reduce $\frac{72}{84}$ to lowest terms.

7. Change $\frac{5}{6}$ to 24ths.

8. Add:
$$\frac{7}{8}$$
$$\frac{5}{6}$$

9. Add:
$$6\frac{3}{5}$$
$$4\frac{2}{3}$$

10. Add: $7\frac{1}{2}$
$$2\frac{11}{16}$$
$$3\frac{5}{8}$$

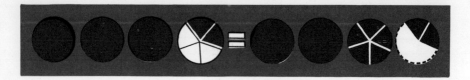

EXERCISE 13

REGROUPING IN SUBTRACTION OF FRACTIONS

I. Aim: To change the form of a given whole number or a mixed number when regrouping is necessary in the subtraction of fractions.

II. Procedure

1. When the given number is a whole number, take one (1) and change it to a fraction, making the numerator and denominator the same. (See sample solution 1.)

2. When the given number is a mixed number and the denominator required is the same as that in the given mixed number, take one (1) and change it and the given fraction to an improper fraction. (See sample solution 2.)

3. When the given number is a mixed number and the denominator required is different from that in the given mixed number, raise the fraction to higher terms, then take one (1) and change it and the fraction to an improper fraction. (See sample solution 3.)

III. Sample Solutions

Find the missing numbers:

1. $7 = 6\frac{}{3}$

$7 = 6\frac{3}{3}$ since the 1 taken from the 7 equals $\frac{3}{3}$.

Answer: $7 = 6\frac{3}{3}$

2. $8\frac{2}{5} = 7\frac{}{5}$

$8\frac{2}{5} = 7\frac{7}{5}$ since the 1 taken from the 8 equals $\frac{5}{5}$ and $\frac{2}{5} + \frac{5}{5} = \frac{7}{5}$.

Answer: $8\frac{2}{5} = 7\frac{7}{5}$

3. $9\frac{1}{2} = 9\frac{}{8} = 8\frac{}{8}$

$9\frac{1}{2} = 9\frac{4}{8} = 8\frac{12}{8}$

Since $\frac{1}{2} = \frac{4}{8}$, therefore $9\frac{1}{2} = 9\frac{4}{8}$.

Also since the 1 taken from the 9 equals $\frac{8}{8}$ and $\frac{4}{8} + \frac{8}{8} = \frac{12}{8}$, therefore, $9\frac{4}{8} = 8\frac{12}{8}$.

Answer: $9\frac{1}{2} = 9\frac{4}{8} = 8\frac{12}{8}$

DIAGNOSTIC TEST

Find the missing numbers:

1. $3 = 2\frac{}{5}$

2. $1\frac{3}{4} = \frac{}{4}$

3. $4\frac{9}{10} = 3\frac{}{10}$

4. $3\frac{7}{8} = 3\frac{}{16} = 2\frac{}{16}$

RELATED PRACTICE EXAMPLES

Find the missing numbers:

SET 1	SET 2	SET 3
1. $4 = 3\frac{}{2}$	**1.** $1\frac{1}{2} = \frac{}{2}$	**1.** $3\frac{2}{3} = 2\frac{}{3}$
2. $3 = 2\frac{}{6}$	**2.** $1\frac{1}{4} = \frac{}{4}$	**2.** $8\frac{7}{8} = 7\frac{}{8}$
3. $7 = 6\frac{}{4}$	**3.** $1\frac{1}{3} = \frac{}{3}$	**3.** $2\frac{1}{2} = 1\frac{}{2}$
4. $9 = 8\frac{}{3}$	**4.** $1\frac{5}{8} = \frac{}{8}$	**4.** $4\frac{4}{5} = 3\frac{}{5}$
5. $12 = 11\frac{}{8}$	**5.** $1\frac{2}{5} = \frac{}{5}$	**5.** $9\frac{3}{4} = 8\frac{}{4}$
6. $8 = 7\frac{}{10}$	**6.** $1\frac{9}{10} = \frac{}{10}$	**6.** $15\frac{5}{6} = 14\frac{}{6}$
7. $6 = 5\frac{}{24}$	**7.** $1\frac{11}{16} = \frac{}{16}$	**7.** $12\frac{8}{9} = 11\frac{}{9}$
8. $5 = 4\frac{}{16}$	**8.** $1\frac{5}{6} = \frac{}{6}$	**8.** $6\frac{3}{10} = 5\frac{}{10}$
9. $14 = 13\frac{}{32}$	**9.** $1\frac{4}{7} = \frac{}{7}$	**9.** $7\frac{9}{16} = 6\frac{}{16}$
10. $2 = 1\frac{}{20}$	**10.** $1\frac{7}{12} = \frac{}{12}$	**10.** $10\frac{11}{12} = 9\frac{}{12}$

SET 4

1. $4\frac{1}{3} = 4\frac{}{9} = 3\frac{}{9}$

2. $7\frac{2}{5} = 7\frac{}{10} = 6\frac{}{10}$

3. $9\frac{3}{4} = 9\frac{}{16} = 8\frac{}{16}$

4. $5\frac{1}{2} = 5\frac{}{16} = 4\frac{}{16}$

5. $6\frac{3}{8} = 6\frac{}{24} = 5\frac{}{24}$

6. $3\frac{1}{7} = 3\frac{}{35} = 2\frac{}{35}$

7. $8\frac{3}{10} = 8\frac{}{100} = 7\frac{}{100}$

8. $2\frac{5}{6} = 2\frac{}{30} = 1\frac{}{30}$

9. $10\frac{7}{16} = 10\frac{}{64} = 9\frac{}{64}$

10. $15\frac{1}{12} = 15\frac{}{36} = 14\frac{}{36}$

MISCELLANEOUS EXAMPLES

Use a ruler to find the answer to each of the following:

1. $4'' = 3\frac{}{8}''$

2. $5'' = 4\frac{}{16}''$

3. $10'' = 9\frac{}{4}''$

4. $1\frac{7}{8}'' = \frac{}{8}''$

5. $9\frac{3}{4}'' = 8\frac{}{4}''$

6. $7\frac{11}{16}'' = 6\frac{}{16}''$

7. $8\frac{1}{8}'' = 7\frac{}{8}''$

8. $6\frac{1}{2}'' = 6\frac{}{4}'' = 5\frac{}{4}''$

9. $4\frac{5}{8}'' = 4\frac{}{16}'' = 3\frac{}{16}''$

10. $11\frac{3}{4}'' = 11\frac{}{16}'' = 10\frac{}{16}''$

EXERCISE 14

SUBTRACTION OF FRACTIONS AND MIXED NUMBERS

I. Aim: To subtract fractions and mixed numbers.

II. Procedure

1. If the fractions have like denominators, subtract the numerators and write the difference over the common denominator. Reduce the answer to lowest terms. (See sample solutions 1 and 2.)

2. If the fractions have unlike denominators, find their lowest common denominator and change the fractions to equivalent fractions having a common denominator. Then subtract as explained in step 1. (See sample solution 3 and Exercise 11.)

3. To subtract a fraction or mixed number from a whole number, take one (1) from the whole number and change it into a fraction making the numerator and common denominator the same. Then subtract fractions and subtract whole numbers. (See sample solution 6 and Exercise 13.)

4. To subtract mixed numbers, first subtract the fractions, then subtract the whole numbers. (See sample solution 4.) If the fraction in the subtrahend is larger than the fraction in the minuend, take one (1) from the whole number in the minuend and increase the fraction. (See sample solutions 7 and 8 and Exercise 13.)

5. Check by going over the work again.

Concept:

From $1\frac{1}{2}$ inches take $\frac{7}{8}$ inch.

In $1\frac{1}{2}$ inches there are $\frac{12}{8}$. If $\frac{7}{8}$ are taken away, $\frac{5}{8}$ will be left. Therefore,

$1\frac{1}{2}$ inches $- \frac{7}{8}$ inch $= \frac{5}{8}$ inch

or $\qquad 1\frac{1}{2} - \frac{7}{8} = \frac{5}{8}$.

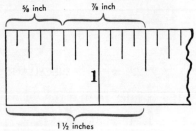

III. Sample Solutions

Subtract in the following examples:

1. $\dfrac{\dfrac{4}{5}}{\dfrac{\dfrac{1}{5}}{\dfrac{3}{5}}}$

   Answer: $\frac{3}{5}$

2. $\dfrac{\dfrac{11}{16}}{\dfrac{\dfrac{5}{16}}{\dfrac{6}{16}}} = \frac{3}{8}$

   Answer: $\frac{3}{8}$

3. $\begin{array}{c} \frac{7}{8} = \frac{7}{8} \\ \frac{1}{4} = \frac{2}{8} \\ \hline \frac{5}{8} \end{array}$

   Answer: $\frac{5}{8}$

4. $\begin{array}{c} 6\frac{4}{5} = 6\frac{8}{10} \\ 3\frac{1}{2} = 3\frac{5}{10} \\ \hline 3\frac{3}{10} \end{array}$

   Answer: $3\frac{3}{10}$

5. $7\frac{2}{3}$
$\underline{\quad 3 \quad}$
$4\frac{2}{3}$

Answer: $4\frac{2}{3}$

6. $8 = 7\frac{16}{16}$
$\underline{1\frac{7}{16} = 1\frac{7}{16}}$
$6\frac{9}{16}$

Answer: $6\frac{9}{16}$

7. $6\frac{1}{8} - \frac{7}{8}$

Solution:

$6\frac{1}{8} = 5\frac{9}{8}$
$\underline{\frac{7}{8} = \quad \frac{7}{8}}$
$\qquad 5\frac{2}{8} = 5\frac{1}{4}$

Answer: $5\frac{1}{4}$

8. $9\frac{1}{3} - 4\frac{5}{6}$

Solution:

$9\frac{1}{3} = 9\frac{2}{6} = 8\frac{8}{6}$
$\underline{4\frac{5}{6} = 4\frac{5}{6} = 4\frac{5}{6}}$
$\qquad\qquad\qquad 4\frac{3}{6} = 4\frac{1}{2}$

Answer: $4\frac{1}{2}$

DIAGNOSTIC TEST

Subtract:

1. $\frac{2}{3}$
$\frac{1}{3}$

2. $\frac{5}{8}$
$\frac{1}{8}$

3. $\frac{5}{6}$
$\frac{1}{2}$

4. $\frac{7}{8}$
$\frac{1}{5}$

5. $\frac{3}{4}$
$\frac{7}{10}$

6. $4\frac{4}{5}$
$3\frac{2}{5}$

7. $8\frac{13}{16}$
$5\frac{3}{16}$

8. $45\frac{1}{3}$
$32\frac{2}{3}$

9. $12\frac{3}{8}$
$7\frac{7}{8}$

10. $38\frac{9}{16}$
$36\frac{9}{16}$

11. $5\frac{15}{32}$
3

12. 6
$2\frac{3}{4}$

13. 9
$\frac{4}{5}$

14. $8\frac{11}{32}$
$5\frac{1}{6}$

15. $9\frac{3}{4}$
$3\frac{1}{3}$

16. $13\frac{7}{16}$
$7\frac{5}{12}$

17. $14\frac{5}{8}$
$5\frac{3}{4}$

18. $8\frac{1}{5}$
$2\frac{1}{3}$

19. $6\frac{3}{10}$
$3\frac{9}{16}$

20. $14\frac{1}{8}$
$13\frac{1}{2}$

21. $1\frac{1}{4}$
$\frac{5}{6}$

22. $\frac{15}{16} - \frac{3}{4}$

23. $14\frac{1}{4} - 5\frac{2}{3}$

24. Subtract $1\frac{5}{8}$ from 6.

RELATED PRACTICE EXAMPLES

Subtract:

SET 1

| $\frac{4}{5}$ | $\frac{5}{7}$ | $\frac{5}{8}$ | $\frac{3}{4}$ | $\frac{27}{32}$ |
| $\frac{3}{5}$ | $\frac{3}{7}$ | $\frac{2}{8}$ | $\frac{2}{4}$ | $\frac{18}{32}$ |

SET 2

| $\frac{3}{4}$ | $\frac{9}{16}$ | $\frac{5}{6}$ | $\frac{7}{10}$ | $\frac{53}{64}$ |
| $\frac{1}{4}$ | $\frac{3}{16}$ | $\frac{1}{6}$ | $\frac{3}{10}$ | $\frac{29}{64}$ |

Set 3

$$\frac{7}{8} \quad \frac{2}{3} \quad \frac{3}{4} \quad \frac{17}{20} \quad \frac{15}{16}$$
$$\frac{3}{16} \quad \frac{1}{6} \quad \frac{5}{12} \quad \frac{3}{5} \quad \frac{21}{32}$$

Set 4

$$\frac{1}{2} \quad \frac{3}{4} \quad \frac{7}{8} \quad \frac{2}{3} \quad \frac{3}{5}$$
$$\frac{1}{3} \quad \frac{2}{5} \quad \frac{2}{3} \quad \frac{7}{16} \quad \frac{7}{12}$$

Set 5

$$\frac{1}{4} \quad \frac{5}{6} \quad \frac{7}{12} \quad \frac{5}{8} \quad \frac{11}{16}$$
$$\frac{1}{6} \quad \frac{3}{8} \quad \frac{3}{16} \quad \frac{1}{12} \quad \frac{9}{20}$$

Set 6

$$6\frac{3}{5} \quad 8\frac{8}{9} \quad 15\frac{2}{4} \quad 34\frac{13}{16} \quad 53\frac{7}{8}$$
$$2\frac{1}{5} \quad 7\frac{3}{9} \quad 4\frac{1}{4} \quad 21\frac{8}{16} \quad 25\frac{2}{8}$$

Set 7

$$3\frac{5}{8} \qquad 6\frac{11}{16} \qquad 9\frac{7}{12} \qquad 11\frac{9}{10} \qquad 31\frac{17}{20}$$
$$1\frac{3}{8} \qquad 3\frac{5}{16} \qquad 7\frac{5}{12} \qquad 6\frac{3}{10} \qquad 19\frac{13}{20}$$

Set 8

$$9\frac{2}{5} \qquad 5\frac{3}{7} \qquad 16\frac{9}{16} \qquad 18\frac{1}{4} \qquad 36\frac{1}{5}$$
$$4\frac{4}{5} \qquad 1\frac{6}{7} \qquad 7\frac{12}{16} \qquad 14\frac{2}{4} \qquad 18\frac{4}{5}$$

Set 9

$$7\frac{1}{6} \qquad 15\frac{5}{8} \qquad 13\frac{3}{10} \qquad 8\frac{13}{16} \qquad 17\frac{5}{32}$$
$$1\frac{5}{6} \qquad 6\frac{7}{8} \qquad 10\frac{9}{10} \qquad 6\frac{15}{16} \qquad 13\frac{29}{32}$$

Set 10

$$6\frac{1}{2} \qquad 11\frac{3}{4} \qquad 29\frac{2}{5} \qquad 43\frac{3}{10} \qquad 32\frac{11}{12}$$
$$5\frac{1}{2} \qquad 4\frac{3}{4} \qquad 16\frac{2}{5} \qquad 28\frac{3}{10} \qquad 23\frac{11}{12}$$

Set 11

$$4\frac{1}{2} \qquad 9\frac{3}{4} \qquad 15\frac{3}{8} \qquad 43\frac{9}{10} \qquad 39\frac{25}{32}$$
$$2 \qquad\quad 6 \qquad\quad 9 \qquad\quad 27 \qquad\quad 14$$

Set 12

$$9 \qquad\quad 3 \qquad\quad 13 \qquad\quad 42 \qquad\quad 27$$
$$2\frac{1}{4} \qquad 1\frac{3}{5} \qquad 6\frac{5}{8} \qquad 17\frac{7}{20} \qquad 20\frac{13}{16}$$

Set 13

$$5 \qquad\quad 9 \qquad\quad 4 \qquad\quad 12 \qquad\quad 10$$
$$\frac{3}{8} \qquad \frac{7}{12} \qquad \frac{1}{2} \qquad \frac{9}{10} \qquad \frac{2}{3}$$

Set 14

$$8\frac{5}{6} \qquad 11\frac{11}{12} \qquad 14\frac{3}{4} \qquad 18\frac{9}{10} \qquad 42\frac{7}{8}$$
$$6\frac{1}{3} \qquad 8\frac{1}{4} \qquad 3\frac{1}{8} \qquad 15\frac{2}{5} \qquad 9\frac{3}{16}$$

Set 15

$7\frac{1}{3}$ $20\frac{3}{5}$ $11\frac{2}{3}$ $23\frac{13}{16}$ $40\frac{4}{5}$

$4\frac{1}{5}$ $12\frac{7}{16}$ $5\frac{1}{2}$ $17\frac{2}{3}$ $8\frac{3}{4}$

Set 16

$8\frac{3}{4}$ $3\frac{7}{12}$ $7\frac{15}{16}$ $13\frac{9}{10}$ $32\frac{13}{20}$

$5\frac{1}{6}$ $1\frac{3}{8}$ $2\frac{5}{6}$ $9\frac{3}{4}$ $27\frac{5}{8}$

Set 17

$6\frac{1}{2}$ $9\frac{3}{8}$ $10\frac{5}{16}$ $16\frac{3}{10}$ $17\frac{5}{32}$

$3\frac{3}{4}$ $5\frac{9}{16}$ $7\frac{3}{4}$ $8\frac{1}{2}$ $12\frac{9}{16}$

Set 18

$10\frac{1}{3}$ $13\frac{1}{4}$ $9\frac{1}{6}$ $36\frac{2}{3}$ $25\frac{3}{4}$

$4\frac{1}{2}$ $8\frac{2}{3}$ $2\frac{3}{5}$ $17\frac{7}{8}$ $21\frac{4}{5}$

Set 19

$9\frac{3}{4}$ $7\frac{1}{6}$ $18\frac{5}{6}$ $23\frac{3}{8}$ $24\frac{7}{12}$

$1\frac{9}{10}$ $5\frac{3}{8}$ $12\frac{15}{16}$ $11\frac{5}{12}$ $14\frac{7}{10}$

Set 20

$8\frac{11}{16}$ $4\frac{7}{8}$ $7\frac{1}{3}$ $13\frac{3}{4}$ $19\frac{2}{5}$

$8\frac{7}{16}$ $4\frac{1}{2}$ $6\frac{2}{3}$ $12\frac{5}{6}$ $18\frac{9}{10}$

Set 21

$5\frac{1}{2}$ $3\frac{9}{16}$ $1\frac{7}{10}$ $1\frac{1}{3}$ $1\frac{3}{4}$

$\frac{3}{4}$ $\frac{7}{8}$ $\frac{5}{6}$ $\frac{1}{2}$ $1\frac{5}{16}$

Set 22

Subtract as indicated:

1. $\frac{3}{5} - \frac{1}{5}$

2. $\frac{5}{8} - \frac{1}{4}$

3. $\frac{1}{2} - \frac{1}{6}$

4. $\frac{4}{5} - \frac{3}{4}$

5. $\frac{13}{16} - \frac{7}{10}$

6. $2\frac{3}{8} - 1$

7. $2 - 1\frac{3}{8}$

8. $4 - \frac{9}{16}$

9. $6\frac{1}{2} - \frac{1}{2}$

10. $3\frac{5}{6} - \frac{1}{3}$

SET 23

Subtract as indicated:

1. $6\frac{7}{8} - 2\frac{3}{8}$
2. $2\frac{1}{2} - 1\frac{3}{4}$
3. $8\frac{1}{4} - 4\frac{2}{5}$
4. $11\frac{1}{2} - 2\frac{1}{3}$
5. $14\frac{3}{8} - 9\frac{1}{10}$

6. $24\frac{9}{16} - 8\frac{3}{4}$
7. $21\frac{3}{10} - 13\frac{1}{4}$
8. $10\frac{5}{6} - 10\frac{7}{12}$
9. $8\frac{7}{8} - 7\frac{15}{16}$
10. $4\frac{1}{6} - 3\frac{2}{3}$

SET 24

1. From $\frac{7}{8}$ subtract $\frac{5}{16}$.
2. From $1\frac{4}{5}$ take $\frac{9}{10}$.
3. From 7 subtract $2\frac{11}{16}$.

4. Take 3 from $4\frac{5}{8}$.
5. Subtract $2\frac{1}{2}$ from $9\frac{1}{2}$.
6. Take $5\frac{3}{4}$ from $7\frac{1}{8}$.

7. Find the difference between $6\frac{1}{3}$ and $5\frac{5}{6}$.
8. Find the difference between $4\frac{5}{8}$ and $2\frac{9}{10}$.
9. Find the difference between $15\frac{1}{4}$ and $8\frac{1}{2}$.
10. Find the difference between 9 and $3\frac{3}{4}$.

PRACTICAL APPLICATIONS

1. Two months ago Marian weighed $123\frac{1}{4}$ lb. Now she weighs $116\frac{3}{4}$ lb. How many pounds did she lose?

2. If normal body temperature is $98\frac{3}{5}$ degrees, how many degrees above normal is a temperature of 101 degrees?

3. Helen bought $4\frac{3}{8}$ yards of material for a dress. If her mother plans to use only $3\frac{3}{4}$ yards, how much extra material did Helen buy?

4. A $4\frac{1}{4}$-lb. chicken weighed $3\frac{1}{8}$ lb. when dressed. Find the loss in weight.

5. A merchant sold $7\frac{5}{8}$ yards of cloth to a customer. If it was cut from a bolt that contained $18\frac{2}{3}$ yards, what length remained in the bolt?

6. During the baseball season a newspaper reported that the 6th place team was 16 games behind the leader while the 5th place team was $13\frac{1}{2}$ games behind the leader. How many games behind the 5th place team was the 6th place team?

7. Find the net change in a stock if it opened at $63\frac{7}{8}$ points and closed at $65\frac{1}{4}$ points.

8. In arranging an $8\frac{1}{2}$ by 11 inch piece of paper in the drawing class, pupils were directed to draw a line $\frac{1}{4}$ inch from each edge. What are the inside dimensions between the lines?

9. The running time of a crack streamliner from Philadelphia to Chicago is $14\frac{3}{4}$ hours. Another train takes $15\frac{2}{3}$ hours to make the same trip. How much faster is the first train?

10. A pilot finds that winds slow his progress in reaching his destination. His trip out takes $2\frac{3}{4}$ hr. How long should his return trip take if he must return at the end of $4\frac{1}{2}$ hr. flying time?

11. If one mechanic can assemble a motor in $6\frac{1}{2}$ hr. while another mechanic can do the same job in $7\frac{5}{6}$ hr., how much more quickly can the first mechanic do the job?

12. A $2\frac{1}{2}$-inch nail is driven through a piece of wood, $1\frac{1}{8}$ inches thick, supporting a joist. How far into the joist did the nail extend?

13. After flying for $3\frac{1}{4}$ hr., a pilot was forced to land at an alternate airport, 490 miles from his destination. Following a delay of $\frac{1}{2}$ hr., the airplane took off. If the pilot wishes to arrive on schedule, $5\frac{3}{4}$ hr. after his original take-off, how fast must he fly?

14. A plumber, in installing water pipes, used pieces measuring $5\frac{1}{2}$ ft., $3\frac{3}{4}$ ft., and $1\frac{2}{3}$ ft. If they were cut from a 15-foot length of pipe, how many feet of pipe remained? Disregard waste.

15. The wall thickness of certain tubing is $\frac{5}{16}$ in. and its outside diameter is $2\frac{7}{8}$ in. What is the inside diameter?

REFRESH YOUR SKILLS

1. Add:

68,322
87,947
48,279
70,976
91,385

2. Subtract:

832,506
95,708

3. Multiply:

869
798

4. Divide:

$2,240\overline{)1,543,360}$

5. Round off 269,826,140 to the nearest million.

6. Reduce $\frac{54}{90}$ to lowest terms.   **7.** Change $\frac{3}{4}$ to 64ths.

8. Add: $4\frac{5}{6}$
$2\frac{3}{4}$
$5\frac{7}{12}$

9. Subtract: $10\frac{5}{6}$
$8\frac{1}{3}$

10. Subtract: 9
$2\frac{13}{16}$

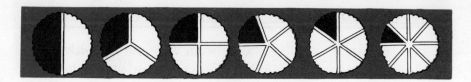

EXERCISE 15

COMPARING FRACTIONS

(Also see page 146)

I. Aim: To compare fractions.

II. Procedure

1. Change the given fractions to fractions having a common denominator.

2. Then take the given fraction that is equal to the fraction having the larger numerator and common denominator as the larger fraction.

III. Sample Solutions

1. Which is larger: $\frac{2}{5}$ or $\frac{1}{2}$?

$$\frac{2}{5} = \frac{4}{10}$$
$$\frac{1}{2} = \frac{5}{10}$$

Answer: $\frac{1}{2}$ is larger

2. Which is smaller: $\frac{3}{4}$ or $\frac{5}{6}$?

$$\frac{3}{4} = \frac{9}{12}$$
$$\frac{5}{6} = \frac{10}{12}$$

Answer: $\frac{3}{4}$ is smaller

3. Arrange in order of size (largest first): $\frac{3}{4}$, $\frac{7}{8}$, and $\frac{2}{3}$

$$\frac{3}{4} = \frac{18}{24}, \qquad \frac{7}{8} = \frac{21}{24}, \qquad \text{and} \qquad \frac{2}{3} = \frac{16}{24}$$

Answer: $\frac{7}{8}$, $\frac{3}{4}$, and $\frac{2}{3}$

DIAGNOSTIC TEST

Which is larger:

1. $\frac{1}{3}$ or $\frac{1}{2}$?

2. $\frac{5}{6}$ or $\frac{7}{8}$?

Which is smaller:

3. $\frac{1}{4}$ or $\frac{1}{10}$?

4. $\frac{5}{8}$ or $\frac{11}{16}$?

Arrange in order of size (largest first):

5. $\frac{7}{32}$, $\frac{3}{8}$, and $\frac{13}{16}$.

Arrange in order of size (smallest first):

6. $\frac{3}{5}$, $\frac{7}{12}$, and $\frac{1}{2}$.

114

RELATED PRACTICE EXAMPLES

Which is larger: Which is smaller:

SET 1   SET 2   SET 3   SET 4

1. $\frac{1}{4}$ or $\frac{1}{3}$? **1.** $\frac{2}{3}$ or $\frac{5}{8}$? **1.** $\frac{1}{2}$ or $\frac{1}{6}$? **1.** $\frac{5}{16}$ or $\frac{1}{4}$?

2. $\frac{1}{6}$ or $\frac{1}{10}$? **2.** $\frac{4}{5}$ or $\frac{3}{4}$? **2.** $\frac{1}{8}$ or $\frac{1}{10}$? **2.** $\frac{5}{8}$ or $\frac{7}{12}$?

3. $\frac{1}{2}$ or $\frac{1}{16}$? **3.** $\frac{7}{16}$ or $\frac{2}{5}$? **3.** $\frac{1}{16}$ or $\frac{1}{12}$? **3.** $\frac{2}{5}$ or $\frac{3}{8}$?

4. $\frac{1}{5}$ or $\frac{1}{8}$? **4.** $\frac{3}{8}$ or $\frac{1}{4}$? **4.** $\frac{1}{3}$ or $\frac{1}{5}$? **4.** $\frac{2}{3}$ or $\frac{11}{16}$?

5. $\frac{1}{12}$ or $\frac{1}{10}$? **5.** $\frac{13}{16}$ or $\frac{5}{6}$? **5.** $\frac{1}{8}$ or $\frac{1}{4}$? **5.** $\frac{7}{10}$ or $\frac{3}{4}$?

SET 5   SET 6

Arrange in order of size (largest first):

Arrange in order of size (smallest first):

1. $\frac{1}{2}$, $\frac{1}{5}$, and $\frac{1}{3}$

2. $\frac{5}{8}$, $\frac{2}{3}$, and $\frac{3}{5}$

3. $\frac{3}{4}$, $\frac{9}{16}$, and $\frac{7}{12}$

4. $\frac{7}{8}$, $\frac{5}{6}$, and $\frac{4}{5}$

5. $\frac{1}{4}$, $\frac{5}{16}$, and $\frac{3}{8}$

1. $\frac{1}{4}$, $\frac{1}{2}$, and $\frac{1}{6}$

2. $\frac{1}{2}$, $\frac{2}{5}$, and $\frac{3}{10}$

3. $\frac{11}{16}$, $\frac{5}{8}$, and $\frac{3}{4}$

4. $\frac{2}{3}$, $\frac{11}{12}$, and $\frac{5}{6}$

5. $\frac{5}{8}$, $\frac{3}{5}$, and $\frac{3}{4}$

MISCELLANEOUS EXAMPLES

1. To round off a mixed number to the nearest whole number, drop the fraction. However, add 1 to the whole number if the fraction is one half or more. If the fraction is less than one half, do not add anything.

Round off the following mixed numbers to the nearest whole numbers:

SET 1   SET 2   SET 3

(a) $4\frac{1}{4}$ (a) $3\frac{2}{3}$ (a) $1\frac{5}{6}$

(b) $9\frac{3}{8}$ (b) $5\frac{4}{5}$ (b) $6\frac{5}{12}$

(c) $7\frac{2}{5}$ (c) $8\frac{1}{2}$ (c) $2\frac{9}{16}$

(d) $12\frac{7}{16}$ (d) $16\frac{17}{32}$ (d) $27\frac{3}{5}$

(e) $28\frac{13}{32}$ (e) $34\frac{7}{8}$ (e) $53\frac{27}{64}$

2. (a) Which is larger: $\frac{1}{2}$ of a gallon or $\frac{1}{2}$ of a quart?

(b) Which is smaller: $\frac{3}{4}$ of a foot or $\frac{3}{4}$ of a yard?

(c) Which weighs more: $\frac{2}{3}$ of a ton or $\frac{2}{3}$ of a pound?

(d) Which is longer: $\frac{1}{6}$ of an hour or $\frac{1}{6}$ of a minute?

CHANGING MIXED NUMBERS TO IMPROPER FRACTIONS

I. Aim: To change a mixed number to an improper fraction.

II. Procedure

1. Multiply the whole number by the denominator of the fraction. Add the numerator of the fraction to this product.

2. Write this sum over the denominator of the fraction.

III. Sample Solutions

1. Change $1\frac{3}{8}$ to an improper fraction. $\qquad\qquad 1\frac{3}{8} = \frac{11}{8}$

Multiply 1 by 8, then add 3 to the product. Write this sum (11) over the denominator (8) of the given fraction. This is a brief way of saying

$$1\frac{3}{8} = 1 + \frac{3}{8} = \frac{8}{8} + \frac{3}{8} = \frac{11}{8}$$

Answer: $\frac{11}{8}$

2. Change $4\frac{2}{5}$ to an improper fraction. $\qquad\qquad 4\frac{2}{5} = \frac{22}{5}$

Multiply 4 by 5, then add 2 to the product. Write this sum (22) over the denominator (5) of the given fraction. Here $4\frac{2}{5} = 4 + \frac{2}{5} = \frac{20}{5} + \frac{2}{5} = \frac{22}{5}$

Answer: $\frac{22}{5}$

DIAGNOSTIC TEST

Change the following mixed numbers to improper fractions:

1. $1\frac{1}{3} =$ **2.** $1\frac{3}{4} =$ **3.** $7\frac{1}{2} =$ **4.** $5\frac{7}{8} =$

RELATED PRACTICE EXAMPLES

Change the following mixed numbers to improper fractions:

SET 1	SET 2	SET 3	SET 4(a)	SET 4(b)	SET 4(c)
1. $1\frac{1}{5} =$	**1.** $1\frac{5}{8} =$	**1.** $8\frac{1}{5} =$	**1.** $4\frac{2}{3} =$	**1.** $7\frac{4}{5} =$	**1.** $3\frac{5}{6} =$
2. $1\frac{1}{4} =$	**2.** $1\frac{2}{3} =$	**2.** $3\frac{1}{7} =$	**2.** $3\frac{3}{4} =$	**2.** $6\frac{2}{9} =$	**2.** $8\frac{7}{10} =$
3. $1\frac{1}{2} =$	**3.** $1\frac{7}{12} =$	**3.** $9\frac{1}{6} =$	**3.** $2\frac{5}{8} =$	**3.** $5\frac{4}{7} =$	**3.** $4\frac{3}{8} =$
4. $1\frac{1}{8} =$	**4.** $1\frac{13}{16} =$	**4.** $16\frac{1}{3} =$	**4.** $3\frac{7}{12} =$	**4.** $4\frac{13}{32} =$	**4.** $10\frac{9}{16} =$
5. $1\frac{1}{16} =$	**5.** $1\frac{9}{32} =$	**5.** $14\frac{1}{4} =$	**5.** $5\frac{3}{16} =$	**5.** $2\frac{11}{12} =$	**5.** $13\frac{3}{5} =$

MISCELLANEOUS EXAMPLES

1. How many half-inches in $5\frac{1}{2}$ inches? in $9\frac{1}{2}$ inches?

2. How many eighths of an inch in $4\frac{7}{8}$ inches? in $2\frac{3}{8}$ inches?

3. How many sixteenths of an inch in $2\frac{13}{16}$ inches? in $1\frac{9}{16}$ inches?

4. How many quarters of an inch in $6\frac{3}{4}$ inches? in $7\frac{1}{4}$ inches?

5. How many thirty-seconds of an inch in $1\frac{17}{32}$ inches? in $3\frac{5}{32}$ inches?

PRACTICAL APPLICATIONS

1. A bag contains $37\frac{1}{2}$ pounds of sugar. How many $\frac{1}{2}$-pound bags can be filled?

2. How many pieces $\frac{1}{4}$ inch long can be cut from a strip of metal $14\frac{3}{4}$ inches long?

3. If it takes $\frac{1}{8}$ yard of material to make a certain necktie, how many similar neckties can be made from a bolt of goods containing $15\frac{3}{8}$ yards?

4. How many pieces of wood $\frac{1}{3}$ foot long can be cut from a board $6\frac{2}{3}$ feet long?

5. How many $\frac{1}{10}$-ounce tea bags can be made from $9\frac{3}{10}$ ounces of tea?

REFRESH YOUR SKILLS

1. Add: **2.** Subtract: **3.** Multiply: **4.** Divide:

59,864	968,325	5,280	$3,600\overline{)2,512,800.}$
46,239	898,296	905	
67,403			
76,216			
85,945			

5. Round off 7,899,846 to the nearest thousand.

6. Reduce $\frac{54}{96}$ to lowest terms.   **7.** Change $\frac{3}{5}$ to 60ths

8. Arrange in order of size   **9.** Add: **10.** Subtract:
(largest first):

$\frac{2}{3}, \frac{7}{8}, \frac{9}{10}$ $8\frac{1}{4}$ $1\frac{3}{10}$

$5\frac{3}{16}$ $\frac{4}{5}$

$2\frac{5}{8}$

MULTIPLICATION OF FRACTIONS AND MIXED NUMBERS

I. Aim: To multiply fractions and mixed numbers.

II. Procedure

1. Change each mixed number to an improper fraction. (See Exercise 16.) A whole number may be expressed in fractional form by using the whole number as the numerator and the figure 1 as the denominator. (See sample solution 4.)

2. Wherever it is possible, first divide any numerator and denominator by the greatest possible number that is exactly contained in both (greatest common factor) to simplify computation.

3. Multiply the resulting numerators to obtain the numerator of the answer.

4. Multiply the resulting denominators to obtain the denominator of the answer.

5. Where necessary, reduce the answer to simplest form.

6. When multiplying a mixed number and a whole number, the vertical form may also be used. (See sample solution 7.)

7. Check by going over the work again.

Concept:

(a) Find $\frac{2}{3}$ of 3 inches.

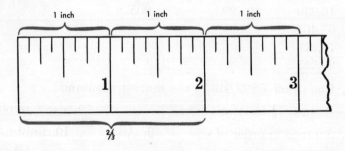

3 inches can be divided into 3 equal parts, each 1 inch.
$\frac{2}{3}$ means 2 of 3 equal parts. Therefore,

$$\frac{2}{3} \text{ of 3 inches} = 2 \text{ inches} \qquad \text{or} \qquad \frac{2}{\cancel{3}} \times \cancel{3}^{1} = 2.$$

(b) Find $\frac{1}{2}$ of $\frac{3}{4}$ inch.

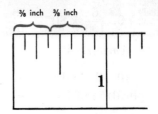

⅜ inch ⅜ inch

$\frac{3}{4}$ inch can be divided into 2 equal parts, each $\frac{3}{8}$ inch.

$\frac{1}{2}$ means 1 of 2 equal parts. Therefore,

$\frac{1}{2}$ of $\frac{3}{4}$ inch $= \frac{3}{8}$ inch   or $\frac{1}{2} \times \frac{3}{4} = \frac{3}{8}$.

Note that when a number is multiplied by a fraction, the product is always smaller than the given number because a fractional part of the given number is being found.

III. Sample Solutions

Multiply in the following examples:

1. $\frac{7}{8} \times \frac{3}{5} = \frac{21}{40}$

Answer: $\frac{21}{40}$

2. $\frac{2}{3} \times 5 = \frac{10}{3} = 3\frac{1}{3}$

Answer: $3\frac{1}{3}$

3. $\frac{4}{5} \times \frac{15}{16} = \frac{\overset{1}{\cancel{4}}}{\cancel{5}} \times \frac{\overset{3}{\cancel{15}}}{\underset{4}{\cancel{16}}} = \frac{3}{4}$

Answer: $\frac{3}{4}$

4. $6 \times \frac{3}{8} = \frac{\overset{3}{\cancel{6}}}{1} \times \frac{3}{\underset{4}{\cancel{8}}} = \frac{9}{4} = 2\frac{1}{4}$

Answer: $2\frac{1}{4}$

5. $2\frac{1}{2} \times 1\frac{1}{5} = \frac{\overset{1}{\cancel{5}}}{\underset{1}{\cancel{2}}} \times \frac{\overset{3}{\cancel{6}}}{\underset{1}{\cancel{5}}} = \frac{3}{1}$ or 3

Answer: 3

6. $2\frac{5}{8} \times 1\frac{1}{4} = \frac{21}{8} \times \frac{5}{4} = \frac{105}{32} = 3\frac{9}{32}$

Answer: $3\frac{9}{32}$

7.
$\begin{array}{r} 21 \\ \times\, 3\frac{1}{2} \\ \hline 63 \\ +\,10\frac{1}{2} \\ \hline 73\frac{1}{2} \end{array}$
   $\frac{1}{2} \times 21 = \frac{21}{2} = 10\frac{1}{2}$

Answer: $73\frac{1}{2}$

8. $1\frac{4}{5} \times \frac{2}{3} \times 3\frac{1}{8} = \frac{\overset{3}{\cancel{9}}}{\underset{1}{\cancel{5}}} \times \frac{\overset{1}{\cancel{2}}}{\underset{1}{\cancel{3}}} \times \frac{\overset{5}{\cancel{25}}}{\underset{4}{\cancel{8}}} = \frac{15}{4} = 3\frac{3}{4}$

Answer: $3\frac{3}{4}$

9. $\dfrac{6}{100} \times 800 = \dfrac{6}{\cancel{100}} \times \cancel{800} = 48$

Answer: 48

10. To find a fractional part of a number, multiply as in multiplication of fractions.

Find $\dfrac{5}{8}$ of 48. $\dfrac{5}{\cancel{8}} \times \cancel{48}^{\,6} = 30$

Answer: 30

11. Reduction may be used in examples involving both multiplication and division as follows:

Simplify: $\dfrac{5{,}280 \times 60}{3{,}600} = \dfrac{\overset{88}{\cancel{5{,}280}} \times \overset{1}{\cancel{60}}}{\underset{\underset{1}{6}}{\cancel{3{,}600}}} = \dfrac{88}{1}$ or 88

Answer: 88

DIAGNOSTIC TEST

Multiply as indicated:

1. $\frac{1}{5} \times \frac{1}{3}$	**9.** $\frac{2}{3} \times 6$	**17.** $5 \times \frac{3}{16}$	**25.** $6\frac{1}{4} \times \frac{3}{8}$
2. $\frac{3}{4} \times \frac{5}{8}$	**10.** $\frac{3}{4} \times 2$	**18.** $4\frac{1}{2} \times 4$	**26.** $\frac{5}{16} \times 9\frac{3}{5}$
3. $\frac{1}{2} \times \frac{2}{3}$	**11.** $\frac{5}{6} \times 10$	**19.** $1\frac{7}{12} \times 8$	**27.** $\frac{5}{6} \times 1\frac{9}{16}$
4. $\frac{3}{8} \times \frac{4}{5}$	**12.** $\frac{3}{5} \times 7$	**20.** $3\frac{1}{3} \times 5$	**28.** $5\frac{1}{3} \times 1\frac{1}{8}$
5. $\frac{3}{4} \times \frac{8}{15}$	**13.** $10 \times \frac{9}{10}$	**21.** $12 \times 1\frac{5}{6}$	**29.** $2\frac{5}{8} \times 2\frac{2}{5}$
6. $\frac{9}{16} \times \frac{5}{6}$	**14.** $48 \times \frac{7}{12}$	**22.** $10 \times 2\frac{9}{16}$	**30.** $4\frac{1}{2} \times 2\frac{1}{4}$
7. $\frac{5}{2} \times \frac{10}{3}$	**15.** $4 \times \frac{7}{8}$	**23.** $7 \times 3\frac{1}{4}$	
8. $\frac{7}{8} \times 8$	**16.** $12 \times \frac{5}{8}$	**24.** $2\frac{1}{2} \times \frac{4}{5}$	

31. $\frac{1}{2} \times \frac{8}{15} \times \frac{5}{6}$ **33.** $\begin{array}{r} 18 \\ 7\frac{1}{3} \end{array}$ **34.** $\begin{array}{r} 12\frac{5}{6} \\ \underline{8} \end{array}$

32. $1\frac{3}{4} \times 3\frac{1}{7} \times 1\frac{3}{5}$

35. Find the product of $2\frac{7}{8}$ and $1\frac{3}{4}$.

36. $\frac{5}{100} \times 900$

37. Simplify: $\dfrac{132 \times 3{,}600}{5{,}280}$

38. Find $\frac{3}{4}$ of 18.

RELATED PRACTICE EXAMPLES

Multiply as indicated:

Set 1

$\frac{1}{4} \times \frac{1}{2}$ $\frac{1}{8} \times \frac{1}{3}$ $\frac{1}{5} \times \frac{1}{4}$ $\frac{1}{2} \times \frac{1}{10}$ $\frac{1}{16} \times \frac{1}{4}$

Set 2

$\frac{1}{2} \times \frac{3}{5}$ $\frac{5}{6} \times \frac{7}{8}$ $\frac{7}{16} \times \frac{3}{4}$ $\frac{9}{10} \times \frac{3}{8}$ $\frac{5}{12} \times \frac{1}{3}$

Set 3

$\frac{1}{3} \times \frac{3}{5}$ $\frac{4}{5} \times \frac{3}{4}$ $\frac{3}{10} \times \frac{1}{3}$ $\frac{2}{3} \times \frac{1}{2}$ $\frac{5}{6} \times \frac{6}{7}$

Set 4

$\frac{5}{6} \times \frac{3}{8}$ $\frac{6}{7} \times \frac{11}{12}$ $\frac{4}{5} \times \frac{7}{8}$ $\frac{3}{10} \times \frac{5}{14}$ $\frac{1}{3} \times \frac{9}{10}$

Set 5

$\frac{2}{5} \times \frac{5}{12}$ $\frac{9}{10} \times \frac{2}{3}$ $\frac{5}{8} \times \frac{16}{25}$ $\frac{8}{9} \times \frac{3}{4}$ $\frac{4}{21} \times \frac{7}{8}$

Set 6

$\frac{5}{6} \times \frac{4}{5}$ $\frac{3}{16} \times \frac{6}{7}$ $\frac{7}{8} \times \frac{12}{21}$ $\frac{10}{12} \times \frac{14}{15}$ $\frac{15}{16} \times \frac{9}{10}$

Set 7

$\frac{5}{4} \times \frac{2}{3}$ $\frac{7}{2} \times \frac{4}{5}$ $\frac{4}{3} \times \frac{3}{4}$ $\frac{21}{10} \times \frac{15}{14}$ $\frac{10}{9} \times \frac{15}{8}$

Set 8

$\frac{1}{2} \times 2$ $\frac{5}{6} \times 6$ $\frac{11}{8} \times 8$ $\frac{7}{16} \times 16$ $\frac{3}{5} \times 5$

Set 9

$\frac{3}{4} \times 8$ $\frac{5}{8} \times 16$ $\frac{7}{6} \times 72$ $\frac{5}{12} \times 36$ $\frac{9}{16} \times 64$

Set 10

$\frac{3}{8} \times 4$ $\frac{7}{16} \times 2$ $\frac{5}{12} \times 3$ $\frac{11}{24} \times 12$ $\frac{9}{10} \times 5$

Set 11

$\frac{3}{8} \times 6$ $\frac{9}{16} \times 20$ $\frac{19}{12} \times 8$ $\frac{7}{10} \times 26$ $\frac{5}{6} \times 4$

Set 12

$\frac{1}{3} \times 7$ $\frac{3}{5} \times 9$ $\frac{9}{8} \times 5$ $\frac{13}{16} \times 3$ $\frac{3}{10} \times 21$

Set 13

$4 \times \frac{3}{4}$ $8 \times \frac{5}{8}$ $12 \times \frac{13}{12}$ $32 \times \frac{29}{32}$ $16 \times \frac{15}{16}$

Set 14

$12 \times \frac{5}{6}$ $24 \times \frac{3}{8}$ $32 \times \frac{17}{16}$ $8 \times \frac{3}{4}$ $30 \times \frac{2}{5}$

SET 15

$2 \times \frac{3}{8}$	$4 \times \frac{5}{16}$	$2 \times \frac{7}{4}$	$5 \times \frac{3}{10}$	$6 \times \frac{13}{24}$

SET 16

$12 \times \frac{7}{16}$	$18 \times \frac{15}{32}$	$16 \times \frac{19}{12}$	$14 \times \frac{5}{8}$	$15 \times \frac{3}{10}$

SET 17

$4 \times \frac{2}{3}$	$9 \times \frac{4}{5}$	$3 \times \frac{9}{8}$	$7 \times \frac{5}{12}$	$13 \times \frac{9}{10}$

SET 18

$2\frac{1}{8} \times 16$	$3\frac{1}{4} \times 12$	$1\frac{2}{3} \times 9$	$7\frac{1}{2} \times 6$	$4\frac{3}{5} \times 10$

SET 19

$2\frac{5}{6} \times 3$	$5\frac{7}{8} \times 6$	$3\frac{11}{12} \times 8$	$1\frac{9}{10} \times 12$	$6\frac{13}{16} \times 20$

SET 20

$2\frac{1}{5} \times 4$	$3\frac{1}{2} \times 7$	$5\frac{2}{3} \times 2$	$4\frac{5}{8} \times 3$	$3\frac{9}{16} \times 5$

SET 21

$8 \times 5\frac{1}{4}$	$16 \times 2\frac{5}{8}$	$12 \times 3\frac{5}{6}$	$48 \times 1\frac{13}{16}$	$24 \times 5\frac{11}{12}$

SET 22

$15 \times 1\frac{7}{10}$	$8 \times 2\frac{9}{16}$	$18 \times 5\frac{5}{8}$	$4 \times 3\frac{1}{6}$	$16 \times 4\frac{7}{12}$

SET 23

$2 \times 6\frac{1}{3}$	$5 \times 4\frac{3}{8}$	$3 \times 9\frac{1}{2}$	$9 \times 5\frac{7}{16}$	$7 \times 1\frac{3}{4}$

SET 24

$3\frac{1}{3} \times \frac{3}{5}$	$2\frac{1}{5} \times \frac{5}{6}$	$6\frac{3}{4} \times \frac{2}{3}$	$3\frac{1}{8} \times \frac{8}{15}$	$4\frac{1}{2} \times \frac{2}{9}$

SET 25

$2\frac{1}{2} \times \frac{3}{4}$	$5\frac{2}{3} \times \frac{5}{8}$	$1\frac{3}{8} \times \frac{1}{2}$	$3\frac{7}{16} \times \frac{3}{4}$	$4\frac{5}{6} \times \frac{11}{16}$

SET 26

$\frac{1}{2} \times 3\frac{1}{5}$	$\frac{5}{6} \times 2\frac{3}{10}$	$\frac{7}{8} \times 3\frac{1}{7}$	$\frac{9}{16} \times 1\frac{1}{3}$	$\frac{5}{12} \times 2\frac{1}{4}$

SET 27

$\frac{7}{8} \times 1\frac{1}{4}$	$\frac{1}{2} \times 3\frac{3}{8}$	$\frac{1}{5} \times 4\frac{1}{3}$	$\frac{9}{10} \times 1\frac{1}{2}$	$\frac{3}{4} \times 2\frac{3}{16}$

SET 28

$1\frac{1}{4} \times 1\frac{3}{5}$	$5\frac{1}{3} \times 4\frac{1}{2}$	$2\frac{5}{8} \times 1\frac{5}{7}$	$3\frac{3}{4} \times 1\frac{1}{5}$	$2\frac{2}{3} \times 3\frac{3}{8}$

SET 29

$$2\frac{1}{3} \times 1\frac{1}{5} \qquad 2\frac{1}{6} \times 2\frac{2}{3} \qquad 2\frac{2}{5} \times 1\frac{3}{16} \qquad 1\frac{7}{16} \times 1\frac{5}{9} \qquad 1\frac{3}{4} \times 3\frac{1}{3}$$

SET 30

$$2\frac{1}{8} \times 1\frac{1}{2} \qquad 3\frac{3}{4} \times 2\frac{7}{8} \qquad 1\frac{9}{16} \times 4\frac{1}{3} \qquad 2\frac{5}{6} \times 1\frac{3}{8} \qquad 4\frac{1}{8} \times 3\frac{13}{16}$$

SET 31

$$\frac{1}{4} \times \frac{5}{6} \times \frac{2}{5} \qquad \frac{2}{3} \times \frac{5}{8} \times \frac{3}{10} \qquad \frac{5}{12} \times \frac{3}{16} \times \frac{4}{5}$$

$$\frac{2}{5} \times \frac{3}{4} \times \frac{15}{16} \qquad \frac{3}{4} \times \frac{3}{5} \times \frac{1}{2}$$

SET 32

$$2\frac{3}{4} \times 1\frac{1}{8} \times 3\frac{5}{6} \qquad 1\frac{1}{2} \times \frac{4}{5} \times 2\frac{1}{6} \qquad 3\frac{1}{5} \times 1\frac{1}{4} \times 1\frac{1}{3}$$

$$1\frac{5}{16} \times 2\frac{2}{3} \times 3\frac{1}{7} \qquad 4\frac{1}{6} \times 3\frac{1}{5} \times 1\frac{3}{10}$$

SET 33

28	16	35	6	29
$4\frac{1}{2}$	$5\frac{3}{4}$	$7\frac{5}{8}$	$8\frac{4}{5}$	$2\frac{2}{3}$

SET 34

$32\frac{1}{4}$	$24\frac{3}{8}$	$17\frac{3}{5}$	$5\frac{5}{6}$	$14\frac{3}{16}$
8	6	10	9	8

SET 35

1. Multiply $4\frac{7}{8}$ by 6.
2. Multiply $2\frac{3}{4}$ by $4\frac{1}{2}$.
3. Find the product of $1\frac{3}{4}$ and $3\frac{1}{7}$.
4. Find the product of $1\frac{1}{8}$ and $5\frac{1}{3}$.
5. Find the product of $2\frac{3}{16}$ and $2\frac{2}{5}$.

SET 36

1. $\frac{3}{100} \times 400$
2. $\frac{4}{100} \times 500$
3. $\frac{2}{100} \times 1,000$
4. $\frac{6}{100} \times 2,500$
5. $\frac{8}{100} \times 4,800$

SET 37

Simplify:

1. $\frac{1,760 \times 30}{60}$ 2. $\frac{75 \times 32}{25 \times 24}$ 3. $\frac{22 \times 21 \times 21}{7 \times 2 \times 2}$ 4. $\frac{33 \times 6 \times 14}{231}$

5. $\frac{18 \times 12 \times 16}{144}$ 6. $\frac{5,280 \times 120}{3,600}$ 7. $\frac{3,600 \times 66}{5,280}$

8. $\frac{5,280 \times 4}{6,080}$ 9. $\frac{5,280 \times 100}{3,600}$ 10. $\frac{6,080 \times 12}{5,280}$

Finding Fractional Parts of a Number

Find:

SET 38(a)	SET 38(b)	SET 38(c)	SET 38(d)
1. $\frac{1}{2}$ of 48	1. $\frac{1}{3}$ of 96	1. $\frac{1}{8}$ of 104	1. $\frac{1}{6}$ of 78
2. $\frac{1}{2}$ of 32¢	2. $\frac{1}{3}$ of 8	2. $\frac{1}{8}$ of $136	2. $\frac{1}{6}$ of $120
3. $\frac{1}{2}$ of $60	3. $\frac{1}{4}$ of 52¢	3. $\frac{1}{8}$ of $\frac{2}{5}$	3. $\frac{1}{6}$ of 4
4. $\frac{1}{2}$ of 17	4. $\frac{1}{4}$ of $1,000	4. $\frac{1}{16}$ of 288	4. $\frac{1}{12}$ of 84¢
5. $\frac{1}{2}$ of $2\frac{1}{2}$	5. $\frac{1}{4}$ of $1\frac{3}{5}$	5. $\frac{1}{16}$ of 24	5. $\frac{1}{12}$ of $2\frac{1}{4}$

SET 38(e)	SET 38(f)	SET 38(g)	SET 38(h)
1. $\frac{1}{5}$ of $285	1. $\frac{3}{4}$ of 16	1. $\frac{2}{5}$ of 45¢	1. $\frac{3}{8}$ of 24¢
2. $\frac{1}{5}$ of 19	2. $\frac{3}{4}$ of $272	2. $\frac{2}{5}$ of 12	2. $\frac{5}{8}$ of $168
3. $\frac{1}{10}$ of 80¢	3. $\frac{3}{4}$ of $\frac{3}{8}$	3. $\frac{3}{5}$ of $235	3. $\frac{7}{8}$ of 6
4. $\frac{1}{20}$ of 45	4. $\frac{2}{3}$ of 87¢	4. $\frac{3}{5}$ of $1\frac{2}{3}$	4. $\frac{15}{16}$ of $1,120
5. $\frac{1}{100}$ of 1,400	5. $\frac{2}{3}$ of $1\frac{11}{16}$	5. $\frac{4}{5}$ of 585	5. $\frac{9}{16}$ of $\frac{2}{3}$

SET 38(i)		SET 38(j)	
1. $\frac{7}{10}$ of 180	4. $\frac{17}{20}$ of 12	1. $\frac{5}{6}$ of 72¢	4. $\frac{5}{12}$ of $2,400
2. $\frac{9}{100}$ of 250	5. $\frac{3}{10}$ of $1\frac{1}{2}$	2. $\frac{5}{6}$ of 16	5. $\frac{7}{12}$ of $2\frac{2}{5}$
3. $\frac{41}{100}$ of $5,000		3. $\frac{11}{12}$ of 132	

PRACTICAL APPLICATIONS

1. A sewing class is making costumes for the school play. If each costume requires $3\frac{5}{8}$ yards of goods, how many yards are needed to make 26 costumes?

2. How many feet of wood are needed to make 15 shelves each $6\frac{2}{3}$ feet long?

3. Find the cost of: (a) $1\frac{1}{2}$ dozen eggs at 58¢ per dozen.

(b) $1\frac{3}{4}$ lb. of cake at 48¢ per lb.

(c) $3\frac{1}{4}$ lb. of bananas at 12¢ per lb.

(d) $2\frac{3}{8}$ lb. of string beans at 24¢ per lb.

(e) $1\frac{7}{16}$ lb. of cheese at 64¢ per lb.

4. The cooking class is divided into 6 teams. If each team uses a recipe that requires $2\frac{1}{2}$ cups cake flour, $2\frac{1}{4}$ teaspoons baking powder, $\frac{1}{2}$ cup shortening, and $1\frac{1}{4}$ cups sugar, how much of each ingredient does the entire class need?

5. Paul wishes to buy a record player priced at $60. He pays $\frac{1}{5}$ in cash and the rest in 6 equal monthly installments. How much must he pay each month?

6. A house worth $19,500 is assessed at $\frac{2}{3}$ of its value. What is the assessed value of the house?

7. Mr. Rodgers earns $3 per hour. If he gets time and a half for overtime, what is his hourly rate for overtime work?

8. The premium rate for a 3-year fire insurance policy is $2\frac{1}{2}$ times the annual rate. What is the rate for a 3-year policy if the annual rate is: (*a*) 18¢ per $100; (*b*) 32¢ per $100; (*c*) 25¢ per $100; (*d*) 19¢ per $100; (*e*) 37¢ per $100.

9. How much will a trip over a distance of 12 miles cost at $7\frac{3}{4}$ cents per mile?

10. A family budgets $\frac{1}{4}$ of its annual income of $5,400 for food, $\frac{3}{10}$ for shelter including operating expenses and furnishings, $\frac{1}{8}$ for clothing, $\frac{3}{20}$ for savings, and the remainder for miscellaneous expenses. How much is allowed for each item annually?

11. (*a*) If the scale on a chart is 1 inch = 30 miles, how many miles do $6\frac{1}{2}$ inches represent?

(*b*) Using the scale 1 inch = 150 miles, find the distance represented by $\frac{3}{4}$ inch.

12. (*a*) In constructing a vector diagram the scale 1 inch = 48 m.p.h. is used. What speed in m.p.h. will a line $2\frac{3}{16}$ inches in length represent?

(*b*) What is the wind velocity if it is represented by a line $\frac{5}{8}$ inch and the scale 1 inch = 64 m.p.h. is used?

(*c*) What is the air speed if it is represented by a line $3\frac{1}{2}$ inches long and the scale 1 inch = 50 m.p.h. is used?

(*d*) What is the ground speed if it is represented by a line $4\frac{3}{4}$ inches long and the scale 1 inch = 60 m.p.h. is used?

13. To change Fahrenheit temperature readings to Centigrade readings, first subtract 32 degrees from the Fahrenheit reading, then take $\frac{5}{9}$ of the answer.

Change the following Fahrenheit readings to Centigrade:
(*a*) 68° F.   (*b*) 104° F.   (*c*) 41° F.   (*d*) 32° F.   (*e*) 212° F.

14. (*a*) The diameter of a circle is twice the radius. Find the length of the diameter if the radius is: (1) $1\frac{3}{4}$ in.   (2) $17\frac{1}{2}$ ft. (3) $\frac{5}{8}$ in.   (4) $\frac{3}{16}$ in.   (5) $6\frac{1}{4}$ ft.

(*b*) The radius of a circle is one half the diameter. Find the length of the radius if the diameter is: (1) 18 ft.   (2) 33 ft. (3) $4\frac{7}{8}$ in.   (4) $\frac{3}{4}$ in.   (5) $1\frac{11}{16}$ in.

(c) The circumference (distance around) of a circle is $3\frac{1}{7}$ times the diameter. Find the circumference when the diameter is: (1) 56 ft.   (2) 15 ft.   (3) $10\frac{1}{2}$ in.   (4) $8\frac{3}{4}$ in.   (5) $\frac{7}{8}$ in.

15. The temperature of a parcel of air decreases at the rate of $5\frac{1}{2}°$ Fahrenheit for each 1,000 feet it rises following the dry adiabat.

(a) If the temperature at the surface is 68° F., find the temperature at an altitude of 4,000 feet.

(b) What is the temperature at the surface if the temperature at an altitude of 5,000 feet is 42° F.?

16. A plane encounters a wind which cuts its ground speed to $\frac{2}{3}$ of its scheduled speed. If the pilot planned to fly at a ground speed of 360 m.p.h. and reach a point 720 miles distant, how much longer will it take him to get to his destination, flying at the reduced speed?

17. If 1 cu. ft. holds about $7\frac{1}{2}$ gal., how many gallons of oil will a tank hold if its volume is $24\frac{1}{2}$ cu. ft.?

18. If 1 cu. ft. of water weighs $62\frac{1}{2}$ lb., find the weight of a column of water containing 32 cu. ft.

19. A ship steams at $18\frac{1}{2}$ knots. At that rate how many nautical miles does it go in $6\frac{1}{4}$ hours? (1 knot = 1 nautical m.p.h.)

20. The speed of a certain submarine when submerged is $\frac{3}{5}$ of its surface speed. If its maximum surface speed is $17\frac{1}{2}$ knots, what is its maximum speed when submerged?

REFRESH YOUR SKILLS

1. Round off 687,473 to the nearest hundred.

2. Add:	**3.** Subtract:	**4.** Multiply:	**5.** Divide:
627	800,000	5,280	365)149,285
4,963	706,094	5,280	
81,896			
97,988			
8,569			

6. Reduce $\frac{36}{54}$ to lowest terms.

7. Add:	**8.** Subtract:	**9.** Multiply:	**10.** Multiply:
$3\frac{7}{10}$	$4\frac{1}{3}$	$\frac{7}{8} \times \frac{3}{4}$	$4\frac{3}{8} \times 3\frac{1}{5}$
$6\frac{5}{12}$	$3\frac{5}{6}$		

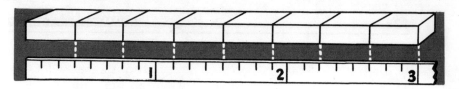

EXERCISE 18

DIVISION OF FRACTIONS AND MIXED NUMBERS

I. Aim: To divide fractions and mixed numbers.

II. Procedure

1. Change each mixed number to an improper fraction. (See Exercise 16.) Express each whole number in fraction form by using the whole number as the numerator and the figure 1 as the denominator.

2. Since division by a number gives the same result as multiplication by the reciprocal of this number (see page 148), invert the divisor to find the reciprocal and then multiply as in the multiplication of fractions, using reduction where possible. (See Exercise 17.)

3. To simplify a complex fraction, divide the fraction in the numerator by the fraction in the denominator.

4. Check by going over the work again.

Concept:

(a) 3 inches $\div \frac{3}{4}$ inch.

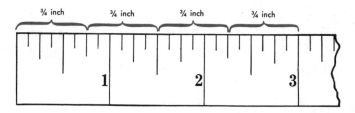

To divide 3 inches by $\frac{3}{4}$ inch means to find how many $\frac{3}{4}$ inch are contained in 3 inches. In 3 inches, $\frac{3}{4}$ inch can be contained 4 times. Therefore,

$$3 \text{ inches} \div \tfrac{3}{4} \text{ inch} = 4$$

or $\qquad 3 \div \dfrac{3}{4} = \overset{1}{\cancel{3}} \times \dfrac{4}{\underset{1}{\cancel{3}}} = 4$

127

(b) $3\frac{1}{4}$ inches $\div$ $1\frac{5}{8}$ inches

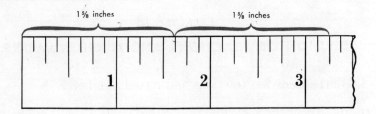

To divide $3\frac{1}{4}$ inches by $1\frac{5}{8}$ inches means to find how many $1\frac{5}{8}$ inches are contained in $3\frac{1}{4}$ inches. In $3\frac{1}{4}$ inches, $1\frac{5}{8}$ inches can be contained twice. Therefore, $3\frac{1}{4}$ inches $\div$ $1\frac{5}{8}$ inches $= 2$

$$\text{or} \quad 3\frac{1}{4} \div 1\frac{5}{8} = \frac{13}{4} \div \frac{13}{8} = \frac{\overset{1}{\cancel{13}}}{\underset{1}{\cancel{4}}} \times \frac{\overset{2}{\cancel{8}}}{\underset{1}{\cancel{13}}} = \frac{2}{1} \text{ or } 2$$

Note that when a number is divided by a fraction, the quotient is always greater than the given number. When a number is divided by a mixed number, the quotient is always smaller than the given number.

III. Sample Solutions

Divide in the following examples:

1. $\dfrac{2}{5} \div \dfrac{5}{8} = \dfrac{2}{5} \times \dfrac{8}{5} = \dfrac{16}{25}$

Answer: $\frac{16}{25}$

3. $15 \div \dfrac{3}{8} = \dfrac{15}{1} \times \dfrac{8}{\underset{1}{\cancel{3}}}^{5} = \dfrac{40}{1}$ or 40

Answer: 40

2. $\dfrac{2}{3} \div \dfrac{5}{6} = \dfrac{2}{\underset{1}{\cancel{3}}} \times \dfrac{\overset{2}{\cancel{6}}}{5} = \dfrac{4}{5}$

Answer: $\frac{4}{5}$

4. $8\frac{3}{4} \div 7 = \dfrac{35}{4} \div 7 = \dfrac{\overset{5}{\cancel{35}}}{4} \times \dfrac{1}{\underset{1}{\cancel{7}}} = \dfrac{5}{4} = 1\frac{1}{4}$

Answer: $1\frac{1}{4}$

5. $2\frac{1}{2} \div \dfrac{3}{4} = \dfrac{5}{2} \div \dfrac{3}{4} = \dfrac{5}{\underset{1}{\cancel{2}}} \times \dfrac{\overset{2}{\cancel{4}}}{3} = \dfrac{10}{3} = 3\frac{1}{3}$

Answer: $3\frac{1}{3}$

6. $2\frac{3}{16} \div 1\frac{1}{4} = \dfrac{35}{16} \div \dfrac{5}{4} = \dfrac{\overset{7}{\cancel{35}}}{\underset{4}{\cancel{16}}} \times \dfrac{\overset{1}{\cancel{4}}}{\underset{1}{\cancel{5}}} = \dfrac{7}{4} = 1\frac{3}{4}$

Answer: $1\frac{3}{4}$

7. (a) $\left(2\frac{1}{2} \div \frac{5}{6}\right) \div \frac{2}{3} = \left(\frac{\cancel{5}^{1}}{\cancel{2}_{1}} \times \frac{\cancel{6}^{3}}{\cancel{5}_{1}}\right) \div \frac{2}{3} = \frac{3}{1} \div \frac{2}{3} = \frac{3}{1} \times \frac{3}{2} = \frac{9}{2} = 4\frac{1}{2}$

Answer: $4\frac{1}{2}$

(b) $2\frac{1}{2} \div \left(\frac{5}{6} \div \frac{2}{3}\right) = 2\frac{1}{2} \div \left(\frac{5}{\cancel{6}_{2}} \times \frac{\cancel{3}^{1}}{2}\right) = 2\frac{1}{2} \div \frac{5}{4} = \frac{\cancel{5}^{1}}{\cancel{2}_{1}} \times \frac{\cancel{4}^{2}}{\cancel{5}_{1}} = \frac{2}{1} = 2$

Answer: 2

The associative property does not hold for division. See pages 5 and 6.

8. Simplify the following complex fraction:

$$\frac{\frac{9}{16}}{\frac{3}{8}} = \frac{9}{16} \div \frac{3}{8} = \frac{\cancel{9}^{3}}{\cancel{16}_{2}} \times \frac{\cancel{8}^{1}}{\cancel{3}_{1}} = \frac{3}{2} = 1\frac{1}{2}$$

Answer: $1\frac{1}{2}$

IV. Definition

A complex fraction is a fraction in which the numerator or denominator or both have a fraction as a term.

DIAGNOSTIC TEST
Divide as indicated:

1. $\frac{1}{3} \div \frac{3}{4}$	7. $\frac{7}{8} \div 2$	13. $1\frac{2}{3} \div 4$	19. $2\frac{5}{8} \div \frac{3}{5}$
2. $\frac{2}{3} \div \frac{5}{16}$	8. $8 \div \frac{1}{2}$	14. $15 \div 1\frac{7}{8}$	20. $1\frac{7}{16} \div \frac{2}{3}$
3. $\frac{3}{5} \div \frac{9}{10}$	9. $5 \div \frac{15}{16}$	15. $6 \div 4\frac{1}{2}$	21. $\frac{7}{8} \div 1\frac{3}{4}$
4. $\frac{3}{4} \div \frac{3}{8}$	10. $2 \div \frac{3}{5}$	16. $4 \div 5\frac{1}{3}$	22. $\frac{3}{4} \div 1\frac{3}{5}$
5. $\frac{5}{6} \div \frac{7}{12}$	11. $4\frac{1}{2} \div 18$	17. $7 \div 2\frac{3}{4}$	23. $11\frac{1}{3} \div 2\frac{5}{6}$
6. $\frac{3}{4} \div 6$	12. $4\frac{2}{3} \div 2$	18. $2\frac{1}{2} \div \frac{5}{6}$	24. $3\frac{3}{16} \div 2\frac{1}{8}$

25. $1\frac{1}{6} \div 9\frac{1}{3}$

26. $5\frac{3}{8} \div 1\frac{2}{5}$

27. $6\frac{3}{5} \div 6\frac{3}{5}$

28. Divide $9\frac{1}{3}$ by $3\frac{1}{7}$.

29. $\left(1\frac{1}{8} \div 2\frac{1}{4}\right) \div 4\frac{2}{3}$

30. $7\frac{1}{3} \div \left(3\frac{1}{7} \times 2\frac{4}{5}\right)$

Simplify:

31. $\dfrac{\frac{2}{3}}{\frac{5}{8}}$

RELATED PRACTICE EXAMPLES
Divide as indicated:

SET 1

$\frac{1}{4} \div \frac{1}{3}$ $\frac{3}{4} \div \frac{4}{5}$ $\frac{1}{2} \div \frac{2}{3}$ $\frac{2}{5} \div \frac{9}{16}$ $\frac{3}{5} \div \frac{11}{12}$

SET 2

$\frac{1}{2} \div \frac{1}{5}$ $\frac{7}{8} \div \frac{2}{3}$ $\frac{9}{10} \div \frac{1}{3}$ $\frac{11}{12} \div \frac{4}{7}$ $\frac{4}{9} \div \frac{7}{16}$

SET 3

$\frac{1}{4} \div \frac{3}{4}$ $\frac{5}{8} \div \frac{5}{6}$ $\frac{3}{16} \div \frac{5}{12}$ $\frac{2}{3} \div \frac{4}{5}$ $\frac{5}{6} \div \frac{7}{8}$

SET 4

$\frac{5}{6} \div \frac{5}{12}$ $\frac{7}{8} \div \frac{7}{16}$ $\frac{2}{3} \div \frac{2}{9}$ $\frac{5}{8} \div \frac{5}{8}$ $\frac{4}{5} \div \frac{4}{15}$

SET 5

$\frac{1}{2} \div \frac{7}{16}$ $\frac{2}{5} \div \frac{3}{10}$ $\frac{7}{8} \div \frac{5}{12}$ $\frac{4}{5} \div \frac{7}{10}$ $\frac{5}{12} \div \frac{3}{16}$

SET 6

$\frac{2}{3} \div 4$ $\frac{4}{5} \div 2$ $\frac{7}{8} \div 7$ $\frac{9}{10} \div 6$ $\frac{3}{5} \div 9$

SET 7

$\frac{3}{5} \div 8$ $\frac{1}{2} \div 10$ $\frac{7}{16} \div 3$ $\frac{11}{12} \div 5$ $\frac{5}{8} \div 4$

SET 8

$6 \div \frac{1}{3}$ $7 \div \frac{1}{8}$ $8 \div \frac{4}{5}$ $10 \div \frac{5}{16}$ $4 \div \frac{2}{5}$

SET 9

$18 \div \frac{9}{10}$ $6 \div \frac{4}{5}$ $10 \div \frac{2}{3}$ $12 \div \frac{15}{16}$ $15 \div \frac{21}{32}$

SET 10

$5 \div \frac{3}{4}$ $13 \div \frac{2}{3}$ $9 \div \frac{7}{8}$ $14 \div \frac{5}{6}$ $7 \div \frac{9}{16}$

SET 11

$1\frac{1}{2} \div 3$ $4\frac{2}{3} \div 14$ $5\frac{3}{5} \div 7$ $2\frac{7}{16} \div 13$ $3\frac{3}{8} \div 9$

SET 12

$3\frac{3}{4} \div 3$ $7\frac{1}{2} \div 5$ $8\frac{2}{5} \div 6$ $18\frac{3}{4} \div 10$ $11\frac{7}{8} \div 5$

SET 13

$1\frac{5}{8} \div 2$ $2\frac{1}{16} \div 4$ $8\frac{1}{2} \div 3$ $5\frac{3}{4} \div 5$ $3\frac{4}{5} \div 8$

SET 14

$6 \div 1\frac{1}{2}$ $8 \div 1\frac{1}{3}$ $27 \div 2\frac{1}{4}$ $68 \div 3\frac{2}{5}$ $57 \div 2\frac{3}{8}$

SET 15

$8 \div 2\frac{2}{5}$ $10 \div 1\frac{7}{8}$ $14 \div 1\frac{5}{16}$ $40 \div 5\frac{1}{3}$ $6 \div 2\frac{1}{4}$

Set 16

$$5 \div 6\tfrac{2}{3} \qquad 8 \div 9\tfrac{3}{5} \qquad 3 \div 6\tfrac{3}{4} \qquad 6 \div 7\tfrac{7}{8} \qquad 2 \div 4\tfrac{4}{5}$$

Set 17

$$6 \div 1\tfrac{2}{3} \qquad 4 \div 6\tfrac{3}{5} \qquad 8 \div 1\tfrac{4}{5} \qquad 1 \div 2\tfrac{1}{3} \qquad 3 \div 1\tfrac{5}{8}$$

Set 18

$$1\tfrac{1}{2} \div \tfrac{9}{16} \qquad 1\tfrac{1}{8} \div \tfrac{3}{32} \qquad 8\tfrac{3}{4} \div \tfrac{7}{8} \qquad 1\tfrac{7}{8} \div \tfrac{3}{16} \qquad 9\tfrac{1}{3} \div \tfrac{7}{24}$$

Set 19

$$1\tfrac{3}{5} \div \tfrac{2}{3} \qquad 2\tfrac{1}{3} \div \tfrac{7}{8} \qquad 1\tfrac{5}{6} \div \tfrac{5}{12} \qquad 3\tfrac{1}{4} \div \tfrac{5}{6} \qquad 2\tfrac{1}{8} \div \tfrac{9}{10}$$

Set 20

$$4\tfrac{1}{4} \div \tfrac{3}{5} \qquad 2\tfrac{3}{5} \div \tfrac{5}{8} \qquad 3\tfrac{1}{7} \div \tfrac{3}{4} \qquad 2\tfrac{2}{3} \div \tfrac{9}{16} \qquad 2\tfrac{3}{8} \div \tfrac{4}{5}$$

Set 21

$$\tfrac{5}{12} \div 8\tfrac{1}{3} \qquad \tfrac{5}{6} \div 1\tfrac{1}{9} \qquad \tfrac{3}{5} \div 2\tfrac{2}{5} \qquad \tfrac{7}{8} \div 3\tfrac{3}{4} \qquad \tfrac{13}{16} \div 1\tfrac{7}{32}$$

Set 22

$$\tfrac{2}{3} \div 1\tfrac{1}{4} \qquad \tfrac{7}{8} \div 3\tfrac{1}{3} \qquad \tfrac{3}{16} \div 1\tfrac{3}{5} \qquad \tfrac{1}{3} \div 2\tfrac{9}{16} \qquad \tfrac{4}{5} \div 4\tfrac{5}{8}$$

Set 23

$$14\tfrac{3}{8} \div 2\tfrac{7}{8} \qquad 7\tfrac{1}{2} \div 1\tfrac{1}{4} \qquad 14\tfrac{1}{2} \div 3\tfrac{5}{8} \qquad 18\tfrac{1}{3} \div 1\tfrac{5}{6} \qquad 50\tfrac{1}{4} \div 4\tfrac{3}{16}$$

Set 24

$$3\tfrac{1}{5} \div 1\tfrac{1}{3} \qquad 1\tfrac{5}{8} \div 1\tfrac{7}{32} \qquad 4\tfrac{2}{3} \div 1\tfrac{3}{5} \qquad 11\tfrac{1}{4} \div 2\tfrac{1}{2} \qquad 2\tfrac{1}{16} \div 1\tfrac{3}{8}$$

Set 25

$$2\tfrac{1}{4} \div 3\tfrac{3}{8} \qquad 1\tfrac{3}{5} \div 3\tfrac{1}{5} \qquad 1\tfrac{13}{16} \div 2\tfrac{1}{4} \qquad 2\tfrac{1}{12} \div 3\tfrac{3}{4} \qquad 1\tfrac{17}{32} \div 2\tfrac{5}{8}$$

Set 26

$$1\tfrac{2}{5} \div 2\tfrac{2}{3} \qquad 4\tfrac{1}{4} \div 2\tfrac{4}{5} \qquad 3\tfrac{3}{8} \div 3\tfrac{1}{5} \qquad 1\tfrac{1}{2} \div 1\tfrac{7}{9} \qquad 1\tfrac{2}{3} \div 1\tfrac{7}{16}$$

Set 27

$$\tfrac{3}{8} \div \tfrac{3}{8} \qquad 1\tfrac{5}{12} \div 1\tfrac{5}{12} \qquad 2\tfrac{2}{3} \div 2\tfrac{2}{3} \qquad 9\tfrac{1}{2} \div 9\tfrac{1}{2} \qquad 6\tfrac{13}{16} \div 6\tfrac{13}{16}$$

Set 28

1. Divide $4\tfrac{1}{2}$ by $\tfrac{3}{5}$.
2. Divide $6\tfrac{1}{4}$ by 8.
3. Divide $2\tfrac{2}{3}$ by $7\tfrac{1}{2}$.
4. Divide $3\tfrac{3}{4}$ by $4\tfrac{2}{5}$.
5. Divide $1\tfrac{7}{8}$ by $1\tfrac{1}{3}$.

Set 29(a)

1. $(\tfrac{7}{8} \div \tfrac{3}{16}) \div \tfrac{21}{32}$
2. $(\tfrac{3}{4} \div \tfrac{4}{5}) \div \tfrac{3}{8}$
3. $(1\tfrac{1}{2} \div \tfrac{5}{8}) \div 1\tfrac{1}{5}$
4. $(4\tfrac{1}{5} \div 1\tfrac{3}{4}) \div 2\tfrac{7}{10}$
5. $(6\tfrac{2}{3} \div 3\tfrac{1}{5}) \div 3\tfrac{3}{4}$

Set 29(b)

1. $\tfrac{9}{10} \div (\tfrac{3}{5} \div \tfrac{3}{4})$
2. $\tfrac{3}{8} \div (\tfrac{5}{6} \div \tfrac{7}{12})$
3. $5\tfrac{1}{2} \div (\tfrac{11}{12} \div 2\tfrac{2}{3})$
4. $1\tfrac{7}{8} \div (3\tfrac{3}{4} \div 2\tfrac{2}{5})$
5. $4\tfrac{2}{3} \div (3\tfrac{1}{2} \div 1\tfrac{3}{4})$

SET 30(a)	SET 30(b)	SET 30(c)
1. $(\frac{5}{16} \div \frac{3}{8}) \times \frac{4}{5}$	1. $\frac{7}{8} \times (\frac{3}{4} \div \frac{15}{16})$	1. $\frac{5}{12} \div (\frac{1}{6} \times \frac{2}{3})$
2. $(1\frac{1}{4} \div 4\frac{1}{2}) \times \frac{9}{16}$	2. $\frac{25}{32} \times (\frac{9}{10} \div \frac{5}{8})$	2. $\frac{1}{2} \div (\frac{3}{4} \times \frac{7}{8})$
3. $(\frac{2}{3} \times \frac{3}{4}) \div \frac{3}{5}$	3. $6\frac{2}{3} \times (\frac{13}{16} \div 5\frac{1}{5})$	3. $8\frac{3}{4} \div (\frac{15}{16} \times 2\frac{4}{5})$
4. $(1\frac{7}{8} \times 1\frac{1}{2}) \div 2\frac{1}{4}$	4. $1\frac{1}{2} \times (1\frac{3}{4} \div 1\frac{4}{5})$	4. $4\frac{1}{2} \div (2\frac{1}{4} \times 1\frac{2}{3})$
5. $(2\frac{1}{5} \times 3\frac{1}{2}) \times 4\frac{2}{3}$	5. $2\frac{5}{6} \times (5\frac{1}{4} \div 1\frac{5}{16})$	,5. $7\frac{4}{5} \div (8\frac{2}{3} \times 3\frac{3}{8})$

Simplify:

SET 31(a)

$$\frac{\frac{3}{5}}{\frac{3}{8}} \qquad \frac{\frac{1}{2}}{\frac{3}{4}} \qquad \frac{\frac{7}{16}}{\frac{5}{6}} \qquad \frac{\frac{4}{5}}{\frac{7}{8}} \qquad \frac{\frac{9}{16}}{\frac{2}{5}}$$

SET 31(b)

$$\frac{2\frac{2}{3}}{5\frac{1}{3}} \qquad \frac{3\frac{3}{8}}{4\frac{1}{2}} \qquad \frac{3\frac{15}{16}}{2\frac{5}{8}} \qquad \frac{10\frac{5}{8}}{4\frac{1}{4}} \qquad \frac{4\frac{2}{5}}{2\frac{3}{4}}$$

SET 31(c)

$$\frac{\frac{5}{8}}{2} \qquad \frac{2\frac{9}{16}}{6} \qquad \frac{1\frac{5}{6}}{3} \qquad \frac{9\frac{1}{2}}{4} \qquad \frac{2\frac{1}{8}}{10}$$

SET 31(d)

$$\frac{87\frac{1}{2}}{100} \qquad \frac{33\frac{1}{3}}{100} \qquad \frac{12\frac{1}{2}}{100} \qquad \frac{62\frac{1}{2}}{100} \qquad \frac{16\frac{2}{3}}{100}$$

SET 31(e)

$$\frac{4}{\frac{2}{5}} \qquad \frac{6}{1\frac{1}{2}} \qquad \frac{5}{3\frac{3}{4}} \qquad \frac{1}{2\frac{2}{3}} \qquad \frac{8}{5\frac{3}{8}}$$

SET 31(f)

$$\frac{\frac{1}{2} + \frac{1}{4}}{\frac{3}{8}} \qquad \frac{\frac{5}{6}}{3 - 1\frac{1}{3}} \qquad \frac{\frac{3}{4} + \frac{7}{8}}{\frac{11}{16} - \frac{1}{2}} \qquad \frac{4\frac{1}{2} + 1\frac{1}{2}}{7\frac{1}{4} + 2\frac{5}{8}} \qquad \frac{8\frac{1}{6} - 2\frac{2}{3}}{6 - 3\frac{3}{5}}$$

PRACTICAL APPLICATIONS

1. How many athletic association membership cards $1\frac{3}{8}$ inches wide can be cut from stock 22 inches wide?

2. If each costume for the school show requires $3\frac{1}{3}$ yards of material, how many costumes can be made from a 30-yard bolt of material?

3. Betty wishes to use a recipe but it makes twice the quantity she needs. If the recipe requires $\frac{1}{4}$ cup cake flour, $2\frac{1}{2}$ tablespoons lemon juice, 1 cup milk, and $\frac{3}{4}$ cup sugar, how much of each ingredient should she take to make the quantity she wants?

4. If a board $10\frac{1}{4}$ ft. long was cut into 6 pieces of equal length, what would the length of each piece be? Disregard waste.

5. How much does a pound of each of the following items cost if: (a) $2\frac{1}{2}$ lb. of peas cost 50¢?

(b) $1\frac{3}{4}$ lb. of asparagus cost 63¢?

(c) $3\frac{5}{8}$ lb. of apples cost 58¢?

6. If a pilot flies 560 mi. in $1\frac{3}{4}$ hr., what is his average ground speed per hour?

7. A ship steamed a distance of 90 nautical miles in $8\frac{1}{3}$ hr. Find its average speed in knots. (1 knot = 1 nautical m.p.h.)

8. A bus is scheduled to go a distance of $87\frac{1}{2}$ mi. in $2\frac{1}{2}$ hr. What average speed must be maintained to arrive on schedule?

9. What are the actual dimensions of a porch which, drawn to the scale of $\frac{1}{4}$ inch = 1 foot, measures $1\frac{3}{4}$ inches by $2\frac{1}{2}$ inches.

10. The scale on a blueprint of a factory is $\frac{1}{8}$ inch = 1 foot. Find the actual dimensions of a room measuring $2\frac{7}{8}$ by $3\frac{5}{16}$ inches.

11. (a) Two cities, 252 miles apart, are plotted on a chart $5\frac{1}{4}$ inches apart. Find the scale of the chart. (b) Find the scale if:

Actual distance	217 mi.	350 mi.	100 mi.	8,125 yd.	$268\frac{3}{4}$ mi.
Distance on chart	$3\frac{7}{8}$ in.	$8\frac{3}{4}$ in.	$1\frac{9}{16}$ in.	$6\frac{1}{2}$ in.	$5\frac{3}{8}$ in.

12. (a) On a map a distance of 84 mi. is represented by $2\frac{5}{8}$ in. How long should a line be to represent a distance of 96 mi.?

(b) How long should a line be to represent a distance of 25 mi. if a distance of 350 mi. on the chart is represented by $1\frac{3}{4}$ in.?

(c) If the distance between Chicago and Cleveland, 360 miles, is represented on a road map by a length of $4\frac{1}{2}$ inches, what is the distance between Detroit and Memphis represented on the same map by a length of $9\frac{1}{8}$ inches?

13. The temperature of a parcel of air decreases at the rate of $5\frac{1}{2}°$ F. for each 1,000 feet it rises following the dry adiabat.

(a) Find the altitude where the temperature is $53\frac{1}{2}°$ F. when the surface temperature is 70° F.

(b) At what altitude is the temperature 45° F. when the surface temperature is 78° F.?

(c) Find the altitude where the temperature is $40\frac{1}{2}°$ F. when the surface temperature is $62\frac{1}{2}°$ F.

14. (a) If the weight of a column of water is 1,125 lb., how many cubic feet does it occupy? (1 cu. ft. of water weighs about $62\frac{1}{2}$ lb.)

(b) A railroad tank car has a capacity of 6,000 gallons of oil. What is its capacity in cubic feet? (1 cu. ft. = $7\frac{1}{2}$ gallons.)

(c) A storage bin has a capacity of 1,190 cu. ft. How many bushels of wheat can it hold? (1 bu. = $1\frac{1}{4}$ cu. ft.)

15. (a) How many lengths of pipe $3\frac{1}{2}$ feet long can be cut from a pipe 28 feet long? Disregard waste in cutting.

(b) A floor is 24 feet wide. How many floor boards $2\frac{1}{4}$ inches wide are needed to cover it?

(c) How many pieces $3\frac{3}{8}$ inches long can be cut from 50 metal rods each 54 inches long? Disregard waste.

16. The diameter of a circle is equal to the circumference (distance around) of the circle divided by $3\frac{1}{7}$. Find the diameter when the circumference is: (a) 88 ft. (b) 50 ft. (c) $\frac{11}{16}$ in. (d) $9\frac{5}{8}$ in. (e) $16\frac{1}{2}$ in.

REFRESH YOUR SKILLS

1. Add: **2.** Subtract: **3.** Multiply: **4.** Divide:

92,838	156,072	3,600	1,728)1,394,496
79,665	75,483	905	
83,756			
44,973			
58,786			

5. Round off 18,639,708 to the nearest thousand.

6. Add: **7.** Subtract: **8.** Multiply: **9.** Divide:

$2\frac{3}{8}$ $11\frac{1}{2}$ $2\frac{7}{10} \times 3\frac{3}{4}$ $9\frac{1}{6} \div 3\frac{1}{7}$

$\frac{11}{12}$ $5\frac{2}{3}$

$9\frac{1}{6}$

10. Reduce $\frac{96}{128}$ to lowest terms.

EXERCISE 19

FINDING WHAT PART ONE NUMBER IS OF ANOTHER

I. Aim: (1) To find what part one number is of another and (2) to compare numbers by using fractions.

II. Procedure

1. To find what part one number is of another, make a fraction taking the number of parts used as the numerator and the number of parts in the whole unit or group as the denominator. Reduce the fraction to lowest terms.

2. To compare numbers by using fractions, make a fraction taking the number that is being compared as the numerator and the number with which it is being compared as the denominator. Change the fraction to simplest form.

III. Sample Solutions

1. What part of 5 is 4?

Answer: $\frac{4}{5}$

2. 9 is what part of 12?

$$\frac{9}{12} = \frac{3}{4}$$

Answer: $\frac{3}{4}$

3. Compare 10 with 16.

$$\frac{10}{16} = \frac{5}{8}$$

Answer: $\frac{5}{8}$

4. Compare 9 with 6.

$$\frac{9}{6} = \frac{3}{2} \text{ or } 1\frac{1}{2}$$

Answer: $\frac{3}{2}$ or $1\frac{1}{2}$

DIAGNOSTIC TEST

Find the following:

1. What part of 6 is 1?

2. 2 is what part of 3?

3. What part of 56 is 35?

4. What part of 100 is 40?

5. Compare 3 with 5.

6. Compare 12 with 16.

7. Compare 11 with 8.

8. Compare 15 with 9.

9. Compare 8 with 1.

10. Compare 24 with 24.

RELATED PRACTICE EXAMPLES

Find the following:

SET 1

1. What part of 4 is 1?
2. What part of 5 is 1?
3. What part of 8 is 7?
4. What part of 24 is 13?
5. What part of 9 is 5?

SET 2

1. 2 is what part of 5?
2. 3 is what part of 4?
3. 7 is what part of 10?
4. 8 is what part of 15?
5. 29 is what part of 32?

SET 3(*a*)

1. What part of 12 is 6?
2. What part of 18 is 3?
3. What part of 64 is 16?
4. What part of 80 is 5?
5. What part of 75 is 25?

SET 3(*b*)

1. 12 is what part of 18?
2. 16 is what part of 20?
3. 49 is what part of 56?
4. 27 is what part of 36?
5. 45 is what part of 54?

SET 3(*c*)

1. What part of 72 is 30?
2. 78 is what part of 90?
3. What part of 112 is 21?
4. 66 is what part of 108?
5. What part of 144 is 135?

SET 4

1. What part of 100 is 28?
2. 75 is what part of 100?
3. What part of 100 is 64?
4. $37\frac{1}{2}$ is what part of 100?
5. What part of 100 is $66\frac{2}{3}$?

SET 5

Compare:
1. 1 with 8
2. 3 with 7
3. 5 with 6
4. 1 with 2
5. 12 with 25

SET 6

Compare:
1. 6 with 10
2. 21 with 28
3. 84 with 96
4. 25 with 30
5. 36 with 54

SET 7

Compare:
1. 7 with 6
2. 13 with 8
3. 9 with 4
4. 5 with 3
5. 17 with 5

SET 8

Compare:
1. 10 with 8
2. 18 with 15
3. 21 with 12
4. 24 with 10
5. 40 with 16

SET 9

Compare:
1. 2 with 1
2. 5 with 1
3. 10 with 1
4. 50 with 1
5. 28 with 1

SET 10

Compare:
1. 8 with 8
2. 10 with 5
3. 24 with 6
4. 150 with 150
5. 96 with 4

PRACTICAL APPLICATIONS

1. What part of a class attended school on a certain day if 39 pupils of the 42 enrolled were present?

2. Janet missed 5 examples in an arithmetic test of 25 examples. What part of the test did she get right?

3. There are 16 boys and 20 girls in a class. What part of the class is boys? What part is girls?

4. If 175 out of 200 freshmen passed their physical examination, what part of the freshmen passed?

5. On the final report 6 pupils in the mathematics class received A. The teacher also announced there were 12 B's, 10 C's, 8 D's, and 4 E's. What part of the class received A? B? E? D? C?

6. In 24 times at bat, Joe hit safely 9 times. What part of the time did he hit safely?

7. George made two errors in 25 fielding chances. What part of his chances did he field the ball cleanly?

8. The Springfield School team won 9 games and lost 6. What part of the games played did it win?

9. John Miller, a pitcher, won 8 games and lost 4. What part of the games did he win?

10. At bat 36 times, Thompson made 7 singles, 2 doubles, 1 triple, and 2 home runs. What part of the time did he hit safely?

11. What part of his annual income of $4,800 does a man save if he deposits $60 each month in his savings account?

12. If brass contains 3 parts copper and 2 parts zinc, what part of brass is copper? What part is zinc?

13. A certain hydrochloric acid solution contains 4 parts acid and 8 parts water. What part of the solution is acid? How many quarts of acid are there in 18 quarts of the solution?

14. (*a*) What part of a dollar is a dime? (*b*) 50 minutes is what part of an hour? (*c*) 3 things are what part of a dozen? (*d*) 12 ounces is what part of a pound? (*e*) What part of a bushel is a peck? (*f*) 6 inches is what part of a foot?

15. A bag of mixed grass seed contains 4 pounds of rye-grass, 3 pounds of fescue, 1 pound of clover, and 2 pounds of bluegrass seed. What part of the mixture is rye-grass seed? fescue? clover? bluegrass?

Ratio*

Ratio is the answer obtained when two numbers are compared by division.

The ratio of 4 to 12 is $\frac{4}{12}$ or $\frac{1}{3}$, read "1 to 3" which indicates that 4 when compared to 12 is $\frac{1}{3}$ of 12.

The ratio of 12 to 4 is $\frac{12}{4}$ or $\frac{3}{1}$, read "3 to 1" which indicates that 12 when compared to 4 is 3 times 4.

Quantities that are being compared must be expressed in the same units.

1. Find the ratio of:

SET 1	SET 2	SET 3
(a) 4 to 6	(a) 6 to 4	(a) 2 in. to 8 in.
(b) 9 to 12	(b) 8 to 5	(b) 10 in. to 1 ft.
(c) 5 to 7	(c) 24 to 3	(c) 16 in. to 1 yd.
(d) 8 to 32	(d) 15 to 9	(d) 20 lb. to 12 lb.
(e) 25 to 40	(e) 18 to 16	(e) 18 min. to 1 hr.

2. (a) What is the ratio of a nickel to a quarter? (b) Compare 2 things to a dozen. (c) What is the ratio of 35 minutes to 15 minutes? (d) Compare 1 dollar to 3 quarters. (e) Compare $\frac{1}{4}$ hour to 2 hours.

3. Find the ratio of two meshed gears if one gear has 48 teeth and the other 36 teeth.

4. The pitch of a roof is the ratio of the rise to the span. What is the pitch of a roof if the rise is 5 feet and the span is 20 feet?

5. The following recipe will make 6 servings of custard: 3 eggs, 1 pint milk, $\frac{1}{4}$ teaspoon salt, $\frac{1}{2}$ teaspoon vanilla, $\frac{1}{4}$ cup sugar. How much of each ingredient should be used to make 12 servings? 3 servings? 2 servings? 9 servings? 4 servings?

6. A mixture used to make concrete contains 1 part cement, 2 parts sand, 4 parts gravel, and water. If 4 bags of sand are used, how many bags of cement and bags of gravel are required?

7. The Lift-Drag Ratio (L/D) is the ratio of the lift of an airplane to its drag. Find the Lift-Drag Ratio if:

Lift (lb.)	900	1,400	1,050	2,700	3,000
Drag (lb.)	150	100	175	200	180

*See page 522.

FINDING A NUMBER WHEN A FRACTIONAL PART OF IT IS KNOWN

I. Aim: To find a number when a fractional part of it is known.

II. Procedure

1. Divide the given number representing the fractional part of the unknown number by the given fraction or just multiply the given number by the reciprocal of the given fraction. See page 148.

2. Or follow method 2 shown in the sample solutions.

III. Sample Solutions

1. $\frac{1}{6}$ of what number is 18?

Method 1

$18 \div \frac{1}{6} = 18 \times 6 = 108$

Method 2

Since $\frac{1}{6}$ of the number $= 18$
$\frac{6}{6}$ of the number $= 6 \times 18 = 108$
Therefore, the number $= 108$

Answer: 108

2. $\frac{3}{4}$ of what number is 21?

Method 1

$$21 \div \frac{3}{4} = \overset{7}{\cancel{21}} \times \frac{4}{\underset{1}{\cancel{3}}} = 28$$

Method 2

Since $\frac{3}{4}$ of the number $= 21$
$\frac{1}{4}$ of the number $= 21 \div 3 = 7$
$\frac{4}{4}$ of the number $= 4 \times 7 = 28$
Therefore, the number $= 28$

Answer: 28

DIAGNOSTIC TEST

Find the following:

      1. $\frac{1}{4}$ of what number is 12?

      2. $\frac{5}{8}$ of what number is 45?

RELATED PRACTICE EXAMPLES

Find the following:

SET 1(a)

1. $\frac{1}{2}$ of what number is 5?
2. $\frac{1}{2}$ of what number is 12?
3. $\frac{1}{2}$ of what number is 38?
4. $\frac{1}{2}$ of what number is 275?
5. $\frac{1}{2}$ of what number is 500?

SET 1(b)

1. $\frac{1}{3}$ of what number is 4?
2. $\frac{1}{3}$ of what number is 18?
3. $\frac{1}{4}$ of what number is 8?
4. $\frac{1}{4}$ of what number is 27?
5. $\frac{1}{4}$ of what number is 250?

SET 1(c)

1. $\frac{1}{8}$ of what number is 2?
2. $\frac{1}{8}$ of what number is 8?
3. $\frac{1}{8}$ of what number is 19?
4. $\frac{1}{16}$ of what number is 10?
5. $\frac{1}{16}$ of what number is 21?

SET 1(d)

1. $\frac{1}{6}$ of what number is 7?
2. $\frac{1}{6}$ of what number is 24?
3. $\frac{1}{6}$ of what number is 52?
4. $\frac{1}{12}$ of what number is 36?
5. $\frac{1}{12}$ of what number is 200?

SET 1(e)

1. $\frac{1}{5}$ of what number is 6?
2. $\frac{1}{5}$ of what number is 125?
3. $\frac{1}{10}$ of what number is 40?
4. $\frac{1}{100}$ of what number is 9?
5. $\frac{1}{20}$ of what number is 150?

SET 2(a)

1. $\frac{3}{4}$ of what number is 9?
2. $\frac{3}{4}$ of what number is 15?
3. $\frac{3}{4}$ of what number is 26?
4. $\frac{2}{3}$ of what number is 14?
5. $\frac{2}{3}$ of what number is 110?

SET 2(b)

1. $\frac{2}{5}$ of what number is 42?
2. $\frac{3}{5}$ of what number is 3?
3. $\frac{3}{5}$ of what number is 96?
4. $\frac{4}{5}$ of what number is 8?
5. $\frac{4}{5}$ of what number is 55?

SET 2(c)

1. $\frac{5}{8}$ of what number is 20?
2. $\frac{3}{8}$ of what number is 12?
3. $\frac{7}{8}$ of what number is 35?
4. $\frac{11}{16}$ of what number is 33?
5. $\frac{3}{16}$ of what number is 9?

Set 2(d)	Set 2(e)

<table>
<tr><td>

Set 2(d)

1. $\frac{9}{10}$ of what number is 18?
2. $\frac{7}{10}$ of what number is 105?
3. $\frac{11}{20}$ of what number is 55?
4. $\frac{3}{100}$ of what number is 60?
5. $\frac{47}{100}$ of what number is 94?

</td><td>

Set 2(e)

1. $\frac{5}{6}$ of what number is 10?
2. $\frac{5}{6}$ of what number is 28?
3. $\frac{7}{12}$ of what number is 21?
4. $\frac{11}{12}$ of what number is 66?
5. $\frac{5}{12}$ of what number is 45?

</td></tr>
</table>

MISCELLANEOUS EXAMPLES

Find the following:

<table>
<tr><td>

Set 1

1. 16 is $\frac{1}{2}$ of what number?
2. 35 is $\frac{1}{3}$ of what number?
3. 23 is $\frac{1}{4}$ of what number?
4. 9 is $\frac{1}{8}$ of what number?
5. 40 is $\frac{1}{12}$ of what number?

</td><td>

Set 2

1. 6 is $\frac{3}{4}$ of what number?
2. 30 is $\frac{5}{8}$ of what number?
3. 44 is $\frac{11}{12}$ of what number?
4. 27 is $\frac{2}{3}$ of what number?
5. 56 is $\frac{7}{16}$ of what number?

</td></tr>
</table>

PRACTICAL APPLICATIONS

1. If 138 students or $\frac{3}{8}$ of the graduating class selected the college preparatory course, how many pupils were in the graduating class?

2. The school athletic association sold 1,295 student membership tickets. If $\frac{7}{8}$ of the school became members, what is the school enrollment?

3. Charlotte received $\frac{5}{6}$ of all the votes cast in the election for school treasurer. If she received 885 votes, how many students voted?

4. If the school baseball team won 16 games or $\frac{2}{3}$ of the games played, how many games were lost?

5. Herbert, being paid at the rate of $\frac{3}{20}$ of his sales, received $51 commission. What was the amount of his sales?

6. Marilyn bought a pair of ice-skates at a sale for $10. What was the regular price of the skates if they were reduced one third?

7. How much does a pound of each of the following cost if:
(a) $\frac{1}{2}$ pound of cake costs 35¢? (b) $\frac{1}{4}$ pound of cookies costs 20¢?
(c) $\frac{3}{4}$ pound of butter costs 54¢? (d) $\frac{5}{8}$ pound of liver costs 55¢?
(e) $\frac{7}{8}$ pound of flounder costs 63¢? (f) $\frac{15}{16}$ pound of cheese costs 60¢?

REVIEW OF UNIT II

1. Reduce each of the following fractions to lowest terms:

(a) $\frac{18}{24}$　　(b) $\frac{16}{36}$　　(c) $\frac{45}{75}$　　(d) $\frac{84}{108}$　　(e) $\frac{105}{140}$

2. Change each of the following improper fractions to a whole number or a mixed number:

(a) $\frac{9}{5}$　　(b) $\frac{15}{3}$　　(c) $\frac{20}{6}$　　(d) $\frac{35}{8}$　　(e) $\frac{76}{24}$

3. Change each of the following mixed numbers to simplest form:

(a) $8\frac{3}{3}$　　(b) $9\frac{24}{8}$　　(c) $2\frac{36}{60}$　　(d) $4\frac{11}{5}$　　(e) $12\frac{28}{16}$

4. Change each of the following to equivalent fractions having denominators as specified:

(a) $\frac{1}{4} = \frac{}{64}$　　　　(b) $\frac{2}{3} = \frac{}{45}$　　　　(c) $\frac{17}{20} = \frac{}{100}$
(d) Change $\frac{5}{8}$ to 32nds.　　(e) Change $\frac{11}{12}$ to 60ths.

5. Find the lowest common denominator of each of the following groups of fractions:

(a) $\frac{3}{5}$ and $\frac{7}{10}$　　　　(b) $\frac{1}{2}$ and $\frac{2}{3}$　　　　(c) $\frac{5}{6}$ and $\frac{3}{4}$
(d) $\frac{7}{8}$, $\frac{1}{4}$, and $\frac{5}{16}$　　(e) $\frac{3}{10}$, $\frac{7}{12}$, and $\frac{5}{8}$

6. Add:

(a) $\frac{5}{16}$　　(b) $1\frac{7}{8}$　　(c) $3\frac{9}{10}$　　(d) $6\frac{3}{4}$　　(e) $4\frac{11}{12} + 3\frac{3}{8} + 1\frac{9}{16}$
　　$\frac{3}{4}$　　　　$2\frac{2}{3}$　　　$10\frac{5}{8}$　　　$\frac{5}{12}$
　　　　　　　　　　　　　　　　　　　　　$2\frac{1}{6}$

7. Find the missing numbers:

(a) $6 = 5\frac{}{8}$　　　　(b) $1\frac{5}{12} = \frac{}{12}$　　　　(c) $10\frac{1}{6} = 9\frac{}{6}$
(d) $7\frac{3}{4} = 7\frac{}{16} = 6\frac{}{16}$　　(e) $5\frac{2}{3} = 5\frac{}{24} = 4\frac{}{24}$

8. Subtract:

(a) $\frac{7}{10}$　　(b) $6\frac{4}{5}$　　(c) 9　　(d) $4\frac{1}{8}$　　(e) Subtract $11\frac{3}{4}$ from $12\frac{9}{16}$.
　　$\frac{1}{2}$　　　$4\frac{2}{3}$　　$2\frac{17}{32}$　　$2\frac{5}{6}$

9. Which is smaller:　(a) $\frac{1}{3}$ or $\frac{1}{5}$?　　(b) $\frac{3}{4}$ or $\frac{2}{3}$?
　　Which is larger:　　(c) $\frac{1}{8}$ or $\frac{1}{12}$?　　(d) $\frac{7}{16}$ or $\frac{1}{2}$?
　　(e) Arrange in order of size, smallest first: $\frac{11}{16}$, $\frac{3}{4}$, $\frac{7}{12}$

10. Change the following mixed numbers to improper fractions:

(a) $1\frac{5}{6}$　　(b) $8\frac{1}{2}$　　(c) $5\frac{2}{3}$　　(d) $15\frac{7}{10}$　　(e) $2\frac{13}{16}$

11. Multiply:

(*a*) $\frac{3}{4} \times \frac{13}{16}$ (*b*) $18 \times 4\frac{5}{6}$ (*c*) $6\frac{3}{8} \times \frac{4}{5}$ (*d*) $5\frac{1}{4} \times 2\frac{2}{3}$ (*e*) 29
$$6\frac{1}{2}$$

12. Divide:

(*a*) $\frac{9}{10} \div \frac{3}{5}$ (*b*) $6\frac{2}{3} \div 10$ (*c*) $14 \div 3\frac{1}{7}$

(*d*) $4\frac{11}{16} \div 3\frac{3}{4}$ (*e*) Divide $\frac{5}{8}$ by $2\frac{1}{3}$.

13. (*a*) What part of 16 is 9?   (*b*) 45 is what part of 72?

14. (*a*) $\frac{1}{3}$ of what number is 20?   (*b*) $\frac{3}{5}$ of what number is 27?

15. Find the total weight if a metal can weighs $2\frac{7}{8}$ ounces and its contents $12\frac{3}{4}$ ounces.

16. Jerry's sister typed 225 words in $7\frac{1}{2}$ minutes. How many words did she average per minute?

17. A certain stock sold at $39\frac{5}{8}$ when the stock market opened for the day and at $37\frac{3}{4}$ when it closed. How many points did the stock lose?

18. Tom's father wishes to make 4 shelves each $2\frac{3}{4}$ feet long and 3 shelves each $3\frac{1}{4}$ feet long. Will a 20-foot board be long enough? How much more or less will he need?

19. The directions tell you to add 3 cans of water to 1 can of orange juice concentrate. What is the ratio of the water to the concentrate? Of the concentrate to the water?

20. The radiator of a certain automobile holds 15 quarts. If this radiator contains 6 quarts of anti-freeze and the rest water, what part of the solution is anti-freeze? What part is water?

CUMULATIVE PRACTICE

1. Add:

8,621
19,470
267,922
84,534
741

2. Subtract:

390,000
290,070

3. Multiply:

830
580

4. Divide

$497)\overline{4,476,976}$

5. Add:

$3\frac{5}{8}$
$6\frac{13}{16}$

6. Subtract:

$1\frac{7}{12}$
$\frac{3}{4}$

7. Multiply:

$4\frac{2}{3} \times 19$

8. Divide:

$5\frac{5}{16} \div 2\frac{5}{6}$

9. Round off 624,258,921 to the nearest million.

10. Reduce $\frac{64}{96}$ to lowest terms.

KEYED ACHIEVEMENT TEST

For additional practice turn to the exercises indicated by the numerals in the circles.

1. Write 1,978,246,523 as a word statement. ①

2. Round off 3,602,754 to the nearest thousand. ②

3. Add:
   82,579
   21,429
   51,678 ③
   30,199
   92,389

4. Subtract:
   9,850,601
   9,788,963 ④

5. Multiply:
   8,349
   768 ⑤

6. Divide:
   984)951,528 ⑥

7. Reduce $\frac{54}{60}$ to lowest terms. ⑦

8. Change $\frac{5}{6}$ to 48ths. ⑩

9. Which is larger: $\frac{5}{8}$ or $\frac{2}{3}$? ⑮

10. Add:
    $7\frac{3}{4}$
    $8\frac{2}{3}$ ⑫
    $1\frac{1}{6}$

11. Subtract:
    $20\frac{1}{2}$
    $6\frac{7}{8}$ ⑭

12. Multiply:
    $3\frac{1}{7} \times 8\frac{1}{6}$ ⑰

13. Divide:
    $\frac{9}{16} \div 6\frac{3}{4}$ ⑱

14. What part of 80 is 64? ⑲

15. $\frac{5}{8}$ of what number is 65? ⑳

REFRESH YOUR SKILLS

1. Add:
   635,944
   867,278
   368,985
   923,969
   278,577

2. Subtract:
   1,700,105
   690,999

3. Multiply:
   9,527
   6,845

4. Divide:
   909)7,280,181

5. Add: $6\frac{7}{8} + 1\frac{3}{5} + 4\frac{1}{3}$

6. Subtract: $10 - 5\frac{5}{6}$

7. Multiply: $8\frac{3}{4} \times 7\frac{2}{3}$

8. Divide: $9 \div 6\frac{3}{4}$

9. Reduce $\frac{56}{98}$ to lowest terms.

10. Which is greater: $\frac{5}{13}$ or $\frac{7}{18}$?

11. What part of 65 is 26?

12. $\frac{9}{16}$ of what number is 72?

ADDITIONAL TOPICS

Equivalent Fractions

Fractions that name the same number are called equivalent fractions. A set of equivalent fractions may be developed from the name of the fractional number in simplest form by expressing it successively in higher terms.

> The set of fractions equivalent to $\frac{1}{3}$ is $\{\frac{1}{3}, \frac{2}{6}, \frac{3}{9}, \frac{4}{12}, \cdots\}$.
> The set of equivalent fractions of which $\frac{9}{12}$ is a member is $\{\frac{3}{4}, \frac{6}{8}, \frac{9}{12}, \cdots\}$.

To test whether one fraction is equivalent to another, first express each fraction in lowest terms, then check whether the resulting fractions are the same.

> $\frac{4}{16}$ and $\frac{3}{12}$ are equivalent fractions since $\frac{4}{16} = \frac{1}{4}$ and $\frac{3}{12} = \frac{1}{4}$.

Or use the equal cross products method where you find the product of the numerator of the first fraction and the denominator of the second fraction and the product of the numerator of the second fraction and the denominator of the first fraction. If the two cross products are equal, the two fractions are equivalent.

> $\frac{4}{16}$ and $\frac{3}{12}$ are equivalent fractions or $\frac{4}{16} = \frac{3}{12}$ if $4 \times 12 = 3 \times 16$.
> Since $4 \times 12 = 48$ and $3 \times 16 = 48$, then $4 \times 12 = 3 \times 16$, and $\frac{4}{16}$ and $\frac{3}{12}$ are equivalent fractions.

PRACTICE PROBLEMS

1. Write the set of fractions equivalent to:

(a) $\frac{1}{2}$ (c) $\frac{3}{5}$ (e) $\frac{5}{8}$ (g) $\frac{11}{12}$ (i) $\frac{3}{4}$ (k) $\frac{9}{13}$ (m) $\frac{4}{11}$ (o) $\frac{17}{20}$

(b) $\frac{1}{9}$ (d) $\frac{2}{3}$ (f) $\frac{13}{16}$ (h) $\frac{5}{6}$ (j) $\frac{7}{10}$ (l) $\frac{8}{15}$ (n) $\frac{19}{25}$ (p) $\frac{31}{50}$

2. For each of the following write the set of equivalent fractions of which it is a member:

(a) $\frac{7}{42}$ (c) $\frac{9}{36}$ (e) $\frac{35}{84}$ (g) $\frac{48}{54}$ (i) $\frac{55}{80}$ (k) $\frac{21}{70}$ (m) $\frac{170}{200}$ (o) $\frac{24}{225}$

(b) $\frac{24}{30}$ (d) $\frac{56}{64}$ (f) $\frac{54}{63}$ (h) $\frac{77}{132}$ (j) $\frac{76}{96}$ (l) $\frac{52}{72}$ (n) $\frac{145}{250}$ (p) $\frac{110}{121}$

Test whether each of the following pairs of fractions are equivalent by using the method of:

3. Lowest terms:

(a) $\frac{6}{16}$ and $\frac{15}{40}$ (d) $\frac{28}{35}$ and $\frac{35}{42}$ (g) $\frac{3}{6}$ and $\frac{10}{18}$

(b) $\frac{15}{18}$ and $\frac{36}{48}$ (e) $\frac{21}{27}$ and $\frac{24}{33}$ (h) $\frac{10}{24}$ and $\frac{30}{65}$

(c) $\frac{42}{63}$ and $\frac{16}{24}$ (f) $\frac{39}{52}$ and $\frac{51}{68}$ (i) $\frac{35}{80}$ and $\frac{21}{48}$

4. Equal cross products:

(a) $\frac{16}{28}$ and $\frac{24}{36}$ (d) $\frac{24}{33}$ and $\frac{18}{26}$ (g) $\frac{48}{75}$ and $\frac{35}{50}$

(b) $\frac{10}{16}$ and $\frac{15}{24}$ (e) $\frac{42}{54}$ and $\frac{28}{35}$ (h) $\frac{68}{80}$ and $\frac{102}{120}$

(c) $\frac{15}{25}$ and $\frac{36}{60}$ (f) $\frac{27}{48}$ and $\frac{45}{80}$ (i) $\frac{49}{105}$ and $\frac{77}{165}$

5. Either method:

(a) $\frac{14}{35}$ and $\frac{6}{15}$ (d) $\frac{24}{32}$ and $\frac{42}{56}$ (g) $\frac{10}{25}$ and $\frac{36}{90}$

(b) $\frac{15}{24}$ and $\frac{12}{20}$ (e) $\frac{40}{56}$ and $\frac{49}{63}$ (h) $\frac{45}{54}$ and $\frac{70}{84}$

(c) $\frac{36}{40}$ and $\frac{42}{48}$ (f) $\frac{132}{144}$ and $\frac{77}{84}$ (i) $\frac{26}{40}$ and $\frac{36}{54}$

Comparing Fractions

In Exercise 15 we studied how to compare two fractions by expressing the fractions as equivalent fractions with a common denominator. However, we may also use the following cross products method.

If the product of the numerator of the first fraction and the denominator of the second fraction is greater than the product of the numerator of the second fraction and the denominator of the first fraction, then the first fraction is greater than the second fraction.

The sentence $\frac{3}{5} > \frac{7}{12}$ is true if $3 \times 12 > 5 \times 7$. Since $3 \times 12 = 36$ and $5 \times 7 = 35$, then $3 \times 12 > 5 \times 7$ and $\frac{3}{5} > \frac{7}{12}$.

If the product of the numerator of the first fraction and the denominator of the second fraction is less than the product of the numerator of the second fraction and the denominator of the first fraction, then the first fraction is less than the second fraction.

The sentence $\frac{3}{8} < \frac{2}{5}$ is true if $3 \times 5 < 2 \times 8$. Since $3 \times 5 = 15$ and $2 \times 8 = 16$, then $3 \times 5 < 2 \times 8$ and $\frac{3}{8} < \frac{2}{5}$.

Summarizing:

If a represents the numerator of the first fraction; b, the denominator of the first fraction; c, the numerator of the second fraction; and d, the denominator of the second fraction, then:

(1) $\frac{a}{b} = \frac{c}{d}$ if $a \times d = c \times b$ Two fractions are equivalent.

(2) $\frac{a}{b} > \frac{c}{d}$ if $a \times d > c \times b$ First fraction is greater.

(3) $\frac{a}{b} < \frac{c}{d}$ if $a \times d < c \times b$ First fraction is smaller.

PRACTICE PROBLEMS

Use the cross product test to determine which of the following statements are true:

1. $\frac{1}{3} > \frac{1}{5}$ 6. $\frac{7}{12} > \frac{9}{16}$ 11. $\frac{5}{6} > \frac{3}{4}$ 16. $\frac{27}{36} < \frac{35}{42}$

2. $\frac{1}{8} > \frac{1}{6}$ 7. $\frac{19}{24} < \frac{7}{9}$ 12. $\frac{9}{10} > \frac{15}{16}$ 17. $\frac{15}{24} > \frac{21}{30}$

3. $\frac{2}{3} < \frac{3}{5}$ 8. $\frac{11}{16} < \frac{16}{25}$ 13. $\frac{3}{11} < \frac{5}{18}$ 18. $\frac{49}{56} < \frac{60}{72}$

4. $\frac{7}{8} < \frac{9}{10}$ 9. $\frac{8}{9} > \frac{11}{13}$ 14. $\frac{19}{75} < \frac{6}{25}$ 19. $\frac{27}{81} > \frac{18}{48}$

5. $\frac{3}{4} > \frac{5}{8}$ 10. $\frac{9}{17} < \frac{3}{5}$ 15. $\frac{17}{18} > \frac{19}{20}$ 20. $\frac{36}{84} < \frac{28}{63}$

Number Pairs

Some mathematicians indicate fractions by ordered number pairs. Each ordered number pair consists of a pair of numerals written with parentheses in a specific order. (3, 4) is an ordered pair of numbers with 3 called the first number and 4 the second number. It represents the fraction $\frac{3}{4}$. (4, 3) is a different ordered number pair since 4 is the first number and 3 is the second number and represents the fraction $\frac{4}{3}$.

PRACTICE PROBLEMS

1. Write each of the following ordered pairs of numbers as a numeral naming a fraction:

     (a) (8, 15)   (c) (2, 9)   (e) (10, 3)   (g) (22, 7)   (i) (5, 16)

     (b) (4, 5)   (d) (19, 24)   (f) (17, 8)   (h) (31, 6)   (j) (18, 13)

2. Write each of the following fractions as an ordered pair:

     (a) $\frac{5}{6}$ (c) $\frac{9}{7}$ (e) $\frac{8}{25}$ (g) $\frac{19}{12}$ (i) $\frac{89}{100}$

     (b) $\frac{7}{10}$ (d) $\frac{11}{5}$ (f) $\frac{21}{13}$ (h) $\frac{25}{32}$ (j) $\frac{50}{27}$

Multiplicative Inverse

If the product of two numbers is one (1), then each factor is called the multiplicative inverse or reciprocal of the other. Zero has no inverse for multiplication.

---

6 and $\frac{1}{6}$ are multiplicative inverses of each other because $6 \times \frac{1}{6} = 1$

$\frac{4}{3}$ and $\frac{3}{4}$ are multiplicative inverses of each other because $\frac{4}{3} \times \frac{3}{4} = 1$

Observe that when two numbers are multiplicative inverses of each other, the numerator of one fraction is the denominator of its reciprocal and the denominator is the numerator of its reciprocal.

Division is the inverse operation of multiplication. When we divide 12 by 4, the quotient is 3. When we multiply 12 by $\frac{1}{4}$, the product is 3. Dividing 12 by 4 gives the same answer as multiplying 12 by the reciprocal of 4 (which is $\frac{1}{4}$). Thus to divide a number by another number, we may instead multiply the first number by the reciprocal of the second number (divisor).

Observe in the following model how the multiplicative inverse and the multiplicative identity one (1) are used to develop this principle which is very useful in the division of fractions (page 127).

$$\frac{2}{3} \div \frac{3}{4} = \frac{\frac{2}{3}}{\frac{3}{4}} = \frac{\frac{2}{3}}{\frac{3}{4}} \times 1 = \frac{\frac{2}{3} \times \frac{4}{3}}{\frac{3}{4} \times \frac{4}{3}} = \frac{\frac{2}{3} \times \frac{4}{3}}{1} = \frac{2}{3} \times \frac{4}{3} = \frac{8}{9}$$

We multiply both numerator and denominator by $\frac{4}{3}$, the multiplicative inverse of the denominator $\frac{3}{4}$, to get 1 as a denominator.

PRACTICE PROBLEMS

Write the multiplicative inverse or reciprocal of each of the following:

1. (a) 2   (b) 9   (c) 0   (d) 15   (e) 28   (f) 1   (g) 50

2. (a) $\frac{1}{3}$ (b) $\frac{1}{18}$ (c) $\frac{7}{12}$ (d) $\frac{11}{16}$ (e) $\frac{23}{24}$ (f) $\frac{5}{4}$ (g) $\frac{19}{8}$

3. Find the missing numbers:

(a) $\frac{2}{5} \times \frac{5}{2} = ?$ (c) $? \times \frac{1}{48} = 1$

(b) $17 \times ? = 1$ (d) $\frac{5}{6} \times ? = 1$

UNIT III . . . DECIMAL FRACTIONS

INTRODUCTION

A decimal fraction is a fractional number whose denominator is some power of ten (10; 100; 1,000; etc.) and is named by a numeral in which the denominator is not written as it is in a common fraction but is expressed by place value. Only the numerators appear in decimal notation.

In Exercise 1 we learned that the value of each place on the decimal scale is $\frac{1}{10}$ the value of the next place to the left. To express parts of a unit, we now extend the scale to the right of the units' place. The first place to the right of the units' place has the value of $\frac{1}{10}$ of a whole number unit; it expresses "tenths." A decimal point is used to separate the whole number from the fractional parts. Thus, .6 or 0.6 and $\frac{6}{10}$ are numerals which name the same number.

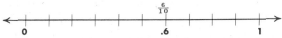

The second place to the right of the units' place expresses hundredths (.01 $= \frac{1}{100}$), the third place expresses thousandths (.001 $= \frac{1}{1,000}$), the fourth place expresses ten-thousandths (.0001 $= \frac{1}{10,000}$), the fifth place expresses hundred-thousandths (.00001 $= \frac{1}{100,000}$), and the sixth place millionths (.000001 $= \frac{1}{1,000,000}$), etc.

Hundred Millions	Ten Millions	Millions	Hundred Thousands	Ten Thousands	Thousands	Hundreds	Tens	Units or Ones and	Tenths	Hundredths	Thousandths	Ten-Thousandths	Hundred-Thousandths	Millionths
4	2	7	5	1	8	2	0	3 .	9	6	4	2	8	7

A mixed decimal is a number containing a whole number and a decimal fraction. The numeral in the above scale names a mixed decimal.

Since multiples of one are expressed in the places to the left of the one's place and parts of one are expressed in the places to the right of the one's place, the one's place is the center of the numeration system and not the decimal point.

THE DAILY TRIBUNE
2.1 INCHES
SNOWFALL

INDIANAPOLIS SPEEDWAY
WINNING SPEED
128.49 MPH

READING AND WRITING DECIMALS

I. Aim: To read and write numerals naming decimal fractions.

II. Procedure

1. In reading a numeral naming a decimal fraction, read the numeral to the right of the decimal point as you would a numeral for a whole number and use the name that applies to the place value of the last figure.

2. In reading a numeral naming a mixed decimal, first read the numeral for the whole number and then the numeral for the decimal fraction. Use the word *and* to show the position of the decimal point. Sometimes the numeral may have a zero written in the units' place just preceding the decimal point.

3. In writing a numeral naming a decimal fraction, write the figures as you do to name a whole number, but insert a decimal point so that the name of the part corresponds to the place value of the last figure. Prefix as many zeros as are required between the decimal point and the first figure when it is necessary to make the name of the part and place value of the last figure correspond.

4. In writing a numeral naming a mixed decimal, write the numeral for the whole number, insert a decimal point for the word *and*, then write the numeral for the decimal fraction.

5. To write numerals by expanded notation, see page 215.

III. Sample Solutions

1. Read .734 (sometimes written as 0.734)
   Answer: Seven hundred thirty-four thousandths.

2. Read 14.06
   Answer: Fourteen and six hundredths.

3. Write as a decimal numeral:
   One hundred and fifty-nine thousandths.
   Answer: 100.059

DIAGNOSTIC TEST A

Read the following decimal numerals (or write them as word statements):

1. .2	**5.** 3.73	**8.** .289	**11.** .17925
2. .06	**6.** .004	**9.** 14.708	**12.** .000456
3. .58	**7.** .076	**10.** .0037	**13.** 129.4261
4. 1.5			

RELATED PRACTICE EXAMPLES

Read the following decimal numerals (or write them as word statements):

SET 1	SET 2	SET 3	SET 4	SET 5
1. .8	**1.** .03	**1.** .24	**1.** 1.6	**1.** 2.51
2. .1	**2.** .07	**2.** .85	**2.** 2.9	**2.** 7.37
3. .5	**3.** .02	**3.** .91	**3.** 14.3	**3.** 30.46
4. .4	**4.** .08	**4.** .60	**4.** 38.5	**4.** 89.03
5. .9	**5.** .05	**5.** .37	**5.** 126.4	**5.** 248.19

SET 6	SET 7	SET 8	SET 9	SET 10
1. .005	**1.** .024	**1.** .832	**1.** 6.005	**1.** .0007
2. .008	**2.** .063	**2.** .946	**2.** 21.769	**2.** .0089
3. .001	**3.** .080	**3.** .253	**3.** 34.094	**3.** .0574
4. .007	**4.** .092	**4.** .798	**4.** 186.528	**4.** .3962
5. .003	**5.** .035	**5.** .465	**5.** 200.042	**5.** .9350

SET 11	SET 12	SET 13
1. .00006	**1.** .000001	**1.** 8.0025
2. .00392	**2.** .000534	**2.** 23.9317
3. .09413	**3.** .080076	**3.** 49.08329
4. .25004	**4.** .175283	**4.** 354.3625
5. .72815	**5.** .800560	**5.** 571.05875

DIAGNOSTIC TEST B

Write each of the following as a decimal numeral:

1. Three tenths
2. Four and eight tenths
3. Seven hundredths
4. Twenty-five hundredths
5. One hundred nine and eighty-four hundredths
6. Nine thousandths
7. Ninety-four thousandths
8. Five hundred twenty-seven thousandths
9. Seven hundred and ninety-three thousandths
10. Four thousand six hundred thirty-six ten-thousandths
11. Eight hundred forty-two hundred-thousandths
12. Four millionths
13. Two hundred sixty and three hundred forty-seven ten-thousandths

RELATED PRACTICE EXAMPLES

Write each of the following as a decimal numeral:

SET 1
1. Four tenths
2. Eight tenths
3. Two tenths
4. Nine tenths
5. One tenth

SET 2
1. Six and five tenths
2. Three and four tenths
3. Nine and seven tenths
4. Five and one tenth
5. Twenty and six tenths

SET 3
1. Eight hundredths
2. Two hundredths
3. Six hundredths
4. Four hundredths
5. Five hundredths

SET 4
1. Thirty-six hundredths
2. Fifty-seven hundredths
3. Eighty-four hundredths
4. Seventeen hundredths
5. Forty-nine hundredths

SET 5

1. Six and four hundredths
2. Five and sixty-two hundredths
3. Seventy-three and eighteen hundredths
4. Two hundred and five hundredths
5. Four hundred seven and twenty-five hundredths

SET 6

1. Three thousandths
2. Seven thousandths
3. Five thousandths
4. Eight thousandths
5. One thousandth

SET 7

1. Sixty-nine thousandths
2. Forty-seven thousandths
3. Twenty-four thousandths
4. Sixteen thousandths
5. Eighty-three thousandths

SET 8

1. Two hundred seventy-four thousandths
2. Four hundred thirty-nine thousandths
3. Seven hundred twenty-one thousandths
4. Three hundred six thousandths
5. One hundred eighty thousandths

SET 9

1. Two and seventeen thousandths
2. Eight hundred and thirty-five thousandths
3. Thirty-six and two hundred fifty-three thousandths
4. Fifty-seven and seven hundred eighty-four thousandths
5. Nineteen and one hundred twenty-two thousandths

SET 10

1. Eight ten-thousandths
2. Thirty-six ten-thousandths
3. Four hundred ninety-four ten-thousandths
4. Three thousand five hundred sixty ten-thousandths
5. Eighteen ten-thousandths

SET 11

1. Three hundred-thousandths
2. Forty-two hundred-thousandths
3. Four hundred fifty-six hundred-thousandths

4. Six thousand eight hundred twenty-two hundred-thousandths

5. Fifteen thousand seven hundred eighty-six hundred-thousandths

SET 12

1. Six millionths

2. Ninety-five millionths

3. Three hundred seven millionths

4. Seventy-two thousand one hundred forty-nine millionths

5. Five thousand thirteen millionths

SET 13

1. Five hundred and fifty-eight ten-thousandths

2. Two and three hundred twenty-five ten-thousandths

3. Seventy and two thousand five hundred twelve ten-thousandths

4. Eighty-five and seven hundred thirty-two hundred-thousandths

5. Six hundred forty-three and sixty-seven millionths

REFRESH YOUR SKILLS

1. Add: **2.** Subtract: **3.** Multiply: **4.** Divide:

439,378	8,200,061	6,029	725)7,111,525
192,106	410,858	8,709	
359,281			
846,092			
399,164			

5. Add: **6.** Subtract: **7.** Multiply: **8.** Divide:

$2\frac{4}{5} + 1\frac{3}{4} + 6\frac{7}{10}$ $5\frac{1}{2} - 1\frac{11}{12}$ $11\frac{2}{3} \times 3\frac{9}{10}$ $14 \div 8\frac{1}{6}$

9. Round off 805,822,149 to the nearest million.

10. Write as a decimal numeral: Four hundred and twenty-seven thousandths.

EXERCISE 22

ROUNDING OFF DECIMALS

I. Aim: To round off decimals.

II. Procedure

1. Rewrite as many figures as are needed and omit the rest.

2. If the first figure dropped is 5 or more, increase the preceding figure by 1.

3. In finding an answer correct to the nearest cent when the answer contains a fractional part of a cent, drop the fraction. However, if the fraction represents one-half cent or more, add one cent. (See sample solutions 10 and 11.)

III. Sample Solutions

Find

1.	.26	correct to nearest tenth.	*Answer:* .3
2.	4.542	correct to nearest tenth.	*Answer:* 4.5
3.	.633	correct to nearest hundredth.	*Answer:* .63
4.	7.2051	correct to nearest hundredth.	*Answer:* 7.21
5.	8.1584	correct to nearest thousandth.	*Answer:* 8.158
6.	.00257	correct to nearest ten-thousandth.	*Answer:* .0026
7.	.001834	correct to nearest hundred-thousandth.	*Answer:* .00183
8.	.0000286	correct to nearest millionth.	*Answer:* .000029
9.	$3.658	correct to nearest cent.	*Answer:* $3.66
10.	5.24\frac{3}{4}$	correct to nearest cent.	*Answer:* $5.25
11.	$.49$\frac{1}{3}$	correct to nearest cent.	*Answer:* $.49
12.	23.8	correct to nearest whole number.	*Answer:* 24
13.	5.499	correct to nearest whole number.	*Answer:* 5

DIAGNOSTIC TEST

Find the following correct to

1. Nearest tenth:
   (a) .68
   (b) 5.425

2. Nearest hundredth:

   (a) 8.349
   (b) .5146

3. Nearest thousandth:
   (a) 1.9685
   (b) 3.24728

4. Nearest ten-thousandth:
   (a) .42769
   (b) 26.58634

5. Nearest hundred-thousandth:
   (a) .005924
   (b) 54.632857

6. Nearest millionth:
   (a) .0000985
   (b) 2.0500302

7. Nearest cent: (a) $2.386 (b) $4.843 (c) $7.23⅔ (d) $1.68⅜

8. Nearest whole number: (a) 57.18 (b) 89.562

RELATED PRACTICE EXAMPLES

Finding the following correct to

Nearest tenth: Nearest hundredth:

SET 1(a)	SET 1(b)	SET 2(a)	SET 2(b)
1. .25	1. .14	1. .517	1. .323
2. .87	2. .32	2. .308	2. .934
3. .984	3. 1.83	3. 5.845	3. 6.544
4. 4.16	4. 3.718	4. 9.3794	4. 8.3025
5. 2.39	5. 5.205	5. 15.2263	5. 14.0412

Nearest thousandth: Nearest ten-thousandth:

SET 3(a)	SET 3(b)	SET 4(a)	SET 4(b)
1. .2146	1. .5452	1. .20585	1. .34143
2. .3998	2. .9293	2. .932473	2. .528129
3. 3.0815	3. 5.0341	3. 4.00619	3. 2.30751
4. 1.5929	4. 2.0084	4. 7.451852	4. 18.781304
5. 16.76876	5. 24.82509	5. 43.020471	5. 39.56372

Nearest hundred-thousandth:

Nearest millionth:

SET 5(a)	SET 5(b)	SET 6(a)	SET 6(b)
1. .000083	1. .000079	1. .0000029	1. .0000052
2. .005142	2. .030585	2. .0001538	2. .0000194
3. 1.079324	3. 2.000467	3. .0254985	3. .0039481
4. 25.415291	4. 23.075306	4. 1.0038296	4. 5.0006373
5. 83.591243	5. 71.114248	5. 4.1830547	5. 8.2751254

Nearest cent:

SET 7(a)	SET 7(b)	SET 7(c)	SET 7(d)
1. $.267	1. $.643	1. $.62$\frac{1}{2}$	1. $.46$\frac{1}{4}$
2. $0.59	2. $.834	2. $.28$\frac{3}{5}$	2. $.73$\frac{1}{3}$
3. $1.316	3. $6.572	3. 3.84\frac{7}{12}$	3. 1.57\frac{2}{5}$
4. $5.8682	4. $14.9615	4. 9.20\frac{7}{8}$	4. 4.89\frac{5}{12}$
5. $24.6754	5. $30.2137	5. 15.14\frac{5}{6}$	5. 12.30\frac{11}{24}$

Nearest whole number:

SET 8(a)		SET 8(b)	
1. 6.3	4. 34.28	1. 9.6	4. 25.989
2. 19.4	5. 858.126	2. 68.5	5. 399.704
3. 2.09		3. 100.81	

PRACTICAL APPLICATIONS

1. Round off the following conversion factors correct to the nearest hundredth:

    (a) 1 nautical mile = 1.1515 statute miles.

    (b) 1 meter = 1.0936 yards.

    (c) 1 kilogram = 2.2046 pounds.

2. Round off correct to the nearest tenth:

    (a) 1 centimeter = 0.3937 inch.

    (b) 1 bushel = 2,150.42 cubic inches.

    (c) 1 cubic inch = 16.3872 cubic centimeters.

3. Round off correct to the nearest thousandth:

    (a) 1 statute mile = 0.8684 nautical mile.

    (b) 1 square inch = 6.4516 square centimeters.

    (c) 1 liquid quart = 0.9463 liter.

EXERCISE 23

ADDITION OF DECIMALS

I. Aim: To add decimals.

II. Procedure

1. If it is necessary to write the numerals in columns, write each addend so that the decimal points are directly under each other. Zeros may be annexed to the numerals naming decimal fractions so that the addends may have the same number of decimal places. (See sample solutions 4 and 5.)

2. Add as in the addition of whole numbers. (See Exercise 3.)

3. Place the decimal point in the sum directly under the decimal points in the addends.

4. When a decimal answer ends in one or more zeros to the right of the decimal point, the zeros may be dropped unless it is necessary to show the exact degree of measurement. (See sample solution 3.)

5. Check by adding the columns in the opposite direction or by adding the sum of each column as shown in Exercise 3.

Concept:

(a) $.8 + .5$

Since $.8 = \frac{8}{10}$ and $.5 = \frac{5}{10}$,

$$\text{then} \quad \begin{array}{r} \frac{8}{10} \\ + \frac{5}{10} \\ \hline \frac{13}{10} = 1\frac{3}{10} \end{array} \qquad \text{or using decimals} \qquad \begin{array}{r} .8 \\ + .5 \\ \hline 1.3 \end{array}$$

1.3 is the same as $1\frac{3}{10}$

(b) $.46 + .7$

Since $.46 = \frac{46}{100}$ and $.7 = \frac{7}{10}$,

$$\text{then} \quad \begin{array}{r} \frac{46}{100} = \frac{46}{100} \\ + \frac{7}{10} = \frac{70}{100} \\ \hline \frac{116}{100} = 1\frac{16}{100} \end{array} \qquad \text{or using decimals} \qquad \begin{array}{r} .46 \\ + .7 \\ \hline 1.16 \end{array}$$

1.16 is the same as $1\frac{16}{100}$

III. Sample Solutions

Add in the following examples:

1. .5
    .8
    .9
  2.2

Answer: 2.2

2. 2.08
   4.07
   1.03
   7.18

Answer: 7.18

3. .26
   .38
   .06
   .70 = .7

Answer: .70 or .7

4. 2.9 + .12

Solution:

  2.9   2.90
   .12 or 0.12
  3.02   3.02

Answer: 3.02

5. Find the sum of:
  .523, 4.16, 3, and 2.2

Solution:

  .523   0.523
 4.16 or 4.160
 3.   3.000
 2.2   2.200
 9.883   9.883

Answer: 9.883

6. $2.58 + $34.74 + $.69 + $5.87

Solution:

    $2.58
   34.74
     .69
    5.87
  $43.88

Answer: $43.88

DIAGNOSTIC TEST

Add:

1. .4
   .3
   .2

2. .6
   .9
   .4

3. .02
   .01
   .03

4. .08
   .03
   .02
   .06

5. .15
   .03
   .48
   .17

6. .52
   .43
   .69
   .74

7. .85
   .10
   .05

8. 1.5
   2.1
   4.3

9. 6.4
   8.9
   4.4
   3.5

10. 3.06
    4.09
    2.08

11. 4.57
    2.93
    4.87

12. 7.49
    3.5

13. 2.86
    .7
    .12

14. 8
    .05

15. 2.103
    4.839
    3.542

16. 50.48
    37.59
    23.84

Test continued on next page.

17. 326.04	**18.** 19.47	**19.** $.50
183.75	8.46	.28
225.39	592.75	.79
491.26	74.81	.84
	126.78	.67
	91.33	

20. $42.85
   9.74   **21.** .08 + 1.5
 223.30
  54.67   **22.** .752 + 4.53 + 6
   7.98   **23.** $1.43 + $.89 + $5.07 + $.36 + $9.58

24. Find the sum of: 6.4, .976, and 2.87

RELATED PRACTICE EXAMPLES

Set 1	Set 2	Set 3	Set 4	Set 5	Set 6
.2	.9	.03	.06	.68	.43
.6	.7	.04	.09	.26	.89
.3	.5	.03	.05	.57	.38
.2	.8	.02	.05	.04	.45
.2	.4	.03	.07	.18	.22
.2	.4	.01	.02	.12	.14
.3	.8	.03	.07	.23	.32
.1	.7	.02	.04	.45	.51
.2	.4	.03	.05	.16	.28
.1	.9	.02	.04	.31	.82
.2	.6	.01	.07	.17	.59
.3	.9	.01	.08	.09	.77
.3	.2	.05	.03	.24	.31
.1	.5	.03	.09	.23	.27
.3	.7	.01	.06	.18	.74
.2	.4	.02	.08	.29	.51
.1	.8	.01	.04	.03	.93
.2	.3	.02	.09	.25	.89

Set 7	Set 8	Set 9	Set 10	Set 11	Set 12
.53	2.4	7.8	8.05	3.26	6.25
.47	3.5	6.5	4.08	2.15	4.6
.48	6.2	4.1	9.08	6.27	6.74
.26	9.3	1.5	8.03	2.83	9.3
.16	8.3	7.4	1.07	5.76	1.87
.52	4.1	2.8	1.04	2.19	9.03
.81	2.2	1.4	3.08	3.82	8.2
.49	1.1	8.2	4.01	5.27	4.19
.68	9.2	7.5	2.05	1.38	2.3
.27	2.2	1.6	6.01	3.41	5.7
.95	1.4	5.3	8.07	2.54	4.3
.32	5.1	4.4	4.05	4.68	9.25
.66	1.1	3.2	2.09	5.27	8.75
.17	9.2	8.5	6.08	3.86	4.92
.08	3.2	4.9	2.03	2.29	8.1
.49	4.3	6.3	9.07	4.57	9.6
.27	2.1	7.4	4.09	5.18	2.43
.99	7.1	5.6	7.03	1.33	1.8

Set 13*	Set 14*	Set 15*	Set 16*	Set 17*
.9	.6	5.01	20.56	138.35
5.28	4.	2.999	14.27	253.42
9.5	.94	3.728	36.87	639.32
.33	7.	2.517	8.26	182.08
.19	.8	9.282	15.84	24.19
1.4	8.	7.053	1.38	8.3407
.7	.53	.96	16.48	.0038
.29	2.1	8.524	9.27	1.153
2.45	.68	1.8	.84	7.4619
.81	3.9	1.516	28.45	.00532
.9	.49	6.24	42.83	.13847
3.9	6.	.006	56.19	.32296
4.62	.57	4.518	18.28	.48325

*Continued on next page.

5.27	.36	4.783	32.28	335.48
7.4	4.68	1.829	14.85	618.37
.35	.2	5.318	9.74	407.54
3.82	9.	2.175	98.42	250.36
.06	1.7	9.384	.94	195.83

Set 18

.08	1.16	16.91	426.26	596.74
.57	2.65	28.38	9.84	289.57
.13	4.27	19.43	16.59	193.86
.42	1.04	37.21	153.60	319.29
.83	3.53	4.82	74.75	475.43
.66	5.21	.48	8.68	628.58

Set 19

$.24	$.83	$.36	$.22	$.84
.59	.25	.88	.93	.27
.37	.03	.41	.79	.49
.73	.62	.29	.68	.56
.85	.54	.37	.85	.99
			.42	.78

Set 20

$2.33	$8.25	$45.63	$297.82	$355.95
.96	3.70	5.96	4.08	109.82
4.28	9.64	.83	16.29	481.56
.51	8.23	14.71	.62	247.49
9.16	4.72	9.43	148.37	575.37
		18.65	974.46	281.25

Add as indicated:

Set 21(a)

1. .3 + .6
2. .05 + .12
3. 3.6 + 5.1
4. .275 + .38
5. .62 + .573
6. .47 + .1785
7. 18 + .32
8. .9 + 4
9. .017 + 15
10. .16 + .7

Set 21(b)

1. .8 + .5
2. .46 + .04
3. 15.8 + 6.3
4. .94 + .065
5. .824 + .19
6. .1692 + .23
7. 25 + .6
8. .08 + 9
9. 1.56 + 4
10. .036 + .1

Set 22

1. .17 + .38 + .53
2. .52 + 1.6 + 8.26
3. .83 + 7 + 4.45 + .049
4. .06 + 1.2 + 46 + 3.825 + .075
5. 1.5 + .18 + 6.84 + .016 + .27
6. .83 + .37 + 4 + 3.9 + .051
7. 4.92 + 1.853 + 9.7 + 60 + 42.6
8. 1.4 + 26 + .39 + 5.98 + 9
9. 3.3 + .07 + 6 + 2.63 + .174
10. 15.6 + .19 + 4.75 + .836 + 200

Set 23

1. $.23 + $.75
2. $.17 + $.49 + $.83
3. $1.80 + $2.60 + $4.25
4. $2.75 + $3.35 + $.96 + $1.45
5. $.60 + $.38 + $1.50 + $3.25 + $9.70
6. $32.40 + $4.80 + $2.62 + $.61 + $.89
7. $100 + $8.42 + $93.75 + $6.83 + $.14
8. $5.57 + $2.83 + $1.69 + $10.50 + $7.25
9. $.74 + $1.60 + $.99 + $4.88 + $.04
10. $3.42 + $6.51 + $12.54 + $9.49 + $8.68

Set 24

Find sum of:

1. 4.23, 6.832, and 4.4
2. 8.01, .684, and 5.9
3. .07, 19.3, and 7.86
4. .6, 8, and .24
5. 1.4, 3.8, and .87

6. 2.05, .156, 4.69, and .08
7. $7.26, $.85, $.42, $.94, and $2.35
8. $12.59, $9.47, $1.27, $.56, and $3.46
9. $8.41, $2.25, $2.50, $7.64, and $.85
10. $1.20, $4.81, $.39, $.74, and $3.08

PRACTICAL APPLICATIONS

1. The school orchestra bought a violin for $69.95, a saxophone for $108.75, and a trumpet for $72.50. What is the total cost of the new instruments?

2. Marilyn bought her graduation outfit. Her dress cost $19.98; shoes, $12.50; hat, $7.49; and bag, $4.75. How much did she spend?

3. The athletic association ticket sales this year at the Smedley Junior High School were distributed as follows: 7A, $21.75; 7B, $39.50; 8A, $47.25; 8B, $63.00; 9A, $37.75; and 9B, $28.75. What was the total amount of sales?

4. Find the total expenses in producing the Wagner School show if renting and making costumes cost $162.55; royalty fee, $25.00; properties, $43.68; tickets, $12.75; lighting, $32.25; and miscellaneous items, $57.19.

5. The freshmen contributed $39.75 to the Red Cross; the sophomores, $28.40; the juniors, $36.15; and the seniors, $40.90. What was the total amount of their contributions?

6. Jane's mother went to the store and bought meat costing $4.29; vegetables, $.84; fruit, $1.08; bakery items, $.56; dairy items, $1.67; and general grocery items, $2.76. How much was her bill?

7. Charlotte's father took the family on a motor trip. The expenses included gasoline, $18.45; oil, $.90; lodging, $37.00; meals, $59.25; amusements, $24.83; miscellaneous expenses, $19.54. How much did the trip cost?

8. The weather bureau reported that the total rainfall for the first 7 months in a city was 30.93 inches. During the 5 times it rained in August, 1.02 in., 2 in., 1.6 in., 0.58 in., and 0.4 in. of rain fell. What was the total rainfall at the end of the first 8 months?

9. (a) Robert's brother is a salesman. Last week he received $54.50 salary and $29.68 commission. How much did he earn in all? (b) What is his new bank balance if the previous balance was $297.06 and he deposited a check for $36.97?

10. (a) How much should a dealer sell a radio for if it cost him $28.75 and he wishes to make a profit of $12.75? (b) Tom paid $37.85 for a bicycle. What was the original price if the storekeeper gave Tom a reduction of $5.75?

Micrometer Caliper Readings

Measurement by a micrometer caliper involves the addition of decimals. On the barrel of the micrometer each exposed number indicates a tenth (.1) of an inch, each uncovered subdivision that follows indicates .025 inch, and on the thimble each of the 25 divisions indicates .001 inch.

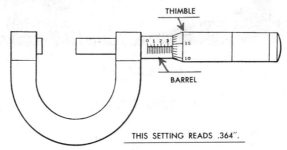

THIMBLE

BARREL

THIS SETTING READS .364".

Find in each case the complete micrometer reading by adding the following given measurements:

	Largest Exposed Number on Barrel Indicating	Uncovered Subdivisions on Barrel Indicating	Divisions on Thimble Indicating
1. Piece A	.5 inch	.075 inch	.013 inch
2. Piece B	.3 inch	.05 inch	.009 inch
3. Piece C	.8 inch	.025 inch	.021 inch
4. Piece D	.2 inch	.05 inch	.018 inch
5. Piece E	.9 inch	.075 inch	.001 inch

REFRESH YOUR SKILLS

1. Add:

9,514
35,825
27,202
83,916
431

2. Subtract:

600,000
81,703

3. Multiply:

5,026
608

4. Divide:

597)5,387,925

5. Add:

$4\frac{3}{5}$
$5\frac{7}{10}$

6. Subtract:

16
$9\frac{11}{12}$

7. Multiply:

$5\frac{5}{8} \times 6\frac{2}{3}$

8. Divide:

$8 \div \frac{3}{4}$

9. Write as a decimal numeral: Two hundred and forty-three thousandths

10. Round off 8.276 to the nearest hundredth.

11. Add: 7.5
4.2
3.6
1.7

12. Add:

$9.46 + .628 + 80.2$

EXERCISE 24

SUBTRACTION OF DECIMALS

I. Aim: To subtract decimals.

II. Procedure

1. If it is necessary to write the numerals, write the subtrahend under the minuend so that the decimal points are directly under each other. Zeros may be annexed to the numeral naming a decimal fraction or a decimal point and zeros to the numeral naming a whole number in the minuend so that the minuend and subtrahend may have the same number of decimal places. (See sample solutions 4, 7, 8, and 9.)

2. Subtract as in the subtraction of whole numbers. (See Exercise 4.)

3. Place the decimal point in the remainder (or difference) directly under the decimal points of the subtrahend and minuend.

4. When a decimal answer ends in one or more zeros to the right of the decimal point, the zeros may be dropped unless it is necessary to show the exact degree of measurement. (See sample solution 5.)

5. Check by adding the remainder to the subtrahend. Their sum should equal the minuend. (See Exercise 4.)

Concept:

(a) $.9 - .2$

Since $.9 = \frac{9}{10}$ and $.2 = \frac{2}{10}$,

then
$$\begin{array}{r} \frac{9}{10} \\ - \frac{2}{10} \\ \hline \frac{7}{10} \end{array}$$
or using decimals
$$\begin{array}{r} .9 \\ - .2 \\ \hline .7 \end{array}$$

$.7$ is the same as $\frac{7}{10}$

(b) $4.5 - 1.6$

Since $4.5 = 4\frac{5}{10}$ and $1.6 = 1\frac{6}{10}$,

then
$$\begin{array}{r} 4\frac{5}{10} = 3\frac{15}{10} \\ - 1\frac{6}{10} = 1\frac{6}{10} \\ \hline 2\frac{9}{10} \end{array}$$
or using decimals
$$\begin{array}{r} 4.5 \\ - 1.6 \\ \hline 2.9 \end{array}$$

2.9 is the same as $2\frac{9}{10}$

III. Sample Solutions. Subtract in the following examples:

1. .59	**2.** .47	**3.** 16.2	**4.** 5.61	5.61
.25	.38	4.6	.9 or	.90
.34	.09	11.6	4.71	4.71

Answer: .34   *Answer:* .09   *Answer:* 11.6   *Answer:* 4.71

5. 9.354	**6.** $71.46	**7.** .82 − .5
.854	15.24	.82 .82
8.500 = 8.5	$56.22	.5 or .50

Answer: 8.500 or 8.5   *Answer:* $56.22   .32   .32

                                            Answer: .32

8. .6 − .524	**9.** $20 − $6.38	**10.** Subtract .27 from 2.7
Solution:	*Solution:*	*Solution:*
.600	$20.00	2.70
.524	6.38	.27
.076	$13.62	2.43

Answer: .076   *Answer:* $13.62   *Answer:* 2.43

DIAGNOSTIC TEST

Subtract:

1. .8	**8.** 5.4	**15.** .34617	**22.** 5.
.2	2.8	.14596	1.43

2. .38	**9.** 6.5	**16.** .4583	**23.** 4.2
.24	2.5	.2783	.372

3. .67	**10.** .679	**17.** .85328	**24.** $176.27
.48	.398	.84793	93.48

4. .05	**11.** 3.72	**18.** 6.531	**25.** .15 − .08
.02	1.95	5.975	

5. .86	**12.** 15.8	**19.** 8.000	**26.** .375 − .2
.79	3.9	1.742	

6. .57	**13.** .6593	**20.** 3.56	**27.** .7 − .625
.37	.4978	.8	

7. 4.6	**14.** 83.452	**21.** .9	**28.** 4.2 − .83
3.1	49.596	.735	

29. 9 − .05   **30.** $16 − $1.50   **31.** Subtract .08 from .3

RELATED PRACTICE EXAMPLES

Subtract:

		SET 1					SET 2		
.9	.4	.6	.7	.5	.29	.47	.73	.98	.64
.5	.3	.1	.2	.4	.03	.26	.32	.65	.21

		SET 3					SET 4		
.36	.44	.25	.83	.58	.08	.06	.09	.07	.09
.18	.27	.09	.36	.29	.01	.04	.03	.05	.06

		SET 5					SET 6		
.85	.92	.54	.25	.13	.58	.46	.25	.74	.92
.76	.84	.45	.17	.08	.28	.36	.05	.54	.42

		SET 7					SET 8		
8.4	4.7	6.8	5.6	9.5	7.5	9.3	4.6	8.2	6.1
4.2	2.5	1.7	3.2	4.4	4.7	1.9	2.8	5.4	4.3

		SET 9					SET 10		
5.3	7.6	9.2	2.8	8.4	.835	.594	.967	.076	.749
3.3	2.6	6.2	1.8	4.4	.214	.287	.378	.043	.729

		SET 11					SET 12		
7.64	6.51	9.68	4.29	9.01	18.5	17.3	24.5	38.4	42.7
3.53	4.32	5.95	1.76	7.84	6.2	5.8	3.5	7.1	5.9

SET 13

.9355	.1327	60.07	375.3	5.724
.8492	.1219	42.38	190.4	3.856

SET 14

.25683	34.645	9.4538	849.54	5,986.3
.14974	17.859	6.7425	258.46	2,894.7

SET 15

.5844	.4683	6.2937	.83572	43.596
.2837	.1678	4.2843	.43564	35.589

SET 16

| .7856 | .3895 | 5.8362 | .92041 | 82.475 |
| .3256 | .1995 | 3.7362 | .52041 | 17.275 |

SET 17

| .6848 | .04965 | .00325 | .97424 | .03741 |
| .6827 | .04894 | .00255 | .96712 | .03659 |

SET 18

| 4.6 | 5.83 | 9.786 | 1.904 | 7.0352 |
| 3.8 | 4.96 | 8.895 | 1.737 | 6.9446 |

SET 19

| 4.000 | 9.000 | 6.0000 | 10.000 | 24.000 |
| 1.753 | 4.068 | 5.9325 | 8.469 | 13.307 |

SET 20

| 1.4 | 2.5 | 8.65 | 7.543 | 5.0046 |
| .9 | .7 | .8 | .28 | 4.307 |

SET 21

| .36 | .78 | .07 | .6 | .4 |
| .034 | .1561 | .0628 | .49 | .003 |

SET 22

| 8 | 3 | 7 | 6 | 28 |
| 7.3 | 1.2 | 2.84 | 4.005 | 9.756 |

SET 23

| 5 | 9 | 3 | 1.6 | 4.9 |
| .6 | .09 | .753 | .54 | .807 |

SET 24(a)

| $4.85 | $1.36 | $36.80 | $84.25 | $25.00 |
| 2.60 | .89 | 17.42 | 9.75 | 16.68 |

SET 24(b)

| $193.45 | $200.00 | $476.13 | $1,250.00 | $5,000.00 |
| 108.91 | 127.18 | 85.75 | 975.80 | 3,752.69 |

Subtract as indicated:

Set 25	Set 26	Set 27
1. .3 − .2	**1.** .45 − .4	**1.** .6 − .45
2. .8 − .3	**2.** .84 − .3	**2.** .8 − .36
3. .49 − .25	**3.** .97 − .6	**3.** .9 − .83
4. .38 − .09	**4.** .384 − .2	**4.** .4 − .176
5. .536 − .008	**5.** .518 − .46	**5.** .35 − .285
6. .837 − .325	**6.** .039 − .01	**6.** .06 − .043
7. .372 − .056	**7.** .6482 − .3	**7.** .2 − .1356
8. .0045 − .0023	**8.** .8056 − .74	**8.** .41 − .2538
9. .1534 − .0976	**9.** .5842 − .095	**9.** .685 − .5903
10. .00316 − .00286	**10.** .0034 − .003	**10.** .006 − .0005

Set 28	Set 29	Set 30
1. 3.6 − .24	**1.** 8 − .5	**1.** $.50 − $.25
2. 4.7 − .83	**2.** 2 − 1.7	**2.** $.78 − $.09
3. 23.4 − 1.75	**3.** 1 − .16	**3.** $2.74 − $.86
4. 5.82 − .004	**4.** 3 − 1.38	**4.** $3.35 − $2.25
5. 6.03 − .307	**5.** 6 − .09	**5.** $10 − $5.60
6. 12.54 − 1.054	**6.** 4 − .875	**6.** $15.42 − $9
7. 81.2 − 4.18	**7.** 7 − 3.0625	**7.** $100 − $84.53
8. 3.4 − .0056	**8.** 10 − .375	**8.** $200 − $133.62
9. 2.875 − .375	**9.** 12 − 8.2003	**9.** $446.58 − $279.49
10. 18.01 − .0002	**10.** 27 − .0067	**10.** $3,500 − $2,938.75

Set 31

1. From .8 subtract .35
2. From 1.4 subtract .07
3. From 45.9 take 6.38
4. From $2.84 take $1.75
5. Subtract .004 from .08
6. Subtract $.62 from $.79
7. Take .45 from 1.5
8. Take $8.40 from $12
9. Find the difference between .03 and .003
10. Find the difference between 4.81 and .481

PRACTICAL APPLICATIONS

1. In addition to his weekly allowance of $2.50, Richard earned $4.65 after school. How much money should he have left at the end of the week if his expenses were: carfare, $.75; school lunches and supplies, $1.97; movies, $.45; church, $.25; and savings, $1.25?

2. How much change should you receive from a:
(a) $1 bill if you owe $.59? $.83? $.46? $.11? $.78?
(b) $5 bill if you owe $1.89? $2.98? $3.04? $.69? $4.44?
(c) $10 bill if you owe $8.45? $5.09? $.97? $9.61? $2.28?

3. Harry bought a new suit costing $44.95; shoes, $10.75; hat, $6.85; shirt, $3.98; and tie, $1.50. If his father gave him $70, how much money is left over after he pays for these articles?

4. (a) John bought a baseball mitt that regularly sold for $7.49 at a reduction of $1.98. How much did he pay? (b) He also left a deposit of $3.75 on a baseball uniform that cost $12.25. What balance does he owe?

5. A boy ran the 100-yard dash in 13.4 seconds, then later ran the same distance in 11.7 seconds. How many seconds less did he take the second time?

6. In measuring a 1-inch block of metal by a precision instrument, a student found the average of all his readings to be 0.9996 inch. Find the amount of error.

7. The passenger ship, *United States*, on her maiden voyage established a record of 35.59 knots crossing the Atlantic Ocean. If the record speed of the *Queen Mary* is 30.99 knots, how much faster is the *United States*?

8. The outside diameter of certain copper tubing is 2.375 in. and its wall thickness is .083 in. What is the inside diameter?

9. During the month a merchant made deposits of $439.76, $180.53, $263.98, and $129.49. Checks and cash withdrawals were: $163.20, $248.00, $92.85, $310.94, and $8.52. If his previous monthly bank balance was $716.91, find his new bank balance.

10. The net worth of a business is equal to its assets minus its liabilities. Find the net worth of a business whose assets are: cash, $982.75; merchandise, $12,369; accounts receivable, $536.89; other assets, $1,750; and liabilities are: notes payable, $400; accounts payable, $109.38; other liabilities, $327.67.

REFRESH YOUR SKILLS

1. Add: **2.** Subtract: **3.** Multiply: **4.** Divide:

149,526   821,427   1,760   407)3,538,865
312,997   291,398   500
500,725
832,589
294,217
381,726

5. Round off 30,246,701 to the nearest million.

6. Reduce $\frac{54}{72}$ to lowest terms.

7. Change $\frac{3}{5}$ to 100ths.

8. Which fraction is larger: $\frac{7}{8}$ or $\frac{4}{5}$?

9. Add: **10.** Subtract: **11.** Multiply: **12.** Divide:

$6\frac{5}{12}$ $5\frac{1}{2}$ $3\frac{1}{7} \times 56$ $5\frac{1}{4} \div \frac{7}{8}$
$2\frac{1}{4}$ $3\frac{13}{16}$
$3\frac{5}{6}$

13. What part of 135 is 45?   **14.** $\frac{3}{16}$ of what number is 27?

15. Write the numeral 800.08 in words.

16. Write as a decimal numeral: Three and fifty-nine thousandths.

17. Round off $5.8273 to the nearest cent.

18. Add: **19.** Subtract: **20.** Subtract:

.693 + 4.82 + 37.6   4.37 $18 − $2.67
                             .6

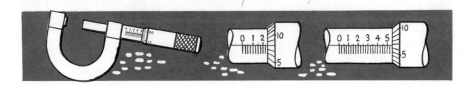

EXERCISE 25

COMPARING DECIMALS

I. Aim: To compare decimals.

II. Procedure

1. If necessary, change the given numbers to decimals containing the same number of decimal places. Take the larger number as the larger decimal. (See sample solution 1.)

2. A mixed decimal or whole number is larger than a decimal fraction.

III. Sample Solutions

1. Which is larger: .03 or .3?

.03 = .03
.3 = .30

Answer: .3 is larger

2. Which is smaller: 1.7 or .283?

1.7 = 1.700
.283 = .283

Answer: .283 is smaller

3. Arrange in order of size (smallest first):
.65, .635, 6.1, and .069

.65 = .650 and 6.1 = 6.100
.635 and .069 are already expressed in thousandths.
Answer: .069, .635, .65, and 6.1

DIAGNOSTIC TEST

Which is larger:

1. .5 or .45?

2. .154 or 1.02?

Which is smaller:

3. .7 or .699?

4. 5.53 or .553?

5. Arrange in order of size (largest first):
.06, 1.4, .19, and .388

6. Arrange in order of size (smallest first):
4.72, .493, 4.8, and .465

RELATED PRACTICE EXAMPLES

Which is larger:

Set 1

1. .3 or .29?
2. .04 or .004?
3. .91 or .893?
4. .7 or .074?
5. .156 or .1561?

Set 2

1. 1.47 or .278?
2. .63 or 4.5?
3. .28 or 2.8?
4. 2.9 or .899?
5. 4.504 or 4.5035?

Which is smaller:

Set 3

1. .89 or .9?
2. .2 or .21?
3. .50 or .05?
4. .36 or .4?
5. .0051 or .006?

Set 4

1. 4.1 or 3.010?
2. 5.06 or 1.059?
3. 1.638 or .5376?
4. 2.0439 or 2.04395?
5. 9.3 or 8.754?

Set 5

Arrange in order of size (largest first):

1. .01, .001, .1, and .0001
2. 2.25, .253, .2485, and 2.249
3. .38, 1.5, .475, and .0506
4. .006, 5.02, .503, and .1483
5. .98, .89, .934, and .9

Set 6

Arrange in order of size (smallest first):

1. .201, .19, 1.2, and .21
2. .465, .4053, .47, and 4.5
3. .51, .583, .60, and .5126
4. .04, 1.25, .156, and 2.3
5. .76, .7, .076, and .0710

PRACTICAL APPLICATIONS

In the manufacture of a certain part 1 inch in length, a tolerance of ± .002 inch is permitted, that is, the part will be accepted if it measures anywhere from 0.998 inch to 1.002 inches.

Which of the following lengths fall within the acceptable range:

1. (a) 1.015 inches   (b) 0.9991 inch   (c) 1.0031 inches
2. (a) 0.9989 inch   (b) 1.0012 inches   (c) 0.99 inch
3. (a) 1.02 inches   (b) 0.989 inch   (c) 1.0007 inches

MULTIPLICATION OF DECIMALS

I. Aim: To multiply decimals.

II. Procedure

1. Write the given numerals and multiply as in the multiplication of whole numbers. The decimal point in the multiplier does not necessarily have to be under the decimal point in the multiplicand.

2. Find the total number of decimal places in the multiplicand and multiplier and point off in the product, counting from right to left, as many decimal places as there are in the multiplicand and multiplier together.

3. When the product contains fewer figures than the required number of decimal places, prefix as many zeros as are necessary. (See sample solutions 3, 4, and 6.)

4. When a decimal answer ends in one or more zeros to the right of the decimal point, the zeros may be dropped unless it is necessary to show the exact degree of measurement. (See sample solutions 4, 5, and 9.)

5. Check by interchanging the multiplier and multiplicand and multiplying again, or by dividing the product by either the multiplier or multiplicand. (See Exercise 5.)

Concept:

(a) $.2 \times .8$

Since $.2 = \frac{2}{10}$ and $.8 = \frac{8}{10}$,

then $\frac{2}{10} \times \frac{8}{10} = \frac{16}{100}$ or using decimals $.2 \times .8 = .16$

.16 is the same as $\frac{16}{100}$

(b) $.3 \times .02$

Since $.3 = \frac{3}{10}$ and $.02 = \frac{2}{100}$,

then $\frac{3}{10} \times \frac{2}{100} = \frac{6}{1000}$ or using decimals $.3 \times .02 = .006$

.006 is the same as $\frac{6}{1000}$

III. Sample Solutions

Multiply in the following examples:

1. $\begin{array}{r} 46 \\ .04 \\ \hline 1.84 \end{array}$
    2. $\begin{array}{r} .2389 \\ 2 \\ \hline .4778 \end{array}$
    3. $\begin{array}{r} .02 \\ .03 \\ \hline .0006 \end{array}$
    4. $\begin{array}{r} 1.35 \\ .06 \\ \hline .0810 = .081 \end{array}$

Answer: 1.84   *Answer:* .4778   *Answer:* .0006   *Answer:* .081

5. $\begin{array}{r} .625 \\ 48 \\ \hline 5\,000 \\ 25\,00 \\ \hline 30.000 \end{array}$
    6. $2.6 \times .002 = .0052$

              Answer: .0052

7. Find $\frac{3}{4}$ of $1.68

    Solution:

    $\frac{3}{4} \times \overset{\$.42}{\$1.68} = \$1.26$

Answer: 30   *Answer:* $1.26

8. Find .56 of 2.43

    Solution:

    $\begin{array}{r} 2.43 \\ .56 \\ \hline 1458 \\ 1\,215 \\ \hline 1.3608 \end{array}$

    Answer: 1.3608

9. Find $.37\frac{1}{2}$ of $28.96

    Solution:

    $\begin{array}{r} \$28.96 \\ .37\frac{1}{2} \\ \hline 20272 \\ 8688 \\ \hline 107152 \\ 1448 \\ \hline \$10.8600 \end{array}$
    $\frac{1}{2} \times 2896 = 1448$

    Answer: $10.86

10. Find $.16\frac{2}{3}$ of $37.25 correct to nearest cent.

    $\begin{array}{r} \$37.25 \\ .16\frac{2}{3} \\ \hline 22350 \\ 3725 \\ \hline 59600 \\ 2483\frac{1}{3} \\ \hline \$6.2083\frac{1}{3} = \$6.21 \end{array}$
    Solution:

    $\frac{2}{3} \times 3725 = \frac{7450}{3} = 2483\frac{1}{3}$

    Answer: $6.21

11. Find $\frac{5}{6}$ of $4.19 correct to nearest cent.

    Solution:

$$\frac{5}{6} \times \$4.19 = \frac{\$20.95}{6} = \$3.49\frac{1}{6} = \$3.49$$

    Answer: $3.49

DIAGNOSTIC TEST

Multiply:

1. .3
  8
	7. .03
	  2
		13. .58
		  .6
			19. .147
			  .03

2. 43
 .24
	8. 14
	 .007
		14. .21
		  .4
			20. 3.1416
			   .75

3. .351
  86
	9. .002
	  4
		15. .56
		 .37
			21. .059
			 .064

4. .6739
   7
	10. 3.14
	  18
		16. .05
		 .01
			22. .012 × .005

5. 75 .48	**11.** .6 .2	**17.** 16.2 .045	
6. 37 .05	**12.** .3 .3	**18.** 34.89 .875	

In examples involving money, find product correct to nearest cent:

23. $.25
  8
	24. $3.80
	  24
		25. $3.62
		 .06
			26. $4.28
			 .125

27. Find $\frac{1}{2}$ of $.84

28. Find $\frac{5}{8}$ of $3.45

29. Find .46 of 150

30. $15.38
 .62$\frac{1}{2}$

31. $23.89
 .33$\frac{1}{3}$

RELATED PRACTICE EXAMPLES

Multiply:

Set 1

4	6	12	.5	.9
.1	.7	.8	3	5

Set 2

.23	7	84	.98	39
9	.56	.42	18	.61

Set 3

.247	.456	3	.572	28
5	34	.409	159	.717

Set 4

.9522	5	46	.1903	8725
8	.4673	.5034	156	.2839

Set 5

25	.95	6	.125	246
.4	20	.35	8	.625

Set 6

.03	.05	10	200	.07
8	17	.04	.08	38

Set 7

.04	.03	.02	3	5
2	3	4	.02	.01

Set 8

.006	.012	.009	5	21
3	7	10	.013	.004

Set 9

.001	.0015	.0007	13	4
9	2	5	.0006	.0014

Set 10

8.7	56.17	24	460	3.1416
6	75	3.6	4.8	32

Set 11

.9	.5	3.6	3	5.7
.8	.6	.7	8.2	2.5

Set 12

.2	.3	.1	.4	.1
.2	.2	.1	.2	.8

Set 13

.34	.95	.7	8.7	1.15
.3	.4	.66	.48	5.2

Set 14

.24	.19	.3	.15	.07
.2	.5	.03	.6	1.3

Set 15

.28	5.93	.45	12.52	256.79
.74	.87	4.91	.06	.03

Set 16

.67	.05	.04	.02	2.14
.02	.76	.09	.02	.03

Set 17

.003	.7	.375	28.2	.009
.4	.002	1.4	.064	36.6

Set 18

.368	32.49	70.84	95.26	453.40
.26	.625	.034	1.125	.375

SET 19

.0002	.179	.057	3.14	.04
.2	.04	.38	.002	1.225

SET 20

.268	3.1416	7.9582	8.504	2.423
.924	6.25	1.39	.015	9.146

SET 21

.00008	.003	.0052	.01	.02167
.6	.009	.05	.0007	1.8

SET 22(a)

1. 5 × .7
2. 8 × .04
3. 3 × .28
4. 6 × .005
5. .06 × 4
6. 9 × .0001
7. 7 × .02
8. 10 × .14
9. 1.2 × 12
10. 18 × .05

SET 22(b)

1. .2 × .3
2. .3 × .04
3. .4 × .35
4. .02 × .09
5. .01 × .005
6. .004 × .02
7. .025 × .008
8. .013 × .01
9. .04 × .029
10. .15 × .060

In examples involving money, find products correct to nearest cent:

SET 23

$.42	$.69	$.80	$.75	$.36
4	18	7	48	15

SET 24

$4.97	$5.76	$10.50	$16.31	$4.25
3	24	60	96	144

SET 25

$89	$.75	$14.25	$152.80	$293.28
.04	.06	.19	.05	.63

SET 26

$840	$3.88	$15.61	$2500	$675.90
.625	.875	.045	.4375	.002

SET 27	SET 28	SET 29
Find:	Find:	Find:
1. $\frac{1}{2}$ of $.98	1. $\frac{1}{2}$ of $.39	1. .25 of 60
2. $\frac{1}{2}$ of $4.63	2. $\frac{3}{4}$ of .58	2. .14 of .36
3. $\frac{1}{4}$ of .56	3. $\frac{1}{6}$ of $1.22	3. .04 of 9
4. $\frac{3}{4}$ of $5.20	4. $\frac{3}{8}$ of $2.58	4. .08 of 1.5
5. $\frac{1}{8}$ of $4.96	5. $\frac{7}{12}$ of $10	5. .75 of $4
6. $\frac{7}{8}$ of 1.44	6. $1\frac{1}{2}$ of $.75	6. .06 of $93
7. $7\frac{1}{3}$ of $.69	7. $2\frac{5}{6}$ of $.83	7. .39 of $3.40
8. $\frac{5}{6}$ of $12.48	8. $4\frac{2}{5}$ of 3.64	8. .86 of 9.57
9. $2\frac{2}{3}$ of $38.16	9. $3\frac{1}{4}$ of $14.20	9. .4 of 200
10. $4\frac{3}{5}$ of $51.40	10. $1\frac{2}{3}$ of $27.68	10. .13 of $15.64

SET 30

$80	$3,000	$.54	$2.80	$18.48
.$12\frac{1}{2}$	.$04\frac{1}{2}$	.$37\frac{1}{2}$	.$03\frac{1}{4}$	.$05\frac{3}{4}$

SET 31

$246	$6,000	$.90	$1.15	$45.71
.$33\frac{1}{3}$	.$08\frac{1}{3}$	.$04\frac{2}{3}$	.$66\frac{2}{3}$	.$83\frac{1}{3}$

PRACTICAL APPLICATIONS

1. Find the cost of each of the following:

(a) 5 lb. of onions @ $.07   (f) 15 sq. yd. of linoleum @ $2.98

(b) 6 chairs @ $5.80   (g) 190 gallons of fuel oil @ $.$12\frac{1}{2}$

(c) 4 tires @ $19.95   (h) $3\frac{5}{8}$ yd. of material @ $1.63

(d) 3 dozen eggs @ $.67   (i) 13 tons of coal @ $21.75

(e) $2\frac{3}{4}$ lb. of meat @ $.89   (j) 24 cans of fruit @ $.29

2. Find the cost per year of each of the following services:

(a) Electricity, $7.80 per month, (b) Gas, $5.94 per month, (c) Telephone, $6.16 per month.

3. Find the earnings per week (time and a half rate over 40 hr.):

Number of hours	32	46	29	43	$51\frac{1}{2}$
Rate per hour	$1.96	$1.20	$1.36	$3.05	$2.80

4. A refrigerator costs $265 cash or $80 down and 12 payments of $17.08 each. How much do you save by paying cash?

5. A finance company can be repaid on a loan of $100 in 6 monthly payments of $18.15, 12 monthly payments of $9.75, or 18 monthly payments of $6.97. Find the amounts paid back and the interest under each plan.

6. A certain plane on a flight used 43.8 gallons of gasoline per hour. If its flight lasted 4.5 hours, how many gallons of gasoline were consumed?

7. An airplane has a ground speed of 325 knots. What is its ground speed in statute m.p.h. if 1 knot = 1.15 statute m.p.h.?

8. Find the distance represented by 6.7 inches if the scale is 1 inch = 50 miles.

9. A vessel heads N. 15° W. for 5 hours at 10.4 knots. Find the distance traveled in nautical miles. (1 knot = 1 nautical m.p.h.)

10. Two ports are 8.1 inches apart on a chart. If the scale is 1 inch = 40 nautical miles, how many hours will it take a ship doing 18 knots to travel between ports?

REFRESH YOUR SKILLS

1. Add: 28,104
625
9,302
29
75,412
828

2. Subtract: 1,500,020
690,175

3. Multiply: 876
938

4. Divide: $289\overline{)285,821}$

5. Add: $\frac{3}{8}$
$\frac{1}{4}$
$\frac{5}{6}$

6. Subtract: $8\frac{7}{12}$
$7\frac{2}{3}$

7. Multiply: $12 \times 3\frac{7}{8}$

8. Divide: $1\frac{11}{16} \div 7\frac{1}{5}$

9. Add: $.88 + .8 + .888$

10. Subtract: $9.6 - .45$

11. Multiply: 3.1416
48

12. Multiply: $.004 \times 2.5$

EXERCISE 27

DIVISION OF DECIMALS

I. Aim: To divide decimals.

II. Procedure

1. If the divisor is a whole number: (See sample solutions 1 to 6.)
   (*a*) Divide as in division of whole numbers. (See Exercise 6.)
   (*b*) Place the decimal point in the quotient directly above the decimal point in the dividend.
2. If the divisor is a decimal: (See sample solutions 7 to 14.)
   (*a*) Make the divisor a whole number by moving its decimal point to the right of the last figure, indicating its new position by a caret ($_\wedge$).
   (*b*) Move the decimal point in the dividend to the right as many places as you moved the decimal point in the divisor and indicate its new position by a caret ($_\wedge$).
   (*c*) Divide as in the division of whole numbers and place the decimal point in the quotient directly above the caret ($_\wedge$) in the dividend.

Observe in the following how the multiplicative identity one (1)* is used to make the divisor a whole number and to allow us to use steps (a), (b), and (c). Both the divisor and dividend are multiplied by the power of ten which makes the divisor a whole number. The caret symbols are used in the sample solutions to indicate the new positions of the decimal points.

$$.12\overline{)\,.492} = \frac{.492}{.12} = \frac{.492}{.12} \times 1 = \frac{.492 \times 100}{.12 \times 100} = \frac{49.2}{12} = 12\overline{)\,49.2}$$

Thus, $.12\overline{)\,.492}$ becomes $12\overline{)\,49.2}$

or using carets, $.12\overline{)\,.492}$ becomes $.12_\wedge\overline{)\,.49_\wedge2}$

(*d*) When the dividend contains fewer decimal places than required, annex as many zeros as are necessary to a

*See page 8.

decimal dividend and a decimal point and the required zeros to a dividend containing a whole number. (See sample solutions 9, 11, 12, 13, and 14.)

3. Check by multiplying the quotient by the divisor and adding the remainder, if any, to the product. The result should equal the dividend. (See Exercise 6.)

4. To find the quotient correct to the nearest required decimal place, find the quotient to one more than the required number of decimal places, then round it off as outlined in Exercise 22. (See sample solution 13.) An alternate method is to find the quotient to the required number of decimal places, adding 1 to the last figure of the quotient if the remainder is equal to one half, or more than one half, of the divisor. (See sample solution 14.)

Concept:

(a) $.468 \div .02$

Since $.468 = \dfrac{468}{1000}$ and $.02 = \dfrac{2}{100}$,

then or using decimals

$$\frac{468}{1000} \div \frac{2}{100} = \frac{\overset{234}{\cancel{468}}}{\cancel{1000}} \times \frac{\cancel{100}}{\underset{1}{\cancel{2}}} = \frac{234}{10} = 23\tfrac{4}{10}$$

$$.02_\wedge)\overline{.46_\wedge 8}\ \ \overset{23.4}{}$$

23.4 is the same as $23\tfrac{4}{10}$

III. Sample Solutions

1. $37.8 \div 6$

$$\begin{array}{r} 6.3 \\ 6)\overline{37.8} \end{array}$$

Answer: 6.3

2. $9.12 \div 8$

$$\begin{array}{r} 1.14 \\ 8)\overline{9.12} \end{array}$$

Answer: 1.14

3. $3.456 \div 4$

$$\begin{array}{r} .864 \\ 4)\overline{3.456} \end{array}$$

Answer: .864

4. Divide .015 by 5

$$\begin{array}{r} .003 \\ 5)\overline{.015} \end{array}$$

Answer: .003

6. Divide \$8.50 by 6. Find answer correct to nearest cent.

$$\begin{array}{r} \$1.41\tfrac{2}{3} = \$1.42 \\ 6)\overline{\$8.50} \end{array}$$

Answer: \$1.42

5. Divide 21 by 56. Find quotient to 3 decimal places.

$$\begin{array}{r} .375 \\ 56)\overline{21.000} \\ 16\ 8 \\ \overline{\ \ 4\ 20} \\ 3\ 92 \\ \overline{\ \ \ \ 280} \\ 280 \end{array}$$

Answer: .375

7. Divide 35.6 by .4

$$8\ 9.$$
$$.4_\wedge\overline{)35.6_\wedge}$$
Answer: 89

8. .0119 ÷ .7

$$.017$$
$$.7_\wedge\overline{).0_\wedge119}$$
Answer: .017

9. $7 ÷ $1.75

$$4.$$
$$\$1.75_\wedge\overline{)\$7.00_\wedge}$$
$$7.00$$
Answer: 4

10. Divide .0006 by .012

$$.05$$
$$.012_\wedge\overline{).000_\wedge60}$$
Answer: .05

11. 15 ÷ .625

$$24.$$
$$.625_\wedge\overline{)15.000_\wedge}$$
$$\underline{12\ 50}$$
$$2\ 500$$
$$\underline{2\ 500}$$
Answer: 24

12. Divide 122.8 by .004

$$30\ 700.$$
$$.004_\wedge\overline{)122.800_\wedge}$$
Answer: 30,700

13. Divide 46 by 16.1 and find quotient correct to nearest thousandth.

$$2\ .8571$$
$$16.1_\wedge\overline{)46.0_\wedge0000}$$
$$\underline{32\ 2}$$
$$13\ 80$$
$$\underline{12\ 88}$$
$$920$$
$$\underline{805}$$
$$1150$$
$$\underline{1127}$$
$$230$$
$$\underline{161}$$
$$69$$
Answer: 2.857

14. Divide 28.5 by .87 and find quotient correct to nearest tenth.

$$32\ .7$$
$$.87\overline{)28.50_\wedge0}$$
$$\underline{26\ 1}$$
$$2\ 40$$
$$\underline{1\ 74}$$
$$660$$
$$\underline{609}$$
$$51$$
Answer: 32.8

Since the remainder (51) is more than one half of the divisor (87), 1 is added to the last figure of the quotient.

DIAGNOSTIC TEST A

Divide:
   1. 4)9.2   **2.** 7)8.96   **3.** 2)5.328

   4. 3).8226   **5.** 6)5.124   **6.** 8).736   **7.** 36)91.44

   8. 8)5.000   **9.** 200)4   **10.** Divide 3.6 by 6

11. Find quotient correct to nearest thousandth: 29)24

12. Find answer correct to nearest cent: 12)$2.57

13. 2 ÷ 16 (Find quotient to 3 decimal places.)

RELATED PRACTICE EXAMPLES
Divide:

SET 1

3)6.9   7)86.1   4)62.4   5)746.5   6)6765.6

SET 2

2).86   4)5.88   7)92.96   6)88.02   8)971.44

SET 3

8).968   5).865   2)7.942   9)9.486   3)73.914

SET 4

4).8936   6).6432   3).5814   5)6.9185   7)8.9789

SET 5

3)2.52   8)5.216   6)2.418   4)3.0612   9)7.5519

SET 6

6).228   2).1346   8).024   7).0133   5).00375

SET 7

12)3.36   48)158.4   24)11.688   75)315.75   144)112.32

SET 8

5)2.0   4)5.00   8)7.000   16)9.0000   32)13.00000

SET 9

60)3   52)13   200)6   48)54   7,000)84

SET 10(a)
Find quotient correct to nearest tenth:

12)7   8)43   90)375   57)845.2   108)20,000

SET 10(b)
Find quotient correct to nearest hundredth:

9)5   6)38   46)2.8   156)108   270)60

SET 10(c)
Find quotient correct to nearest thousandth:

7)285   15)46   12)365   24)13.59   39)258.4

Find answer correct to nearest cent:

Set 11(a)

$3\overline{)\$.72}$ $6\overline{)\$5.40}$ $12\overline{)\$9.60}$ $24\overline{)\$8.16}$ $144\overline{)\$11.52}$

Set 11(b)

$4\overline{)\$.63}$ $6\overline{)\$1.25}$ $12\overline{)\$2.80}$ $72\overline{)\$234}$ $144\overline{)\$1,056}$

Set 12	Set 13
1. $.87 \div 3$	1. Divide 4.2 by 7
2. $1.072 \div 8$	2. Divide .616 by 4
3. $9 \div 12$ (2 decimal places)	3. Divide .0474 by 6
4. $8 \div 7$ (nearest thousandth)	4. Divide .16 by 36 (3 decimal places)
5. $\$2.16 \div 5$ (nearest cent)	5. Divide $10.50 by 12 (nearest cent)

DIAGNOSTIC TEST B

Divide:

1. $.3\overline{)247.8}$ 4. $.6\overline{)2.6898}$ 7. $.6\overline{)12.0}$

2. $.5\overline{)9.25}$ 5. $.2\overline{).0034}$ 8. $.7\overline{)42}$

3. $.8\overline{).896}$ 6. $1.2\overline{)108.72}$ 9. $.4\overline{)2}$

10. Find quotient correct to nearest tenth: $2.7\overline{)18}$

RELATED PRACTICE EXAMPLES

Divide:

Set 1

$.4\overline{)7.6}$ $.5\overline{)89.5}$ $.3\overline{)176.7}$ $.6\overline{)1804.2}$ $.2\overline{)6934.6}$

Set 2

$.3\overline{).84}$ $.2\overline{)4.76}$ $.5\overline{)32.15}$ $.7\overline{)87.92}$ $.4\overline{)733.08}$

Set 3

$.7\overline{).294}$ $.4\overline{)3.024}$ $.8\overline{)9.792}$ $.3\overline{)62.928}$ $.5\overline{)18.725}$

Set 4

$.5\overline{).4205}$ $.3\overline{).7128}$ $.6\overline{)5.2524}$ $.9\overline{)9.3843}$ $.7\overline{)6.4722}$

SET 5

.8).0016   .7).0224   .4).0028   .3).0009   .6).0552

SET 6

1.8)43.74   2.6)14.976   3.5)3041.5   19.6)101.92   24.3)8.8452

SET 7

.4)14.0   .8)20.0   2.8)49.00   6.4)104.000   1.6)15.0000

SET 8

.5)15   .6)24   .4)72   1.8)36   4.2)126

SET 9

.6)3   .8)2   5.6)14   7.2)9   12.8)40

SET 10(*a*)

Find quotient correct to nearest tenth:

.8)9   6.3)15   7.5)456.2   25.4)82.25   2.2)5,000

SET 10(*b*)

Find quotient correct to nearest hundredth:

.3)2   1.4)6   5.4).48   13.2)36   8.4)4.9

SET 10(*c*)

Find quotient correct to nearest thousandth:

.8).45   2.6)740   3.9)85.3   5.7)200   7.5)3,268

DIAGNOSTIC TEST C

Divide:

1. .02)521.56   **4.** .07).89789   **7.** .16)48.00

2. .79)4.661   **5.** .03).0009   **8.** .39)265.2

3. .56)2.4472   **6.** 1.44)135.072   **9.** .25)50

10. Find quotient correct to nearest thousandth: .96)8.8

11. $.04)$1.84

RELATED PRACTICE EXAMPLES
Divide:

SET 1

$.04\overline{).68}$ $.06\overline{)15.06}$ $.65\overline{)17.55}$ $.32\overline{)16.96}$ $.57\overline{)369.36}$

SET 2

$.07\overline{).812}$ $.03\overline{)7.749}$ $.96\overline{)6.912}$ $.25\overline{)24.175}$ $.81\overline{)43.902}$

SET 3

$.02\overline{)4.6954}$ $.08\overline{).7216}$ $.14\overline{).4732}$ $.43\overline{)1.9694}$ $.75\overline{).4725}$

SET 4

$.09\overline{).08928}$ $.05\overline{).15425}$ $.22\overline{).21692}$ $.87\overline{).82563}$ $.36\overline{)1.32156}$

SET 5

$.06\overline{).0018}$ $.01\overline{).0005}$ $.03\overline{).00012}$ $.68\overline{).04216}$ $.42\overline{).00378}$

SET 6

$3.65\overline{)208.05}$ $2.27\overline{)88.303}$ $4.24\overline{)7.0808}$ $8.32\overline{)404.352}$ $5.39\overline{)18.7572}$

SET 7

$.04\overline{)76.00}$ $.36\overline{)18.00}$ $.52\overline{)39.00}$ $.64\overline{)56.000}$ $1.92\overline{)120.000}$

SET 8

$.08\overline{)57.6}$ $.65\overline{)45.5}$ $.78\overline{)670.8}$ $1.47\overline{)3,719.1}$ $2.83\overline{)4,952.5}$

SET 9

$.09\overline{)27}$ $.18\overline{)90}$ $.64\overline{)16}$ $.32\overline{)12}$ $1.36\overline{)119}$

SET 10(*a*)

Find correct to nearest tenth:

$1.15\overline{)825}$ $.87\overline{)79.4}$ $3.14\overline{)853.76}$ $.09\overline{)56.2}$ $39.37\overline{)432}$

SET 10(*b*)

Find correct to nearest hundredth:

$.06\overline{)4}$ $.84\overline{)70}$ $.37\overline{)2.9}$ $1.53\overline{)34}$ $2.21\overline{)13.67}$

SET 10(*c*)

Find correct to nearest thousandth:

$.54\overline{)98}$ $.69\overline{)8.45}$ $.26\overline{)42.7}$ $5.03\overline{)61}$ $2.43\overline{).162}$

Sᴇᴛ 11(a)

$.02)$3.46 $.05)$4 $.38)$27.36 $.40)$57.60 $1.25)$30

Sᴇᴛ 11(b)

$.08)$1.24 $.25)$3.90 $.49)$10.43 $1.80)$44.20 $2.67)$97.90

DIAGNOSTIC TEST D

Divide:

1. .006)74.898   4. .231).00924   7. .125)53.75

2. .018).4554   5. 4.375)11.8125   8. .052)452.4

3. .007)6.53912   6. .048)60.000   9. .014)112

10. Find quotient correct to nearest hundredth: .333)249

RELATED PRACTICE EXAMPLES

Divide:

Sᴇᴛ 1

.007).763   .003)17.862   .043)1.634   .175)49.525   .526)77.322

Sᴇᴛ 2

.006)6.0282   .035).1715   .216)8.1864   .024)1.2144   .382)8.9388

Sᴇᴛ 3

.004).05964   .073).31828   .524).36156   .358).86278   .449)1.50864

Sᴇᴛ 4

.009).00081   .018).0009   .105).00735   .096).00384   .667).04002

Sᴇᴛ 5

2.548)8.1536   4.125).94875   6.875)39.1875   3.002)4.44296

2.383)57.6686

Sᴇᴛ 6

.008)16.000   .056)140.000   .144)108.000   .625)35.000   1.375)132.000

Sᴇᴛ 7

.094)25.38   .008)90.16   .231)147.84   .382)893.88   .292)251.12

Set 8

$.005)\overline{438.5}$ $.072)\overline{691.2}$ $.043)\overline{382.7}$ $.337)\overline{1819.8}$ $.265)\overline{12799.5}$

Set 9

$.059)\overline{177}$ $.108)\overline{972}$ $.007)\overline{210}$ $.591)\overline{2,364}$ $.473)\overline{2,838}$

Set 10(*a*)

Find quotient correct to nearest tenth:

$.542)\overline{158}$ $.003)\overline{.55}$ $.061)\overline{14}$ $1.853)\overline{9.647}$ $.868)\overline{365.9}$

Set 10(*b*)

Find quotient correct to nearest hundredth:

$.006)\overline{25}$ $.013)\overline{56.3}$ $.314)\overline{8.49}$ $.079)\overline{298}$ $.592)\overline{.964}$

Set 10(*c*)

Find quotient correct to nearest thousandth:

$.007)\overline{33}$ $.056)\overline{.428}$ $.723)\overline{62.5}$ $2.381)\overline{356}$ $4.007)\overline{38.25}$

MISCELLANEOUS EXAMPLES

Follow directions given in Exercise 20, except divide by decimal. Also see sample solutions in Exercise 41.

Set 1	Set 2
1. .01 of what number is 8?	1. .5 of what number is 6?
2. .06 of what number is 42?	2. .25 of what number is 15?
3. .02 of what number is 56?	3. .75 of what number is 200?
4. .04 of what number is 19?	4. .8 of what number is 40?
5. .07 of what number is 630?	5. .42 of what number is 21?

Set 3	Set 4
1. .025 of what number is 5?	1. .375 of what number is 9?
2. .005 of what number is 11?	2. .625 of what number is 20?
3. .045 of what number is 18?	3. .125 of what number is 7?
4. .032 of what number is 16?	4. .428 of what number is 107?
5. .094 of what number is 470?	5. .875 of what number is 208?

Set 5	Set 6

Set 5

1. .33⅓ of what number is 4?
2. .16⅔ of what number is 13?
3. .37½ of what number is 27?
4. .66⅔ of what number is 364?
5. .83⅓ of what number is 250?

Set 6

1. 1.25 of what number is 10?
2. 1.75 of what number is 35?
3. 1.06 of what number is 212?
4. 1.625 of what number is 260?
5. 1.87½ of what number is 750?

PRACTICAL APPLICATIONS

1. The neighborhood baseball team bought 12 balls at $1.75 each and 7 bats at $1.95 each. If the 9 boys shared the costs equally, how much was each boy's share?

2. Find amount saved on each can when buying in quantity:

(*a*) 1 dozen cans of peas for $2.04 or $.18 each?

(*b*) 3 cans of corn for $.50 or $.17 each?

(*c*) 1 case of 24 cans of soup for $3.00 or $.14 each?

3. (*a*) At $.17 per lb., how many pounds of apples can you buy for $.85?

(*b*) At $.45 per dozen, how many dozens of oranges can you buy for $1.35?

(*c*) At 10 lb. for $.55, how many pounds of potatoes can you buy for $2.20?

4. (*a*) If 6 dozen pencils cost $2.16, what will one pencil cost?

(*b*) If 5 chairs cost $32.25, how much will 8 chairs cost?

(*c*) If a dozen oranges cost $.30, what will 14 oranges cost?

5. (*a*) A butcher charged $7.44 for a certain cut of meat at $.96 a pound. What was the weight of the meat?

(*b*) The rates of a local laundry are $1.35 for the first 12 pieces and $.09 for each additional piece. If the laundry charged $2.61, how many pieces were laundered?

(*c*) The telephone rates between 2 zones is $.25 for the first 3 minutes and $.05 for each additional minute. How long was a call for which the charges were $.55?

6. An airplane flies 858.2 miles in 2.8 hours. What is its average ground speed?

7. A student measured a 2-inch metal block by a precision instrument and made the following readings: 1.9962 inches,

2.0008 inches, 2.0012 inches, 1.9993 inches, and 2.0015 inches. Find the average reading and the amount of error.

8. The fuel consumption of a certain airplane is 32.5 gallons per hour. Find the number of hours the airplane can fly if its gas tank holds 175.5 gallons.

9. The hold of a freighter has a capacity of 50,000 cu. ft. How many bushels can it hold? (1 bu. = 1.25 cu. ft.)

10. The normal reduction in the temperature of a parcel of air is 3.6° Fahrenheit per 1,000 feet. Find the altitude where the temperature is 46° F. when the surface temperature is 64° F.

REFRESH YOUR SKILLS

1. Add: **2.** Subtract: **3.** Multiply: **4.** Divide:

216,958	8,304,060	3,600	$5,280\overline{)2,101,440}$
133,425	8,293,851	3,600	
590,643			
614,299			
271,086			
484,137			

5. Add: **6.** Subtract: **7.** Multiply: **8.** Divide:

$1\frac{2}{3}$ $15\frac{7}{12}$ $\frac{3}{4} \times 2\frac{5}{8}$ $32 \div 6\frac{2}{3}$

 $\frac{5}{6}$ 9

9. Add: **10.** Subtract: **11.** Multiply: **12.** Divide:

1.4 + .06 + .8   600 − 9.08   14.4 × .09 $.02\overline{)1}$

UNITED STATES MONEY—REVIEW

1. Add:

$.41 + $.27 $2 + $.06 $8.59 + $.94 $6.37 + $15.69

2. Subtract:

$.90 − $.71 $4.85 − $3.49 $6 − $.65 $8.42 − $.87

3. Multiply (find correct to nearest cent):

80 × $.05 $18.75 $46.92 $\frac{7}{8}$ of $6.52 $91.50

               × 27   .03 $.04\frac{1}{2}$

4. Divide:

$8\overline{)$.96}$ $16\overline{)$12}$ $.45\overline{)$10.35}$ $.09\overline{)$27}$ $1.75\overline{)$14}$

MULTIPLYING WHOLE NUMBERS AND DECIMALS BY 10, 100, 1000, ETC.

I. Aim: To multiply whole numbers and decimals by 10, 100, 1,000, etc.

II. Procedure

1. To multiply a whole number by 10, 100, 1,000, etc., annex as many zeros to the right of the given numeral as there are zeros in the given multiplier.

(*a*) If multiplied by 10, annex one zero.

(*b*) If multiplied by 100, annex two zeros.

(*c*) If multiplied by 1,000, annex three zeros, etc.

2. To multiply a decimal by 10, 100, 1,000, etc., first write the figures of the given numeral, then move the decimal point as many places to the right of its original position as there are zeros in the given multiplier.

(*a*) If multiplied by 10, move decimal point 1 place to the right.

(*b*) If multiplied by 100, move decimal point 2 places to the right.

(*c*) If multiplied by 1,000, move decimal point 3 places to the right, etc.

III. Sample Solutions

1. (*a*) $\quad 10 \times 7 = 70 \quad$ *Answer:* 70

   (*b*) $\quad 10 \times .6 = 6 \quad$ *Answer:* 6

   (*c*) $\quad 10 \times .05 = .5 \quad$ *Answer:* .5

   (*d*) $\quad 10 \times 2.741 = 27.41 \quad$ *Answer:* 27.41

2. (*a*) $\quad 100 \times 80 = 8,000 \quad$ *Answer:* 8,000

   (*b*) $\quad 100 \times .6 = 60 \quad$ *Answer:* 60

   (*c*) $\quad 100 \times .05 = 5 \quad$ *Answer:* 5

   (*d*) $\quad 100 \times 2.741 = 274.1 \quad$ *Answer:* 274.1

3. (*a*) $\quad 1,000 \times 9 = 9,000 \quad$ *Answer:* 9,000

   (*b*) $\quad 1,000 \times .6 = 600 \quad$ *Answer:* 600

   (*c*) $\quad 1,000 \times .05 = 50 \quad$ *Answer:* 50

   (*d*) $\quad 1,000 \times 2.741 = 2,741 \quad$ *Answer:* 2,741

DIAGNOSTIC TEST

In examples 1 to 6, multiply the given numbers by 10:

1. 8	**3.** .4	**5.** .06
2. 60	**4.** .78	**6.** 25.324

In examples 7 to 12, multiply the given numbers by 100:

7. 26	**9.** .83	**11.** .0987
8. 500	**10.** .5	**12.** 67.39

In examples 13 to 18, multiply the given numbers by 1,000:

13. 9	**15.** .365	**17.** .8574
14. 420	**16.** .67	**18.** 56.967

RELATED PRACTICE EXAMPLES

In sets 1 to 6, multiply the given numbers by 10:

SET 1	SET 2	SET 3	SET 4	SET 5	SET 6
1. 5	**1.** 40	**1.** .3	**1.** .26	**1.** .03	**1.** 5.8
2. 9	**2.** 80	**2.** .1	**2.** .57	**2.** .09	**2.** 34.6
3. 27	**3.** 100	**3.** .5	**3.** .924	**3.** .085	**3.** 96.34
4. 85	**4.** 150	**4.** .9	**4.** .805	**4.** .007	**4.** 49.927
5. 763	**5.** 3,000	**5.** .8	**5.** .4326	**5.** .0625	**5.** 540.653

In sets 7 to 12, multiply the given numbers by 100:

SET 7	SET 8	SET 9	SET 10	SET 11	SET 12
1. 7	**1.** 20	**1.** .42	**1.** .2	**1.** .721	**1.** 8.54
2. 51	**2.** 60	**2.** .33	**2.** .8	**2.** .039	**2.** 36.46
3. 38	**3.** 300	**3.** .19	**3.** .7	**3.** .5257	**3.** 72.03
4. 423	**4.** 590	**4.** .67	**4.** .9	**4.** .0416	**4.** 5.792
5. 9,564	**5.** 7,400	**5.** .95	**5.** .1	**5.** .8547	**5.** 25.875

In sets 13 to 18, multiply the given numbers by 1,000:

SET 13	SET 14	SET 15	SET 16	SET 17	SET 18
1. 3	**1.** 50	**1.** .657	**1.** .35	**1.** .2653	**1.** 6.582
2. 62	**2.** 90	**2.** .942	**2.** .7	**2.** .5929	**2.** 29.37
3. 597	**3.** 200	**3.** .485	**3.** .09	**3.** .0357	**3.** 81.1
4. 2,055	**4.** 780	**4.** .076	**4.** .4	**4.** .17425	**4.** 176.2563
5. 4,682	**5.** 5,000	**5.** .189	**5.** .98	**5.** .00072	**5.** 250.40575

MISCELLANEOUS EXAMPLES

Write each of the following as a numeral completely:

1. (*a*) 27 hundred   (*b*) 856 hundred   (*c*) 4.5 hundred
(*d*) 980 hundred   (*e*) 9.6 hundred   (*f*) 64 hundred

2. (*a*) 46 thousand   (*b*) 3,024 thousand   (*c*) 7.8 thousand
(*d*) 528.7 thousand   (*e*) 14.4 thousand   (*f*) 3.2 thousand

3. (*a*) 159 million   (*b*) 6.3 million   (*c*) 92.4 million
(*d*) 601.9 million   (*e*) 87.5 million   (*f*) 6.9 million

4. (*a*) 37 billion   (*b*) 4.1 billion   (*c*) 13.2 billion
(*d*) 705.6 billion   (*e*) 20.4 billion   (*f*) 5.3 billion

5. (*a*) 256 hundred cubic feet of gas were consumed.

(*b*) 43.9 thousand tons of almonds were produced.

(*c*) 8.1 million dollars were spent for a new road.

(*d*) The Internal Revenue department collected 66.3 billion dollars.

(*e*) The national income is 299.7 billion dollars.

PRACTICAL APPLICATIONS

1. To change kilowatts (kw.) to watts, multiply the number of kilowatts by 1,000.

Change to watts:

(*a*) 8 kw.   (*b*) 40 kw.   (*c*) 6.5 kw.   (*d*) 139 kw.   (*e*) 27.3 kw.

2. To change centimeters (cm.) to millimeters, multiply the number of centimeters by 10.

Change to millimeters:

(*a*) 3 cm.   (*b*) 15 cm.   (*c*) 4.2 cm.   (*d*) 87 cm.   (*e*) 18.5 cm.

3. To change meters (m.) to centimeters, multiply the number of meters by 100.

Change to centimeters:

(*a*) 5 m.   (*b*) 20 m.   (*c*) 3.7 m.   (*d*) 15.08 m.   (*e*) 9.385 m.

4. (*a*) How many dimes are in 28 dollars?

(*b*) Find the number of pennies in 17 dollars.

5. (*a*) A fuel oil consumer bought 100 gallons of heating oil at $.127 a gallon. How much did he pay for the oil?

(*b*) A poultry farmer bought 1,000 chicks at $.13 each. What did he pay for the chicks?

DIVIDING WHOLE NUMBERS AND DECIMALS BY 10, 100, 1000, ETC.

I. Aim: To divide whole numbers and decimals by 10, 100, 1,000, etc.

II. Procedure

1. First write the numeral for the given whole number or decimal.

2. Then move the decimal point as many places to the left of its original position as there are zeros in the given divisor. In a numeral naming a whole number the decimal point is understood after the units' figure.

(*a*) If divided by 10, move decimal point 1 place to the left.

(*b*) If divided by 100, move decimal point 2 places to the left.

(*c*) If divided by 1,000, move decimal point 3 places to the left, etc.

III. Sample Solutions

1. (*a*) $2,500 \div 10 = 250$ *Answer:* 250
  (*b*) $.5 \div 10 = .05$ *Answer:* .05
  (*c*) $128.4 \div 10 = 12.84$ *Answer:* 12.84
  (*d*) $67 \div 10 = 6.7$ *Answer:* 6.7

2. (*a*) $2,500 \div 100 = 25$ *Answer:* 25
  (*b*) $5 \div 100 = .05$ *Answer:* .05
  (*c*) $128.4 \div 100 = 1.284$ *Answer:* 1.284
  (*d*) $431 \div 100 = 4.31$ *Answer:* 4.31

3. (*a*) $2,500 \div 1,000 = 2.5$ *Answer:* 2.5
  (*b*) $.75 \div 1,000 = .00075$ *Answer:* .00075
  (*c*) $128.4 \div 1,000 = .1284$ *Answer:* .1284
  (*d*) $9,678 \div 1,000 = 9.678$ *Answer:* 9.678

4. (*a*) $6,400,000 \div 1,000,000 = 6.4$ *Answer:* 6.4
  (*b*) $9,200,000,000 \div 1,000,000,000 = 9.2$ *Answer:* 9.2

DIAGNOSTIC TEST

In examples 1 to 5, divide the given numbers by 10:

1. 80	**3.** 6	**5.** 15.683
2. 95	**4.** .7	

In examples 6 to 11, divide the given numbers by 100:

6. 400	**8.** 92	**10.** .34
7. 875	**9.** 8	**11.** 197.2

In examples 12 to 17, divide the given numbers by 1,000:

12. 65,000	**14.** 467	**16.** .675
13. 2,973	**15.** 72	**17.** 527.3

RELATED PRACTICE EXAMPLES

In sets 1 to 5, divide the given numbers by 10:

Set 1	Set 2	Set 3	Set 4	Set 5
1. 20	**1.** 34	**1.** 5	**1.** .2	**1.** 3.5
2. 50	**2.** 79	**2.** 3	**2.** .9	**2.** 9.82
3. 600	**3.** 276	**3.** 9	**3.** .32	**3.** 27.46
4. 300	**4.** 408	**4.** 7	**4.** .08	**4.** 39.239
5. 1,000	**5.** 5,426	**5.** 4	**5.** .936	**5.** 145.948

In sets 6 to 11, divide the given numbers by 100:

Set 6	Set 7	Set 8	Set 9	Set 10	Set 11
1. 200	**1.** 382	**1.** 59	**1.** 4	**1.** .21	**1.** 29.5
2. 700	**2.** 829	**2.** 32	**2.** 9	**2.** .60	**2.** 128.93
3. 3,000	**3.** 4,520	**3.** 67	**3.** 2	**3.** .8	**3.** 502.86
4. 5,000	**4.** 3,948	**4.** 70	**4.** 3	**4.** .045	**4.** 68.24
5. 2,700	**5.** 65,726	**5.** 85	**5.** 7	**5.** .914	**5.** 1,500.75

In sets 12 to 17, divide the given numbers by 1,000:

Set 12	Set 13	Set 14	Set 15	Set 16	Set 17
1. 8,000	**1.** 3,725	**1.** 628	**1.** 85	**1.** .925	**1.** 284.9
2. 2,000	**2.** 2,890	**2.** 314	**2.** 93	**2.** .56	**2.** 500.74
3. 10,000	**3.** 8,575	**3.** 200	**3.** 6	**3.** .3	**3.** 795.82
4. 28,000	**4.** 15,925	**4.** 476	**4.** 8	**4.** .072	**4.** 1,526.1
5. 150,000	**5.** 18,464	**5.** 957	**5.** 38	**5.** .89	**5.** 2,963.45

PRACTICAL APPLICATIONS

1. To change from watt-hours to kilowatt-hours, divide the number of watt-hours by 1,000.

Change to kilowatt-hours:

(*a*) 20,000 watt-hr.   (*b*) 135,000 watt-hr.   (*c*) 27,500 watt-hr.

2. A bag of sugar, weighing 100 pounds, costs $9.30. What is the cost per pound?

3. Taxes

(*a*) If the tax rate is $2.80 per hundred dollars, how much must you pay for taxes on a house assessed for $8,900?

(*b*) Find the amount of taxes on properties having the following assessed valuations and tax rates:

Assessed valuation	$3,400	$7,500	$11,800	$15,000	$10,200
Tax rate per $100	$1.70	$2.45	$3.60	$3.25	$1.84

(*c*) A house is assessed for $6,300 and the tax rate is $2.40 per $100. Which plan will give a greater reduction in taxes, reducing the assessment to $5,700 or reducing the rate to $2.15 per $100? How much greater?

4. Life Insurance

(*a*) What annual premium should a man pay on a $5,000 policy when the rate is $29.18 per $1,000?

(*b*) Find the annual premium on the following amounts of life insurance at the given annual rates per $1,000:

Face of Policy	$3,000	$2,000	$10,000	$5,000	$12,000
Rate per $1,000	$43.95	$18.40	$33.07	$47.72	$52.81

5. Fire Insurance

(*a*) Mr. Daniels wishes to insure his house for $7,000. The rate charged by a fire insurance company is $.24 per $100. What is the annual premium?

(*b*) Find the annual premium on the following amounts of fire insurance at the given annual rates per $100:

Face of Policy	$4,000	$5,000	$3,500	$7,500	$12,800
Rate per $100	$.18	$.75	$.46	$.29	$1.05

6. Interest—6% (or 60-day) Method

To find the interest on a sum of money borrowed or invested (principal) for 60 days at 6%, divide the principal by 100.

(*a*) Find the interest for 60 days at 6% on the following given principals: (1) $2,000   (2) $580   (3) $45   (4) $1,325   (5) $769

(*b*) Find the interest on:

(1) $1,000 for 30 days at 6%   (2) $500 for 30 days at 3%
(3) $1,200 for 15 days at 6%   (4) $4,000 for 90 days at 6%

7. Sometimes a number like 4,500,000 is shortened and expressed as 4.5 million by dividing by 1,000,000.*

Express each of the following numbers in shortened form:

(*a*) In hundreds: (1) 900   (2) 560   (3) 3,480
(*b*) In thousands: (1) 2,000   (2) 7,300   (3) 281,500
(*c*) In millions: (1) 7,000,000   (2) 3,200,000   (3) 196,900,000
(*d*) In billions: (1) 5,000,000,000   (2) 9,400,000,000
                                              (3) 72,100,000,000

REFRESH YOUR SKILLS

1. Add: **2.** Subtract: **3.** Multiply: **4.** Divide:

820,142   4,258,003   8,039   962)7,704,658
963,819   3,167,905   9,670
610,387
241,299
872,175

5. Add: **6.** Subtract: **7.** Multiply: **8.** Divide:

$4\frac{11}{12}$ 20 $1\frac{7}{8} \times 3\frac{3}{4}$ $9\frac{1}{7} \div 4\frac{4}{5}$

$3\frac{4}{5}$ $6\frac{7}{10}$

9. Add: **10.** Subtract: **11.** Multiply: **12.** Divide:

$.638 + 2.47 + 92.5$ $4.68 - \$3$ $500 \times .002$ $\$.08)\overline{\$40}$

---

*See page 196.

EXERCISE 30

CHANGING COMMON FRACTIONS TO DECIMALS
(See page 218)

I. Aim: To change a common fraction or mixed number to a decimal.

II. Procedure

1. To change a common fraction to a decimal (3 methods):
   (a) Divide the numerator by the denominator. (See sample solutions 1 and 4.)
   (b) Or, if the decimal equivalent is known, write the decimal numeral directly. Sometimes it may be necessary first to reduce the given fraction to lowest terms.
   (c) Or, if the given fraction has as its denominator 10, 100, 1,000, etc., drop the denominator and rewrite the numerator, placing a decimal point in the proper location. (See sample solutions 2 and 3.)

2. To change a mixed number to a mixed decimal:
   Change the fraction to a decimal and annex it to the numeral for the whole number. (See sample solution 6.)

III. Sample Solutions

1. Change $\frac{2}{5}$ to a decimal.

$$\frac{2}{5} = \frac{.4}{5)\overline{2.0}}$$

Answer: .4

2. Change $\frac{19}{100}$ to a decimal.

$$\frac{19}{100} = .19$$

Answer: .19

3. Change $\frac{165}{100}$ to a decimal.

$$\frac{165}{100} = 1.65$$

Answer: 1.65

4. Change $\frac{6}{14}$ to a decimal (2 places).

$$\frac{6}{14} = \frac{3}{7} = \frac{.42\frac{6}{7}}{7)\overline{3.00}}$$

Answer: $.42\frac{6}{7}$

5. Change $\frac{5}{4}$ to a decimal.

$$\frac{5}{4} = \frac{1.25}{4)\overline{5.00}}$$

Answer: 1.25

6. Change $1\frac{7}{8}$ to a decimal.

$$\frac{7}{8} = .87\frac{1}{2} \text{ or } .875$$
$$1\frac{7}{8} = 1.87\frac{1}{2} \text{ or } 1.875$$

Answer: $1.87\frac{1}{2}$ or 1.875

DIAGNOSTIC TEST

Express the following common fractions or mixed numbers as decimals (carry out examples 3, 4, and 6 through 16 to 2 decimal places):

1. $\frac{9}{10}$ 4. $\frac{1}{4}$ 7. $\frac{125}{100}$ 10. $\frac{20}{25}$ 13. $1\frac{3}{4}$ 16. $2\frac{7}{16}$

2. $\frac{1}{2}$ 5. $\frac{7}{8}$ 8. $\frac{37\frac{1}{2}}{100}$ 11. $\frac{49}{56}$ 14. $\frac{12}{8}$ 17. $\frac{893}{1000}$

3. $\frac{27}{100}$ 6. $\frac{5}{6}$ 9. $\frac{8}{9}$ 12. $\frac{24}{28}$ 15. $\frac{18}{14}$ 18. $\frac{7429}{10000}$

RELATED PRACTICE EXAMPLES

Express the following common fractions or mixed numbers as decimals (carry out sets 3, 4, and 6 through 16 to 2 decimal places):

SET 1	SET 2	SET 3	SET 4	SET 5	SET 6
1. $\frac{1}{10}$	1. $\frac{4}{5}$	1. $\frac{39}{100}$	1. $\frac{3}{4}$	1. $\frac{3}{8}$	1. $\frac{1}{3}$
2. $\frac{7}{10}$	2. $\frac{1}{5}$	2. $\frac{54}{100}$	2. $\frac{17}{20}$	2. $\frac{5}{8}$	2. $\frac{1}{6}$
3. $\frac{2}{10}$	3. $\frac{1}{2}$	3. $\frac{3}{100}$	3. $\frac{14}{25}$	3. $\frac{1}{8}$	3. $\frac{2}{3}$
4. $\frac{8}{10}$	4. $\frac{2}{5}$	4. $\frac{6}{100}$	4. $\frac{41}{50}$	4. $\frac{9}{16}$	4. $\frac{1}{12}$
5. $\frac{6}{10}$	5. $\frac{3}{5}$	5. $\frac{91}{100}$	5. $\frac{9}{20}$	5. $\frac{1}{16}$	5. $\frac{5}{12}$

SET 7	SET 8	SET 9	SET 10	SET 11	SET 12
1. $\frac{115}{100}$	1. $\frac{33\frac{1}{3}}{100}$	1. $\frac{4}{7}$	1. $\frac{18}{36}$	1. $\frac{15}{40}$	1. $\frac{42}{54}$
2. $\frac{175}{100}$	2. $\frac{62\frac{1}{2}}{100}$	2. $\frac{3}{11}$	2. $\frac{21}{28}$	2. $\frac{45}{54}$	2. $\frac{27}{63}$
3. $\frac{183}{100}$	3. $\frac{16\frac{2}{3}}{100}$	3. $\frac{7}{9}$	3. $\frac{30}{75}$	3. $\frac{34}{51}$	3. $\frac{30}{66}$
4. $\frac{150}{100}$	4. $\frac{5\frac{3}{4}}{100}$	4. $\frac{13}{15}$	4. $\frac{56}{80}$	4. $\frac{84}{96}$	4. $\frac{28}{105}$
5. $\frac{234}{100}$	5. $\frac{87\frac{1}{2}}{100}$	5. $\frac{9}{13}$	5. $\frac{54}{90}$	5. $\frac{80}{128}$	5. $\frac{24}{108}$

SET 13	SET 14	SET 15	SET 16	SET 17	SET 18
1. $1\frac{1}{2}$	1. $\frac{8}{5}$	1. $\frac{14}{9}$	1. $2\frac{3}{8}$	1. $\frac{571}{1000}$	1. $\frac{9514}{10000}$
2. $1\frac{5}{8}$	2. $\frac{14}{8}$	2. $\frac{10}{7}$	2. $3\frac{11}{12}$	2. $\frac{386}{1000}$	2. $\frac{2781}{10000}$
3. $1\frac{3}{7}$	3. $\frac{12}{9}$	3. $\frac{76}{60}$	3. $\frac{96}{36}$	3. $\frac{49}{1000}$	3. $\frac{457}{10000}$
4. $1\frac{2}{5}$	4. $\frac{57}{48}$	4. $\frac{65}{35}$	4. $\frac{66}{21}$	4. $\frac{8}{1000}$	4. $\frac{26}{10000}$
5. $1\frac{7}{16}$	5. $\frac{52}{32}$	5. $\frac{50}{45}$	5. $2\frac{5}{6}$	5. $\frac{647}{1000}$	5. $\frac{5933}{10000}$

Express each of the following measurements as a decimal. Use as many decimal places as you need to make the dividend exactly divisible.

1. (a) $\frac{3}{8}$ inch (b) $\frac{1}{8}$ inch (c) $\frac{3}{4}$ inch (d) $\frac{5}{8}$ inch (e) $\frac{7}{8}$ inch

2. (a) $\frac{5}{16}$ inch (b) $\frac{7}{16}$ inch (c) $\frac{11}{16}$ inch (d) $\frac{3}{16}$ inch (e) $\frac{15}{16}$ inch

3. (a) $\frac{7}{32}$ inch (b) $\frac{25}{32}$ inch (c) $\frac{9}{32}$ inch (d) $\frac{19}{32}$ inch (e) $\frac{13}{32}$ inch

4. (a) $\frac{1}{64}$ inch (b) $\frac{43}{64}$ inch (c) $\frac{17}{64}$ inch (d) $\frac{35}{64}$ inch (e) $\frac{29}{64}$ inch

5. (a) $1\frac{17}{32}$ inches (b) $5\frac{9}{16}$ inches (c) $2\frac{23}{64}$ inches (d) $8\frac{1}{16}$ inches (e) $3\frac{27}{32}$ inches

PRACTICAL APPLICATIONS

1. Which is larger: (a) $\frac{5}{8}$ inch or .619 inch? (b) .5347 inch or $\frac{17}{32}$ inch?

2. Which is smaller: (a) .742 inch or $\frac{3}{4}$ inch? (b) .8129 inch or $\frac{13}{16}$ inch?

3. To find the batting average, first find what fractional part of the times at bat each player hit safely, then change the fraction to a decimal correct to three places:

	At Bat	Hits	Avg.
Paul	32	12	
George	27	9	
Tom	41	13	

4. To find the team standing average, first find what fractional part of the games played is the games won, then change the fraction to a decimal correct to three places:

	Won	Lost	Avg.
Blues	8	4	
Yellows	7	5	
Browns	3	9	

5. To find the fielding average, first find what fractional part of the total chances (the sum of the put-outs, assists, and errors) are the chances properly handled (the sum of the put-outs and assists). Then change the fraction to a decimal correct to three places:

	Put-Outs	Assists	Errors	Avg.
Dave	32	37	6	
Ted	40	15	5	
Jim	14	49	7	
Frank	17	31	8	
Bill	29	27	10	

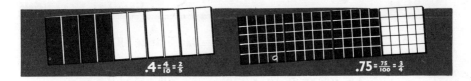

$.4 = \frac{4}{10} = \frac{2}{5}$ $.75 = \frac{75}{100} = \frac{3}{4}$

EXERCISE 31

CHANGING DECIMALS TO COMMON FRACTIONS
(See page 218)

I. Aim: To change a decimal to a common fraction or a mixed number.

II. Procedure

1. To change a decimal to a common fraction (2 methods):
   - (*a*) Write a fraction, using the figures of the decimal numeral as the numerator and a power of ten (10, 100, 1,000, etc.) corresponding to the place value of the last figure of the decimal numeral as the denominator. Then simplify and reduce to lowest terms. (See sample solutions 1, 2, 3, 4, and 6.)
   - (*b*) Or, if the common fraction equivalent is known, write the common fraction directly.
2. To change a mixed decimal to a mixed number:
   - (*a*) Change the decimal fraction to a common fraction. Reduce to lowest terms.
   - (*b*) Annex this answer to the numeral for the whole number. (See sample solution 5.)

III. Sample Solutions

1. Change .05 to a common fraction.

$$.05 = \frac{5}{100} = \frac{1}{20}$$
Answer: $\frac{1}{20}$

2. Change $.33\frac{1}{3}$ to a common fraction.

$$.33\frac{1}{3} = \frac{33\frac{1}{3}}{100} = \frac{100}{300} = \frac{1}{3}$$
Answer: $\frac{1}{3}$

3. Change .625 to a common fraction.

$$.625 = \frac{625}{1000} = \frac{5}{8}$$
Answer: $\frac{5}{8}$

4. Change $.12\frac{1}{2}$ to a common fraction.

$$.12\frac{1}{2} = \frac{12\frac{1}{2}}{100} = 12\frac{1}{2} \div 100$$
$$= \frac{\overset{1}{\cancel{25}}}{2} \times \frac{1}{\underset{4}{\cancel{100}}} = \frac{1}{8}$$
Answer: $\frac{1}{8}$

5. Change 5.875 to a mixed number.

$$5.875 = 5\tfrac{875}{1000} = 5\tfrac{7}{8}$$

Answer: $5\tfrac{7}{8}$

6. Change .0045 to a common fraction.

$$.0045 = \tfrac{45}{10000} = \tfrac{9}{2000}$$

Answer: $\tfrac{9}{2000}$

DIAGNOSTIC TEST

Express the following decimals as common fractions or mixed numbers:

1. .3	**5.** .66⅔	**9.** .672	**13.** .0075
2. .25	**6.** 1.9	**10.** .028	**14.** 7.8125
3. .04	**7.** 2.85	**11.** 3.125	
4. .60	**8.** 1.37½	**12.** .4375	

RELATED PRACTICE EXAMPLES

Express the following decimals as common fractions or mixed numbers:

SET 1	SET 2	SET 3	SET 4	SET 5
1. .6	**1.** .75	**1.** .02	**1.** .40	**1.** $16\tfrac{2}{3}$
2. .2	**2.** .45	**2.** .07	**2.** .70	**2.** $87\tfrac{1}{2}$
3. .5	**3.** .52	**3.** .01	**3.** .90	**3.** $06\tfrac{1}{4}$
4. .1	**4.** .87	**4.** .08	**4.** .10	**4.** $83\tfrac{1}{3}$
5. .9	**5.** .32	**5.** .06	**5.** .80	**5.** $62\tfrac{1}{2}$

SET 6	SET 7	SET 8	SET 9	SET 10
1. 1.2	**1.** 1.25	**1.** $1.33\tfrac{1}{3}$	**1.** .125	**1.** .036
2. 1.5	**2.** 2.42	**2.** $1.12\tfrac{1}{2}$	**2.** .875	**2.** .085
3. 2.8	**3.** 2.67	**3.** $2.66\tfrac{2}{3}$	**3.** .946	**3.** .004
4. 3.4	**4.** 1.32	**4.** $4.08\tfrac{1}{3}$	**4.** .384	**4.** .006
5. 1.7	**5.** 3.84	**5.** $3.87\tfrac{1}{2}$	**5.** .192	**5.** .048

SET 11	SET 12	SET 13	SET 14
1. 1.375	**1.** .3125	**1.** .0025	**1.** 1.4132
2. 1.248	**2.** .5625	**2.** .0054	**2.** 2.0625
3. 2.964	**3.** .0475	**3.** .0068	**3.** 5.0084
4. 3.755	**4.** .9375	**4.** .0015	**4.** 3.5625
5. 1.045	**5.** .15625	**5.** .00075	**5.** 6.6875

TABLE OF EQUIVALENTS
PER CENTS, DECIMALS, AND COMMON FRACTIONS

PER CENT	DECIMAL	COMMON FRACTION
5%	.05	$\frac{1}{20}$
$6\frac{1}{4}\%$	$.06\frac{1}{4}$	$\frac{1}{16}$
$8\frac{1}{3}\%$	$.08\frac{1}{3}$	$\frac{1}{12}$
10%	.10 or .1	$\frac{1}{10}$
$12\frac{1}{2}\%$	$.12\frac{1}{2}$ or .125	$\frac{1}{8}$
$16\frac{2}{3}\%$	$.16\frac{2}{3}$	$\frac{1}{6}$
20%	.20 or .2	$\frac{1}{5}$
25%	.25	$\frac{1}{4}$
30%	.30 or .3	$\frac{3}{10}$
$33\frac{1}{3}\%$	$.33\frac{1}{3}$	$\frac{1}{3}$
$37\frac{1}{2}\%$	$.37\frac{1}{2}$ or .375	$\frac{3}{8}$
40%	.40 or .4	$\frac{2}{5}$
50%	.50 or .5	$\frac{1}{2}$
60%	.60 or .6	$\frac{3}{5}$
$62\frac{1}{2}\%$	$.62\frac{1}{2}$ or .625	$\frac{5}{8}$
$66\frac{2}{3}\%$	$.66\frac{2}{3}$	$\frac{2}{3}$
70%	.70 or .7	$\frac{7}{10}$
75%	.75	$\frac{3}{4}$
80%	.80 or .8	$\frac{4}{5}$
$83\frac{1}{3}\%$	$.83\frac{1}{3}$	$\frac{5}{6}$
$87\frac{1}{2}\%$	$.87\frac{1}{2}$ or .875	$\frac{7}{8}$
90%	.90 or .9	$\frac{9}{10}$
100%	1.00 or 1	

EXERCISE 32

COMMON FRACTIONS AND DECIMALS

I. Aim: To add, subtract, multiply, and divide mixed groups of common fractions and decimals.

II. Procedure

1. When required to use decimals, change the given common fractions to decimal equivalents, then perform the necessary operation. (See sample solutions 1 and 2.)

2. When required to use common fractions, change the given decimals to common fraction equivalents, then perform the necessary operation. (See sample solutions 3 and 4.)

III. Sample Solutions

In examples 1 and 2, change common fractions to their decimal equivalents; in examples 3 and 4, change decimals to their common fraction equivalents, then do as directed:

1. $.62\frac{1}{2} - \frac{1}{2}$ **2.** $\frac{1}{4} \div .5$ **3.** $.12\frac{1}{2} + \frac{3}{8}$ **4.** Find $.33\frac{1}{3}$ of 42

Solution:

$.62\frac{1}{2} = .625$
$-\frac{1}{2} = .5$
$\overline{\hphantom{-\frac{1}{2}=}.125}$

Answer: .125

Solution:

$\frac{1}{4} \div .5$
$= .25 \div .5$

$.5$
$.5_\wedge\overline{)\,.2_\wedge5}$

Answer: .5

Solution:

$.12\frac{1}{2} = \frac{1}{8}$
$+\frac{3}{8} = \frac{3}{8}$
$\overline{\hphantom{+\frac{3}{8}=}\frac{4}{8}} = \frac{1}{2}$

Answer: $\frac{1}{2}$

Solution:

$.33\frac{1}{3} \times 42$

$= \frac{1}{3} \times \overset{14}{\cancel{42}} = 14$

Answer: 14

DIAGNOSTIC TEST A

Change common fractions to their decimal equivalents, then do as directed:

1. Add $\frac{3}{8}$ and .24   **3.** Find $\frac{3}{5}$ of .51

2. $.66\frac{2}{3} - \frac{1}{4}$ **4.** $.87\frac{1}{2} \div \frac{1}{8}$

RELATED PRACTICE EXAMPLES

Change common fractions to their decimal equivalents, then do as directed:

Set 1

1. Add .38 and $\frac{4}{5}$
2. $\frac{1}{4} + .62\frac{1}{2}$
3. Add $\frac{5}{8}$ and .97
4. Find the sum of .83$\frac{1}{3}$ and $\frac{2}{3}$
5. .42 $+ \frac{1}{2}$

Set 2

1. $.48 - \frac{2}{5}$
2. From $\frac{7}{8}$ take .15
3. Subtract $\frac{1}{3}$ from .66$\frac{2}{3}$
4. $\frac{5}{6} - .6$
5. From .25 subtract $\frac{1}{4}$

Set 3

1. Find $\frac{7}{8}$ of .43
2. $\frac{4}{5} \times .14\frac{1}{2}$
3. Multiply $\frac{3}{10}$ by .19
4. Find the product of $\frac{2}{5}$ and .06
5. $\frac{3}{4} \times .08\frac{1}{3}$

Set 4

1. $.75 \div \frac{3}{8}$
2. $\frac{3}{5} \div .12$
3. Divide .37$\frac{1}{2}$ by $\frac{1}{2}$
4. Find the quotient of $\frac{3}{4}$ divided by .15
5. $.2 \div \frac{1}{5}$

DIAGNOSTIC TEST B

Change decimals to their common fraction equivalents, then do as directed:

1. $.83\frac{1}{3} + \frac{2}{3}$
2. Subtract $\frac{5}{8}$ from .75
3. Find .62$\frac{1}{2}$ of 800
4. Divide 24 by .33$\frac{1}{3}$

RELATED PRACTICE EXAMPLES

Change decimals to their common fraction equivalents, then do as directed:

Set 1

1. $.37\frac{1}{2} + \frac{1}{2}$
2. Add .5 and $\frac{3}{4}$
3. $\frac{1}{4} + .87\frac{1}{2}$
4. Find the sum of .33$\frac{1}{3}$ and $\frac{5}{6}$
5. $\frac{2}{5} + .75$

Set 2

1. $.7 - \frac{3}{5}$
2. From $\frac{2}{3}$ subtract .33$\frac{1}{3}$
3. Take $\frac{3}{8}$ from .62$\frac{1}{2}$
4. $.87\frac{1}{2} - \frac{1}{2}$
5. Subtract .1 from $\frac{1}{4}$

SET 3(a)

1. $.75 \times \frac{4}{5}$

2. $.66\frac{2}{3} \times \frac{5}{6}$

3. Multiply $.16\frac{2}{3}$ by 54

4. Find the product of $.37\frac{1}{2}$ and 72

5. Find the product of $.33\frac{1}{3}$ and 900

SET 3(b)

1. Find $.12\frac{1}{2}$ of 16

2. Find $.83\frac{1}{3}$ of 300

3. Find $.33\frac{1}{3}$ of 396

4. Find $.62\frac{1}{2}$ of 472

5. Find $.06\frac{1}{4}$ of 512

SET 4(a)

1. $\frac{1}{3} \div .16\frac{2}{3}$

2. $.25 \div \frac{1}{8}$

3. Divide $.5$ by $\frac{2}{5}$

4. Find the quotient of $.75$ divided by $\frac{3}{10}$

5. Divide $.83\frac{1}{3}$ by $\frac{1}{12}$

SET 4(b)

1. Divide 200 by $.62\frac{1}{2}$

2. Divide 150 by $.66\frac{2}{3}$

3. Divide 12 by $.16\frac{2}{3}$

4. Divide 1,000 by $.33\frac{1}{3}$

5. Divide 287 by $.87\frac{1}{2}$

MISCELLANEOUS EXAMPLES

1. Change mixed number to a mixed decimal, then do as directed:

(a) $7\frac{1}{2} \times 9\frac{1}{2}$ $4\frac{3}{4} \times 5\frac{1}{4}$ $3\frac{1}{4} \times 7\frac{7}{8}$ $4\frac{1}{8} \times 3\frac{5}{8}$ $6\frac{3}{8} \times 9\frac{4}{5}$

(b) $5\frac{1}{4} \div 2\frac{5}{8}$ $4\frac{1}{5} \div 7\frac{1}{2}$ $5 \div .2\frac{1}{2}$ $11.4 \div .3\frac{4}{5}$ $9 \div .04\frac{1}{2}$

2. Divide as indicated:

$$40 \div .2\frac{2}{3} \qquad 4.8\frac{1}{2} \div .8\frac{1}{12} \qquad 13 \div .04\frac{1}{3}$$

$$1.54 \div .12\frac{5}{6} \qquad 10.25 \div .34\frac{1}{6}$$

PRACTICAL APPLICATIONS

Find the cost of:

1. $2\frac{3}{4}$ lb. of steak at \$1.25 per lb.

2. $7\frac{5}{8}$ lb. of turkey at \$.67 per lb.

3. $3\frac{1}{4}$ lb. of bananas at \$.12$\frac{1}{2}$ per lb.

4. $7\frac{1}{2}$ lb. of onions at \$.08$\frac{1}{3}$ per lb.

5. $11\frac{3}{4}$ lb. of potatoes at \$.06$\frac{1}{4}$ per lb.

6. 128 sq. ft. of cedar lining at \$.16$\frac{2}{3}$ per sq. ft.

7. $137\frac{1}{2}$ board feet of lumber at \$.09$\frac{3}{4}$ per bd.-ft.

8. $362\frac{1}{2}$ sq. ft. of ceiling tile at \$.10$\frac{1}{2}$ per sq. ft.

SHORT METHODS IN MULTIPLICATION AND DIVISION

I. Aim: To multiply and divide, using special methods.

II. Procedure

1. To multiply a number by
    (a) 50, multiply it by 100, then divide by 2.
    (b) 25, multiply it by 100, then divide by 4.
    (c) 20, multiply it by 100, then divide by 5.
    (d) $33\frac{1}{3}$, multiply it by 100, then divide by 3.
    (e) $12\frac{1}{2}$, multiply it by 100, then divide by 8.
    (f) $16\frac{2}{3}$, multiply it by 100, then divide by 6.
    (g) $8\frac{1}{3}$, multiply it by 100, then divide by 12.
    (h) $6\frac{1}{4}$, multiply it by 100, then divide by 16.

2. To divide a number by
    (a) 50, multiply it by 2, then divide by 100.
    (b) 25, multiply it by 4, then divide by 100.
    (c) 20, multiply it by 5, then divide by 100.
    (d) $33\frac{1}{3}$, multiply it by 3, then divide by 100.
    (e) $12\frac{1}{2}$, multiply it by 8, then divide by 100.
    (f) $16\frac{2}{3}$, multiply it by 6, then divide by 100.
    (g) $8\frac{1}{3}$, multiply it by 12, then divide by 100.
    (h) $6\frac{1}{4}$, multiply it by 16, then divide by 100.

III. Sample Solutions

1. Multiply 68 by 50.
    (a) $68 \times 100 = 6,800$
    (b) $2\overline{)6,800}$ ... 3,400
    Answer: 3,400

2. Multiply 79 by 25.
    (a) $79 \times 100 = 7,900$
    (b) $4\overline{)7,900}$ ... 1,975
    Answer: 1,975

3. Multiply 18 by $16\frac{2}{3}$.
    (a) $18 \times 100 = 1,800$
    (b) $6\overline{)1,800}$ ... 300   *Answer:* 300

4. Divide 345 by 50.

  (*a*) $345 \times 2 = 690$

  (*b*) $690 \div 100 = 6.9$

  Answer: 6.9

5. Divide 1,375 by 25.

  (*a*) $1,375 \times 4 = 5,500$

  (*b*) $5,500 \div 100 = 55$

  Answer: 55

6. Divide 224 by $12\frac{1}{2}$.

  (*a*) $224 \times 8 = 1,792$

  (*b*) $1,792 \div 100 = 17.92$

  Answer: 17.92

DIAGNOSTIC TEST A

Multiply, using short methods:

1. 50×62	**4.** $33\frac{1}{3} \times 63$	**7.** $8\frac{1}{3} \times 156$
2. 43×25	**5.** $104 \times 12\frac{1}{2}$	**8.** $128 \times 6\frac{1}{4}$
3. 20×56	**6.** $16\frac{2}{3} \times 84$	

RELATED PRACTICE EXAMPLES

Multiply, using short methods:

SET 1(*a*)	SET 1(*b*)	SET 2(*a*)	SET 2(*b*)
1. 50×36	**1.** 24×50	**1.** 25×28	**1.** 32×25
2. 50×94	**2.** 72×50	**2.** 25×52	**2.** 96×25
3. 50×27	**3.** 49×50	**3.** 25×35	**3.** 19×25
4. 50×65	**4.** 63×50	**4.** 25×89	**4.** 51×25
5. 50×128	**5.** 144×50	**5.** 25×112	**5.** 164×25

SET 3	SET 4	SET 5	SET 6
1. 20×34	**1.** $33\frac{1}{3} \times 21$	**1.** $12\frac{1}{2} \times 48$	**1.** $16\frac{2}{3} \times 54$
2. 20×43	**2.** $33\frac{1}{3} \times 87$	**2.** $12\frac{1}{2} \times 64$	**2.** $16\frac{2}{3} \times 78$
3. 20×71	**3.** $33\frac{1}{3} \times 189$	**3.** $12\frac{1}{2} \times 136$	**3.** $16\frac{2}{3} \times 240$
4. 85×20	**4.** $75 \times 33\frac{1}{3}$	**4.** $96 \times 12\frac{1}{2}$	**4.** $90 \times 16\frac{2}{3}$
5. 124×20	**5.** $153 \times 33\frac{1}{3}$	**5.** $216 \times 12\frac{1}{2}$	**5.** $138 \times 16\frac{2}{3}$

SET 7	SET 8
1. $8\frac{1}{3} \times 60$	**1.** $6\frac{1}{4} \times 64$
2. $8\frac{1}{3} \times 96$	**2.** $6\frac{1}{4} \times 32$
3. $8\frac{1}{3} \times 360$	**3.** $6\frac{1}{4} \times 160$
4. $24 \times 8\frac{1}{3}$	**4.** $80 \times 6\frac{1}{4}$
5. $168 \times 8\frac{1}{3}$	**5.** $288 \times 6\frac{1}{4}$

DIAGNOSTIC TEST B

Divide, using short methods:

1. $340 \div 50$ 4. $165 \div 33\frac{1}{3}$ 7. $500 \div 8\frac{1}{3}$
2. $575 \div 25$ 5. $200 \div 12\frac{1}{2}$ 8. $225 \div 6\frac{1}{4}$
3. $638 \div 20$ 6. $727 \div 16\frac{2}{3}$

RELATED PRACTICE EXAMPLES

Divide, using short methods:

SET 1(a)	SET 1(b)	SET 2(a)	SET 2(b)
1. $650 \div 50$	1. $160 \div 50$	1. $450 \div 25$	1. $90 \div 25$
2. $950 \div 50$	2. $220 \div 50$	2. $375 \div 25$	2. $430 \div 25$
3. $1,400 \div 50$	3. $547 \div 50$	3. $1,000 \div 25$	3. $246 \div 25$
4. $2,150 \div 50$	4. $1,235 \div 50$	4. $1,525 \div 25$	4. $854 \div 25$
5. $3,950 \div 50$	5. $2,368 \div 50$	5. $2,450 \div 25$	5. $1,795 \div 25$

SET 3	SET 4	SET 5
1. $460 \div 20$	1. $200 \div 33\frac{1}{3}$	1. $500 \div 12\frac{1}{2}$
2. $150 \div 20$	2. $140 \div 33\frac{1}{3}$	2. $320 \div 12\frac{1}{2}$
3. $790 \div 20$	3. $625 \div 33\frac{1}{3}$	3. $184 \div 12\frac{1}{2}$
4. $228 \div 20$	4. $416 \div 33\frac{1}{3}$	4. $658 \div 12\frac{1}{2}$
5. $346 \div 20$	5. $5,200 \div 33\frac{1}{3}$	5. $1,400 \div 12\frac{1}{2}$

SET 6	SET 7	SET 8
1. $300 \div 16\frac{2}{3}$	1. $600 \div 8\frac{1}{3}$	1. $800 \div 6\frac{1}{4}$
2. $168 \div 16\frac{2}{3}$	2. $200 \div 8\frac{1}{3}$	2. $500 \div 6\frac{1}{4}$
3. $450 \div 16\frac{2}{3}$	3. $940 \div 8\frac{1}{3}$	3. $325 \div 6\frac{1}{4}$
4. $821 \div 16\frac{2}{3}$	4. $375 \div 8\frac{1}{3}$	4. $2,156 \div 6\frac{1}{4}$
5. $1,200 \div 16\frac{2}{3}$	5. $2,400 \div 8\frac{1}{3}$	5. $4,800 \div 6\frac{1}{4}$

PRACTICAL APPLICATIONS

Find the cost of each of the following:

(a) 24 tomato plants at $8\frac{1}{3}$¢ per plant.

(b) 1 sq. ft. of roofing shingles if a bundle of $33\frac{1}{3}$ sq. ft. costs \$2.

(c) 1 lb. of turkey if $12\frac{1}{2}$ lb. cost \$8.

REVIEW OF UNIT III

1. Write each of the following as a decimal numeral:

(a) Nine hundredths (b) Five hundred and forty-three thousandths (c) Eight and five tenths (d) Eleven millionths (e) Seven thousand eight hundred twenty-two ten-thousandths.

2. Write each of the following numerals as a word statement:

(a) .7 (b) .006 (c) 4.09 (d) .80501 (e) 62.5483

3. Round off: (a) .96 correct to nearest tenth (b) 8.2915 correct to nearest hundredth (c) 25.1427 correct to nearest thousandth (d) $4.279 correct to nearest cent (e) $70.16⅖ correct to nearest cent.

4. Add:

(a) 8.2 (b) 8.05 (c) 8.2 + .19 + 24
   5.9   2.03 (d) Find the sum of: 49.2, .871, and 6.45
   4.5   5.04 (e) $6.21 + $58.14 + $.68 + $9.85 + $180.07
         1.08

5. Subtract:

(a) 47.512 (b) .489 − .3 (c) .8 − .375 (d) 10 − .04
   39.835

(e) Subtract $3.25 from $28.

6. Which is larger: (a) .8 or .62? (b) 1.06 or .305?
Which is smaller: (c) .425 or .94? (d) 2.9 or .49?
(e) Arrange in order of size, largest first:

$$1.67, .0167, 0.167, 16.7$$

7. Multiply:

(a) .04 (b) 90.72 (c) .018 × .05
   .2   .125

Find correct to nearest cent:

(d) ¾ of $5.26 (e) $28.93
                     .83⅓

8. Divide:

(a) 78)‾.624 (b) 1.2)‾11.076 (c) 35 ÷ .875 (d) $.04)‾$2

(e) Find correct to nearest tenth: 39.37)‾582

9. Multiply by short method:

(a) 100×90 (c) $1,000 \times .4$ (e) $1,000 \times 28.95$

(b) 10×3.56 (d) $100 \times .08$

10. Divide by short method:

(a) $500 \div 10$ (c) $.7 \div 100$ (e) $654 \div 100$

(b) $240 \div 1,000$ (d) $93.2 \div 1,000$

11. Change each of the following fractions to decimals:

(a) $\frac{3}{5}$ (b) $\frac{83}{100}$ (c) $\frac{17}{25}$ (d) To 3 decimal places: $\frac{49}{56}$

       (e) To 4 decimal places: $\frac{13}{16}$

12. Change each of the following decimals to fractions or mixed numbers:

(a) $.4$ (b) $.25$ (c) $.375$ (d) 9.0625 (e) $.66\frac{2}{3}$

13. Do as directed:

(a) $\frac{4}{5} + .75$ (c) $\frac{7}{10} \times .43$ (e) Find $.12\frac{1}{2}$ of 32

(b) $.66\frac{2}{3} - \frac{1}{3}$ (d) $60 \div .83\frac{1}{3}$

14. Do as directed, using short methods:

     (a) 25×36 (c) $700 \div 50$ (e) $42 \times 16\frac{2}{3}$

     (b) $33\frac{1}{3} \times 60$ (d) $150 \div 12\frac{1}{2}$

15. Find the cost of 235 gallons of fuel oil at $.127 a gallon.

16. A basketball player scored 871 points in 56 games. Find the number of points he averaged per game to the nearest tenth of a point.

17. The best batter in the American League had a batting average of .349. The leading batter in the National League had an average of .355. Who had the higher average and how much higher?

18. The distance by train from St. Louis to Indianapolis is 240 miles, from Indianapolis to Dayton is 109.7 miles, from Dayton to Columbus is 70.7 miles, and from Columbus to Pittsburgh is 109.9 miles. What is the distance by train from St. Louis to Pittsburgh by this route?

19. If the tax rate is $2.95 per $100, how much must you pay for taxes on a house assessed for $9,800?

20. A merchant bought 150 pounds of pears for $19.50. He sold 67 pounds at $.23 a pound, 48 pounds at $.19 a pound, and 29 pounds at $.16 a pound. The rest spoiled. How much profit did he make?

CUMULATIVE PRACTICE

1. Add: 2,958
         47,426
          8,019
            846
        25,625

2. Subtract: 1,600,520
        549,618

3. Multiply: 9,658
        8,692

4. Divide: $456\overline{)176,472}$

5. Add: $8\frac{3}{4}$
     $5\frac{1}{2}$
     $2\frac{11}{16}$

6. Subtract: $4\frac{1}{5}$
        $3\frac{2}{3}$

7. Multiply: 98
        $7\frac{3}{4}$

8. Divide: $6\frac{7}{8} \div 3\frac{1}{7}$

9. Add:
  $8.3 + .75 + 14$

10. Subtract:
  $\$92 - \$3.85$

11. Multiply:
  $2.5 \times .04$

12. Divide:
  $.02\overline{).001}$

KEYED ACHIEVEMENT TEST

For further practice see exercises indicated by circled numerals.

1. Add:
  82,162
  48,279
  14,086
  53,328 ③
  13,497
  62,172

2. Subtract:
  415,037
  316,287 ④

3. Multiply:
  786
  598 ⑤

4. Divide:
  $6,080\overline{)4,839,680}$ ⑥

5. Add:
  $6\frac{9}{10}$
  $4\frac{3}{5}$ ⑫

6. Subtract:
  $7\frac{3}{8}$
  $3\frac{5}{6}$ ⑭

7. Multiply:
  $6\frac{3}{4} \times 4\frac{1}{6}$ ⑰

8. Divide:
  $84 \div 2\frac{5}{8}$ ⑱

9. Reduce $\frac{48}{64}$ to lowest terms. ⑦

10. What part of 90 is 75? ⑲

11. Which is larger: $\frac{2}{3}$ or $\frac{7}{12}$? ⑮

12. Add:
  $.96 + .096 + 9.6$ ㉓

13. Subtract:
  $8.3 - .49$ ㉔

14. Multiply:
  $2.08 \times .15$ ㉖

15. Divide:
  $.04\overline{).006}$ ㉗

16. Write as a decimal numeral: Four hundred and twenty-five thousandths. ㉑

17. Round off 29.426 to the nearest hundredth. ㉒

18. Change $\frac{7}{20}$ to a decimal. ㉚

19. Change .875 to a common fraction. ㉛

20. Multiply 45.02 by 1,000 using the short method. ㉘

ADDITIONAL TOPICS

Writing Decimal Fractions as Polynomials — Expanded Notation

We have seen on page 79 that a numeral for a whole number may be written as the sum of the products of each digit in the numeral and its place value expressed as a power of ten. Here we extend this notation to the decimal fraction.

.1 and $\frac{1}{10}$ are equivalent, and $\frac{1}{10}$ may be written as $\frac{1}{10^1}$.

.01 and $\frac{1}{100}$ are equivalent, and $\frac{1}{100}$ may be written as $\frac{1}{10^2}$.

.001 and $\frac{1}{1,000}$ are equivalent, and $\frac{1}{1,000}$ may be written as $\frac{1}{10^3}$.

.0001 and $\frac{1}{10,000}$ are equivalent, and $\frac{1}{10,000}$ may be written as $\frac{1}{10^4}$.

It can be shown that

$$\frac{1}{10^1} = 10^{-1}, \frac{1}{10^2} = 10^{-2}, \frac{1}{10^3} = 10^{-3}, \frac{1}{10^4} = 10^{-4}; \text{ etc.}$$

and that $10^0 = 1$.

The value of each place in a numeral naming a decimal fraction may be expressed as a power of ten with negative exponents.

.9247
$= 9 \text{ tenths} + 2 \text{ hundredths} + 4 \text{ thousandths} + 7 \text{ ten-thousandths}$
$= 9 \times \frac{1}{10} + 2 \times \frac{1}{100} + 4 \times \frac{1}{1,000} + 7 \times \frac{1}{10,000}$
$= 9 \times \frac{1}{10^1} + 2 \times \frac{1}{10^2} + 4 \times \frac{1}{10^3} + 7 \times \frac{1}{10^4}$
$= (9 \times 10^{-1}) + (2 \times 10^{-2}) + (4 \times 10^{-3}) + (7 \times 10^{-4})$

Also the numeral 685.379 is written in expanded form as:
$(6 \times 10^2) + (8 \times 10^1) + (5 \times 10^0) + (3 \times 10^{-1}) + (7 \times 10^{-2}) +$
(9×10^{-3})

Note that the place values are powers of ten arranged in a decreasing order from left to right.

PRACTICE PROBLEMS

1. Express each of the following as a decimal numeral:

(a) $(7 \times 10^{-1}) + (3 \times 10^{-2}) + (4 \times 10^{-3})$

(b) $(6 \times 10^{-1}) + (1 \times 10^{-2}) + (7 \times 10^{-3}) + (5 \times 10^{-4})$

(c) $(9 \times 10^1) + (3 \times 10^0) + (6 \times 10^{-1}) + (8 \times 10^{-2})$

(d) $(2 \times 10^2) + (0 \times 10^1) + (7 \times 10^0) + (4 \times 10^{-1}) + (9 \times 10^{-2})$

(e) $(4 \times 10^4) + (8 \times 10^3) + (3 \times 10^2) + (6 \times 10^1) + (8 \times 10^0) + (0 \times 10^{-1}) + (2 \times 10^{-2}) + (7 \times 10^{-3})$

(f) $(6 \times 10^3) + (4 \times 10^2) + (9 \times 10^1) + (2 \times 10^0) + (5 \times 10^{-1}) + (0 \times 10^{-2}) + (3 \times 10^{-3}) + (8 \times 10^{-4})$

(g) $(4 \times 10^2) + (9 \times 10^1) + (2 \times 10^0) + (3 \times 10^{-1}) + (6 \times 10^{-2}) + (7 \times 10^{-3}) + (0 \times 10^{-4}) + (6 \times 10^{-5})$

2. Write each of the following numerals in expanded form as a polynomial:

(a) .29	(d) .28145	(g) 89.46	(j) 957.504
(b) .476	(e) .975263	(h) 215.83	(k) 3,146.25
(c) .3509	(f) 8.2	(i) 23.927	(l) 8,372.4916

Scientific Notation

A number is expressed in *scientific notation* when its numeral names a number that is greater than 1 but less than 10 multiplied by some power of ten.

9,800,000 is 9.8 million which may be expressed in scientific notation as 9.8×10^6.

To write a numeral by scientific notation, we rewrite the significant digits:* **(1)** As a numeral for a whole number if there is only one significant digit. **(2)** As a numeral for a mixed decimal if there are two or more significant digits, using the first digit as the numeral for a whole number and all other digits as the numeral for a decimal fraction. Then we indicate that this numeral is multiplied by the required power of ten.

The required power of ten may be determined as follows:

(1) By dividing the whole number or mixed decimal into the given number and changing the quotient into a power of ten.

*See page 472.

Write 58,000 by scientific notation.	Write .0352 by scientific notation.
$58,000 = 5.8 \times$?	$.0352 = 3.52 \times$?
$10,000.$	$.01$
Divide: $5.8_\wedge)\overline{58,000.0_\wedge}$	Divide: $3.52_\wedge)\overline{.03_\wedge 52}$
However, $10,000 = 10^4$	However, $.01 = 10^{-2}$
Thus, $58,000 = 5.8 \times 10^4$	Thus, $.0352 = 3.52 \times 10^{-2}$
Answer: 5.8×10^4	Answer: 3.52×10^{-2}

(2) Or counting the number of places the decimal point is being moved.

$58,000. = 5.8 \times 10^4$	$.0352 = 3.52 \times 10^{-2}$
Decimal point moved 4 places to left.	Decimal point moved 2 places to right.

Observe that when the given number is 10 or greater, a positive integer† is used for the exponent and when the given number is between 0 and 1, a negative integer† is used for the exponent.

PRACTICE PROBLEMS

1. Express each of the following numbers by scientific notation:
   (a) 50   87   400   914   8,000   3,060
   (b) 60,000   79,000   520,000   36,000,000   4,875,000
   (c) 2,000,000,000   308,000,000,000   84,500,000,000,000
   (d) 510000000000   426000000000000000
   (e) 7000000000000000000   9400000000000000000000000
   (f) 17.4   579.3   46.81   62.059   673.37   4,553.88

2. Express each of the following numbers by scientific notation:
   (a) .4   .9   .3   .34   .02   .88   .69
   (b) .057   .007   .983   .0542   .0093   .8167   .2005
   (c) .00018   .00249   .06356   .000784   .0000091
   (d) .0000356   .00000079   .000000801   .0000000036
   (e) .000000000043 .00000000000005 .00000000000000682

†See page 480.

3. Express each of the following numbers by scientific notation:

(*a*) The sun at any second develops 500,000,000,000,000,-000,000,000 horsepower.

(*b*) The star Alpha Herculis is 2,400,000,000 miles in diameter.

Repeating Decimals

Decimals like .33$\overline{3}$ . . . , sometimes written as .$\overline{3}$, and .72$\overline{72}$ . . . , sometimes written as .$\overline{72}$, which have a digit or group of digits repeating endlessly are called repeating decimals. The bar indicates the repeating sequence (period) and the dots, although unnecessary, are sometimes used to indicate that the sequence repeats endlessly.

When $\frac{1}{3}$ is changed to a decimal, the division is not exact; the remainder at each step is the same, one (1), and the digit 3 repeats in the quotient and will keep repeating as the division is extended.

When $\frac{8}{11}$ is changed to a decimal, the division is not exact. The pair of digits 72 repeats in the quotient and will keep repeating endlessly; the remainder at each second step is the same (8).

When $\frac{1}{4}$ is changed to a decimal, the quotient is exactly .25 with a remainder of 0. The decimal form .25 is called a terminating decimal. Since .25 may also be written as .25$\overline{0}$ . . . , terminating decimals may be considered to be repeating decimals.

```
      .333              .7272
  3)1.000          11)8.0000
     9                 7 7
    ──                 ──
    10                 30
     9                 22
    ──                 ──
    10                 80
     9                 77
    ──                 ──
     1                 30
                       22
                       ──
                        8

      .25
  4)1.00
     8
    ──
    20
    20
    ──
     0
```

When a common fraction is changed to a decimal by division and a remainder of 0 occurs in the division, the quotient is a terminating decimal. If, however, after a series of divisions, a remainder other than 0 repeats, then the sequence of digits obtained in the quotient between occurrences of this remainder will repeat endlessly and the quotient is a repeating decimal.

To change a repeating decimal to a common fraction, first multiply the given repeating decimal by some power of 10 so that there is a whole number to the left of the decimal point and the repeating sequence begins to the right of the decimal point. If the repeating sequence has 1 digit, multiply by 10; 2 digits, multiply by 100; etc. Subtract the given number from this product to get a whole number for the difference.

(1)	(2)	(3)
$.77\overline{7}\ldots = ?$	$.2424\overline{24}\ldots = ?$	$.8333\overline{3}\ldots = ?$
Let $n = .777\ldots$	Let $n = .242424\ldots$	Let $n = .83333\ldots$
$10\,n = 7.777\ldots$	$100\,n = 24.242424\ldots$	$100\,n = 83.3333\ldots$
$10\,n - n = 7$	$100\,n - n = 24$	and $10\,n = 8.3333\ldots$
$9\,n = 7$	$99\,n = 24$	then $90\,n = 75$
$n = \frac{7}{9}$	$n = \frac{24}{99}$	$n = \frac{75}{90}$
	$n = \frac{8}{33}$	$n = \frac{5}{6}$
Answer, $\frac{7}{9}$	Answer, $\frac{8}{33}$	Answer, $\frac{5}{6}$

When a repeating decimal begins with digits other than those used in the repeating sequence, another step is necessary as shown in (3).

Then solve the resulting equation (see page 506) to find the required common fraction.

Thus, every common fraction may be expressed as a repeating decimal and every repeating decimal may be expressed as a common fraction.

PRACTICE PROBLEMS

1. Express each of the following as a numeral naming a repeating decimal. Indicate the repeating sequence by a horizontal bar.

$(a)\ \frac{2}{3}$	$(f)\ \frac{11}{16}$	$(k)\ \frac{3}{5}$	$(p)\ \frac{20}{21}$	$(u)\ \frac{11}{12}$
$(b)\ \frac{7}{8}$	$(g)\ \frac{5}{12}$	$(l)\ \frac{11}{18}$	$(q)\ \frac{9}{11}$	$(v)\ \frac{23}{32}$
$(c)\ \frac{1}{6}$	$(h)\ \frac{13}{33}$	$(m)\ \frac{7}{15}$	$(r)\ \frac{3}{4}$	$(w)\ \frac{15}{19}$
$(d)\ \frac{3}{7}$	$(i)\ \frac{7}{11}$	$(n)\ \frac{19}{24}$	$(s)\ \frac{14}{15}$	$(x)\ \frac{28}{33}$
$(e)\ \frac{5}{9}$	$(j)\ \frac{9}{13}$	$(o)\ \frac{8}{27}$	$(t)\ \frac{2}{9}$	$(y)\ \frac{16}{17}$

2. Express each of the following as a numeral naming a common fraction:

$(a)\ .\overline{4}$	$(d)\ .9\overline{4}$	$(g)\ .6\overline{0}$	$(j)\ .15$
$(b)\ .5\overline{4}$	$(e)\ .58\overline{3}$	$(h)\ .375\overline{0}$	$(k)\ .7\overline{3}$
$(c)\ .\overline{148}$	$(f)\ .791\overline{6}$	$(i)\ .\overline{15}$	$(l)\ .52\overline{7}$

UNIT IV . . . PER CENT

INTRODUCTION

The earner, consumer, and business man use per cent, designated by the symbol "%," extensively in their daily affairs. They experience its use in situations like the following:

The earner may find that a 14% withholding tax, $3\frac{5}{8}$% social security tax, and perhaps a 3% state or city income tax are deducted from his paycheck. A salesman may earn 5% commission on what he sells.

A home-owner may receive a 2% discount for paying his real estate taxes in advance, a 3% discount on his gas and electric bills or a 5% discount on his water bills if he pays before the discount period ends. A consumer may buy merchandise at a department store advertising a 40% reduction on certain sales items; he may pay 12% carrying charge on a new automobile; his wife may buy jewelry and cosmetics on which she pays a 10% federal tax and, where required, an additional state sales tax of perhaps 1% to 5%. Labels on her clothing may indicate the content of cloth like 30% mohair, 70% wool.

In business a storekeeper may make a 35% profit on his merchandise; a bank may pay 4% interest on deposits and charge 6% interest on loans.

The student and the teacher also use per cent. A student may receive a mark of 83%. His teacher may find the average daily attendance of the class to be 92%.

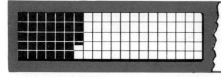 

EXERCISE 34

THE MEANING OF PER CENT

(See page 250)

I. Aim: To find the meaning of per cent.

II. Procedure

In our study of fractions we found that $\frac{27}{100}$ is read twenty-seven *hundredths* meaning 27 parts out of 100 equal parts or 27 out of a group of 100. In the study of decimals we found that

the decimal .27 also represents 27 *hundredths*. Now we study a third way of representing hundredths. It is called per cent and it is indicated by the symbol %. 27% means 27 *hundredths*.

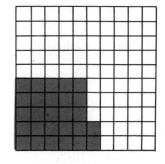

Thus, *hundredths* can be expressed as a per cent, a decimal, or a fraction.

It should be noted that 100% of anything is $\frac{100}{100}$ of it or all of it.

A per cent may also be considered a ratio (see page 522). 27%, which is equivalent to $\frac{27}{100}$, is the ratio of 27 to 100.

III. Sample Solutions

1. Express five hundredths as a per cent.   *Answer: 5%*
2. Express $3\frac{1}{2}$ hundredths as a per cent.   *Answer: $3\frac{1}{2}$%*
3. Express 19 out of 100 as a per cent.   *Answer: 19%*
4. How many hundredths are in 4.9%. *Answer:* 4.9 hundredths
5. Write thirty-seven hundredths as a per cent, decimal, and fraction.   *Answer:* 37%, .37, and $\frac{37}{100}$

DIAGNOSTIC TEST

1. Express eighteen hundredths as a per cent.
2. Express 81 out of 100 as a per cent.
3. How many hundredths are in 35%?
4. Write four hundredths as a per cent, decimal, and fraction.

RELATED PRACTICE EXAMPLES

SET 1

Express each of the following as a per cent:

1. 3 hundredths
2. 9 hundredths
3. 16 hundredths
4. 30 hundredths
5. 74 hundredths
6. 200 hundredths
7. $5\frac{1}{2}$ hundredths
8. $37\frac{1}{2}$ hundredths
9. 62.5 hundredths
10. $\frac{1}{4}$ hundredth

SET 2

Express each of the following as a per cent:

1. 47 out of 100.
2. 68 out of 100.
3. 7 out of 100.
4. 95 out of 100.
5. 1 out of 100.
6. $4\frac{1}{2}$ out of 100.
7. $66\frac{2}{3}$ out of 100.
8. 12.5 out of 100.
9. 20 out of 100.
10. $3\frac{3}{4}$ out of 100.

SET 3

How many hundredths are in:

1. 4%?
2. 7%?
3. 19%?
4. 45%?
5. 60%?
6. 140%?
7. $87\frac{1}{2}$%?
8. $4\frac{3}{4}$%?
9. 3.5%?
10. $\frac{1}{2}$%?

SET 4

Write each of the following statements as a per cent, decimal, and fraction:

1. Six hundredths
2. Eight hundredths
3. Twenty-three hundredths
4. Sixty-four hundredths
5. Seventy hundredths
6. Twelve and one-half hundredths
7. Two and one-fourth hundredths
8. Three hundred hundredths
9. Thirty-two hundredths
10. Three-fourths hundredth

MISCELLANEOUS EXAMPLES

Explain the meaning of each of the following:

1. Cloth bearing the label: 55% Dacron, 45% wool.
2. Plant food containing 5% nitrogen, 10% phosphoric acid, 5% potash.

EXERCISE 35

CHANGING PER CENTS TO DECIMALS

I. Aim: To change a per cent to a decimal.

II. Procedure

1. Rewrite the given numeral, omitting the per cent sign.

2. Move the decimal point two places to the left. In a numeral naming a whole number a decimal point is understood after the units' figure.

III. Sample Solutions

1. $5\% = .05$ *Answer:* .05
2. $84\% = .84$ *Answer:* .84
3. $30\% = .30$ or .3   *Answer:* .3
4. $125\% = 1.25$ *Answer:* 1.25
5. $110\% = 1.10$ or 1.1   *Answer:* 1.10 or 1.1
6. $2\frac{1}{2}\% = .02\frac{1}{2}$ or .025   *Answer:* $.02\frac{1}{2}$ or .025
7. $102\frac{1}{4}\% = 1.02\frac{1}{4}$ or 1.0225   *Answer:* $1.02\frac{1}{4}$ or 1.0225
8. $37.5\% = .375$ *Answer:* .375
9. $8.34\% = .0834$ *Answer:* .0834
10. $.2\%$ or $0.2\% = .002$ *Answer:* .002
11. $\frac{7}{8}\% = .00\frac{7}{8}$ or .00875   *Answer:* $.00\frac{7}{8}$ or .00875
12. $700\% = 7.00$ or 7   *Answer:* 7

DIAGNOSTIC TEST

Express each of the following per cents as a decimal:

1. 8%
2. 53%
3. 90%
4. 119%
5. 160%
6. 500%
7. $12\frac{1}{2}\%$
8. $5\frac{1}{4}\%$
9. $40\frac{5}{8}\%$
10. $105\frac{3}{4}\%$
11. 27.5%
12. 12.25%
13. 8.6%
14. 4.82%
15. 352.875%
16. $.16\%$
17. $\frac{3}{4}\%$

RELATED PRACTICE EXAMPLES

Express each of the following per cents as a decimal:

SET 1	SET 2(a)	SET 2(b)	SET 3	SET 4
1. 6%	1. 16%	1. 27%	1. 40%	1. 134%
2. 9%	2. 38%	2. 81%	2. 70%	2. 157%
3. 1%	3. 45%	3. 99%	3. 20%	3. 148%
4. 3%	4. 67%	4. 13%	4. 60%	4. 106%
5. 4%	5. 58%	5. 42%	5. 10%	5. 175%

SET 5	SET 6	SET 7	SET 8	SET 9
1. 130%	1. 100%	1. $37\frac{1}{2}$%	1. $4\frac{1}{2}$%	1. $60\frac{1}{2}$%
2. 120%	2. 200%	2. $62\frac{1}{2}$%	2. $6\frac{1}{2}$%	2. $20\frac{1}{2}$%
3. 180%	3. 300%	3. $83\frac{1}{3}$%	3. $3\frac{3}{4}$%	3. $10\frac{3}{8}$%
4. 150%	4. 600%	4. $16\frac{2}{3}$%	4. $2\frac{7}{8}$%	4. $50\frac{2}{3}$%
5. 140%	5. 400%	5. $18\frac{3}{4}$%	5. $5\frac{4}{5}$%	5. $70\frac{1}{4}$%

SET 10	SET 11	SET 12	SET 13	SET 14
1. $100\frac{7}{8}$%	1. 87.5%	1. 17.75%	1. 3.5%	1. 1.25%
2. $101\frac{1}{4}$%	2. 12.5%	2. 34.25%	2. 2.8%	2. 3.67%
3. $106\frac{1}{2}$%	3. 46.4%	3. 56.94%	3. 4.7%	3. 5.33%
4. $152\frac{9}{16}$%	4. 57.3%	4. 99.44%	4. 9.3%	4. 2.08%
5. $127\frac{3}{5}$%	5. 95.1%	5. 82.09%	5. 6.4%	5. 7.19%

SET 15	SET 16	SET 17
1. 26.375%	1. .7%	1. $\frac{1}{2}$%
2. 31.625%	2. .02%	2. $\frac{1}{4}$%
3. 128.333%	3. .9%	3. $\frac{5}{8}$%
4. 432.125%	4. .85%	4. $\frac{2}{3}$%
5. 895.667%	5. .49%	5. $\frac{7}{16}$%

MISCELLANEOUS EXAMPLES

Express each of the following per cents as a decimal:

1. Department store sales increased 8%.
2. The increase in the cost of living was 1.5%.
3. The market price of a corporation bond remained at $100\frac{5}{8}$%.

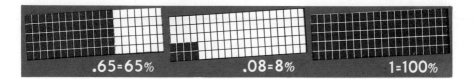

.65=65%   .08=8%   1=100%

EXERCISE 36

CHANGING DECIMALS TO PER CENTS

I. Aim: To change a decimal to a per cent.

II. Procedure

1. Rewrite the given numeral.
2. Move the decimal point two places to the right. Do not write the decimal point if, after moving it, it is located at the end of the numeral.
3. Write the per cent sign, $\%$.

III. Sample Solutions

1. $.07 = 7\%$ *Answer:* 7%
2. $.19 = 19\%$ *Answer:* 19%
3. $1.34 = 134\%$ *Answer:* 134%
4. $.5 = 50\%$ *Answer:* 50%
5. $.06\frac{1}{2} = 6\frac{1}{2}\%$ *Answer:* $6\frac{1}{2}\%$
6. $1.02\frac{3}{4} = 102\frac{3}{4}\%$ *Answer:* $102\frac{3}{4}\%$
7. $.435 = 43.5\%$ *Answer:* 43.5%
8. $.0575 = 5.75\%$ *Answer:* 5.75%
9. $.0036 = .36\%$ *Answer:* $.36\%$ or 0.36%
10. $.00\frac{2}{5} = \frac{2}{5}\%$ *Answer:* $\frac{2}{5}\%$
11. 8 or $8.00 = 800\%$ *Answer:* 800%
12. $.4\frac{1}{2} = .45 = 45\%$ *Answer:* 45%

DIAGNOSTIC TEST

Express each of the following decimals as a per cent:

1. $.06$
2. $.32$
3. $.7$
4. 1.12
5. 1.4
6. $.37\frac{1}{2}$
7. $.04\frac{1}{2}$
8. $.60\frac{3}{4}$
9. $1.66\frac{2}{3}$
10. $.625$
11. $.0467$
12. $.1\frac{1}{4}$
13. 2.875
14. 2
15. $.00\frac{3}{8}$
16. $.0025$

RELATED PRACTICE EXAMPLES

Express each of the following decimals as a per cent:

SET 1	SET 2	SET 3	SET 4	SET 5	SET 6
1. .01	1. .28	1. .6	1. 1.39	1. 1.2	1. .12$\frac{1}{2}$
2. .08	2. .75	2. .3	2. 1.92	2. 1.8	2. .33$\frac{1}{3}$
3. .04	3. .59	3. .8	3. 1.18	3. 1.7	3. .83$\frac{5}{6}$
4. .03	4. .16	4. .1	4. 1.50	4. 1.3	4. .42$\frac{2}{7}$
5. .05	5. .93	5. .9	5. 1.44	5. 1.6	5. .18$\frac{3}{4}$

SET 7	SET 8	SET 9	SET 10	SET 11	SET 12
1. .01$\frac{1}{2}$	1. .10$\frac{1}{2}$	1. 1.37$\frac{1}{2}$	1. .875	1. .2625	1. .2$\frac{1}{2}$
2. .05$\frac{1}{2}$	2. .30$\frac{2}{3}$	2. 1.83$\frac{1}{3}$	2. .125	2. .0525	2. .6$\frac{1}{2}$
3. .03$\frac{3}{4}$	3. .70$\frac{3}{4}$	3. 1.00$\frac{1}{2}$	3. .347	3. .0875	3. .3$\frac{1}{4}$
4. .04$\frac{2}{3}$	4. .50$\frac{1}{2}$	4. 1.16$\frac{2}{3}$	4. .078	4. .0233	4. .1$\frac{3}{4}$
5. .06$\frac{5}{6}$	5. .40$\frac{7}{8}$	5. 1.05$\frac{3}{4}$	5. .989	5. .65125	5. .8$\frac{7}{8}$

SET 13	SET 14	SET 15	SET 16
1. 1.245	1. 1	1. .00$\frac{1}{4}$	1. .005
2. 1.375	2. 3	2. .00$\frac{1}{2}$	2. .0075
3. 2.667	3. 5	3. .00$\frac{3}{5}$	3. .0067
4. 3.7275	4. 4	4. .00$\frac{5}{8}$	4. .008
5. 2.9625	5. 6	5. .00$\frac{2}{3}$	5. .00875

PRACTICAL APPLICATIONS

Baseball Averages

1. The pennant-winning team led the league with the standing of .625. What per cent of the games played did it win?

2. What per cent of the number of times at bat must a batter hit safely to average .300?   .375?   .400?

3. A pitcher has an average of .800. What per cent of the games did he lose?

4. What per cent of the games played must a team win to have a standing of .750?

5. On what per cent of his chances did a shortstop make an error if his fielding average is .875?

EXERCISE 37

CHANGING PER CENTS TO COMMON FRACTIONS

I. Aim: To change a per cent to a common fraction or a mixed number.

II. Procedure

1. To change a per cent to a common fraction (2 methods):
   (*a*) Make a fraction by writing the given numeral as the numerator and the numeral 100 as the denominator. Then reduce to lowest terms. (See sample solution 1.)
   (*b*) Or, if the common fraction equivalent is known, write the common fraction directly. (See sample solution 2.)

2. If the per cent is greater than 100%, the answer is a mixed number. (See sample solution 3.)

III. Sample Solutions

1. $8\% = \frac{8}{100} = \frac{2}{25}$ **2.** $40\% = \frac{2}{5}$ **3.** $130\% = \frac{130}{100} = 1\frac{3}{10}$

Answer: $\frac{2}{25}$ *Answer:* $\frac{2}{5}$ *Answer:* $1\frac{3}{10}$

DIAGNOSTIC TEST

Express each of the following per cents as a common fraction or mixed number:

    1. 75% **2.** $16\frac{2}{3}\%$ **3.** 2% **4.** 125%

RELATED PRACTICE EXAMPLES

Express each of the following per cents as a common fraction or mixed number:

H.W

✓ **SET 1**   **SET 2**

• **1.** 50%	**6.** 60%	**1.** $33\frac{1}{3}\%$	**6.** $37\frac{1}{2}\%$
– **2.** 25%	**7.** 30%	**2.** $87\frac{1}{2}\%$	**7.** $66\frac{2}{3}\%$
3. 10%	**8.** 40%	– **3.** $83\frac{1}{3}\%$	**8.** $6\frac{1}{4}\%$
4. 80%	**9.** 70%	**4.** $8\frac{1}{3}\%$	**9.** $16\frac{2}{3}\%$
5. 90%	**10.** 20%	**5.** $12\frac{1}{2}\%$	**10.** $62\frac{1}{2}\%$

H.W.   Set 3   H.W.   Set 4

1. 6%	6. 24%	1. 110%	6. 230%
2. 4%	7. 52%	2. 150%	7. 148%
~3. 5%	8. 18%	~3. $133\frac{1}{3}$%	8. 106%
4. 9%	9. 85%	4. $162\frac{1}{2}$%	9. 225%
5. 46%	10. 36%	5. 175%	10. 180%

✓ PRACTICAL APPLICATIONS

1. 30% of the pupils at the Southeast High School are in the ninth year. What part of the student body is in the ninth year?

2. If $87\frac{1}{2}$% of a class received a passing mark in a science test, what part of the class failed in the test?

3. What part of a graduating class is planning to go to college if 40% filed applications for entrance?

4. If Mr. Wilson pays 25% down on a house, what part of the purchase price is his down payment?

5. In a certain area $16\frac{2}{3}$% of all the crops were destroyed by floods. What part of the harvest was saved?

H.W.   REFRESH YOUR SKILLS

1. Add: 2. Subtract: 3. Multiply: 4. Divide:

   9,625   526,809   784 $2,240\overline{)2,210,880}$
  84,517 $\underline{348,719}$ $\underline{697}$
    862
  54,163
   $\underline{7,989}$

5. Add: 6. Subtract: 7. Multiply: 8. Divide:

  $6\frac{2}{3} + 1\frac{7}{12} + 4\frac{5}{6}$ $8\frac{1}{4} - 6\frac{7}{10}$ $7\frac{5}{6} \times 1\frac{1}{8}$ $16 \div 3\frac{3}{4}$

9. Add: 10. Subtract: 11. Multiply: 12. Divide:

  $8.9 + .45 + 21$ $8.03 - .7$ $4.06 \times .005$ $.16\overline{).96}$

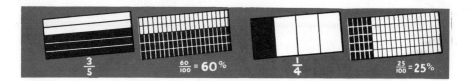

$\frac{3}{5}$ $\frac{60}{100} = 60\%$ $\frac{1}{4}$ $\frac{25}{100} = 25\%$

EXERCISE 38

CHANGING COMMON FRACTIONS TO PER CENTS

I. Aim: To change common fractions and mixed numbers to per cents.

II. Procedure

1. To change a common fraction to a per cent (3 methods):
   - (*a*) *1.* Divide the numerator by the denominator, finding the quotient to two decimal places.
   - *2.* Rewrite the quotient, omitting the decimal point.
   - *3.* Then write the per cent sign, %. (See sample solutions 1 and 4.)
   - (*b*) Or, if the per cent equivalent of the given fraction is known, write the per cent directly. Sometimes it may be necessary to reduce the given fraction to lowest terms. (See sample solution 2.)
   - (*c*) Or if possible, raise the given fraction to higher terms or reduce it to lower terms so that its denominator is 100. Then rewrite the numerator, replacing the denominator with the per cent sign, %. (See sample solution 3.)

2. To change a mixed number to a per cent:

   Change the mixed number to a mixed decimal. Then follow step 1 (*a*), parts *2* and *3*. (See sample solution 7.)

III. Sample Solutions

1. Change $\frac{18}{25}$ to per cent.

$$\frac{18}{25} = 25\overline{)18.00} \quad \begin{array}{r} .72 = 72\% \\ \hline \end{array}$$
$$\begin{array}{r} 17\ 5 \\ \hline 50 \\ 50 \\ \hline \end{array}$$

Answer: 72%

3. Change $\frac{7}{50}$ to per cent.

$$\frac{7}{50} = \frac{14}{100} = 14\% \quad Answer:\ 14\%$$

2. Change $\frac{24}{40}$ to per cent.

$$\frac{24}{40} = \frac{3}{5} = 60\%$$

Answer: 60%

4. Change $\frac{2}{9}$ to per cent.

$$\frac{2}{9} = 9\overline{)2.00} \quad \begin{array}{r} .22\frac{2}{9} = 22\frac{2}{9}\% \\ \hline \end{array}$$

Answer: $22\frac{2}{9}\%$

5. Change $\frac{2}{30}$ to per cent.

$$\frac{2}{30} = \frac{1}{15} = \overset{.06\frac{2}{3} = 6\frac{2}{3}\%}{15\overline{)1.00}}$$

Answer: $6\frac{2}{3}\%$

6. Change $\frac{11}{8}$ to per cent.

$$\frac{11}{8} = \overset{1.37\frac{1}{2} = 137\frac{1}{2}\%}{8\overline{)11.00}}$$

Answer: $137\frac{1}{2}\%$

7. Change $1\frac{1}{4}$ to per cent.

$$1\frac{1}{4} = 1.25 = 125\%$$

Answer: 125%

or　$1\frac{1}{4} = 125\%$

since　$1 = 100\%$ and $\frac{1}{4} = 25\%$

DIAGNOSTIC TEST

Express each of the following fractions and mixed numbers as a per cent:

1. $\frac{3}{4}$	4. $\frac{19}{50}$	7. $\frac{7}{9}$	10. $1\frac{1}{2}$	13. $2\frac{2}{3}$
2. $\frac{2}{3}$	5. $\frac{8}{400}$	8. $\frac{24}{56}$	11. $\frac{7}{4}$	14. $\frac{12}{5}$
3. $\frac{3}{100}$	6. $\frac{9}{36}$	9. $\frac{18}{18}$	12. $\frac{72}{64}$	

RELATED PRACTICE EXAMPLES

Express each of the following fractions and mixed numbers as a per cent:

SET 1	SET 2	SET 3	SET 4	SET 5
1. $\frac{1}{4}$	1. $\frac{5}{6}$	1. $\frac{7}{100}$	1. $\frac{27}{50}$	1. $\frac{18}{200}$
2. $\frac{2}{5}$	2. $\frac{3}{8}$	2. $\frac{39}{100}$	2. $\frac{4}{25}$	2. $\frac{35}{700}$
3. $\frac{1}{2}$	3. $\frac{1}{3}$	3. $\frac{145}{100}$	3. $\frac{13}{20}$	3. $\frac{12}{300}$
4. $\frac{7}{10}$	4. $\frac{7}{8}$	4. $\frac{87\frac{1}{2}}{100}$	4. $\frac{31}{50}$	4. $\frac{60}{500}$
5. $\frac{4}{5}$	5. $\frac{1}{6}$	5. $\frac{81}{100}$	5. $\frac{16}{25}$	5. $\frac{135}{900}$

SET 6	SET 7	SET 8	SET 9	SET 10
1. $\frac{16}{24}$	1. $\frac{5}{7}$	1. $\frac{20}{36}$	1. $\frac{45}{45}$	1. $1\frac{3}{4}$
2. $\frac{39}{65}$	2. $\frac{8}{11}$	2. $\frac{45}{99}$	2. $\frac{7}{7}$	2. $1\frac{2}{5}$
3. $\frac{40}{48}$	3. $\frac{4}{9}$	3. $\frac{42}{49}$	3. $\frac{39}{39}$	3. $1\frac{1}{3}$
4. $\frac{63}{72}$	4. $\frac{7}{15}$	4. $\frac{65}{75}$	4. $\frac{84}{84}$	4. $1\frac{4}{7}$
5. $\frac{33}{88}$	5. $\frac{5}{18}$	5. $\frac{30}{105}$	5. $\frac{156}{156}$	5. $1\frac{5}{8}$

SET 11	SET 12	SET 13	SET 14
1. $\frac{5}{3}$	1. $\frac{57}{38}$	1. $2\frac{5}{8}$	1. $\frac{8}{3}$
2. $\frac{13}{8}$	2. $\frac{65}{52}$	2. $3\frac{4}{5}$	2. $\frac{14}{4}$
3. $\frac{8}{7}$	3. $\frac{36}{27}$	3. $4\frac{2}{3}$	3. $\frac{17}{6}$
4. $\frac{11}{9}$	4. $\frac{70}{49}$	4. $3\frac{1}{7}$	4. $\frac{78}{18}$
5. $\frac{9}{5}$	5. $\frac{90}{48}$	5. $2\frac{3}{4}$	5. $\frac{23}{10}$

PRACTICAL APPLICATIONS

1. If Henry received $\frac{3}{5}$ of all votes cast in a home-room election, what per cent of the votes did he get?

2. What per cent of the community contributed to the welfare fund if $\frac{5}{6}$ of the community contributed?

3. If $\frac{7}{10}$ of the student body participated in the interclass athletic games, what per cent of the students did not participate?

4. A salesman receives a commission of $\frac{3}{20}$ of the amount of his sales. What per cent commission does he receive?

5. A department store advertises a $\frac{1}{4}$ reduction on all merchandise. What is the per cent mark-down in this sale?

REFRESH YOUR SKILLS

1. Add:

692,865
734,192
802,371
563,816
814,935
629,683

2. Subtract:

4,502,097
3,968,498

3. Multiply:

54,008
984

4. Divide:

$675)\overline{6,668,325}$

5. Add:

$8\frac{3}{4} + 3\frac{17}{32}$

6. Subtract:

$6\frac{4}{5} - 2\frac{5}{6}$

7. Multiply:

$3\frac{1}{7} \times 4\frac{2}{3}$

8. Divide:

$10\frac{1}{2} \div 2\frac{2}{5}$

9. Add:

$4.26 + $9.83 + $18.97 + $153.62

10. Subtract:

$100 - $71.06

11. Multiply:

$.62\frac{1}{2} \times $500

12. Divide:

$.24)\overline{$18}$

EXERCISE 39

FINDING A PER CENT OF A NUMBER

(See page 250)

I. Aim: To find a per cent of a number.

II. Procedure

1. Change the per cent to a decimal or common fraction.
2. Multiply the given number by this decimal or common fraction.

III. Sample Solutions

1. Find 23% of 64.   **2.** Find 3% of 18.   **3.** Find 4% of $200.

$$\begin{array}{r} 64 \\ .23 \\ \hline 1\ 92 \\ 12\ 8 \\ \hline 14.72 \end{array}$$

Answer: 14.72

$$\begin{array}{r} 18 \\ .03 \\ \hline .54 \end{array}$$

Answer: .54

$$\frac{4}{100} \times \$200 = \$8$$

Answer: $8

4. Find 60% of 175.

$$\frac{3}{5} \times \overset{35}{\cancel{175}} = 105$$

Answer: 105

5. Find 114% of 240.

$$\begin{array}{r} 240 \\ 1.14 \\ \hline 9\ 60 \\ 24\ 0 \\ 240 \\ \hline 273.60 \end{array}$$

Answer: 273.6

6. Find 3½% of 40.

$$\begin{array}{r} 40 \\ .035 \\ \hline 200 \\ 1\ 20 \\ \hline 1.400 \end{array} \quad \text{or} \quad \begin{array}{r} 40 \\ .03\frac{1}{2} \\ \hline 1\ 20 \\ 20 \\ \hline 1.40 \end{array}$$

$$\frac{1}{2} \times \overset{20}{\cancel{40}} = 20$$

Answer: 1.4

7. Find ¾% of 650.

$$\begin{array}{r} 650 \\ .0075 \\ \hline 3250 \\ 4\ 550 \\ \hline 4.8750 \end{array}$$

Answer: 4.875

8. Find .4% of 52.

$$52$$
$$.004$$
$$\overline{.208}$$

Answer: .208

9. Find 4% of $12.96 to nearest cent.

$$\$12.96$$
$$.04$$
$$\overline{\$.5184} = \$.52$$

Answer: $.52

DIAGNOSTIC TEST

Find the following:

1. 18% of 46   **2.** 6% of 24   **3.** 39% of 6.75

Change per cents to common fractions in examples 4, 5, and 6.

4. 3% of 5,000   **5.** 25% of 36   **6.** $83\frac{1}{3}$% of 582
7. 127% of 743   **8.** 140% of 295   **9.** 200% of 75
10. $4\frac{1}{2}$% of 624   **11.** $50\frac{3}{4}$% of 840   **12.** $\frac{1}{4}$% of 300
13. 7.8% of 45   **14.** .3% of 160   **15.** 5% of $29
16. 2% of $4.68 (to nearest cent)

RELATED PRACTICE EXAMPLES

Find the following:

Set 1	Set 2	Set 3
1. 24% of 52	**1.** 2% of 18	**1.** 2% of 3.6
2. 87% of 41	**2.** 4% of 93	**2.** 5% of 8.24
3. 63% of 75	**3.** 5% of 84	**3.** 3% of 9.62
4. 14% of 80	**4.** 9% of 50	**4.** 18% of 4.7
5. 92% of 48	**5.** 1% of 85	**5.** 27% of 8.73
6. 16% of 240	**6.** 3% of 200	**6.** 1% of 15.40
7. 59% of 936	**7.** 6% of 325	**7.** 6% of 27.75
8. 45% of 819	**8.** 7% of 928	**8.** 5% of 295.08
9. 32% of 2,907	**9.** 8% of 1,540	**9.** 25% of 75.24
10. 21% of 4,384	**10.** 4% of 8,462	**10.** 38% of 251.69

Change per cents to common fractions in sets 4, 5, and 6.

Set 4	Set 5	Set 6
1. 5% of 200	1. 10% of 30	1. $12\frac{1}{2}$% of 800
2. 4% of 4,000	2. 50% of 62	2. $37\frac{1}{2}$% of 312
3. 8% of 9,000	3. 40% of 65	3. $62\frac{1}{2}$% of 672
4. 7% of 3,000	4. 75% of 92	4. $83\frac{1}{3}$% of 5,820
5. 6% of 650	5. 30% of 50	5. $8\frac{1}{3}$% of 8,280
6. 18% of 500	6. 60% of 200	6. $33\frac{1}{3}$% of 768
7. 32% of 2,000	7. 90% of 740	7. $16\frac{2}{3}$% of 804
8. 29% of 10,000	8. 25% of 328	8. $66\frac{2}{3}$% of 987
9. 95% of 5,300	9. 20% of 735	9. $87\frac{1}{2}$% of 4,368
10. 83% of 7,250	10. 80% of 1,225	10. $6\frac{1}{4}$% of 9,328

Set 7	Set 8	Set 9
1. 116% of 28	1. 120% of 45	1. 100% of 72
2. 105% of 57	2. 150% of 274	2. 500% of 400
3. 138% of 120	3. 125% of 848	3. 200% of 325
4. 147% of 825	4. $133\frac{1}{3}$% of 246	4. 400% of 2,000
5. 235% of 1,500	5. $137\frac{1}{2}$% of 5,640	5. 300% of 3,854

Set 10	Set 11	Set 12
1. $2\frac{1}{2}$% of 30	1. $24\frac{1}{2}$% of 20	1. $\frac{1}{2}$% of 48
2. $5\frac{1}{2}$% of 180	2. $142\frac{3}{4}$% of 64	2. $\frac{1}{3}$% of 930
3. $1\frac{1}{2}$% of 2,500	3. $10\frac{1}{2}$% of 36	3. $\frac{3}{4}$% of 219
4. $4\frac{3}{4}$% of 3,000	4. $130\frac{1}{2}$% of 245	4. $\frac{5}{8}$% of 600
5. $5\frac{1}{4}$% of 824	5. $98\frac{7}{8}$% of 5,000	5. $\frac{7}{16}$% of 3,500

Set 13	Set 14
1. 2.5% of 36	1. .2% of 8
2. 4.7% of 840	2. .1% of 95
3. 6.75% of 725	3. .25% of 500
4. 5.625% of 192	4. .375% of 848
5. 15.375% of 2,400	5. $.66\frac{2}{3}$% of 759

Find correct to nearest cent:

Set 15(a)	Set 15(b)	Set 16(a)
1. 4% of $5	1. 113% of $42	1. 3% of $.90
2. 2% of $94	2. 150% of $264	2. 5% of $4.60
3. 6% of $273	3. $2\frac{1}{2}$% of $300	3. 6% of $3.29
4. 1% of $3,000	4. $4\frac{1}{2}$% of $740	4. 4% of $10.55
5. 10% of $50	5. $133\frac{1}{3}$% of $600	5. 6% of $36.48
6. 40% of $240	6. 300% of $493	6. 15% of $8.75
7. 23% of $19	7. 3.5% of $28	7. 34% of $9.23
8. 75% of $760	8. .25% of $400	8. 79% of $25.38
9. $33\frac{1}{3}$% of $6,900	9. $\frac{3}{4}$% of $2,000	9. 50% of $94.81
10. 41% of $5,643	10. $\frac{1}{2}$% of $5,400	10. 25% of $285.96

Set 16(b)

1. $87\frac{1}{2}$% of $.56	6. 200% of $35.86
2. $33\frac{1}{3}$% of $8.16	7. $137\frac{1}{2}$% of $11.12
3. 124% of $6.73	8. 4.3% of $58
4. 160% of $2.25	9. .6% of $18.54
5. $3\frac{1}{2}$% of $9.40	10. $\frac{1}{4}$% of $32.80

PRACTICAL APPLICATIONS

1. How many problems did Joan have right if she received a grade of 85% in a mathematics test of 20 problems?

2. Richard received a grade of 60% in a spelling test of 25 words. How many words did he misspell?

3. The enrollment in the Weston Junior High School is 850. If the attendance for a certain month was 92%, how many absences were there during the month?

4. How many questions out of 28 may a pupil miss and still get a grade of 75%?

5. Arthur's father earns $6,800 a year. He plans to use the following budget: food, 25%; shelter, 20%; clothing, 15%; savings, 10%; miscellaneous, 30%. How much does he plan to spend for each item?

6. Mr. Becker bought a house for $18,250 and made a down payment of 20%. What is the amount of the mortgage?

7. A house worth $9,600 is insured for 80% of its value. How much would the owner receive if the house were destroyed by fire?

8. Mrs. Turner bought a washing machine for $216. She paid 25% in cash and the balance is to be paid in 12 equal monthly installments. How much must she pay each month?

9. Mrs. Ritter stored her fur coat for the winter and was charged 2% of its value. If the coat is valued at $750, how much did she pay?

10. Frank's father received a 10% increase on a salary of $90 per week. Recently his salary was reduced 10%. How does his present salary compare with his original salary before the increase?

11. A certain manganese bronze contains 59% copper. How many pounds of copper are in 300 pounds of manganese bronze?

12. A certain electric motor is 78% efficient. What is the output if the input is 1,400 watts?

13. The true altitude for a certain air density is 5% less than the indicated altitude. What is the true altitude if the indicated altitude is 4,900 feet?

Sales Tax, Discount, Commission,
Profit and Loss, and Interest

A. **Sales Tax**

1. If the sales tax is 2%, what would the tax be on a purchase of $8.50?

2. Find the sales tax to the nearest cent on the following purchases at the given tax rates:

Purchases	$56.00	$17.10	$1.98	$23.00	$9.40	$12.36
Tax Rate	3%	1%	2%	$2\frac{1}{2}$%	$1\frac{1}{2}$%	$3\frac{1}{2}$%

B. **Discount**

The regular or full price of an article is usually called the list price or marked price. Discount is the reduction in price. The price after the discount has been deducted is called the net price or sale price.

1. Mr. Warner bought a camera at a 15% discount. If the regular price was $56, how much discount was he allowed? How much did he pay?

2. Find the discount and the net price on the following:

List Price	$43.00	$.96	$31.68	$170.94	$6.59	$85.31
Rate of Discount	8%	6%	25%	42%	$37\frac{1}{2}\%$	20%

3. How much trade discount is allowed if the catalogue lists a kitchen cabinet sink at $98.75 and the discount sheet shows a 16% discount? What is the net price?

4. Find the cash discount received and the net amount paid if a bill for $27.40 is paid upon receipt. The terms of payment were 3% discount if paid within 10 days or the full amount in 30 days.

5. What is the net price of a refrigerator listed at $227.50 with a trade discount of 12% and an additional cash discount of 5%?

C. Commission

An agent who sells or buys goods for another person is usually paid a sum of money (commission) based on the value of the goods. The amount remaining after the commision has been deducted is called net proceeds.

1. A real estate agent sold a house for $13,500 and was paid a commission of 5%. What was the amount of his commission? How much did the owner of the house receive?

2. Find the commission and the net proceeds on the following:

Sales	$4,275	$324.50	$1,568	$108.25	$2,700	$495
Rate of Comm.	7%	18%	$12\frac{1}{2}\%$	23%	$5\frac{1}{2}\%$	30%

3. Jane's sister works in a department store. She receives $45 per week and 1% commission on sales. How much did she earn in a week when she sold $1,028 worth of merchandise?

4. A salesman sold 9 window fans at $39.95 each and 7 air conditioners at $279.75 each. At 4% commission, how much did he earn?

5. A commission merchant charging $7\frac{1}{2}\%$ commission, sold for a grower 290 boxes of lemons at $4.25 a box and 475 boxes of plums at $3.80 a box. What net proceeds should the grower receive?

D. Profit and Loss

1. A merchant sold a rug costing $139 at a profit of 30%. How much profit did he make? What was the selling price?

2. Find the profit and the selling price at the given rates of profit on the following costs:

Cost	$54.00	$1.25	$98.50	$461.00	$236.15	$29.98
Rate of Profit	25%	40%	16%	$37\frac{1}{2}\%$	9%	$18\frac{1}{2}\%$

3. Shirts cost a merchant $27 a dozen. At what price each must he sell them to make a profit of $33\frac{1}{3}\%$ on the cost?

4. A dealer bought a table for $38.40 and marked it to sell for a profit of 35% on the cost. If he finally sold it at a reduction of 10% on the marked price, what was the selling price and the amount of profit?

5. A storekeeper bought baseballs at $19.20 per dozen. If his overhead expenses are $12\frac{1}{2}\%$ of the cost and he wishes to make a net profit of 25% on the cost, how much should he charge for each ball?

E. Simple Interest

Interest is money paid for the use of money. The money borrowed or invested on which interest is paid is called principal. The sum of the principal and interest is called amount.

Interest is equal to the principal times the rate per year times the time in years. Formula: $i = prt$

1. Mr. Jennings owns a $100 bond bearing 5% interest. How much interest does he receive each year?

2. A man borrowed $600 at 4% simple interest for 3 years. How much interest did he owe? What amount was due?

3. Find the interest and the amount on the following:

Principal	$750	$840	$219	$500	$1,125	$1,600
Rate	2%	4%	3%	$2\frac{1}{2}\%$	6%	$5\frac{1}{2}\%$
Time	1 yr.	2 yr.	5 yr.	12 yr.	$\frac{1}{2}$ yr.	$2\frac{3}{4}$ yr.

4. A man bought a house for $16,700. He paid 25% down and gave a mortgage bearing 6% interest for the remainder. What is the annual interest? Semi-annual interest?

5. Mr. Smith has $2,400 in a savings bank for his son's college education. If the bank pays $2\frac{3}{4}\%$ annual interest and the money has been deposited for the full year, how much interest is earned for the year?

REFRESH YOUR SKILLS

1. Add:
29
6,842
98,386
2,594
73,967

2. Subtract:
1,000,000
908,147

3. Multiply:
846
259

4. Divide:
$1,728\overline{)1,655,424}$

5. Add:
$4\frac{3}{8} + 5\frac{9}{16}$

6. Subtract:
$8\frac{1}{4} - 2\frac{1}{3}$

7. Multiply:
$3\frac{1}{7} \times 4\frac{2}{3}$

8. Divide:
$7\frac{1}{2} \div 6\frac{3}{4}$

9. Add:
6.03
2.39
3.26
7.32

10. Subtract:
$9 - $1.32

11. Multiply: (Nearest cent)
$70.29
.01$\frac{1}{2}$

12. Divide:
$144\overline{)$12.96}$

13. Round off 3,999,506 to the nearest thousand.

14. Reduce $\frac{48}{144}$ to lowest terms.

15. Change .18 to a per cent.

16. Change 60% to a fraction.

17. Change 56% to a decimal.

18. Change $\frac{13}{20}$ to a decimal.

19. Find 3% of $56.25 to nearest cent.

20. Find $133\frac{1}{3}\%$ of 924.

FINDING WHAT PER CENT ONE NUMBER IS OF ANOTHER

(See page 250)

I. Aim: To find what per cent one number is of another.

II. Procedure

1. Make a fraction, indicating what fractional part one number is of the other. If possible, reduce the fraction to lowest terms.
2. Change the fraction to a per cent, using the per cent equivalent if it is known; otherwise change the fraction first to a 2-place decimal by dividing the numerator by the denominator, then change the decimal to a per cent. (See sample solution 2 for a short method.)

III. Sample Solutions

1. 27 is what per cent of 36?

$$\frac{27}{36} = \frac{3}{4} = 75\%$$

or $\dfrac{27}{36} = $

$$\begin{array}{r} .75 = 75\% \\ 36\overline{)27.00} \\ 25\ 2 \\ \hline 1\ 80 \\ 1\ 80 \\ \hline \end{array}$$

Answer: 75%

2. 9 is —— per cent of 20?

$$\frac{9}{20} = \frac{45}{100} = 45\%$$

Answer: 45%

3. What per cent of 26 is 26?

$$\frac{26}{26} = 1 = 100\%$$

Answer: 100%

4. What per cent of 48 is 30?

$$\frac{30}{48} = \frac{5}{8} = 62\frac{1}{2}\%$$

or $\dfrac{30}{48} = $

$$\begin{array}{r} .62\frac{1}{2} = 62\frac{1}{2}\% \\ 48\overline{)30.00} \\ 28\ 8 \\ \hline 1\ 20 \\ 96 \\ \hline 24 \end{array}$$

$$\frac{24}{48} = \frac{1}{2}$$

Answer: 62½%

5. 18 is what per cent of 16?

$$\frac{18}{16} = \frac{9}{8} = \begin{array}{r} 1.12\frac{1}{2} = 112\frac{1}{2}\% \\ 8\overline{)9.00} \end{array}$$

or $\frac{9}{8} = 1\frac{1}{8} = 112\frac{1}{2}\%$

Answer: 112½%

6. $1.50 is what per cent of $7.50?

$$\frac{\$1.50}{\$7.50} = \frac{1}{5} = 20\%$$

Answer: 20%

DIAGNOSTIC TEST

Find the following:

1. 4 is what per cent of 5?
2. What per cent of 12 is 6?
3. What per cent of 8 is 7?
4. 45 is ——% of 54?
5. 2 is what per cent of 7?
6. What per cent of 18 is 10?
7. 37 is what per cent of 37?
8. 8 is ——% of 4?
9. 25 is what per cent of 20?
10. What per cent of 36 is 48?
11. 561 is what per cent of 935?
12. What per cent of $17 is $3.40?
13. $3\frac{1}{2}$ is what per cent of $10\frac{1}{2}$?
14. 9 is ——% of 100? (Use short method.)
15. 13 is what per cent of 25? (Use short method.)
16. What per cent of 400 is 16? (Use short method.)

RELATED PRACTICE EXAMPLES

Find the following:

SET 1(a)

1. 3 is what per cent of 5?
2. 1 is what per cent of 4?
3. 3 is ——% of 4?
4. 1 is ——% of 5?
5. 9 is ——% of 10?

SET 1(b)

1. What per cent of 4 is 1?
2. What per cent of 5 is 2?
3. What per cent of 2 is 1?
4. What per cent of 10 is 7?
5. What per cent of 10 is 3?

SET 2(a)

1. What per cent of 36 is 9?
2. What per cent of 50 is 15?
3. 4 is ——% of 40?
4. 39 is ——% of 52?
5. 42 is what per cent of 60?

SET 2(b)

1. 5 is ——% of 50?
2. 36 is ——% of 45?
3. 72 is what per cent of 96?
4. What per cent of 80 is 56?
5. What per cent of 90 is 81?

Set 3

1. What per cent of 8 is 1?
2. What per cent of 6 is 5?
3. What per cent of 3 is 2?
4. 3 is ——% of 8?
5. 5 is what per cent of 8?

Set 4(a)

1. 9 is ——% of 27?
2. 16 is ——% of 24?
3. 35 is what per cent of 42?
4. What per cent of 40 is 15?
5. What per cent of 72 is 63?

Set 4(b)

1. 9 is what per cent of 54?
2. 28 is what per cent of 32?
3. What per cent of 64 is 24?
4. What per cent of 16 is 10?
5. 5 is ——% of 80?

Set 5

1. 3 is what per cent of 7?
2. 5 is what per cent of 12?
3. What per cent of 9 is 7?
4. What per cent of 13 is 8?
5. 17 is ——% of 18?

Set 6(a)

1. What per cent of 14 is 4?
2. What per cent of 54 is 30?
3. 15 is ——% of 84?
4. 42 is what per cent of 49?
5. 60 is what per cent of 78?

Set 6(b)

1. 32 is ——% of 72?
2. 27 is ——% of 99?
3. 70 is what per cent of 75?
4. What per cent of 96 is 27?
5. What per cent of 48 is 2?

Set 7

1. 8 is what per cent of 8?
2. 40 is what per cent of 40?
3. What per cent of 53 is 53?
4. What per cent of 82 is 82?
5. 250 is ——% of 250?

Set 8

1. 2 is ——% of 1?
2. 8 is ——% of 2?
3. 60 is what per cent of 12?
4. What per cent of 10 is 30?
5. What per cent of 12 is 72?

Set 9

1. 6 is what per cent of 5?
2. 7 is what per cent of 4?
3. What per cent of 24 is 54?
4. What per cent of 50 is 65?
5. 63 is ——% of 35?

Set 10

1. What per cent of 3 is 4?
2. What per cent of 12 is 32?
3. 90 is ——% of 48?
4. 64 is ——% of 28?
5. 85 is what per cent of 75?

Set 11

1. 492 is what per cent of 656?
2. 516 is what per cent of 774?
3. 645 is ——% of 1,032?
4. What per cent of 1,225 is 98?
5. 1,014 is ——% of 2,535?

Set 12(a)

1. What per cent of 10 is 2.5?
2. What per cent of 7.5 is 3?
3. .54 is ——% of 9?
4. 4.3 is what per cent of 6.45?
5. 9.6 is what per cent of 6.4?

Set 12(b)

1. $.75 is ——% of $18.75?
2. $1.30 is ——% of $6.50?
3. $9 is what per cent of $6.75?
4. What per cent of $12.25 is $10?
5. What per cent of $15 is $3.75?

Set 13

1. $2\frac{1}{4}$ is what per cent of 9?
2. $1\frac{2}{3}$ is what per cent of $8\frac{1}{3}$?
3. What per cent of $4\frac{2}{3}$ is $3\frac{1}{2}$?
4. What per cent of $1\frac{7}{8}$ is $1\frac{1}{4}$?
5. $4\frac{1}{8}$ is ——% of $6\frac{7}{8}$?

Use short method:

Set 14

1. 15 is ——% of 100?
2. 125 is ——% of 100?
3. 4.5 is what per cent of 100?
4. What per cent of 100 is 7?
5. What per cent of 100 is $33\frac{1}{3}$?

Set 15

1. 27 is what per cent of 50?
2. 7 is what per cent of 20?
3. What per cent of 50 is 34?
4. What per cent of 25 is 21?
5. 2 is ——% of 25?

Set 16

1. What per cent of 200 is 6?
2. What per cent of 900 is 60?
3. 120 is ——% of 1,000?
4. 32 is what per cent of 800?
5. 480 is what per cent of 2,400?

MISCELLANEOUS EXAMPLES

Find each of the following correct to nearest tenth of a per cent:

Set 1

1. 5 is what % of 9?
2. What % of 21 is 13?
3. $.11 is ——% of $.15?
4. What % of 16 is 1?
5. $7 is what % of $12?

Set 2

1. What % of 63 is 27?
2. 30 is what % of 78?
3. What % of $42 is $39?
4. $.60 is ——% of $1.44?
5. What % of $171 is $135?

PRACTICAL APPLICATIONS

1. There are 40 pupils in a class. On a certain day 38 pupils were present. What per cent of the class attended school? What per cent of the class attendance does each pupil's attendance represent?

2. There are 18 girls and 27 boys in a class. What per cent of the class are boys?

3. Charles answered 19 questions correctly and missed 6 questions. What per cent of the questions did he answer correctly?

4. The school team won 9 games and lost 6. What per cent of the games did the team lose?

5. Gloria guessed the length of the schoolroom to be 28 feet. When she measured it, she found it to be 32 feet. What was her per cent of error?

6. Mr. Graham saves $70 each month. If his annual income is $6,000, what per cent of his income does he save annually?

7. To find the efficiency of an electric motor, find what per cent the output is of the input. Find the efficiency of a motor if its output is 1,520 watts when the input is 1,600 watts.

8. Rate of Commission—% commission on sales, purchases, collections.

(*a*) Find the rate of commission when: (1) commission is $60 and sales are $1,000; (2) commission is $130 and purchases are $3,250.

(*b*) A lawyer collected a debt of $412 for a client, charging $61.80 for his services. What rate of commission did he charge?

9. Rate of Profit or Loss—% profit or loss on cost or on selling price.

(*a*) Find the rate of profit or loss on cost when: (1) cost is $75 and selling price is $96; (2) cost is 60¢ and selling price is 50¢.

(*b*) Find the rate of profit or loss on selling price when: (1) cost is $19 and selling price is $25; (2) cost is $162 and selling price is $144.

(*c*) Mr. Adams sold for $7,800 a house which originally cost him $7,200. What was his per cent of profit on the cost?

(*d*) Robert's uncle bought a car for $1,040. He sold it for $910. What was his per cent of loss on the cost?

10. Annual Rate of Interest—% annual interest on principal.

(*a*) Find the annual rate of interest when: (1) yearly interest on $900 is $45; (2) yearly interest on $400 is $14; (3) interest for $\frac{1}{2}$ year on $500 is $10.

(*b*) A man pays $150 interest each year on a mortgage of $2,500. Find the rate of interest.

(*c*) What is the rate of interest on the mortgage if a man semi-annually pays $82.50 interest on a mortgage of $3,000?

(d) A man bought a $100 bond for $96. If he receives an annual interest of $6, what is his rate of income?

11. Rate of Increase or Decrease—*% increase or decrease on original amount.*

(a) Find the rate of increase or decrease when (1) enrollment increased from 250 pupils to 300 pupils; (2) lateness dropped from 42 cases to 35 cases; (3) price changed from 30¢ to 40¢; from 40¢ to 30¢.

(b) A certain factory produced 1,605 units last month and 1,284 units the month before. What was the per cent of increase in production?

12. Rate of Discount—*% discount on regular, marked, or list price.*

(a) Find the rate of discount when: (1) discount is $4 and regular price is $32; (2) marked price is $80 and sale price is $68; (3) list price is $175 and net price is $140; (4) discount is $.50 and sale price is $4.50.

(b) A discount of $1.35 was given on a football regularly priced at $8.10. What was the rate of discount?

REFRESH YOUR SKILLS

1. Add:

7,124
83,259
61,435
816
9,527
84,349

2. Subtract:

815,008
747,598

3. Multiply:

403
807

4. Divide:

$794\overline{)235,818}$

5. Add:

$7\frac{2}{3}$
$4\frac{5}{6}$

6. Subtract:

$8\frac{3}{4}$
$2\frac{4}{5}$

7. Multiply:

$4\frac{3}{8} \times 2\frac{3}{10}$

8. Divide:

$\frac{13}{16} \div 1\frac{1}{12}$

9. Add:

$3.8 + .47 + 25$

10. Subtract:

$6.825 - .97$

11. Multiply:

3.14×80

12. Divide:

$1.15\overline{)46}$

13. Find 8% of 60.9

14. Find $87\frac{1}{2}$% of $526

15. What per cent of 144 is 64?

16. What per cent of $1.25 is $.50?

EXERCISE 41

FINDING A NUMBER WHEN A PER CENT OF IT IS KNOWN
(See page 250)

I. Aim: To find a number when a per cent of it is known.

II. Procedure

1. Change the per cent to a decimal or common fraction.

2. (*a*) Divide the given number representing the given per cent of the unknown number by this decimal or common fraction.

(*b*) Or follow the alternate method shown in the sample solutions.

3. Check by finding the given per cent of the answer.

III. Sample Solutions

1. 16% of what number is 48?

Method 1	*Method 2*
16% = .16	16% of the number = 48
Divide 48 by .16	1% of the number = 48 ÷ 16 = 3
$$\begin{array}{r} 3\ 00. \\ .16_\wedge \overline{)48.00_\wedge} \end{array}$$	100% of the number = 100 × 3 = 300
	Therefore the number = 300

Check:

16% of 300 = 48

Answer: 300

2. 50% of what number = 40?

Method 1	*Method 2*
50% = $\frac{1}{2}$	50% of the number = 40
Divide 40 by $\frac{1}{2}$	$\frac{1}{2}$ of the number = 40
40 ÷ $\frac{1}{2}$ = 40 × 2 = 80	$\frac{2}{2}$ of the number = 2 × 40 = 80
	Therefore the number = 80

Check:

50% of 80 = 40

Answer: 80

3. 31 is 4% of what number?

$4\% = .04$

Divide 31 by .04

$$.04_\wedge\overline{)31.00_\wedge}\ \ 7\ 75.$$

Answer: 775

4. $3\frac{1}{4}\%$ of —— = 65?

$3\frac{1}{4}\% = .0325$

Divide 65 by .0325

$$.0325_\wedge\overline{)65.0000_\wedge}\ \ 2000.$$

Answer: 2,000

5. .2% of what number is 6.4?

$.2\% = .002$

Divide 6.4 by .002

$$.002_\wedge\overline{)6.400_\wedge}\ \ 3\ 200.$$

Answer: 3,200

6. $\frac{3}{8}\%$ of what number = 15?

$\frac{3}{8}\% = .00375$

Divide 15 by .00375

$$.00375_\wedge\overline{)15.00000_\wedge}\ \ 4000.$$
$$\underline{15\ 00}$$

Answer: 4,000

DIAGNOSTIC TEST

Find the missing numbers:

1. 12% of what number is 24?
2. 18 is 36% of what number?
3. 25% of what number is 6?
4. $66\frac{2}{3}\%$ of what number is 14?
5. 6% of what number is 12?
6. 20 is 20% of what number?
7. 100% of what number is 70?
8. 120% of what number is 108?
9. 40% of what number is 12.6?
10. 2.5% of what number is 2?
11. $4\frac{1}{2}\%$ of what number is 90?
12. $187\frac{1}{2}\%$ of what number is 105?
13. .5% of what number is 4?
14. $\frac{3}{4}\%$ of what number is 27?

RELATED PRACTICE EXAMPLES

Find the missing numbers:

SET 1

1. 45% of what number is 90?
2. 65% of what number is 260?
3. 74% of what number is 370?
4. 15% of what number is 18?
5. 31% of what number is 279?

SET 2

1. 12 is 24% of what number?
2. 44 is 55% of what number?
3. 9 is 15% of what number?
4. 40 is 45% of what number?
5. 17 is 85% of what number?

Set 3

1. 20% of what number is 3?
2. 40% of —— = 48?
3. 18 is 60% of what number?
4. 91 = 70% of ——?
5. 75% of what number is 108?

Set 4

1. $33\frac{1}{3}$% of what number is 78?
2. $62\frac{1}{2}$% of —— = 200?
3. 4 is $16\frac{2}{3}$% of what number?
4. 462 = $66\frac{2}{3}$% of ——?
5. $83\frac{1}{3}$% of what number is 290?

Set 5

1. 2% of what number is 10?
2. 4% of —— = 26?
3. 95 is 6% of what number?
4. 15 = 1% of ——?
5. 5% of what number is 45?

Set 6

1. 50 is 50% of what number?
2. 30 = 30% of ——?
3. 28% of what number is 28?
4. 79% of what number is 79?
5. 43% of —— = 43?

Set 7

1. 100% of what number is 59?
2. 300% of —— = 240?
3. 5 is 100% of what number?
4. 36 = 200% of ——?
5. 100% of what number is 180?

Set 8

1. 160% of what number is 72?
2. 175% of —— = 42?
3. 513 is 114% of what number?
4. 78 = 156% of ——?
5. 245% of what number is 98?

Set 9

1. 42% of what number is 115.5?
2. 60% of —— = 46.8?
3. 102.7 is 65% of what number?
4. 371.2 = 58% of ——?
5. 70% of what number is 667.8?

Set 10

1. 4.75% of what number is 38?
2. 15.4% of —— = 130.9?
3. 8.1 is 8.1% of what number?
4. 16.5 = 4.125% of ——?
5. 26.3% of —— = 18.41?

Set 11

1. $4\frac{3}{4}$% of what number is 19?
2. $6\frac{1}{8}$% of —— = 12.25?
3. 18 is $2\frac{1}{2}$% of what number?
4. 72 = $28\frac{4}{5}$% of ——?
5. $18\frac{5}{8}$% of —— = 931.25?

Set 12

1. $116\frac{2}{3}$% of what number is 21?
2. $287\frac{1}{2}$% of —— = 230?
3. 39 is $162\frac{1}{2}$% of what number?
4. 644 = $233\frac{1}{3}$% of ——?
5. $183\frac{1}{3}$% of —— = 440?

Set 13

1. .4% of what number is 2?
2. .875% of —— = 70?
3. 2 is .1% of what number?
4. 12 = $.33\frac{1}{3}$% of ——?
5. .25% of what number is 2.5?

Set 14

1. $\frac{1}{2}$% of what number is 10?
2. $\frac{5}{12}$% of —— = 100?
3. 9 is $\frac{3}{20}$% of what number?
4. 60 is $\frac{2}{3}$% of ——?
5. $\frac{1}{4}$% of what number is 6.25?

↳ PRACTICAL APPLICATIONS

1. Betty bought a camera at a 20% reduction sale. If she paid $18 for it, what was the regular price?

2. If the annual amount of depreciation is $170 based on a 2% rate of depreciation, what is the value of the property?

3. If 45% of the school are boys and the girls number 858, how many boys are enrolled?

4. Ted's brother receives $30 per week as salary and an additional 9% commission on the amount of his sales. If he earned $93 as his total income in a week, find the amount of his sales.

5. A dealer wishes to make a 25% profit on the selling price of a rug that cost him $60. What should the selling price be?

6. How much money must be invested at 4% to earn $1,000 per year?

7. If an ore contains 16% copper, how many tons of ore are needed to get 20 tons of copper?

8. The mark-up on a lamp is $12. How much did the lamp cost the dealer if he uses a 40% rate of mark-up on the cost?

REFRESH YOUR SKILLS

1. Add:

23,845
74,583
96,148
31,599
83,172

2. Subtract:

403,070
392,989

3. Multiply:

8,004
9,050

4. Divide:

$365\overline{)79,205}$

5. Add: $4\frac{5}{8}$
$\frac{3}{4}$
$8\frac{11}{16}$

6. Subtract: $1\frac{1}{6}$
$\frac{1}{2}$

7. Multiply: $6\frac{2}{3} \times 7\frac{7}{8}$

8. Divide: $4\frac{1}{6} \div 2\frac{13}{16}$

9. Add: $8.29 + .58 + $46.75

10. Subtract: $49 - $.89

11. Multiply: $2.8 \times .003$

12. Divide: $20\overline{).1}$

13. Find $2\frac{1}{2}$% of $6,000

14. What per cent of 120 is 75?

15. 2% of what number is 5?

16. 96% of what number is 288?

PER CENT—SOLVING BY PROPORTION

Ratio and proportion may be used to solve problems involving per cent. See pages 522 and 523.

We generally think of a per cent as another way of writing a fraction. A per cent may also be considered a ratio. 75%, which is equivalent to $\frac{75}{100}$, is the ratio of 75 to 100.

By means of proportion the three basic types of percentage problems may be treated as one.

(1) Find 8% of 25.

8% is the ratio of 8 to 100 or $\frac{8}{100}$.

To find 8% of 25 means to determine the number (n) which compared to 25 is the same as 8 compared to 100.

The proportion $\frac{n}{25} = \frac{8}{100}$ is formed and solved.

$$\frac{n}{25} = \frac{8}{100}$$
$$100\,n = 200$$
$$n = 2$$
Answer: 2

(2) What per cent of 25 is 2?

To find what per cent of 25 is 2 means to find the number (n) per 100 or the ratio of a number to 100 which has the same ratio as 2 to 25. The proportion $\frac{n}{100} = \frac{2}{25}$ is formed and solved.

$$\frac{n}{100} = \frac{2}{25}$$
$$25\,n = 200$$
$$n = 8$$
Answer: 8%

(3) 8% of what number is 2?

8% is the ratio of 8 to 100 or $\frac{8}{100}$.

To find the number of which 8% is 2 means to determine the number (n) such that 2 compared to this number is the same as 8 compared to 100.

The proportion $\frac{2}{n} = \frac{8}{100}$ is formed and solved.

$$\frac{2}{n} = \frac{8}{100}$$
$$8\,n = 200$$
$$n = 25$$
Answer: 25

PER CENT—SOLVING BY EQUATION

The simple equation may also be used to find (1) a per cent of a number, (2) what per cent one number is of another, and (3) a number when a per cent of it is known. See page 504.

To use this method:

(*a*) Read each problem carefully to find the facts which are related to the missing number.

(*b*) Represent this unknown by a letter.

(*c*) Form an equation by translating two equal facts, with at least one containing the unknown, into algebraic expressions and writing one expression equal to the other. Where necessary, change the per cent to a common fraction or decimal equivalent.

(d) Solve the equation and check.

(1) Find 8% of 25	(2) What % of 25 is 2?	(3) 8% of what number is 2?
$8\% \times 25 = n$	$n\% \times 25 = 2$	$8\% \times n = 2$
$.08 \times 25 = n$	$\dfrac{n}{100} \times 25 = 2$	$.08\,n = 2$
$2 = n$	$\dfrac{n}{4} = 2$	$\dfrac{.08\,n}{.08} = \dfrac{2}{.08}$
$n = 2$	$n = 8$	$n = 25$
Answer, 2	*Answer,* 8%	*Answer,* 25

1. Write each of the following as a ratio:

(a) 6%   (d) 70%   (g) 300%   (j) 2.4%   (m) 57%

(b) 18%   (e) 4%   (h) $62\frac{1}{2}\%$ (k) $\frac{1}{2}\%$ (n) $33\frac{1}{3}\%$

(c) 93%   (f) 120%   (i) $5\frac{1}{4}\%$ (l) 25%   (o) 0.7%

2. Find each of the following:

(a) 37% of 16   (e) 3% of $940   (i) $4\frac{3}{4}\%$ of 924

(b) 8% of 729   (f) 180% of 685   (j) $\frac{1}{4}\%$ of 600

(c) 45% of $300   (g) $16\frac{2}{3}\%$ of 732   (k) 200% of 350

(d) 60% of $1,200   (h) 5.9% of 28   (l) $60\frac{1}{2}\%$ of 520

3. Find each of the following:

(a) 2 is what per cent of 5?   (g) 6 is what per cent of 3?

(b) 18 is what per cent of 54?   (h) What per cent of 8 is 10?

(c) What per cent of 105 is 70?   (i) What per cent of 1.5 is 1.2?

(d) What per cent of 84 is 63?   (j) 7 is what per cent of 11?

(e) 49 is what per cent of 56?   (k) What per cent of $.45 is $.27?

(f) What per cent of 72 is 60?   (l) $1.50 is what per cent of $9?

4. Find each of the following:

(a) 15% of what number is 3?   (g) 160% of what number is 56?

(b) 9% of what number is 72?   (h) 65 is $33\frac{1}{3}\%$ of what number?

(c) 24 is 75% of what number?   (i) 140 is $62\frac{1}{2}\%$ of what number?

(d) 7.8 is 4% of what number?   (j) 3.4% of what number is 10.2?

(e) 100% of what number is 17?   (k) 19 is $\frac{1}{2}\%$ of what number?

(f) 48 is 80% of what number?   (l) .7% of what number is 21?

REVIEW OF UNIT IV

1. Write each of the following as a per cent, decimal, and fraction:

(*a*) Seven hundredths   (*b*) Fifty-six hundredths   (*c*) 53 out of 100   (*d*) 91 out of 100   (*e*) Thirty-nine and one-third hundredths

2. Express each of the following per cents as a decimal:

(*a*) 4%   (*b*) 59%   (*c*) 150%   (*d*) $100\frac{3}{4}\%$ (*e*) 6.9%

3. Express each of the following decimals as a per cent:

(*a*) .03   (*b*) .3   (*c*) 1.18   (*d*) .942   (*e*) $.66\frac{2}{3}$

4. Express each of the following per cents as a common fraction or mixed number:

(*a*) 25%   (*b*) $83\frac{1}{3}\%$ (*c*) 6%   (*d*) $162\frac{1}{2}\%$ (*e*) 250%

5. Express each of the following fractions or mixed numbers as a per cent:

(*a*) $\frac{3}{5}$ (*b*) $\frac{11}{25}$ (*c*) $\frac{5}{4}$ (*d*) $\frac{71}{71}$ (*e*) $3\frac{2}{3}$

6. Find the following:

(*a*) 82% of 350   (*b*) 6% of \$39   (*c*) 75% of 2,000
          (*d*) $4\frac{1}{2}\%$ of \$92.75   (*e*) 180% of 560

7. Find the following:

(*a*) 16 is what per cent of 24?   (*b*) What per cent of 50 is 29? (*c*) \$.48 is what per cent of \$3.20   (*d*) 5 is what per cent of 2? (*e*) What per cent of 9 is 4?   (Correct to nearest tenth)

8. Find the missing numbers:

(*a*) 28% of what number is 7?   (*b*) 72 is 9% of what number? (*c*) 54 is 3.6% of what number?   (*d*) $2\frac{1}{4}\%$ of what number is 81? (*e*) $137\frac{1}{2}\%$ of what number is 55?

9. Richard's father bought a new car for \$3,060. He paid 20% down. If the balance is to be paid in 24 equal monthly installments, how much must he pay each month?

10. What per cent was a television set reduced if it was marked \$225 and sold for \$195?

11. A fur coat with a 10% tax included sells for \$825. What is the selling price of the coat without the tax?

12. On which is the rate of discount greater and how much greater, a suit reduced from \$60 to \$50 or one reduced from \$50 to \$40?

CUMULATIVE PRACTICE

1. Add:
124,173
790,321
525,808
153,349
630,775
219,683

2. Subtract:
815,927
7,549

3. Multiply:
5,807
609

4. Divide:
$495\overline{)4,006,530}$

5. Add:
$4\frac{2}{3}$
$5\frac{7}{8}$

6. Subtract:
20
$6\frac{13}{16}$

7. Multiply:
$\frac{3}{8} \times 4\frac{9}{16}$

8. Divide:
$12 \div \frac{3}{4}$

9. Add:
$\$.06 + \$9$

10. Subtract:
$.4 - .39$

11. Multiply:
$\$2.96$
$.045$

12. Divide:
$\$.05\overline{)\$3}$

13. Find 8% of $427

14. What per cent of 60 is 56?

15. 35% of what number is 14?

KEYED ACHIEVEMENT TEST

For additional practice turn to the exercises indicated by the numerals in the circles.

1. Round off 93,482,576 to the nearest thousand. ②

2. Write as a decimal: Sixty and five thousandths ㉑

3. Add:
82,197
4,825
399 ③
47,286
8,678

4. Subtract:
250,105
176,298 ④

5. Multiply:
6,043
7,008 ⑤

6. Divide:
$809\overline{)247,554}$ ⑥

7. Add:
$6\frac{1}{3}$
$4\frac{3}{4}$ ⑫
$3\frac{7}{12}$

8. Subtract:
$8\frac{1}{2}$
$2\frac{2}{3}$ ⑭

9. Multiply:
$6\frac{1}{4} \times 3\frac{3}{5}$ ⑰

10. Divide:
$2\frac{5}{16} \div \frac{7}{8}$ ⑱

11. Add: ㉓
$4.29 + 97.2 + .687$

12. Subtract:
$\$6.50 - \$3$ ㉔

13. Multiply:
$.24 \times .002$ ㉖

14. Divide:
$.06\overline{).3}$ ㉗

Continued on next page.

15. Change $\frac{3}{8}$ to a decimal fraction. ㉚

16. Change .8 to a common fraction. ㉛

17. Change .069 to a per cent. ㊱

18. Find 5% of $32.68 ㊴

19. 45 is what per cent of 72? ㊵

20. 6% of what number is 270? ㊶

ESTIMATING ANSWERS

In each of the following first estimate your answer, then compute to check the amount of error:

1. 53 times 67
2. 98 times 29
3. $4\frac{7}{8}$ times $3\frac{1}{8}$
4. 2.03 times .96
5. 697 times 3.1

6. 781 divided by 19
7. 5,367 divided by 62
8. $11\frac{2}{3}$ divided by $3\frac{1}{6}$
9. $18\frac{1}{4}$ divided by $1\frac{15}{16}$
10. 26.9 divided by 8.75

MEANINGS AND UNDERSTANDINGS

1. What is the answer called when:

(*a*) One number is subtracted from another? (*b*) Two numbers are multiplied? (*c*) One number is divided by another? (*d*) Two numbers are added?

2. Which is equal to 0:

(*a*) Any number, other than zero, divided by itself or (*b*) Any number subtracted from itself?

3. Is the product *greater than*, *equal to*, or *smaller than* a given number when the given number is multiplied by:

(*a*) 1? (*b*) A number greater than 1? (*c*) A number smaller than 1?

4. Is the quotient *greater than*, *equal to*, or *smaller than* a given number when the given number is divided by:

(*a*) 1? (*b*) A number greater than 1? (*c*) A number smaller than 1 (zero excluded)?

5. Does the value of the fraction change when the numerator and denominator of a given fraction are each:

(*a*) Multiplied by the same number? (*b*) Divided by the same number?

UNIT V . . . SQUARES AND SQUARE ROOTS

INTRODUCTION

The *square* of a number is the product obtained when a given number is multiplied by itself. The *square root* of a number is that number which when multiplied by itself produces the given number. The square of 9 is 81 but the square root of 9 is 3.

A number that is both a non-terminating and non-repeating decimal is an irrational number. The square roots of positive numbers (see page 258) other than perfect squares (numbers having an exact square root) cannot be expressed as a quotient of two whole numbers (with division by zero excluded) and therefore are irrational numbers. For example, the $\sqrt{5}$ is an irrational number.

There is a point on the number line that corresponds to each irrational number. To locate the point corresponding to $\sqrt{2}$ on the number line, construct a square with the side measuring the unit length. By the Rule of Pythagoras it can be shown that the length of the diagonal of this square is $\sqrt{2}$. Thus, to locate the points corresponding to $\sqrt{2}$ and $-\sqrt{2}$ (see page 483) on the number line, describe an arc using the diagonal as the radius. The points where the arc intersects the number line are the required points.

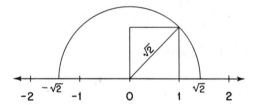

SQUARING A NUMBER

I. Aim: To square a number.

II. Procedure

Multiply the given number by itself.

III. Sample Solutions

1. Square 46

$$\begin{array}{r} 46 \\ \times\,46 \\ \hline 276 \\ 1\,84 \\ \hline 2{,}116 \end{array}$$

Answer: 2,116

2. Square .03

$$\begin{array}{r} .03 \\ \times\,.03 \\ \hline .0009 \end{array}$$

Answer: .0009

3. Square $\frac{4}{5}$

$\frac{4}{5} \times \frac{4}{5} = \frac{16}{25}$

Answer: $\frac{16}{25}$

IV. Definitions

1. Squaring a number means multiplying the number by itself.

2. The square of a number is the product obtained when the given number is multiplied by itself. The square of 5 is 25 because 25 is the product obtained when 5 is multiplied by 5.

3. A short way of writing 5×5, or 5 squared, is 5^2. The small figure 2, written to the right and a little above the number 5, is called an exponent. The exponent 2 indicates the square of a number.

DIAGNOSTIC TEST

Square the following numbers:

1. 8   **2.** 57   **3.** .25   **4.** $\frac{3}{8}$ **5.** $2\frac{1}{4}$

RELATED PRACTICE EXAMPLES

Square the following numbers:

SET 1 —	SET 2 —	SET 3 —	SET 4 —	SET 5 —
1. 4	1. 16	1. .2	1. $\frac{1}{2}$	1. $1\frac{1}{2}$
2. 1	2. 24	2. .7	2. $\frac{5}{6}$	2. $1\frac{2}{3}$
3. 9	3. 39	3. .01	3. $\frac{2}{5}$	3. $2\frac{1}{8}$
4. 7	4. 50	4. .09	4. $\frac{1}{3}$	4. $2\frac{3}{4}$
5. 10	5. 78	5. .75	5. $\frac{7}{8}$	5. $3\frac{1}{3}$
6. 3	6. 100	6. .18	6. $\frac{3}{16}$	6. $1\frac{1}{4}$
7. 6	7. 156	7. 1.47	7. $\frac{11}{12}$	7. $4\frac{1}{2}$
8. 2	8. 247	8. 2.05	8. $\frac{5}{7}$	8. $1\frac{5}{8}$
9. 12	9. 1,760	9. 3.14	9. $\frac{4}{9}$	9. $2\frac{2}{5}$
10. 11	10. 5,280	10. 18.73	10. $\frac{7}{10}$	10. $1\frac{1}{6}$

PRACTICAL APPLICATIONS

1. To find the area of a square when the length of its side is known, square the given side.

Find the area of a square of its side measures:

(*a*) 7 in.   (*b*) 13 in.   (*c*) $2\frac{1}{2}$ ft.   (*d*) 25 ft.   (*e*) 19 yd.

In evaluating formulas it is sometimes necessary to square numbers.

2. The formula for finding the lift of an airplane involves squaring its air speed.

Square the following numbers representing air speeds:

(*a*) 100 ft. per sec.   (*b*) 132 ft. per sec.   (*c*) 228 ft. per sec.

3. The formula for finding the distance a body falls involves squaring the number of seconds the body falls.

Square the following numbers representing intervals of time:

(*a*) 5 sec.   (*b*) 12 sec.   (*c*) 30 sec.   (*d*) 27 sec.   (*e*) 45 sec.

4. The formula for finding the area of a circle involves squaring the radius.

Square the following numbers representing radii of circles:

(*a*) 6 in.   (*b*) 14 ft.   (*c*) $7\frac{1}{2}$ in.   (*d*) $\frac{3}{4}$ ft.   (*e*) 26 yd.

SQUARE ROOT

I. Aim: To find the square root of a number.

II. Procedure

1. Write the numeral under the square root symbol $\left(\sqrt{} \right)$ and separate the numeral into groups of two figures each, starting at the decimal point and forming the groups, first to the left and then to the right of the decimal point.

If there is an odd number of figures to the left of the decimal point, there will be one group containing a single figure. However, if there is an odd number of figures to the right of the decimal point, annex a zero so that each group contains two figures.

2. Find the largest square which can be subtracted from the first group at the left. Write it under the first group.

3. Write the square root of this largest square above the first group as the first figure of the square root.

4. Subtract the square number from the first group. Annex the next group to the remainder.

5. Form the trial divisor by multiplying the root already found by 2 and annexing a zero which is not written but is used mentally.

6. Divide the dividend (Step 4) by the trial divisor (Step 5). Annex the quotient to the root already found; also annex it to the trial divisor to form the complete divisor.

7. Multiply the complete divisor by the new figure of the root.

8. Subtract this product (Step 7) from the dividend (Step 4).

9. Continue this process until all the groups have been used or the desired number of decimal places has been obtained.

10. Since each figure of the root is placed directly above its corresponding group, the decimal point in the root is placed directly above the decimal point in the numeral for the given number.

11. Check by squaring the root (multiplying the answer by itself) to obtain the given number.

III. Sample Solutions

1. Find the square root of 676.

```
      2  6    Check:
   √6 76          26
   4               26
 46)2 76         156
   2 76           52
   . . .         676
```
Answer: 26

2. Find the square root of 5,184.

```
      7  2    Check:
   √51 84          72
   49              72
 142) 2 84        144
   2 84          5 04
   . . .         5,184
```
Answer: 72

3. Find the square root of 214,369.

```
      4  6  3    Check:
   √21 43 69          463
   16                 463
 86) 5 43          1 389
   5 16            27 78
 923)  27 69       185 2
   27 69           214,369
```
Answer: 463

4. Find the square root of 94,249.

```
      3  0  7    Check:
   √9 42 49          307
   9                 307
 607)  42 49       2 149
   42 49           92 10
   . . . .         94,249
```
Answer: 307

5. Find the square root of .2916

```
          .5  4       Check:
       √.29 16            .54
       25                 .54
    104)  4 16           216
       4 16              270
Answer: .54   . . .      .2916
```

6. Find the square root of 7 correct to the nearest hundredth:

```
      2.  6  4  5 = 2.65        Check:
   √7.00 00 00                     2.645
   4                               2.645
 46)3 00                          13 225
   2 76                           105 80
 524)  24 00                     1 587 0
   20 96                         5 290
 5285) 3 04 00                   6 996 025
   2 64 25                          3 975
      39 75    Answer: 2.65       7.000 000
```

IV. Definition

The square root of a number is that number which when multiplied by itself produces the given number. The square root of 36 is 6 because 6 is the number which multiplied by itself equals 36.

DIAGNOSTIC TEST

Find the square root of each of the following numbers. If there is a remainder, find answer correct to nearest hundredth.

1. 64	**5.** 6,084	**9.** 2,673,225	**13.** .8836
2. 8,100	**6.** 71,289	**10.** 52,649,536	**14.** 42
3. .09	**7.** 343,396	**11.** 36,048,016	**15.** 768.4
4. 529	**8.** 167,281	**12.** 409,600	

RELATED PRACTICE EXAMPLES

Find the square root of each of the following numbers. If there is a remainder, find answer correct to nearest hundredth:

Set 1	Set 2	Set 3	Set 4	Set 5
1. 4	**1.** 400	**1.** .04	**1.** 196	**1.** 2,601
2. 49	**2.** 2,500	**2.** .64	**2.** 625	**2.** 4,356
3. 25	**3.** 100	**3.** .81	**3.** 784	**3.** 5,929
4. 9	**4.** 6,400	**4.** .25	**4.** 576	**4.** 8,836
5. 81	**5.** 900	**5.** .01	**5.** 324	**5.** 3,481
6. 16	**6.** 1,600	**6.** .16	**6.** 961	**6.** 1,369
7. 36	**7.** 8,100	**7.** .49	**7.** 484	**7.** 7,396
8. 1	**8.** 3,600	**8.** .0009	**8.** 289	**8.** 9,801
9. 64	**9.** 4,900	**9.** .0036	**9.** 841	**9.** 5,625
10. 100	**10.** 10,000	**10.** .0001	**10.** 729	**10.** 1,444

Set 6	Set 7	Set 8
1. 16,384	**1.** 140,625	**1.** 40,401
2. 60,516	**2.** 682,276	**2.** 11,881
3. 97,344	**3.** 398,161	**3.** 93,636
4. 70,225	**4.** 175,561	**4.** 43,264
5. 21,904	**5.** 877,969	**5.** 164,836
6. 56,169	**6.** 341,056	**6.** 497,025
7. 35,721	**7.** 208,849	**7.** 254,016
8. 23,716	**8.** 487,204	**8.** 815,409
9. 85,849	**9.** 565,504	**9.** 643,204
10. 45,369	**10.** 799,236	**10.** 368,449

SET 9	SET 10	SET 11
1. 1,628,176	1. 17,297,281	1. 1,014,049
2. 3,912,484	2. 46,403,344	2. 4,016,016
3. 5,499,025	3. 10,349,089	3. 9,030,025
4. 1,108,809	4. 31,315,216	4. 64,096,036
5. 6,620,329	5. 19,351,201	5. 16,024,009
6. 1,580,049	6. 58,491,904	6. 25,090,081
7. 5,692,996	7. 72,914,521	7. 36,024,004
8. 9,872,164	8. 92,871,769	8. 81,018,001
9. 8,826,841	9. 40,640,625	9. 49,112,064
10. 3,418,801	10. 65,999,376	10. 36,072,036

SET 12	SET 13	SET 14	SET 15
1. 52,900	1. .1296	1. 2	1. .1
2. 313,600	2. .0324	2. 8	2. .59
3. 774,400	3. .0841	3. 15	3. 147.6
4. 2,992,900	4. .5476	4. 39	4. 3.5
5. 67,404,100	5. .9409	5. 128	5. 207.59
6. 1,040,400	6. 190.44	6. 346	6. 6.283
7. 50,268,100	7. 3.0276	7. 983	7. 25.9
8. 2,250,000	8. 88.5481	8. 1,000	8. .924
9. 27,040,000	9. 7,157.16	9. 2,382	9. 94.617
10. 58,982,400	10. 1,070.5984	10. 4,976	10. 503.419

Square Root by Estimation, Division, and Average

The approximate square root of a number may also be found by estimation, division and average as follows:

(1) Estimate the square root of the given number.

(2) Divide the given number by the estimated squared root.

(3) Find the average of the resulting quotient and estimated square root.

(4) Divide the given number by this average (step 3).

(5) Find the average of the divisor used and quotient found in step 4.

(6) Continue this process to obtain a greater degree of approxi-

mation as the divisor and quotient will eventually approximate each other.

Find the square root of 12.

Since 12 is between 9 and 16, its square root will be between 3 and 4.

                               3.4
                      3.5   + 3.5
             3.4)$\overline{12.00}$ 2)6.9(3.45

(1) Use 3.4 as the estimate.
(2) Divide 12 by 3.4 to get the quotient 3.5.

                              3.45
(3) The average of 3.4 and   3.48   + 3.48
3.5 is 3.45.   3.45)$\overline{12.0000}$ 2)6.93(3.465

(4) Divide 12 by 3.45 to get the quotient 3.48.
(5) The average of 3.45 and 3.48 is 3.465.

                              3.465
(6) Divide 12 by 3.465 to   3.463   3.463
get the quotient 3.463. 3.465)$\overline{12.000000}$ 2)6.928(3.464
The average of 3.465 and 3.463 is 3.464.

                       Answer: 3.464

PRACTICE PROBLEMS

Find the square root of each of the following numbers by estimation, division, and average:

(a) 6	(d) 59	(g) 105	(j) 92	(m) 550
(b) 14	(e) 38	(h) 86	(k) 125	(n) 972
(c) 21	(f) 75	(i) 41	(l) 300	(o) 697

Square Root by Use of Table

Square roots of whole numbers 1 to 99 inclusive and of the perfect squares (squares of whole numbers) given in the table may be found directly from the table of squares and square roots on page 559.

To find the square root of any whole number from 1 to 99 inclusive, first locate the given number in the "No." column and then move to the right to the corresponding "Square Root" column to obtain the required square root.

To find the square root of a perfect square given in the table, first locate this number in the "Square" column and then move to the left to the corresponding "No." column to obtain the required square root.

PRACTICE PROBLEMS

Find the square root of each of the following numbers by use of the table (see page 559):

(a) 19	(e) 48	(i) 33	(m) 9,216	(q) 2,809
(b) 57	(f) 29	(j) 91	(n) 784	(r) 7,921
(c) 95	(g) 66	(k) 324	(o) 2,209	(s) 3,481
(d) 73	(h) 84	(l) 1,225	(p) 5,476	(t) 3,969

PRACTICAL APPLICATIONS

1. To find the length of the side of a square when its area is known, find the square root of the area of the square.

Find the length of the side of a square if its area is:

(a) 25 sq. in.　(b) 144 sq. in.　(c) 6,889 sq. ft.　(d) 1 acre

2. To find the number of seconds it takes a freely falling body to fall a given distance, divide the distance by 16, then find the square root of the quotient.

Find the number of seconds it takes a freely falling body to fall:

(a) 64 ft.　(b) 400 ft.　(c) 4,624 ft.　(d) 7,056 ft.　(e) 10,000 ft.

3. To find the radius of a circle when its area is known, divide the area of the circle by $\frac{22}{7}$, then find the square root of the quotient. Find the radius of a circle when its area is:

(a) 88 sq. in.　(b) 132 sq. ft.　(c) 198 sq. yd.　(d) 440 sq. ft.

4. To find the length of the edge of a cube when the total area of its outside surface is known, divide the total area by 6, then find the square root of the quotient. Find the length of the edge of a cube when its total surface area is:

(a) 294 sq. in. (b) 1,536 sq. ft. (c) 3,750 sq. ft. (d) 8,214 sq. in.

5. To find the diameter of a circle when its area is known, divide the area of the circle by .7854, then find the square root of the quotient. Find the diameter of a circle when its area is:

(a) 78.54 sq. in.　　(b) 1,963.5 sq. ft.　　(c) 314.16 sq. ft.
(d) 706.86 sq. in.

NOW THAT YOU HAVE HAD THE OPPORTUNITY TO CORRECT YOUR WEAKNESSES IN ARITHMETIC, CHECK YOUR PROGRESS AND YOUR LEVEL OF ACHIEVEMENT BY TRYING THE EXAMPLES IN THE FOLLOWING TESTS.

IF YOU STILL NEED HELP, TURN TO THE EXERCISES CORRESPONDING TO THE ORDER NUMBERS OF THE EXAMPLES WHICH YOU COULD NOT DO CORRECTLY.

1. Read the numeral 85,267,428 or write it as a word statement.
2. Round off 581,560 to the nearest thousand.
3. Add: $472 + 5,973 + 15,682 + 33 + 280$
4. Take 638 from 4,000.   5. Multiply: $8 \times 14 \times 1,728$
6. Divide: $48\overline{)33,744}$ 7. Reduce $\frac{28}{48}$ to lowest terms.
8. Change $\frac{9}{2}$ to a mixed number.
9. Reduce $6\frac{7}{3}$ to simplest form.
10. Change $\frac{7}{12}$ to 60ths.
11. Find the lowest common denominator of the following fractions: $\frac{2}{3}, \frac{3}{4},$ and $\frac{11}{12}$
12. Add: $9\frac{1}{2} + 3\frac{2}{5}$
13. Find the missing number: $2\frac{5}{6} = 1\frac{}{24}$
14. Subtract: $4\frac{1}{4}$ 15. Which is smaller: $\frac{5}{8}$ or $\frac{5}{6}$?
        $2\frac{1}{3}$ 16. Change to an improper fraction: $6\frac{3}{8}$
17. Multiply: $3\frac{7}{8} \times 2$
18. Divide: $\frac{3}{4} \div 6$
19. What part of 32 is 20?
20. $\frac{9}{20}$ of what number is 36?
21. Write as a decimal numeral: Fifteen and seven tenths.
22. Find correct to nearest hundredth: 26.8539
23. Add: $6.57
        .36
        12.40
        .82
24. Subtract: $54.3 - 8.28$
25. Which is larger: .46 or .462?
26. Multiply: 3.14×15
27. Divide: $.06\overline{)\$7.44}$
28. Multiply by short method: 10×8.69
29. Divide by short method: $1.95 \div 100$
30. Change $1\frac{3}{8}$ to a decimal (2 places).
31. Change 2.75 to a mixed number.
32. Add: $\frac{1}{4} + .87\frac{1}{2}$
33. Multiply 392 by $12\frac{1}{2}$, using short method.
34. Write sixty hundredths as a per cent, decimal, and fraction.
35. Express 7% as a decimal.
36. Express $.00\frac{7}{8}$ as a per cent.
37. Express 40% as a common fraction.
38. Express $\frac{3}{25}$ as a per cent.
39. Find 125% of 560.
40. 52 is what per cent of 64?
41. 75% of what number is 60?
42. Square 140.   43. Find the square root of 290,521.

1. Read the numeral 7,015,673 or write it as a word statement.
2. Round off 496,280,074 to the nearest million.

3. Add: 462,741   4. Subtract: 178,346
     893,826   77,482
     652,158   5. Multiply 3,600 by 807.
     894,923   6. Divide 72,576 by 1,728.
     579,109   7. Reduce $\frac{63}{105}$ to lowest terms.

8. Change $\frac{21}{12}$ to a mixed number.
9. Reduce $15\frac{10}{16}$ to simplest form.   10. Change $\frac{2}{3}$ to 27ths.
11. Find the lowest common denominator of the following fractions: $\frac{5}{8}$ and $\frac{11}{16}$

12. Add: $\frac{3}{4}$ 13. Find the missing numbers:
       $2\frac{5}{16}$ $8\frac{3}{4} = 8\frac{}{32} = 7\frac{}{32}$
       $4\frac{19}{32}$

14. Subtract $3\frac{3}{8}$ from 4.   15. Which is larger: $\frac{9}{10}$ or $\frac{11}{12}$?
16. Change $4\frac{5}{16}$ to an improper fraction.
17. Multiply: $2\frac{1}{3} \times 3\frac{1}{7}$ 18. Divide: $\frac{15}{16} \div 1\frac{1}{2}$
19. 60 is what part of 100?   20. $\frac{1}{6}$ of what number is 17?
21. Write as a decimal numeral: Five hundred and six thousandths.
22. Find correct to nearest cent: $4.2046
23. Add: 1.93 + .541 + 43.8   24. Subtract:
25. Which is smaller: .92 or .919? $452.46
26. Multiply 6.42 by .25   189.57
27. Divide: $.04\overline{)\,.00012}$
28. Multiply by short method: 100×250
29. Divide by short method: $18.53 \div 1,000$
30. Change $\frac{3}{7}$ to a decimal (2 places).
31. Change .016 to a common fraction. 32. Subtract: $.8 - \frac{3}{4}$
33. Divide 125 by $33\frac{1}{3}$, using short method.
34. Write ninety-four hundredths as a per cent, decimal, and fraction.
35. Express 4.5% as a decimal. 36. Express 1.05 as a per cent.
37. Express 175% as a mixed number.
38. Express $\frac{24}{300}$ as a per cent.
39. Find 8.3% of $15 (nearest cent).
40. What per cent of $7.00 is $1.75?
41. $6\frac{1}{2}\%$ of what number is 26?   42. Square $1\frac{3}{5}$.
43. Find the square root of 6 correct to nearest hundredth.

1. Read the numeral 5,965,408,000 or write it as a word statement.

2. Round off 147,492,350 to the nearest hundred thousand.

3. Add: 15,976
    2,734
   38,592
   21,085
    6,588

4. From 823,849 subtract 812,958.

5. Find the product of 6,009 and 7,908.

6. Divide: 4,843,630 ÷ 605

7. Reduce $\frac{1400}{3600}$ to lowest terms.

8. Change $\frac{51}{16}$ to a mixed number.

9. Reduce $24\frac{18}{4}$ to simplest form.

10. Change $\frac{13}{16}$ to 64ths.

11. Find the lowest common denominator of the following fractions: $\frac{3}{5}$, $\frac{1}{4}$, and $\frac{2}{3}$ Add: $4\frac{1}{8} + \frac{7}{10}$

13. Find the missing numbers: $12\frac{5}{8} = 12\frac{}{24} = 11\frac{}{24}$

14. Subtract: $8\frac{3}{16} - \frac{7}{8}$ 15. Which is smaller: $\frac{9}{32}$ or $\frac{5}{16}$?

16. Change $4\frac{7}{12}$ to an improper fraction.

17. Multiply: $1\frac{1}{2} \times 2\frac{1}{4} \times 1\frac{1}{3}$ 18. Divide: $(3\frac{3}{4} \div 2\frac{1}{2}) \div \frac{3}{4}$

19. What part of 184 is 115?   20. $\frac{9}{16}$ of what number is 45?

21. Write as a decimal numeral: Four hundred seventy-one thousandths.

22. Find correct to nearest ten-thousandth: .00385

23. Add: $8.24 + $5.62 + $.76 + $10.08

24. Subtract .02 from .2   25. Which is larger: .201 or .21?

26. Find $1\frac{3}{4}$ of $6.25 (to nearest cent).   27. Divide 27 by 1.5

28. Multiply by short method: $1,000 \times 48.21$

29. Divide by short method: $37.2 \div 10$

30. Change $\frac{25}{30}$ to a decimal (2 places).

31. Change $.37\frac{1}{2}$ to a common fraction.

32. Divide: $.83\frac{1}{3} \div \frac{5}{12}$

33. Multiply 276 by $16\frac{2}{3}$, using short method.

34. Write eighteen and one-half hundredths as a per cent, decimal, and fraction.

35. Express 150% as a decimal.

36. Express .046 as a per cent.

37. Express 8% as a common fraction.

38. Express $\frac{8}{18}$ as a per cent.

39. Find $\frac{1}{2}$% of $30.   40. 12 is what per cent of 6?

41. 125% of what number is 70?

42. Square 3.5

43. Find the square root of 0.9 correct to nearest hundredth.

1. Read the numeral 4,306,009,085 or write it as a word statement.

2. Round off 6,382,957,429 to the nearest hundred million.

3. Add: 93,574
69,898
74,379
58,486
96,798

4. Subtract 37,989 from 5,000,000

5. Multiply: 7,963 × 5,897

6. Divide 79,183,450 by 9,806

7. Reduce $\frac{39}{169}$ to lowest terms.

8. Change $\frac{100}{24}$ to a mixed number.

9. Reduce $11\frac{15}{6}$ to simplest form.

10. Change $\frac{13}{15}$ to 120ths.

11. Find the lowest common denominator of the following fractions: $\frac{5}{8}$, $\frac{7}{12}$, and $\frac{9}{20}$.

12. Add: $5\frac{5}{6} + \frac{7}{8} + 4\frac{11}{12}$

13. Find the missing number: $16\frac{1}{8} = 15\frac{}{8}$

14. Subtract: $9\frac{2}{5} - 6\frac{3}{4}$ 15. Which is greater: $\frac{7}{15}$ or $\frac{12}{25}$?

16. Change $14\frac{7}{12}$ to an improper fraction.

17. Multiply: $11\frac{3}{16} \times 4\frac{2}{3}$ 18. Divide: $6\frac{1}{4} \div (\frac{5}{8} \div 3\frac{1}{3})$

19. What part of 98 is 21?   20. $\frac{13}{18}$ of what number is 91?

21. Write as a decimal numeral: Fifty and nine hundredths

22. Find correct to the nearest millionth: .0015867

23. Add: .06 + 6.0 + .60   24. Subtract: .803 − .79

25. Which is smaller: .9 or .885?   26. Multiply: .004 × .05

27. Divide: $.012)\overline{.6}$

28. Multiply by short method: 1,000 × 86.05

29. Divide by short method: 63.49 ÷ 1,000

30. Change $\frac{11}{16}$ to a decimal (2 places)

31. Change .65 to a common fraction.

32. From .75 subtract $\frac{3}{4}$.

33. Divide 900 by $16\frac{2}{3}$, using short method.

34. Write thirty-one hundredths as a per cent, decimal, and fraction.

35. Express 7.4% as a decimal.

36. Express .086 as a per cent.

37. Express 275% as a mixed number.

38. Express $\frac{36}{40}$ as a per cent.

39. Find $\frac{1}{4}$% of $660.   40. What per cent of 60 is 72?

41. 8% of what number is 12?

42. Square 1.73   43. Find the square root of 4.2849

PART II

ANCIENT
AND
NON-DECIMAL
MODERN SYSTEMS
OF
NUMERATION

INTRODUCTION

A system of numeration is a method of naming numbers by writing numerals. The base of a numeration system is the unit of grouping or the number it takes in any one place to make one (1) in the next higher place.

This section includes a description of the ancient numeration systems of the Egyptians, Babylonians, Chinese, Mayans, Greeks and Romans. The Egyptians used different symbols for grouping instead of using the positions of the symbols in the numeral. The Babylonians and Mayans used bases other than ten; the Babylonians the base of sixty, the Mayans the base of twenty. The Chinese used the base of ten but wrote symbols to represent powers of ten instead of using place value.

In modern numeration systems, number symbols from zero up to, but not including, the symbol for the base are arranged by position to represent numbers. Place value and the principles of addition and multiplication are used in these systems. A description of the decimal system of numeration is found on page 4.

This test is keyed by page number. Explanatory material may be found on the page indicated by the numeral at the end of each problem.

1. Name 267 by its equivalent:
   - (a) Roman numeral **276**   (d) Egyptian numeral   **272**
   - (b) Chinese numeral **273**   (e) Greek numeral   **274**
   - (c) Mayan numeral **273**   (f) Babylonian numeral   **272**

2. Name CCCXLV by its equivalent: **276**
   - (a) decimal numeral **272**   (d) Babylonian numeral **272**
   - (b) Egyptian numeral **272**   (e) Chinese numeral   **273**
   - (c) Greek numeral   **274**   (f) Mayan numeral   **273**

3. Name ΣΛΗ by its equivalent: **274**
   - (a) decimal numeral **272**   (d) Mayan numeral   **273**
   - (b) Roman numeral **276**   (e) Babylonian numeral **272**
   - (c) Chinese numeral **273**   (f) Egyptian numeral   **272**

4. Name 3,597 by its equivalent:
   - (a) Chinese numeral **273**   (c) Roman numeral   **276**
   - (b) Egyptian numeral **272**

5. Make as many dots on your paper as are represented   **277**
   by each of the following numerals. Group them to show the meaning of each numeral.   (a) 23_{four} (b) 54_{eight} (c) 36_{seven}

6. What is the value of the place where the digit: **277**
   - (a) 7 is located in the numeral 7563_{nine}?
   - (b) E is located in the numeral $9E854_{twelve}$?
   - (c) 1 is located in the numeral 100000000_{two}?

7. What numeral is the successor of: (a) 4344_{five}?   **277**
   (b) 66666_{seven}?   (c) 32333_{four}?

8. Express 34121_{five} in expanded form as a polynomial.   **280**

9. Express 210221_{three} as a base ten numeral.   **281**

10. Express 32416_{seven} as a base twelve numeral.   **281**

11. Express 14532_{six} as a base two numeral.   **281**

12. Add: **284** 13. Subtract: **284**   Multiply: **284**

$$21012_{three}$$
$$2212_{three}$$
$$12221_{three}$$
$$\underline{2102_{three}}$$

$$6403_{seven}$$
$$\underline{3645_{seven}}$$

$$342_{five}$$
$$\underline{413_{five}}$$

15. Divide: $101_{two})\overline{1001011_{two}}$ **284**

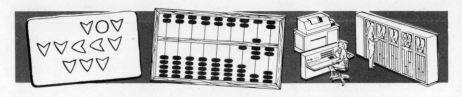

ANCIENT SYSTEMS OF NUMERATION

EGYPTIAN

The ancient Egyptians used the following number symbols in their system of notation:

Symbol | ∩ 9 𝄉 (⋙ ☥

Value   1   10   100   1,000   10,000   100,000   1,000,000

To write numerals for numbers, they used, when necessary, any symbol as many as nine times but used the next higher number symbol if ten of any one symbol were required. The symbols were written next to each other and the sum of their value represented the number.

𝄉 9 9 9 ∩ ∩ ∩ ∩ | | consists of symbols representing

$1,000 + 100 + 100 + 100 + 10 + 10 + 10 + 10 + 1 + 1$ or   the number 1,342.

BABYLONIAN

The Babylonians used wedge-shaped number symbols.

Symbol   ∨   ◁   ∨   ◁

Value   1   10   60   600

To write numerals for numbers from 1 to 59 inclusive, they used the symbol for one as many as nine times when necessary and the symbol for ten as many as five times when necessary. To write numerals for numbers greater than 59 they used 60 as the base.

∨ ◁ ◁ ◁ ∨ ∨   consists of symbols represent-

ing $60 + 10 + 10 + 10 + 1 + 1$, or the number 92.

CHINESE

The Chinese use the following traditional number symbols to express numbers one to nine inclusive and powers of ten:

Symbol	—	=	≡	⊏⊐	五	六
Value	1	2	3	4	5	6

Symbol	七	八	九	十	百	千
Value	7	8	9	10	100	1,000

Chinese numerals are written vertically. When a symbol that represents any number from 1 through 9 precedes (written above) a symbol that represents a power of ten, it indicates how many times that power is taken.

30 is expressed as 3 times 10   800 is expressed as 8 times 100

or ≡ 十   or 八 百

The following numeral represents:

千 2 times 1,000 plus

九 百 9 times 100 plus

⊏⊐ 十 4 times 10 plus

八 8 or the number 2,948.

MAYAN

The Mayans of Central America used a dot for one and a bar for five. They formed combinations of dots and bars to represent numbers from 1 to 19 as follows:

Symbol	•	••	•••	••••	—	•̲	•̲•̲	•̲•̲•̲	•̲•̲•̲•̲	=
Value	1	2	3	4	5	6	7	8	9	10

Symbol	•̿	••̿	•••̿	••••̿	≡	•̳	••̳	•••̳	••••̳
Value	11	12	13	14	15	16	17	18	19

However, they used 20 as the base of their system. The

symbol representing 0 was  . When this symbol was written under any of the symbols for 1 to 17 inclusive, it indicated, acting as a place holder, that the number was 20 times as large. ⬤ expressed 5×20 or 100.

Mayan numerals were written vertically.

$\overset{\bullet\bullet}{\underset{\equiv}{\bullet\bullet\bullet\bullet}}$ represented 2×20 plus 19 or the number 59.

GREEK

The Greeks used alphabetic numerals. The first nine letters of their alphabet represented numbers 1 to 9 inclusive, the next nine letters represented the tens, and other letters represented the hundreds.

Symbol	A	B	Γ	Δ	E	F	Z	H	θ
Value	1	2	3	4	5	6	7	8	9

Symbol	I	K	Λ	M	N	Ξ	O	Π	ꟼ
Value	10	20	30	40	50	60	70	80	90

Symbol	P	Σ	T	Υ	Φ	X	Ψ	Ω	⅀
Value	100	200	300	400	500	600	700	800	900

The Greek numerals were formed by writing the letters next to each other with the letters representing ones on the right, tens to the left of the ones, and hundreds to the left of the tens. Sometimes an accent mark was written after the letter to indicate that it was a numeral.

ΩKθ represented $800 + 20 + 9$ or the number 829.

PRACTICE PROBLEMS

1. What decimal number is expressed by each of the following numerals?

(a) ꟼꟼ੭∩∩∩||||

(b) ੧੧੧∩∩∩||||
ſſſℲ੧੧੧∩∩∩||||
∩∩∩

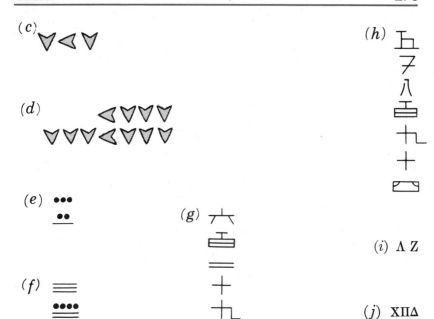

2. (a) Write as an Egyptian numeral: (1) 65 (2) 243 (3) 5,418
   (b) Write as a Mayan numeral: (1) 37 (2) 112 (3) 271
   (c) Write as a Babylonian numeral: (1) 28 (2) 76 (3) 145
   (d) Write as a Chinese numeral: (1) 54 (2) 628 (3) 7,934
   (e) Write as a Greek numeral: (1) 69 (2) 475 (3) 892

3. Name 46 by its equivalent:
   (a) Egyptian numeral   (d) Greek numeral
   (b) Mayan numeral   (e) Chinese numeral
   (c) Babylonian numeral

4. Name 269 by its equivalent:
   (a) Babylonian numeral   (d) Mayan numeral
   (b) Greek numeral   (e) Egyptian numeral
   (c) Chinese numeral

5. Name TNH by its equivalent:
   (a) decimal numeral   (d) Babylonian numeral
   (b) Chinese numeral   (e) Mayan numeral
   (c) Egyptian numeral

ROMAN

The Romans used as number symbols I for 1, V for 5, X for 10, L for 50, C for 100, D for 500, and M for 1,000.

Roman numerals were formed by writing from left to right as a sum, first the symbol for the largest possible value, with symbols I, X, C, and M used as many as three times when necessary, then the symbol for the next smaller value, etc.

$$
\begin{array}{ll}
\multicolumn{2}{c}{\text{MDCCXCIII}} \\
\text{Since} & M = 1,000 \\
 & D = 500 \\
 & CC = 200 \\
 & XC = 90 \\
 & III = 3 \\
 \cline{2-2}
 & 1,793 \\
\multicolumn{2}{c}{\text{MDCCXCIII} = 1,793}
\end{array}
$$

When symbols I, X, or C preceded a Roman number symbol of greater value, its value was subtracted from the larger value.

$$IV = 5 - 1 = 4 \qquad IX = 10 - 1 = 9 \qquad XL = 50 - 10 = 40$$
$$XC = 100 - 10 = 90 \qquad CD = 500 - 100 = 400$$
$$CM = 1,000 - 100 = 900$$

The symbols V, L, and D never preceded a Roman number symbol of greater value and were never used in succession.

PRACTICE PROBLEMS

1. What decimal number does each of the following Roman numerals represent?

 (a) II　　　　VIII　　　　IX　　　　XVII　　　　XXIV
 (b) XXXIX　　　LXVI　　　XLVII　　　XC　　　LIV
 (c) XCVIII　　　CXII　　　CCCXC　　　CDXI
 (d) DCCXLI　　MDCLXVI　　MCCLIV　　MCMLXV

2. Write the Roman numeral for each of the following numbers:

 (a)　　7　　　　4　　　　19　　　　34　　　　21　　　　38
 (b)　63　　　　76　　　　48　　　　97　　　104　　　299
 (c) 386　　　847　　　459　　　1492　　　1970　　　1995

3. Name LXXIV by an equivalent:

 (a) decimal numeral　　　　(d) Greek numeral
 (b) Babylonian numeral　　(e) Egyptian numeral
 (c) Mayan numeral　　　　(f) Chinese numeral

4. Name CMXCIX by an equivalent:

 (a) Chinese numeral　　　　(c) Egyptian numeral
 (b) Greek numeral

NON-DECIMAL MODERN SYSTEMS OF NUMERATION

Reading and Writing Numerals; Place Value

The number symbols required by a modern system of numeration and the place value used in the system depend on the base of the system. Each system of numeration has its own place value.

In each modern system, as we have already seen in the decimal system on page 4, number symbols from zero up to, but not including, the symbol for the base are arranged by position to represent numbers. No digit whose value is equal to or greater than the value of the digit representing the base number may be used. The binary (base 2) system uses only digits 0 and 1; the ternary (base 3) system uses only digits 0, 1, and 2; the quaternary (base 4) system uses only digits 0, 1, 2, and 3; etc. Thus, any number less than the base number is represented by its respective symbol and any number equal to or greater than the base number is represented by a numeral containing more than one digit.

The base of the numeration system is indicated by a subscript written at the lower right of the numeral.

14_{five} or 14_5 is read "one four, base five."

935_{twelve} or 935_{12} is read "nine three five, base twelve."

1011_{two} or 1011_2 is read "one zero one one, base two."

A numeral that does not have an identifying subscript or some other identification is assumed to be a numeral belonging to the decimal system.

If fourteen dots are grouped

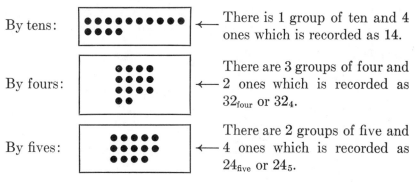

By tens: ←— There is 1 group of ten and 4 ones which is recorded as 14.

By fours: ←— There are 3 groups of four and 2 ones which is recorded as 32_{four} or 32_4.

By fives: ←— There are 2 groups of five and 4 ones which is recorded as 24_{five} or 24_5.

By sevens:  ← There are 2 groups of seven and no ones which is recorded as 20_{seven} or 20_7.

If the system is base 2 (binary system), there are two number symbols, 0 and 1, and the value of each place is two times the value of the next place to the right. Two of any one group will make one of the next larger group. 2 ones make 1 two; 2 twos make 1 four; 2 fours make 1 eight, and so forth.

Binary

1	1	1	1	0	1	┆	1	1
32's	16's	8's	4's	2's	1's	┆	$\frac{1}{2}$'s	$\frac{1}{4}$'s

Point

If the system is base 5 (quinary system), there are five number symbols, 0, 1, 2, 3, and 4, and the value of each place is five times the value of the next place to the right. Five of any one group will make one of the next larger group. 5 ones make 1 five; 5 fives makes 1 twenty-five, and so forth.

Quinary

1	2	0	3	1	4	┆	2	3
3,125's	625's	125's	25's	5's	1's	┆	$\frac{1}{5}$'s	$\frac{1}{25}$'s

Point

If the system is base 12 (duodecimal system), there are twelve number symbols, 0, 1, 2, 3, 4, 5, 6, 7, 8, 9, T (ten), and E (eleven), and the value of each place is twelve times the value of the next place to the right. Twelve of any one group will make one of the next larger group. 12 ones make 1 twelve; 12 twelves make 1 one hundred forty-four, and so forth.

Duodecimal

7	E	4	T	8	┆	3	5
20,736's	1728's	144's	12's	1's	┆	$\frac{1}{12}$'s	$\frac{1}{144}$'s

Point

The place values of some of the systems of numeration used in this book are given in the following table. Observe that the values increase going to the left.

SYSTEM	← PLACE VALUES ←				
Base 2	16's	8's	4's	2's	1's
Base 3	81's	27's	9's	3's	1's
Base 4	256's	64's	16's	4's	1's
Base 5	625's	125's	25's	5's	1's
Base 6	1,296's	216's	36's	6's	1's
Base 7	2,401's	343's	49's	7's	1's
Base 8	4,096's	512's	64's	8's	1's
Base 9	6,561's	729's	81's	9's	1's
Base 10	10,000's	1,000's	100's	10's	1's
Base 12	20,736's	1,728's	144's	12's	1's

To write successive numerals in a modern system of numeration, first add one to each number to make each succeeding counting number (successor). Write the corresponding numerals using the digits of the respective system until the largest digit is used, then form a new group as shown below:

Base 10	0	1	2	3	4	5	6	7	8	9	10
Base 2	0	1	10	11	100	101	110	111	1000	1001	1010
Base 3	0	1	2	10	11	12	20	21	22	100	101
Base 4	0	1	2	3	10	11	12	13	20	21	22

PRACTICE PROBLEMS

1. Read, or write in words, each of the following:

(a) 53_six (d) 8495_twelve (g) 5326_seven (j) 24013_five

(b) 40_five (e) 101101_two (h) 74308_nine (k) 36142_seven

(c) 121_three (f) 2013_four (i) 65774_eight (l) 10001101_two

2. Write each of the following as a numeral:

(a) Six two, base eight

(b) One three, base five

(c) One zero one zero, base two

(d) Three four two, base six

(e) Eight one five six, base twelve

(f) One zero zero two, base four

3. Name all the digits that are used to write numerals in each of the following numeration systems:

(a) Base seven   (c) Base six   (e) Base twelve

(b) Base nine   (d) Base eight   (f) Base five

4. (*a*) Make a row of twenty-three dots. Group them by sevens. Write a numeral in base seven naming this number of dots.

(*b*) Make another row of twenty-three dots. Group them by nines. Write a numeral in base nine naming this number of dots.

5. (*a*) Make a row of eighteen dots. Group them by fives. Write a numeral in base five naming this number of dots.

(*b*) Make another row of eighteen dots. Group them by sixes. Write a numeral in base six naming this number of dots.

6. Group dots on your paper to show the meaning of each of the following:

    (*a*) 16_{seven} (*b*) 21_{four} (*c*) 55_{six} (*d*) 40_{nine} (*e*) 34_{five}

7. Find the value of the place in which each indicated digit appears in the numeral:

(*a*) Digit 3 in:	(1) 836_{nine}	(2) 3241_{five}	(3) 630927_{ten}
(*b*) Digit 1 in:	(1) 100000_{two}	(2) 20102_{three}	(3) 133230_{four}
(*c*) Digit 7 in:	(1) $752E_{twelve}$	(2) 6275_{eight}	(3) 37584_{nine}
(*d*) Digit 2 in:	(1) 1203_{five}	(2) 42530_{six}	(3) 21303_{four}
(*e*) Digit 4 in:	(1) 6743_{eight}	(2) $43TE0_{twelve}$	(3) 34101_{five}
(*f*) Digit 0 in:	(1) 3012_{four}	(2) 20111_{three}	(3) 10111111_{two}
(*g*) Digit 5 in:	(1) 4235_{six}	(2) 51836_{nine}	(3) $95E40_{twelve}$
(*h*) Digit 6 in:	(1) 565_{eight}	(2) $863T5_{twelve}$	(3) 61354_{seven}
(*i*) Digit 8 in:	(1) 18266_{nine}	(2) 87454_{twelve}	(3) 36869_{ten}
(*j*) Digit 9 in:	(1) 3987_{twelve}	(2) 90705_{ten}	(3) $T9E83_{twelve}$

8. Write the next three numerals that immediately follow:

(*a*) 122_{three}	(*d*) 10111_{two}	(*g*) 7888_{nine}	(*j*) 21212_{three}
(*b*) 555_{six}	(*e*) 4343_{five}	(*h*) 33333_{four}	(*k*) $T9EE_{twelve}$
(*c*) 767_{eight}	(*f*) TET_{twelve}	(*i*) 6565_{seven}	(*l*) 1111101_{two}

9. (*a*) Write the first sixty base four numerals beginning with 0.

(*b*) Write the first forty base nine numerals beginning with 0.

10. Make a chart showing the first fifty numerals beginning with 0 in base two, base five, base seven, and base twelve.

Expanded Notation

A non-decimal numeral may be written in expanded form as a polynomial by using the powers of the base expressed in decimal values or in digits of the base.

$3132_{four} = 3$ sixty-fours $+ 1$ sixteen $+ 3$ fours $+ 2$ ones

in decimal digits:

$$= (3 \times 4^3) + (1 \times 4^2) + (3 \times 4^1) + (2 \times 1)$$

or in digits of base 4:

$$= (3 \times 10^3{}_{four}) + (1 \times 10^2{}_{four}) + (3 \times 10^1{}_{four}) + (2 \times 1)$$

PRACTICE PROBLEMS

1. Express as a base five numeral:

$$(4 \times 5^4) + (2 \times 5^3) + (3 \times 5^2) + (1 \times 5^1) + (4 \times 1)$$

2. Express as a base nine numeral:

$$(7 \times 9^5) + (6 \times 9^4) + (4 \times 9^3) + (0 \times 9^2) + (8 \times 9^1) + (3 \times 1)$$

3. Express as a base seven numeral:

$$(4 \times 10^3{}_{seven}) + (3 \times 10^2{}_{seven}) + (6 \times 10^1{}_{seven}) + (5 \times 1)$$

4. Write each of the following numerals in expanded form as a polynomial (using decimal digits):

(a) 423_{five} (c) 2656_{seven} (e) 23132_{four} (g) $5TE4_{twelve}$

(b) 675_{eight} (d) 10212_{three} (f) 101101_{two} (h) 936825_{ten}

5. Write each of the following numerals in expanded form as a polynomial (using digits of the base):

(a) 523_{six} (b) $69T8_{twelve}$ (c) 41321_{five} (d) 36514_{seven}

Expressing Numerals as Numerals in Other Bases

To express a numeral given in a base other than ten as a base ten numeral, multiply the value of each digit by its place value and add these products. Then write the decimal numeral for the resulting sum.

Write $4\,TE_{twelve}$ as a base ten numeral. $4 \times 144 = 576$

$4\,TE_{twelve} = $ 4 T E $10 \times 12 = 120$

           144's   12's   1's $11 \times 1 = \underline{\ \ 11}$

         $= 707_{ten}$ 707

Answer: 707_{ten} *(Continued on next page)*

Write 3142_{five} as a base ten numeral.

$3142_{\text{five}} =$

3	1	4	2
125's	25's	5's	1's

$= 422_{\text{ten}}$

Answer: 422_{ten}

$3 \times 125 = 375$
$1 \times 25 = 25$
$4 \times 5 = 20$
$2 \times 1 = 2$
$\overline{422}$

Write 11011_{two} as a base ten numeral.

$11011_{\text{two}} =$

1	1	0	1	1
16's	8's	4's	2's	1's

$= 27_{\text{ten}}$

Answer: 27_{ten}

$1 \times 16 = 16$
$1 \times 8 = 8$
$1 \times 2 = 2$
$1 \times 1 = 1$
$\overline{27}$

To express a base ten numeral as a numeral in a base other than ten, use either the quotients method or remainders method.

Quotients method:

(*a*) Divide the largest possible power of the base into the given number. Then divide the remainder by the next lower power of the base. Continue in this manner until the divisor is the base itself.

(*b*) Take the quotient of each division as the digit for the corresponding position in the required base numeral.

(*c*) Use the final remainder as the digit for the one's place in the required numeral.

Write 992 as a base five numeral.

$$625)\overline{992}(1$$
$$\underline{625}$$
$$125)\overline{367}(2$$
$$\underline{250}$$
$$25)\overline{117}(4$$
$$\underline{100}$$
$$5)\overline{17}(3$$
$$\underline{15}$$
$$2$$

Answer, 12432_{five}

Remainders method:

(*a*) Divide the base into the given number. Then divide the base into the quotient, then divide the base into the new quotient, and so forth. Continue until the quotient is zero.

(*b*) Take the remainders in these divisions as the required digits, using the final remainder as the digit for

$5)992(198$ Remainder 2 ↑
$5)198(39$ Remainder 3
$5)39(7$ Remainder 4
$5)7(1$ Remainder 2
$5)1(0$ Remainder 1

Answer, 12432_{five}

the greatest place value and the first remainder as the digit for the ones' place.

To express one non-decimal numeral as another non-decimal numeral in a different base, first change the given non-decimal numeral to a base ten numeral. Then change the resulting base ten numeral to the numeral of the required base.

Write 11100101_{two} as a base twelve numeral.

11100101_{two} expressed as a base ten numeral is 237_{ten} which is the base twelve numeral 179_{twelve}.

PRACTICE PROBLEMS

1. Express each of the following as a base ten numeral:

(a) (1) 1101_{two} (2) 10010_{two} (3) 10111011_{two} (4) 11101100111_{two}
(b) (1) 324_{five} (2) 1042_{five} (3) 31123_{five} (4) 241234_{five}
(c) (1) $1ET_{twelve}$ (2) 859_{twelve} (3) 2407_{twelve} (4) $5E043_{twelve}$
(d) (1) 211_{three} (2) 222_{three} (3) 12021_{three} (4) 120212_{three}
(e) (1) 86_{nine} (2) 5742_{nine} (3) 4085_{nine} (4) 38167_{nine}
(f) (1) 354_{seven} (2) 4106_{seven} (3) 35214_{seven} (4) 60355_{seven}
(g) (1) 123_{four} (2) 3331_{four} (3) 23103_{four} (4) 323312_{four}
(h) (1) 65_{eight} (2) 754_{eight} (3) 3617_{eight} (4) 25760_{eight}
(i) (1) 452_{six} (2) 5513_{six} (3) 2405_{six} (4) 45124_{six}
(j) (1) 134_{seven} (2) 23130_{four} (3) $T5E4_{twelve}$ (4) 11011110110_{two}

2. Express each of the following base ten numerals as a numeral in the indicated base:

(a) To base two: (1) 93   (2) 245   (3) 1,051
(b) To base five: (1) 36   (2) 461   (3) 2,974
(c) To base twelve: (1) 100   (2) 708   (3) 9,567
(d) To base seven: (1) 59   (2) 357   (3) 3,208
(e) To base three: (1) 31   (2) 125   (3) 1,027
(f) To base nine: (1) 87   (2) 650   (3) 7,500
(g) To base six: (1) 64   (2) 782   (3) 6,000
(h) To base four: (1) 92   (2) 240   (3) 4,209
(i) To base eight: (1) 75   (2) 500   (3) 10,000
(j) (1) $126 = (\ \ )_{six}$ (4) $1,000 = (\ \ )_{nine}$
 (2) $815 = (\ \ )_{seven}$ (5) $407 = (\ \ )_{three}$
 (3) $583 = (\ \ )_{four}$ (6) $1,356 = (\ \ )_{eight}$

3. Express each of the following numerals as a numeral in the indicated base:

(a) $8T5_{twelve}$ to base two
(b) 101101010_{two} to base five
(c) 343_{five} to base two
(d) 1000110111_{two} to base six
(e) $T79_{twelve}$ to base five
(f) 4214_{five} to base twelve
(g) 20112_{three} to base seven
(h) 40545_{six} to base four

(i) 100100101_{two} to base nine
(j) 41356_{seven} to base eight
(k) 33103_{four} to base six
(l) 18357_{nine} to base three
(m) 222022_{three} to base twelve
(n) 56273_{eight} to base seven
(o) 111011100011_{two} to base eight
(p) 64235_{seven} to base five

4. (a) Express 658_{ten} as a base four numeral.
   (b) Express 534_{six} as a base ten numeral.
   (c) Express 100000010_{two} as a base three numeral.
   (d) Express $ET8_{twelve}$ as a base eight numeral.
   (e) Express 2605_{nine} as a base two numeral.
   (f) Express 13624_{seven} as a base twelve numeral.
   (g) Express 212012_{three} as a base five numeral.
   (h) Express 12323_{four} as a base nine numeral.
   (i) Express 52765_{eight} as a base six numeral.
   (j) Express 41033_{five} as a base seven numeral.
   (k) Express 12201_{three} as a base four numeral.
   (l) Express $T4E8_{twelve}$ as a base nine numeral.
   (m) Express 23065_{seven} as a base three numeral.
   (n) Express 34142_{five} as a base twelve numeral.
   (o) Express 5817_{nine} as a base eight numeral.
   (p) Express 231023_{four} as a base two numeral.
   (q) Express 10001110101_{two} as a base six numeral.

Computation in Bases Other than Ten

We add, subtract, multiply, and divide numbers in bases other than ten as we do decimal numbers but we use the number facts belonging to the given base.

The number facts necessary for computation in the binary system are:

$0 + 0 = 0$	$0 - 0 = 0$	$0 \times 0 = 0$	0
$0 + 1 = 1$	$1 - 0 = 1$	$1 \times 0 = 0$	$1\overline{)0}$
$1 + 0 = 1$	$1 - 1 = 0$	$0 \times 1 = 0$	1
$1 + 1 = 10$	$10 - 1 = 1$	$1 \times 1 = 1$	$1\overline{)1}$

Adding the following binary numbers:

11	In the ones' column $1 + 1 = 10$; $10 + 1 = 11$;
1101	$11 + 1 = 100$; $100 + 1 = 101$. Write the last 1 in
111	answer. Carry the 10.
1111	In the twos' column $10 + 1 = 11$; $11 + 1 = 100$;
1111	$100 + 1 = 101$; $101 + 1 = 110$. Write the 0.
110101	Carry the 11.

In the fours' column $11 + 1 = 100$; $100 + 1 = 101$; $101 + 1 = 110$; $110 + 1 = 111$. Write the last 1. Carry the 11.

In the eights' column $11 + 1 = 100$; $100 + 1 = 101$; $101 + 1 = 110$. Write the 110 in the answer.

Answer, 110101

PRACTICE PROBLEMS

1. Binary System

(*a*) Perform the indicated operations on the following:

$1 + 1 =$; $1 + 0 =$; $0 + 1 =$; $0 + 0 =$; $1 \times 1 =$; $1 \times 0 =$; $0 \times 1 =$; $0 \times 0 =$; $10 - 1 =$; $1 - 1 =$; $1 - 0 =$; $0 - 0 =$; $1\overline{)10}$; $1\overline{)0}$; $111 + 1 =$; $1111111 + 1 =$; $111111 + 1 =$; $111111111 + 1 =$; $100 - 1 =$; $10000 - 1 =$; $10000000 - 1 =$; $100000000000 - 1 =$.

(*b*) Compute as directed the following binary numbers:

Add:

				11101
		1101	11011	110111
	101	1011	11111	1101
1011	111	1111	10111	11110
1111	111	1101	11111	110111

Subtract:

101	10111	11000	101000	1100100
10	10101	1010	11011	1011011

Multiply:

10	111	1011	11011	10101
11	101	100	11101	11011

Divide:

$11\overline{)110}$ · $111\overline{)111111}$ $110\overline{)101010}$ $101\overline{)110010}$ $1011\overline{)1001101}$

2. Quinary System

(*a*) Perform the indicated operations on the following:

$2+2=$; $4+1=$; $2+4=$; $3+3=$; $4+4=$; $3+4=$; $3+2=$;

$10-3=$; $12-4=$; $13-4=$; $10-1=$; $11-3=$; $12-3=$; $11-2=$;

$3\times1=$; $2\times4=$; $3\times3=$; $4\times3=$; $4\times4=$; $2\times3=$; $4\times2=$;

$2\overline{)4}$; $1\overline{)3}$; $4\overline{)22}$; $3\overline{)14}$; $4\overline{)31}$; $2\overline{)13}$; $3\overline{)11}$.

(*b*) What new group does 1 more than 444444 make?

(*c*) Compute as directed the following quinary numbers:

Add:

			4132	30143
		132	2433	1344
102	234	434	1424	43
232	243	244	3244	23144

Subtract:

324	312	1423	42102	24010
221	104	1333	1214	12432

Multiply:

12	34	132	343	400
21	43	241	204	432

Divide:

$14\overline{)223}$ $23\overline{)1033}$ $40\overline{)2200}$ $32\overline{)12101}$ $213\overline{)13134}$

3. Duodecimal System

(*a*) Perform the indicated operations on the following duodecimal numbers:

$7+4=$; $8+9=$; $T+E=$; $8+5=$; $E+9=$; $5+T=$; $7+8=$;

$8-5=$; $14-7=$; $1T-T=$; $19-E=$; $17-8=$; $13-9=$; $10-4=$;

$2\times9=$; $5\times T=$; $8\times4=$; $E\times T=$; $9\times7=$; $9\times8=$; $6\times E=$;

$5\overline{)34}$; $7\overline{)53}$; $T\overline{)92}$; $8\overline{)60}$; $E\overline{)T1}$; $4\overline{)28}$; $9\overline{)83}$.

(*b*) What new group does 1 more than *EEEEEEE* make?

(*c*) Compute as directed the following duodecimal numbers:

Add:

			5876	39873
		482	8E09	629
89	2T5	9E4	T427	675E
47	378	56T	2153	82T12

Subtract:

968	524	7605	9734	612T5
742	2E6	358	486T	5319E

Multiply:

37	651	E8	893	70T4
29	82	4T	7E5	16TE

Divide:

$9)\overline{153}$ $E)\overline{362}$ $5T)\overline{6632}$ $110)\overline{2310}$ $216)\overline{40846}$

4. Other Bases

Add:

1102_{three}	2316_{seven}	31321_{four}	4187_{nine}	53425_{six}	32756_{eight}
2112_{three}	3435_{seven}	12323_{four}	3506_{nine}	15304_{six}	14670_{eight}
1221_{three}	1652_{seven}	20133_{four}	5738_{nine}	24135_{six}	25541_{eight}
2121_{three}	2466_{seven}	33203_{four}	7467_{nine}	42043_{six}	43675_{eight}

Subtract:

2112_{three}	6253_{seven}	31012_{four}	65273_{nine}	14542_{six}	63415_{eight}
1221_{three}	3534_{seven}	12103_{four}	27184_{nine}	5324_{six}	43637_{eight}

Multiply:

212_{three}	463_{seven}	231_{four}	835_{nine}	543_{six}	546_{eight}
102_{three}	256_{seven}	321_{four}	647_{nine}	425_{six}	673_{eight}

Divide:

$22_{three})\overline{2101_{three}}$ $36_{seven})\overline{1653_{seven}}$ $210_{four})\overline{120030_{four}}$

$167_{nine})\overline{22051_{nine}}$ $431_{six})\overline{111434_{six}}$ $245_{eight})\overline{115260_{eight}}$

5. Compute as directed:

Add:	Subtract:	Multiply:	Divide:
24134_{five}	52143_{six}	10111_{two}	$33_{four})\overline{2211_{four}}$
31224_{five}	23435_{six}	101_{two}	
23433_{five}			
41424_{five}			

REVIEW OF PART II

1. Name CCXCIX by its equivalent:

    (*a*) decimal numeral   (*d*) Egyptian numeral

    (*b*) Greek numeral   (*e*) Babylonian numeral

    (*c*) Mayan numeral   (*f*) Chinese numeral

2. Make as many dots on your paper as are represented by the numeral 42_{five}. Group them to show the meaning of the numeral.

3. Express 63157_{eight} in expanded form as a polynomial.

4. Express 5024_{six} as a base ten numeral.

5. Express 12586_{nine} as a base five numeral.

6. Express 32311_{four} as a base twelve numeral.

7. Add: **8** Subtract: **9.** Multiply: **10.** Divide:

$$10111_{two} \qquad 3TE4_{twelve} \qquad 635_{seven} \qquad 324_{five}\overline{)342233_{five}}$$
$$1011_{two} \qquad \underline{2978_{twelve}} \qquad \underline{254_{seven}}$$
$$11001_{two}$$
$$\underline{11111_{two}}$$

REFRESH YOUR SKILLS

1. Add: **2.** Subtract: **3.** Multiply: **4.** Divide:

$$69,286 \qquad 8,040,010 \qquad 32,709 \qquad 3,065\overline{)19,637,455}$$
$$3,859 \qquad \underline{995,098} \qquad \underline{8,006}$$
$$457,685$$
$$\underline{35,697}$$

5. Add: **6.** Subtract: **7.** Multiply: **8.** Divide:

$$7\tfrac{11}{32} + 5\tfrac{3}{4} \qquad 10\tfrac{1}{3} - \tfrac{5}{6} \qquad 3\tfrac{1}{7} \times 4\tfrac{9}{10} \qquad 2\tfrac{5}{8} \div 4\tfrac{13}{16}$$

9. Add: **10.** Subtract: **11.** Multiply: **12.** Divide:

$$.52 + .3 \qquad 6.8 - .41 \qquad 6.04 \times .5 \qquad 2.4\overline{).3}$$

13. Add: **14.** Subtract: **15.** Multiply: **16.** Divide:

$$10111_{two} \qquad ET5_{twelve} \qquad 324_{five} \qquad 25_{seven}\overline{)1163_{seven}}$$
$$1101_{two} \qquad \underline{987_{twelve}} \qquad \underline{241_{five}}$$
$$\underline{11111_{two}}$$

17. Find $3\tfrac{1}{2}\%$ of $9,480

18. What per cent of $1.80 is $.72?

19. 6% of what number is 15?

PART III

BASIC UNITS OF MEASURE

INFORMAL GEOMETRY

NUMERICAL TRIGONOMETRY

INTRODUCTION

This section contains the study of the standard units of measure, a comprehensive treatment of informal geometry (see Exercises 45, 47, 49, and 51), numerical trigonometry, and miscellaneous applications where units of measure are used.

Many years ago there were no standard units of measure and people used their fingers, hands, feet, and arms to measure length and distance. Units like the digit (breadth of a finger), palm (width across the open hand at the base of the fingers), span (greatest stretch of the open hand), cubit (length of the forearm from the elbow to the end of the middle finger), and fathom (length across the two outstretched arms) were unsatisfactory because these measurements varied depending upon the size of the individual person.

Measurement, even with the use of standard units of measure, is approximate. See page 470.

The informal geometry of this section includes the study of points, lines, planes, and space, of geometric facts and relationships, and of measurement and construction of geometric figures. The word "geometry" means "earth measure."

In numerical trigonometry the tangent, sine, and cosine ratios are studied. These are included under indirect measurement in Exercise 45.

The miscellaneous applications include scale, budgeting, simple and compound interest, 24-hour clock, navigation, time zones, longitude and latitude, and the magnetic compass.

This test is keyed by page number. Explanatory material may be found on the page indicated by the numeral at the end of each problem.

1. How many yards are in 4 miles? **298**
2. What part of a foot is 3 inches? **298**
3. Subtract 103° 42′ from 180°. **332**
4. Change 108 square inches to square feet. **366**
5. How many cubic inches are in 7 cubic yards? **382**
6. Change 9 gallons to pints. **391**
7. How many bushels are in 96 pecks? **396**
8. What part of a pound is 12 ounces? **400**
9. Change 2 hours 29 minutes to minutes. **405**
10. What part of the year is 10 months? **405**
11. How many gallons will a 30 cubic foot tank hold? **422**
12. Add: **427**
    3 hr. 16 min. 43 sec.
    7 hr. 19 min. 32 sec.
    2 hr. 23 min. 15 sec.
13. Subtract: **427**
    7 ft. 4 in.
    2 ft. 9 in.
14. Multiply: **427**
    9 lb. 6 oz. by 8.
15. Divide: **427**
    5)8 gal. 3 qt.
16. Change 850 centimeters to meters. **439**
17. How many millimeters are in 15 inches? **450**
18. How many miles are in 20 kilometers? **450**
19. Change 30 statute miles per hour to feet per second. **462**
20. Which measurement in each of the following is more precise? **470**
    (a) 6.0 in or 3.17 in. (b) $6\frac{3}{4}$ yd. or $10\frac{1}{2}$ in.
    (c) $5\frac{7}{8}$ lb. or 6 lb. 11 oz.
21. Find the greatest possible error in a measurement of: **470**
    (a) $5\frac{3}{4}$ in. (b) 3.45 ft. (c) .094 in.
22. Find the relative error in a measurement of: **470**
    (a) 1.6 lb. (b) $2\frac{2}{5}$ hr. (c) $4\frac{3}{8}$ in.
23. Which measurement in each of the following is more accurate? **470**
    (a) $4\frac{5}{8}$ in. or $1\frac{9}{16}$ in. (b) 8.7 in. or 87 ft.
    (c) 40,000 mi. or $2\frac{1}{2}$ in.

24. How many significant digits are in each of the fol-   **472**
    lowing? What are they?

    (*a*) 9,008   (*c*) 6,700   (*e*) 89,024
    (*b*) .0040   (*d*) 3.8×10^5 (*f*) 563,000

25. Compute the following approximate numbers as   **473**
    indicated:

    (*a*) $6.7 + 3.41$ (*c*) $5.9 \times .213$
    (*b*) $47.732 - 9.8$ (*d*) $36\overline{)8.67}$

INVENTORY TEST — INFORMAL GEOMETRY
AND NUMERICAL TRIGONOMETRY

This test is keyed by page number. Explanatory material
may be found on the page indicated by the numeral at the end
of each problem.

1. Read, or write in words, each of the following: **305**
   $\overline{BC}, \overleftrightarrow{NR}, \overrightarrow{AT}, \overleftrightarrow{CF}, \overline{SY}, \overrightarrow{PQ}$

2. Name each of the following and express them sym-   **305**
   bolically:

   (*a*) M •――――• S (*b*) ←――•――•――→ D E (*c*) ←―•――•――→ C J

3. (*a*) Find $\overleftrightarrow{AB} \cap \overleftrightarrow{CD} = \{?\}$ **307**
   (*b*) Are points *C*, *E*, and *B* collinear?
   (*c*) Are points *A*, *E*, and *B* collinear?
   (*d*) Are points *B* and *C* collinear? Why?
   (*e*) Are $\overleftrightarrow{AB}$ and $\overleftrightarrow{CD}$ concurrent?

4. Draw a representation of: **306**

   (*a*) a curved line   (*b*) a straight line
              (*c*) a broken line

5. Draw a representation of a line in:

   (*a*) a slanting position (*b*) a vertical position   **306**
              (*c*) a horizontal position

6. Draw a representation of a pair of: **307**

   (*a*) intersecting lines   (*b*) parallel lines
              (*c*) perpendicular lines

7. If the distance from R to A is 50 miles, what is the   **310** distance from A to B?

R   A   B

8. (*a*) With a protractor draw an angle of 125°.   **340**
    (*b*) Name the following angle:
    (*c*) Draw any obtuse angle.
    (*d*) Draw a right angle.
    (*e*) Draw any acute angle.

9. Draw a circle with a diameter of $2\frac{3}{4}$ inches.   **314**

10. Draw a regular hexagon, each side measuring $\frac{7}{8}$ inch.   **345**

11. Construct a triangle with sides measuring $1\frac{5}{8}$ in., $2\frac{1}{8}$ **344** in., and $1\frac{3}{4}$ in.

12. Construct a triangle with sides measuring $1\frac{7}{8}$ in. and   **344** $2\frac{1}{4}$ in. and an included angle of 75°.

13. With the scale of $\frac{1}{4}$ in. $= 1$ ft. construct a triangle   **344** with angles measuring 30° and 60° and an included side measuring 9 ft.

14. Draw any line segment. Use compasses to bisect   **346** this segment.

15. Draw any angle. Use compasses to bisect this angle.   **347**

16. Draw any line. Use compasses to contruct a perpendicular to this line:
    (*a*) At a point on the line.   **347**
    (*b*) From a point outside the line.   **348**

17. Draw with a protractor an angle of 55°. Then con-   **348** struct with compasses an angle equal to it. Check with protractor.

18. Draw any line. Locate a point outside this line.   **349** Through this point construct a line parallel to the first line.

19. What is the complement of an angle of 69°?   **351**

20. What is the supplement of an angle of 108°?   **351**

21. If $\angle 2 = 49°$ and $\angle 3 = 75°$, find the measure of $\angle 1$.   **351** Of $\angle 4$.

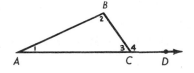

22. If $\angle 3 = 67°$, what is the measure of $\angle 1$? $\angle 2$? $\angle 4$?   **351**

Ex. 22   Ex. 23

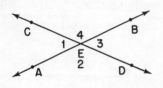 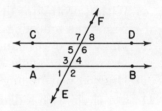

23. Parallel lines AB and CD are cut by the transversal   **352**
EF. If $\angle 6 = 95°$, how many degrees are in $\angle 1$? $\angle 2$?
$\angle 3$? $\angle 4$? $\angle 5$? $\angle 7$? $\angle 8$?

Find the perimeter of:

24. A rectangle 138 yards long and 57 yards wide.   **317**

25. A square whose side measured 106 feet.   **318**

26. A triangle with sides measuring $8\frac{9}{16}$ in., $7\frac{5}{8}$ in., and   **319**
$6\frac{3}{4}$ in.

Find the circumference of:

27. A circle whose radius is 49 feet.   **319**

28. A circle whose diameter is 64 inches.   **319**

Find the area of:

29. A rectangle 293 feet long and 185 feet wide.   **371**

30. A square whose side measures 78 yards.   **372**

31. A parallelogram with an altitude of 98 feet and a   **373**
base of 107 feet.

32. A triangle whose altitude is $10\frac{1}{2}$ inches and base is   **374**
9 inches.

33. A trapezoid with bases of 87 feet and 41 feet and a   **374**
height of 62 feet.

34. A circle whose radius is 3.8 feet.   **375**

35. A circle whose diameter is 56 inches.   **376**

Find the volume of:

36. A rectangular solid 109 feet long, 97 feet wide, and   **385**
63 feet high.

37. A cube whose side measures 2 feet 8 inches. **386**

38. A right circular cylinder with a radius of 8 inches **387** and a height of 10 inches.

39. A sphere whose diameter is 4.5 inches. **388**

40. A right circular cone 10 inches in diameter and 9 **388** inches high.

41. A square pyramid 16 yards on each side of the base **389** and 13 yards high.

Find the total area of the outside surface of:

42. A rectangular solid $7\frac{1}{2}$ inches long, 6 inches wide, and **377** $2\frac{3}{4}$ inches high.

43. A cube whose side measures 9.3 feet. **378**

44. A right circular cylinder 20 inches in diameter and **378** 34 inches high.

45. A sphere whose diameter is 84 inches. **380**

46. Find the base of a right triangle if the hypotenuse is **321** 146 feet and the altitude is 96 feet.

47. Find the hypotenuse of a right triangle if the alti- **321** tude is 112 feet and the base is 384 feet.

48. Find the altitude of a right triangle if the base is 45 **321** yards and the hypotenuse is 117 yards.

49. Find the height of a flagpole that casts a shadow of **324** 450 feet at a time when a girl, $5\frac{1}{2}$ feet tall, casts a shadow of 33 feet.

50. The letters in the following problems represent parts **326** of right triangle ABC (see page 326) with angle C, the right angle; altitude a, the side opposite angle A; and base b, the side opposite angle B.

    (a) Find side a when angle $A = 89°$ and side $b = 250$ feet.

    (b) Find side a when angle $A = 71°$ and side $c = 800$ yards.

    (c) Find side b when angle $A = 47°$ and side $c = 500$ feet.

    (d) How high is the top of a TV tower if, at a horizontal distance of 400 feet from its base, the angle of elevation is 73°?

EXERCISE 44

MEASURE OF LENGTH—BASIC UNITS

I. Aim: To change a given number of linear units of one denomination to units of another denomination.

II. Procedure

Use either of the following methods:

1. *Common Method*

(a) To change to a smaller unit of measure, as changing 5 feet to inches:

> *1.* Find the number of units of the smaller denomination that make one unit of the larger denomination (12 in. = 1 ft.). This number (12) is sometimes called the conversion factor.
>
> *2. Multiply* the given number of units of the larger denomination (5 ft.) by this conversion factor (12). Thus, 5 feet = 5 × 12 = 60 inches.

(b) To change to a larger unit of measure, as changing 60 inches to feet:

> *1.* Find the number of units of the smaller denomination that make one unit of the larger denomination (12 in. = 1 ft.).
>
> *2. Divide* the given number of units of the smaller denomination (60 in.) by this conversion factor (12). Thus, 60 inches = 60 ÷ 12 = 5 feet.

2. *Cancellation of Units*

To change a given number of units of one denomination to units of another denomination, multiply the given number of units by a fraction equal to unity (one), the terms of which are the two members of the required equivalent arranged so that the given unit of measurement may be canceled.

(a) To change 5 feet to inches, multiply 5 feet by the fraction $\dfrac{12 \text{ in.}}{1 \text{ ft.}}$. Thus, $5 \, \cancel{\text{ft.}} \times \dfrac{12 \text{ in.}}{1 \, \cancel{\text{ft.}}} = 60$ in.

(*b*) To change 60 inches to feet, multiply 60 inches by the fraction $\dfrac{1 \text{ ft.}}{12 \text{ in.}}$. Thus, $60 \text{ in.} \times \dfrac{1 \text{ ft.}}{12 \text{ in.}} = 5$ ft.

In the measure of length the following specific rules may also be used:

Part A

To change:

(*a*) Feet to inches, multiply the number of feet by 12.

(*b*) Inches to feet, divide the number of inches by 12.

(*c*) Yards to feet, multiply the number of yards by 3.

(*d*) Feet to yards, divide the number of feet by 3.

(*e*) Yards to inches, multiply the number of yards by 36.

(*f*) Inches to yards, divide the number of inches by 36.

(*g*) Rods to feet, multiply the number of rods by $16\frac{1}{2}$.

(*h*) Feet to rods, divide the number of feet by $16\frac{1}{2}$.

(*i*) Rods to yards, multiply the number of rods by $5\frac{1}{2}$.

(*j*) Yards to rods, divide the number of yards by $5\frac{1}{2}$.

(*k*) Miles to feet, multiply the number of miles by 5,280.

(*l*) Feet to miles, divide the number of feet by 5,280.

(*m*) Miles to yards, multiply the number of miles by 1,760.

(*n*) Yards to miles, divide the number of yards by 1,760.

(*o*) Miles to rods, multiply the number of miles by 320.

(*p*) Rods to miles, divide the number of rods by 320.

Part B

To change:

(*a*) Nautical miles to feet, multiply the number of nautical miles by 6,080.

(*b*) Feet to nautical miles, divide the number of feet by 6,080.

(*c*) Nautical miles to statute miles, multiply the number of nautical miles by 1.15 or divide the number of nautical miles by .87.

(*d*) Statute miles to nautical miles, multiply the number of statute miles by .87 or divide the number of statute miles by 1.15.

(*e*) Fathoms to feet, multiply the number of fathoms by 6.

(*f*) Feet to fathoms, divide the number of feet by 6.

III. Sample Solutions

1. Change 26 mi. to feet.

    Method 1   *Method 2*

$$
\begin{array}{r}
5{,}280 \\
\times\,26 \\
\hline
31\ 680 \\
105\ 60 \\
\hline
137{,}280
\end{array}
$$

$$26\,\cancel{\text{mi.}} \times \frac{5{,}280 \text{ ft.}}{1\,\cancel{\text{mi.}}} = 137{,}280 \text{ ft.}$$

Answer: 137,280 ft.

2. Change 2 ft. 4 in. to inches.

    2 ft. 4 in. = 2 ft. + 4 in. = 24 in. + 4 in. = 28 in.

Answer: 28 in.

3. Change 4 ft. 9 in. to feet.   4. Change 10,000 yd. to miles.

  4 ft. 9 in. = 4 ft. + 9 in.*   Write remainder in yards.

$$= 4 \text{ ft.} + \tfrac{3}{4} \text{ ft.}$$
$$= 4\tfrac{3}{4} \text{ ft.}$$

$$
\begin{array}{r}
5 \\
1{,}760)\overline{10{,}000} \\
8\ 800 \\
\hline
1\ 200
\end{array}
$$

Answer: $4\tfrac{3}{4}$ ft.

* 9 in. = $\tfrac{9}{12}$ ft. = $\tfrac{3}{4}$ ft.   *Answer:* 5 mi. 1,200 yd.

5. Change 4.8 naut. mi. to statute miles.

    Method 1   *Method 2*

$$
\begin{array}{r}
4.8 \\
\times\,1.15 \\
\hline
240 \\
48 \\
4\ 8 \\
\hline
5.520
\end{array}
$$

$$4.8\ \cancel{\text{naut. mi.}} \times \frac{1.15 \text{ stat. mi.}}{1\ \cancel{\text{naut. mi.}}} = 5.52 \text{ stat. mi.}$$

Answer: 5.52 stat. mi.

EQUIVALENTS—MEASURE OF LENGTH

Part A

1 foot (ft.) = 12 inches (in.)	1 rod (rd.) = 16½ feet (ft.)
1 yard (yd.) = 3 feet (ft.)	= 5½ yards (yd.)
= 36 inches (in.)	1 mile (mi.) = 5,280 feet (ft.)
	= 1,760 yards (yd.)
	= 320 rods (rd.)

Part B

1 nautical mile (naut. mi.) = 6,080 feet (6,080.2 ft.)

$\qquad\qquad\qquad\qquad$ = 1.15 statute mile (1.1515 stat. mi.)

1 statute mile (stat. mi.) $\quad$ = 0.87 nautical mile (0.8684 naut. mi.)

$\qquad\qquad\qquad\qquad$ = 5,280 feet (ft.)

$\qquad$ 1 fathom (fath.) = 6 feet (ft.)

DIAGNOSTIC TEST A

Change:

1. 9 ft. to inches
2. 4 ft. 8 in. to inches
3. 16 yd. to feet
4. 7 yd. 2 ft. to feet
5. 23 yd. to inches
6. 5 yd. 1 ft. 3 in. to inches
7. 6 rd. to feet
8. 2 rd. 4 ft. to feet
9. 40 mi. to feet
10. 9 mi. 500 ft. to feet
11. 15 rd. to yards
12. 4 rd. 3 yd. to yards
13. 21 mi. to yards
14. 6 mi. 850 yd. to yards
15. 4 mi. to rods
16. 7 mi. 100 rd. to rods
17. 48 in. to feet
18. What part of a foot is 10 inches?
19. 3 ft. 2 in. to feet
20. 34 in. to feet (Write remainder in inches.)
21. 27 ft. to yards
22. 8 yd. 1 ft. to yards
23. 13 ft. to yards (Write remainder in feet.)
24. 252 in. to yards
25. What part of a yard is 12 inches?
26. 5 yd. 24 in. to yards
27. 207 in. to yards (Write remainder in feet and inches.)
28. 132 ft. to rods
29. 26 ft. to rods (Write remainder in feet.)
30. 33 yd. to rods
31. 71 yd. to rods (Write remainder in yards.)
32. 26,400 ft. to miles
33. 42 mi. 3,960 ft. to miles
34. 6,800 ft. to miles (Write remainder in feet.)
35. 7,040 yd. to miles
36. 25 mi. 880 yd. to miles
37. 11,500 yd. to miles (Write remainder in yards.)
38. 960 rd. to miles
39. 7 mi. 120 rd. to miles
40. 500 rd. to miles (Write remainder in rods.)
41. 3 mi. to inches
42. 126,720 in. to miles

RELATED PRACTICE EXAMPLES

Change to inches:

Set 1(a)	Set 1(b)	Set 2
1. 8 ft.	1. $\frac{3}{4}$ ft.	1. 1 ft. 10 in.
2. 17 ft.	2. $\frac{1}{2}$ ft.	2. 9 ft. 3 in.
3. $3\frac{1}{2}$ ft.	3. $\frac{1}{4}$ ft.	3. 5 ft. 11 in.
4. 7.25 ft.	4. $\frac{5}{6}$ ft.	4. 16 ft. 9 in.
5. 50 ft.	5. $\frac{7}{8}$ ft.	5. 21 ft. 7 in.

Change to feet:

Set 3(a)	Set 3(b)	Set 4
1. 6 yd.	1. $\frac{1}{3}$ yd.	1. 3 yd. 1 ft.
2. 25 yd.	2. $\frac{5}{6}$ yd.	2. 8 yd. 2 ft.
3. $4\frac{2}{3}$ yd.	3. $\frac{1}{2}$ yd.	3. 5 yd. 2 ft.
4. 1.4 yd.	4. $\frac{2}{3}$ yd.	4. 12 yd. 1 ft.
5. 81 yd.	5. $\frac{3}{8}$ yd.	5. 35 yd. $1\frac{1}{2}$ ft.

Change to inches:

Set 5(a)	Set 5(b)	Set 6
1. 9 yd.	1. $\frac{1}{2}$ yd.	1. 1 yd. 2 ft.
2. 16 yd.	2. $\frac{2}{3}$ yd.	2. 3 yd. 1 ft.
3. $7\frac{1}{2}$ yd.	3. $\frac{3}{4}$ yd.	3. 2 yd. 11 in.
4. .25 yd.	4. $\frac{1}{4}$ yd.	4. 6 yd. 2 ft. 7 in.
5. 60 yd.	5. $\frac{5}{8}$ yd.	5. 4 yd. 1 ft. 4 in.

Change to feet:

Set 7	Set 8	Set 9	Set 10
1. 4 rd.	1. 3 rd. 10 ft.	1. 6 mi.	1. 2 mi. 120 ft.
2. 15 rd.	2. 1 rd. 3 ft.	2. 17 mi.	2. 5 mi. 2,500 ft.
3. $5\frac{3}{4}$ rd.	3. 8 rd. 5 ft.	3. $31\frac{7}{8}$ mi.	3. 11 mi. 1,000 ft.
4. 3.2 rd.	4. 20 rd. 7 ft.	4. 9.5 mi.	4. 19 mi. 4,790 ft.
5. 26 rd.	5. 34 rd. 2 ft.	5. 100 mi.	5. 27 mi. 3,700 ft.

Change to yards:

Set 11	Set 12	Set 13	Set 14
1. 2 rd.	1. 1 rd. 4 yd.	1. 7 mi.	1. 4 mi. 200 yd.
2. 19 rd.	2. 3 rd. 2 yd.	2. 38 mi.	2. 7 mi. 880 yd.
3. $6\frac{1}{4}$ rd.	3. 7 rd. 3 yd.	3. $4\frac{1}{2}$ mi.	3. 2 mi. 1,240 yd.
4. 4.6 rd.	4. 13 rd. 1 yd.	4. 13.1 mi.	4. 16 mi. 925 yd.
5. 25 rd.	5. 21 rd. 5 yd.	5. 20 mi.	5. 11 mi. 1,300 yd.

Change to rods:

Change to feet:

SET 15	SET 16	SET 17
1. 5 mi.	**1.** 3 mi. 150 rd.	**1.** 24 in.
2. 14 mi.	**2.** 9 mi. 70 rd.	**2.** 192 in.
3. 23¼ mi.	**3.** 13 mi. 225 rd.	**3.** 38 in.
4. 6.75 mi.	**4.** 25 mi. 180 rd.	**4.** 57 in.
5. 39 mi.	**5.** 40 mi. 200 rd.	**5.** 588 in.

SET 18

1. What part of a foot is 8 inches?
2. 6 inches is what part of a foot?
3. What part of a foot is 9 inches?
4. What part of a foot is 5 inches?
5. 2 inches is what part of a foot?

Change to feet:

In set 20 write the remainder in inches.

SET 19	SET 20
1. 1 ft. 6 in.	**1.** 14 in.
2. 6 ft. 10 in.	**2.** 29 in.
3. 2 ft. 7 in.	**3.** 56 in.
4. 8 ft. 3 in.	**4.** 33 in.
5. 15 ft. 9 in.	**5.** 87 in.

Change to yards:

In set 23 write the remainder in feet.

SET 21	SET 22	SET 23	SET 24
1. 6 ft.	**1.** 5 yd. 1 ft.	**1.** 7 ft.	**1.** 72 in.
2. 21 ft.	**2.** 2 yd. 1 ft.	**2.** 14 ft.	**2.** 180 in.
3. 44 ft.	**3.** 9 yd. 2 ft.	**3.** 50 ft.	**3.** 60 in.
4. 7.5 ft.	**4.** 13 yd. 2 ft.	**4.** 35 ft.	**4.** 84 in.
5. 90 ft.	**5.** 27 yd. 1 ft.	**5.** 130 ft.	**5.** 468 in.

SET 25

1. What part of a yard is 24 inches?
2. 21 inches is what part of a yard?
3. What part of a yard is 30 inches?
4. 7 inches is what part of a yard?
5. What part of a yard is 16 inches?

Change to yards:

In set 27 write the remainder in feet and inches.

Sᴇᴛ 26　　　　　　　　　　　　　　　Sᴇᴛ 27

1. 2 yd. 18 in.　4. 8 yd. 1 ft. 4 in.　　1. 50 in.　　4. 176 in.
2. 4 yd. 28 in.　5. 14 yd. 2 ft. 3 in.　2. 79 in.　　5. 549 in.
3. 1 yd. 9 in.　　　　　　　　　　　　3. 121 in.

Change to rods:

In set 29 write the remainder in feet.　In set 31 write the remainder in yards.

Sᴇᴛ 28	Sᴇᴛ 29	Sᴇᴛ 30	Sᴇᴛ 31
1. 33 ft.	1. 40 ft.	1. 11 yd.	1. 7 yd.
2. 231 ft.	2. $21\frac{1}{2}$ ft.	2. 198 yd.	2. 23 yd.
3. $8\frac{1}{4}$ ft.	3. 75 ft.	3. $41\frac{1}{4}$ yd.	3. 45 yd.
4. 39.6 ft.	4. 102 ft.	4. 15 yd.	4. $18\frac{1}{2}$ yd.
5. 627 ft.	5. $38\frac{1}{2}$ ft.	5. 264 yd.	5. 98 yd.

Change to miles:

In set 34 write the remainder in feet.

Sᴇᴛ 32	Sᴇᴛ 33	Sᴇᴛ 34
1. 15,840 ft.	1. 3 mi. 1,760 ft.	1. 6,000 ft.
2. 36,960 ft.	2. 9 mi. 2,640 ft.	2. 8,400 ft.
3. 3,300 ft.	3. 12 mi. 1,320 ft.	3. 15,000 ft.
4. 10,000 ft.	4. 8 mi. 1,980 ft.	4. 9,750 ft.
5. 132,000 ft.	5. 45 mi. 4,400 ft.	5. 22,000 ft.

In set 37 write the remainder in yards.

Sᴇᴛ 35	Sᴇᴛ 36	Sᴇᴛ 37
1. 8,800 yd.	1. 6 mi. 1,320 yd.	1. 1,800 yd.
2. 22,880 yd.	2. 8 mi. 440 yd.	2. 2,500 yd.
3. 4,840 yd.	3. 1 mi. 110 yd.	3. 4,000 yd.
4. 6,000 yd.	4. 12 mi. 1,540 yd.	4. 6,800 yd.
5. 70,400 yd.	5. 23 mi. 1,650 yd.	5. 12,000 yd.

In set 40 write the remainder in rods.

Sᴇᴛ 38	Sᴇᴛ 39	Sᴇᴛ 40
1. 2,240 rd.	1. 2 mi. 40 rd.	1. 350 rd.
2. 6,720 rd.	2. 9 mi. 280 rd.	2. 600 rd.
3. 160 rd.	3. 5 mi. 32 rd.	3. 800 rd.
4. 1,200 rd.	4. 10 mi. 80 rd.	4. 975 rd.
5. 16,000 rd.	5. 14 mi. 100 rd.	5. 1,300 rd.

Change to inches: Change to miles:

SET 41	SET 42
1. 4 mi.	1. 316,800 in.
2. 6 mi.	2. 696,960 in.
3. $3\frac{1}{8}$ mi.	3. 500,000 in.
4. 1.5 mi.	4. 1,000,000 in.
5. 2.75 mi.	5. 5,000,000 in.

RELATED PROBLEMS

1. Harry is $5\frac{1}{2}$ feet tall. His father is 6 feet 1 inch. How much taller is his father?

2. An automobile wheel goes 9 feet 2 inches in one revolution. How many times does it revolve in 1 mile?

3. How many yards of ribbon are needed to make 30 school officer badges if it takes 9 inches of ribbon to make one badge?

4. If the floor boards are 2 inches wide, how many will be required to cover a floor 17 feet wide?

5. According to rocket readings the Fahrenheit temperature at an altitude of 8 miles is 70 degrees below zero. Express this altitude in feet.

6. How many miles high is Mount Everest if its elevation is 29,028 feet? Find answer correct to nearest tenth.

7. What is the ratio of: (*a*) 6 in. to 8 ft.? (*b*) 2 ft. 3 in. to 2 yd.?

8. Cirrus clouds sometimes reach 35,000 feet above the earth's surface. Find the upper level of these clouds in miles.

DIAGNOSTIC TEST B

Change:

1. 4 naut. mi. to feet

2. 3 naut. mi. to yards

3. 16 naut. mi. to statute miles

4. 12,160 ft. to nautical miles

5. 18,240 yd. to nautical miles

6. 100 stat. mi. to nautical miles

7. 15 fath. to feet

8. 54 ft. to fathoms

RELATED PRACTICE EXAMPLES

Change to feet: Change to yards: Change to statute miles:

SET 1	SET 2	SET 3
1. 6 naut. mi.	**1.** 2 naut. mi.	**1.** 7 naut. mi.
2. 15 naut. mi.	**2.** 12 naut. mi.	**2.** 50 naut. mi.
3. $4\frac{1}{4}$ naut. mi.	**3.** $\frac{7}{8}$ naut. mi.	**3.** $36\frac{1}{2}$ naut. mi.
4. 2.8 naut. mi.	**4.** 8.25 naut. mi.	**4.** 9.3 naut. mi.
5. 40 naut. mi.	**5.** 26 naut. mi.	**5.** 145 naut. mi.

Change to nautical miles:

SET 4	SET 5	SET 6
1. 30,400 ft.	**1.** 6,080 yd.	**1.** 5 stat. mi.
2. 18,240 ft.	**2.** 42,560 yd.	**2.** 90 stat. mi.
3. 10,000 ft.	**3.** 4,000 yd.	**3.** $28\frac{3}{4}$ stat. mi.
4. 7,600 ft.	**4.** 11,500 yd.	**4.** 51.25 stat. mi.
5. 152,000 ft.	**5.** 54,720 yd.	**5.** 130 stat. mi.

Change to feet: Change to fathoms:

SET 7		SET 8	
1. 9 fath.	**4.** 25.4 fath.	**1.** 18 ft.	**4.** 100 ft.
2. 36 fath.	**5.** 60 fath.	**2.** 96 ft.	**5.** 198 ft.
3. $17\frac{2}{3}$ fath.		**3.** 39 ft.	

RELATED PROBLEMS

1. A plane flew a distance of 140 nautical miles. Find the distance in statute miles.

2. A submarine sank to a depth of 18 fathoms. How many feet below the surface did the submarine submerge?

3. The distance from Manila to Shanghai is 1,338 statute miles. The distance from New York to Havana is 1,227 nautical miles. Which route is longer? How many nautical miles longer?

4. The air distance from San Francisco to Honolulu is 2,407 statute miles. Find the distance in nautical miles.

5. An observer at sea level can see an object 10 feet in height at a distance of 3.6 nautical miles. What is this distance in feet?

INFORMAL GEOMETRY AND NUMERICAL TRIGONOMETRY

(Also see Exercises 47, 49, and 51)

Points, Lines, Line Segments, and Rays

A geometric point is an exact location in space. It has no size nor can it be seen. Any dot that is used to indicate a geometric point is only a representation of it. Points

Ṙ is "point R."

that lie on the same straight line are called collinear points. A capital letter is used to label and name a point.

A geometric line is a set of points. Pencil and chalk lines are only representations of geometric lines. A geometric line can not be seen. A geometric line has an infinite number of points but no endpoints and it may be extended indefinitely in both directions because it is endless. Arrowheads are used to show this. A definite part of a line has length but no width or thickness.

To name a line, use two labeled points on it or a small letter near the line.

A•———•B.	is read "line AB" or "line BA" expressed in symbols as $\overleftrightarrow{AB}$ or $\overleftrightarrow{BA}$ respectively.
p•———→	is read "line p."

A point separates a line into two half-lines. Each half-line extends indefinitely in one direction only and 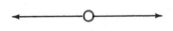 does not include the point that separates the line into two half-lines.

A definite part of a line that includes both of its endpoints is called a line segment. It consists of two endpoints and all the points between the endpoints.

To name a line segment, name its endpoints or the letter between the endpoints.

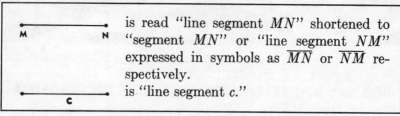

is read "line segment MN" shortened to "segment MN" or "line segment NM" expressed in symbols as $\overline{MN}$ or $\overline{NM}$ respectively.

is "line segment c."

The symbol $m(MN)$ is read "the measure of line segment MN" and represents the length of the segment.

A definite part of a line excluding its endpoints is called an interval.

A half-line which includes one endpoint is called a ray. This endpoint is the one that separates the line into two half-lines.

To name a ray, use the letter first which names the endpoint and then the letter which names one other point on the ray.

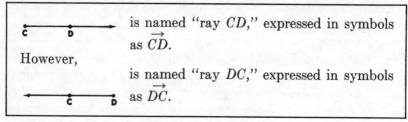

is named "ray CD," expressed in symbols as $\overrightarrow{CD}$.

However,

is named "ray DC," expressed in symbols as $\overrightarrow{DC}$.

KINDS OF LINES

Lines may be straight, curved, or broken. Usually a straight line is simply called a line. All these lines are sometimes called curves.

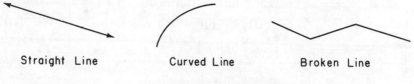

Straight Line   Curved Line   Broken Line

POSITION OF LINES

Lines may be in vertical, horizontal, or slanting (sometimes called oblique) positions.

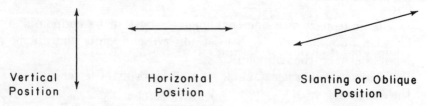

Vertical   Horizontal   Slanting or Oblique
Position   Position   Position

INTERSECTING, PARALLEL, AND PERPENDICULAR LINES

Lines that meet are intersecting lines. Lines that have a common point are called concurrent lines. Intersecting lines are concurrent lines.

Two lines in the same plane (see page 349) that do not meet are called parallel lines. Two lines not in the same plane that do not meet are called skew lines.

Two intersecting lines or rays or segments or a line and a ray or a line and a segment or a ray and a segment that form a right angle (see page 347) are said to be perpendicular to each other.

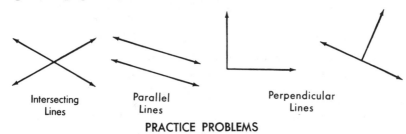

| Intersecting Lines | Parallel Lines | Perpendicular Lines |

PRACTICE PROBLEMS

1. Read, or write in words, each of the following:

(a) $\overrightarrow{RT}$ (c) $\overleftrightarrow{EB}$ (e) $\overline{DF}$ (g) $\overleftrightarrow{ST}$ (i) $\overline{EF}$

(b) $\overline{BN}$ (d) $\overrightarrow{MO}$ (f) $\overleftrightarrow{AC}$ (h) $\overrightarrow{NR}$ (j) $\overleftrightarrow{TV}$

2. Name each of the following and also express them symbolically:

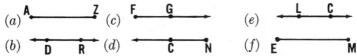

(a) A•————•Z (c) F•——G•——▶ (e) ◀——L•——C•——

(b) ◀——•D——•R—— (d) ◀——•C——•N—— (f) E•————M

3. Name the endpoints in each of the above drawings.

4. (a) Name the line segments in the figure.
   (b) Name the endpoints in each segment.
   (c) Find each of the following:

(1) What is the point of intersection of $\overline{CD}$ and $\overline{DF}$?

(2) $\overline{CD} \cap \overline{DF} = \{?\}$ (3) $\overline{CE} \cap \overline{EF} = \{?\}$

(4) $\overline{DF} \cap \overline{EF} = \{?\}$ (5) $\overline{CE} \cap \overline{CD} = \{?\}$

5. Find each of the following. Use the figure at the top of the next page in which $\overleftrightarrow{HG}$ and $\overleftrightarrow{AB}$ are parallel. (a) $\overleftrightarrow{HG} \cap \overleftrightarrow{DE} = \{?\}$

(b) $\overleftrightarrow{DE} \cap \overleftrightarrow{AB} = \{?\}$ (c) $\overleftrightarrow{AB} \cap \overleftrightarrow{HG} = \{?\}$

    (*d*) Are points *A*, *F*, and *B* collinear?

    (*e*) Are points *H*, *C*, and *G* collinear?

    (*f*) Are points *A*, *D*, and *B* collinear?

    (*g*) Are points *C*, *D*, *E*, and *F* collinear?

    (*h*) Are points *B* and *F* collinear?

    (*i*) Are points *H*, *C*, and *E* collinear?

    (*j*) Are points *A* and *D* collinear? Why?

    (*k*) Are points *E*, *C*, and *G* collinear?

    (*l*) Are points *F* and *G* collinear? Why?

    (*m*) Are $\overleftrightarrow{HG}$ and $\overleftrightarrow{AB}$ concurrent?

    (*n*) Are $\overleftrightarrow{HG}$ and $\overleftrightarrow{DE}$ concurrent?

    (*o*) Are $\overleftrightarrow{DE}$ and $\overleftrightarrow{AB}$ concurrent?

6. Draw a representation of:

    (*a*) a broken line   (*b*) a straight line   (*c*) a curved line

7. Draw a representation of a line in:

    (*a*) a vertical position   (*b*) a slanting position

            (*c*) a horizontal position

8. Draw a representation of a pair of:

    (*a*) perpendicular lines   (*b*) intersecting lines

            (*c*) parallel lines

  9. Develop the idea that an *infinite number of lines can be drawn through a point* by doing the following:

Label a point on your paper as *D*. Draw a line through point *D*. Draw a different line through point *D*. Draw a third, fourth, fifth, and sixth line through point *D*. Can more lines be drawn through point *D*? How many lines can be drawn through a point? Are these lines concurrent?

  10. Show that *one and only one line can pass through any two points* and that *two points determine a line* by doing the following:

Label two points on your paper as *M* and *N*. Draw a line through points *M* and *N*. Draw another line through *M* and *N*. How many lines can be drawn through two points? Are any two points collinear?

  11. Show that *two straight lines can intersect in only one point* by doing the following:

Draw a pair of intersecting lines. How many points in common does this pair of intersecting lines have? Draw another pair of intersecting lines. At how many points do these two straight lines intersect?

12. Show that *the shortest path between two points is along a straight line* by doing the following:

Label two points on your paper as *A* and *B*. Draw a straight line segment from *A* to *B*. Draw a curved line from *A* to *B*. Draw a broken line from *A* to *B*. Along which line is the shortest path between points *A* and *B*?

MEASURING AND DRAWING LINE SEGMENTS

Measuring the length of a line segment means to find the number of standard units of length (linear units) contained in the line segment.

A ruler is an instrument used commonly to measure lengths and to draw lines of given lengths. It is calibrated in inches ($''$) and subdivisions of the inch.

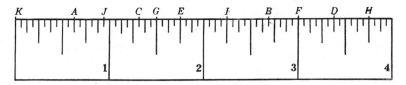

Use the above section of a ruler to answer questions 1 to 7:

1. What markings are represented by points: *A*? *B*? *C*? *D*? *E*? *F*? *G*? *H*? *I*? *J*? *K*?

2. How far from point *B* are points: *F*? *E*? *G*? *A*? *H*? *K*? *C*? *J*? *I*? *D*?

3. How many eighths of an inch are in the length from point *A* to point *D*? from point *G* to point *H*?

4. How many sixteenths of an inch are in $\frac{3}{4}''$? $\frac{5}{8}''$? $3''$? $2\frac{1}{2}''$? $1\frac{13}{16}''$? How many eighths of an inch are in $\frac{1}{4}''$? $1\frac{1}{2}''$? $2''$? $3\frac{5}{8}''$?

5. $2\frac{1}{2}$ in. $= \frac{}{2}''$, $\frac{}{4}''$, $\frac{}{8}''$, $\frac{}{16}''$.

6. What is (*a*) half of $\frac{3}{4}$ in.? (*b*) two times $\frac{7}{8}$ in.?

7. (*a*) Find the $1\frac{9}{16}''$ mark on the ruler. Add $1\frac{5}{8}''$. What is your answer?

(*b*) Find the $1\frac{3}{8}''$ mark on the ruler; add $\frac{13}{16}''$; add $1\frac{1}{4}''$; subtract $2\frac{9}{16}''$. What is your answer?

8. Estimate, then measure the length and width of this page. Find the amount of error in each case.

9. Draw line segments measuring $3\frac{1}{2}$ in., $1\frac{3}{4}$ in., $2\frac{7}{8}$ in., $\frac{11}{16}$ in., and $1\frac{3}{16}$ in.

10. Draw a line segment 10 inches long. Using compasses, lay off on this line consecutive lengths equal to the lines given in example 9.

SCALE

Line segments are used to represent distances. Often line segments drawn to scale represent distances. The scale shows the relationship between the dimensions of a drawing, plan, or map and the actual dimensions.

A scale like 1 inch = 2 feet means that 1 inch on the drawing represents 2 real feet. This scale may also be written as $\frac{1}{2}$ inch = 1 foot or as the representative fraction (R.F.) $\frac{1}{24}$ meaning 1 inch represents 24 inches or 2 feet.

On maps we usually find a scale that is like the one shown in problem 12.

Use the following procedure to solve the problems:

(*a*) *To find the actual distance* when the corresponding scale distance and the scale are known, multiply the scale distance by the scale value of a unit (inch).

(*b*) *To find the scale distance* when the corresponding actual distance and the scale are known, divide the actual distance by the scale value of a unit (inch).

(*c*) *To find the scale*, divide the actual distance by the corresponding scale distance.

1. The scale $\frac{1}{4}$ inch = 1 foot is the same as the scale 1 inch = ? feet.

2. The scale $\frac{1}{16}$ inch = 1 mile is the same as the scale 1 inch = ? miles.

3. The representative fraction $\frac{1}{48}$ is the same as the scale 1 inch = ? feet.

4. The representative fraction $\frac{1}{120}$ is the same as the scale 1 inch = ? feet.

5. If 1 inch = 20 miles, what distance is represented by 7 inches? $2\frac{1}{2}$ inches? $\frac{3}{4}$ inch? $4\frac{5}{8}$ inches?

6. If 1 inch = 40 miles, how many inches represent 160 miles? 60 miles? 110 miles? 15 miles?

7. If $\frac{1}{4}$ inch = 1 foot, what distance is represented by 5 inches? $8\frac{1}{2}$ inches? $16\frac{3}{4}$ inches? $26\frac{7}{8}$ inches?

8. If $\frac{1}{8}$ inch = 1 foot, how many inches represent 24 feet? 20 feet? 3 feet? 50 feet?

9. (a) If the scale is $\frac{1}{24}$, how many inches represent 8 ft.? 15 ft.? $23\frac{1}{2}$ ft.? $32\frac{3}{4}$ ft.? What distance is represented by 6 in.? $4\frac{1}{2}$ in.? $13\frac{1}{4}$ in.? $9\frac{5}{8}$ in.?

(b) If the R.F. is $\frac{1}{7200}$ (or 1 to 7,200), what actual distance on the ground in feet does 1 inch on the map represent? $5\frac{1}{2}$ in.? $9\frac{3}{4}$ in.?

(c) The sectional aeronautical maps of the United States are made at a scale of 1 to 500,000. How many miles do 3 inches represent on a sectional map?

10. Using the scale 1 inch = 48 miles, draw lines representing 240 mi., 36 mi., 90 mi., 123 mi.

11. What are the actual dimensions if floor plans, drawn to the scale of $\frac{1}{8}$ inch = 1 foot, show scale dimensions of: (a) $1\frac{3}{4}$ in. by $1\frac{7}{8}$ in.? (b) $2\frac{7}{16}$ in. by $3\frac{1}{2}$ in.?

12. Use the scale of miles:  to find the distance represented by each of the following line segments:

(a)   (b)   (c)

13. (a) Draw a plan of a schoolroom 33 ft. long and 18 ft. wide, using the scale 1 inch = 12 feet.

(b) Draw a diagram of a football field 360 ft. long and 160 ft. wide, using the scale $\frac{1}{8}$ inch = 5 feet.

14. Line segments sometimes represent speeds or forces. Using the scale 1 inch = 80 m.p.h., draw lines representing 160 m.p.h., 120 m.p.h., 100 m.p.h., 210 m.p.h., 75 m.p.h.

15. Find the scales used to draw the line segments at the right representing the given distances:

(a)   140 mi.

(b)   56 mi.

(c)   22 ft.

PLANES AND SPACE

A geometric plane or flat surface is a set of points. We cannot
see a geometric plane. It is endless and extends beyond any line
boundaries we use to represent it.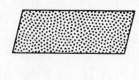
When the plane is limited, it has
length and width which can be
measured but no height or thick-
ness. A wall, floor, and desk top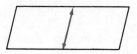
are common representations of a
limited plane. A line separates a
plane into two half-planes.

To name a plane, use letters which name three points not on the
same line belonging to the plane or by two capital letters at
opposite outside corners or by one capital letter in an interior
corner.

Points that lie in the same plane are called
coplanar points. Lines that are in the same
plane are called coplanar lines.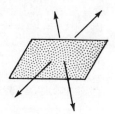

Space is the infinite set of all points. Its
length, width, and height are endless. A
limited space can be measured. A plane separates space into two half-spaces.

PRACTICE PROBLEMS

1. Show that:
   (*a*) Through 3 points on a line more than one plane can
   pass.
   (*b*) *Through 3 points not on a line one and only one plane
   can pass.*

2. Develop the idea that *a geometric plane contains an infinite
number of points and lines* by doing the following:
Draw a representation of a plane and indicate as many points
by dots as you wish. How many points does a geometric plane
have? Draw several lines in the plane. How many more lines

can be drawn in this plane? How many lines does a geometric plane contain?

3. Show that *when two different planes intersect, their intersection is a straight line* by drawing two different planes and their intersection.

GEOMETRIC FIGURES

Geometric figures consist of sets of points. Plane geometric figures are figures with all their points in the same plane.

Angles

An angle is the figure formed by two different rays having the same endpoint. See pages 332 to 365 inclusive for the complete study of angles.

Simple closed plane figures or simple closed curves

Polygons and circles (see page 346) are simple closed plane geometric figures or simple closed curves. Each of these begins at a point and returns to this point without crossing itself, dividing the plane into three sets of points, those in the interior, those in the exterior, and those on the figure. It should be carefully noted that the set of points contained on the line or lines is the figure and not the region enclosed by the figure.

Polygons

A polygon is a simple closed plane figure made up of line segments (called sides). It is the union of three or more line segments. Each pair of intersecting sides meets in a point called the vertex. A polygon with all sides of equal length and all angles of equal measure is called a regular polygon. A polygon is named by reading the letters at the vertices. A line segment connecting two nonadjacent vertices of a polygon is called a diagonal.

Some common polygons are: triangle, consisting of 3 sides; quadrilateral, 4 sides; pentagon, 5 sides; hexagon, 6 sides; octagon, 8 sides; decagon, 10 sides; and dodecagon, 12 sides.

Triangles

When all three sides of a triangle are equal in length, the triangle

is called an equilateral triangle; when two sides are
equal, an isosceles triangle; when no sides are equal,
a scalene triangle. When all three angles of a triangle
are equal in size, the triangle is called an equiangular

triangle; a triangle with a right angle, a right triangle; with an obtuse angle, an obtuse triangle; and with three
acute angles, an acute triangle. The altitude of a triangle is the
perpendicular segment from any vertex of a triangle to the opposite side or extension of that side. The median of a triangle is the
line segment connecting any vertex of a triangle to the midpoint
of the opposite side.

Quadrilaterals

The following properties describe special quadrilaterals:

The rectangle has two pairs of opposite sides which are equal
and parallel and four angles which are right angles.

The square has four equal sides with the opposite sides parallel
and four angles which are right angles.

The parallelogram has two pairs of opposite sides which are
parallel and equal.

The trapezoid has only one pair of opposite sides that are parallel.

The square is a special rectangle, and the rectangle and square
are special parallelograms.

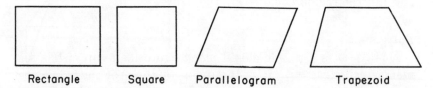

Rectangle   Square   Parallelogram   Trapezoid

Circles

A circle is the set of points in a plane which are equidistant from
a fixed point in the plane called the center. It is a simple closed
curve. The radius of a circle is the line segment which has one
endpoint at the center of the circle and the other endpoint on the
circle. The diameter of a circle is the line segment which has both
of its endpoints on the circle but passes through the center. A
chord of a circle is the line segment which has both of its endpoints
on the circle. An arc is a part of the circle. If the endpoints of an
arc are the endpoints of a diameter, the arc is a semi-circle. An

angle whose vertex is at the center of a circle is called a central angle. The circumference is the distance around the circle.

Concentric circles are circles in the same plane which have the same center but different radii.

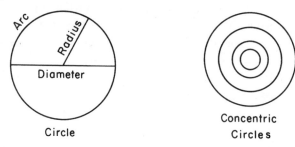

Circle   Concentric Circles

Solid or Space Figures

A closed geometric figure consisting of four or more polygons and their interiors, all in different planes, is called a polyhedron. The polygons and their interiors are called faces. These faces intersect in line segments called edges. These edges intersect in points called vertices.

Common polyhedra are the rectangular solid (right rectangular prism), the cube, and the pyramid.

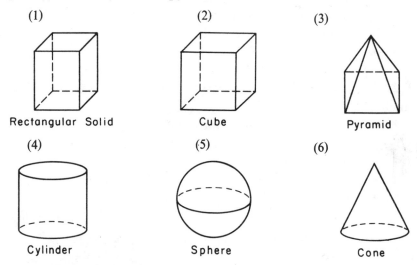

(1)   (2)   (3)

Rectangular Solid   Cube   Pyramid

(4)   (5)   (6)

Cylinder   Sphere   Cone

(1) The rectangular solid has six rectangular faces.
(2) The cube has six squares for its faces. All the edges are equal in length.

(3) The pyramid has any polygon as its base and triangular faces that meet in a common vertex.

Other common solid geometric figures are the cylinder, sphere, and cone.

(4) The cylinder has two equal and parallel circles as bases and a lateral curved surface.

(5) The sphere has a curved surface on which every point is the same distance from the center within.

(6) The cone has a circle for the base and a curved surface that comes to a point called the vertex.

Euler Formula

The Euler formula expresses the relationship of the faces, edges and vertices of a polyhedron. The formula $F + V - E = 2$ tells us that "the number of faces plus the number of vertices minus the number of edges is equal to two."

PRACTICE PROBLEMS

1. What kind of triangle is one that has:
(a) Sides measuring 7 in., $8\frac{1}{2}$ in., and 7 in.?
(b) Angles measuring 60°, 60°, and 60°?
(c) Sides measuring 16 in., 14 in., and 15 in.?
(d) Angles measuring 48°, 42°, and 90°?
(e) Sides measuring 20 ft., 20 ft., and 20 ft.?

2. What is the difference between the altitude of a triangle and the median of a triangle?

3. Draw any (a) parallelogram (b) hexagon (c) pentagon (d) octagon. Determine how many diagonals can be drawn from any one vertex in each figure.

4. Are all polygons regular polygons? If not, draw one that is not a regular polygon.

5. Is a rectangle a special square or is it a special parallelogram?

6. Which of the following are simple closed curves?
(a) a circle   (c) an angle   (e) a straight line
(b) a triangle   (d) a rectangle   (f) a pentagon

7. How many faces (F) does a cube have? How many vertices (V)? How many edges (E)? Does $F + V - E = 2$?

PERIMETER

The distance around a polygon is called the perimeter. It is the sum of the lengths of the sides of the polygon.

I. Rectangle

The perimeter of a rectangle is equal to twice the length added to twice the width.

Formula: $p = 2\,l + 2\,w$

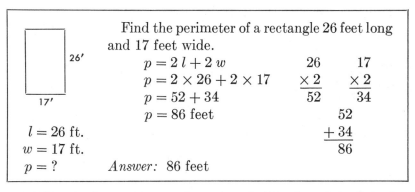

Find the perimeter of a rectangle 26 feet long and 17 feet wide.

$$p = 2\,l + 2\,w$$
$$p = 2 \times 26 + 2 \times 17$$
$$p = 52 + 34$$
$$p = 86 \text{ feet}$$

$$
\begin{array}{cc}
26 & 17 \\
\times 2 & \times 2 \\
\hline
52 & 34
\end{array}
$$

$$
\begin{array}{r}
52 \\
+ 34 \\
\hline
86
\end{array}
$$

$l = 26$ ft.
$w = 17$ ft.
$p = ?$ *Answer:* 86 feet

1. What is the perimeter of a rectangle if its length is 47 inches and width is 21 inches?

2. Find the perimeters of rectangles having the following dimensions:

(a)

Length	16 in.	63 ft.	125 rd.	208 yd.	432 ft.
Width	9 in.	49 ft.	98 rd.	346yd .	327 ft.

(b)

Length	3.5 ft.	8.375 yd.	$7\frac{3}{8}$ in.	$6\frac{2}{3}$ yd.	2 ft. 7 in.
Width	9.75 ft.	1.875 yd.	$4\frac{13}{16}$ in.	$2\frac{1}{2}$ yd.	1 ft. 10 in.

3. How many feet of fencing are required to inclose a rectangular garden 59 ft. long and 39 ft. wide? If each 7-foot section costs $3.69, how much will the fencing cost.

4. How many yards of fringe are needed for a border on a bedspread 72 in. by 105 in.?

5. Fred wishes to make a frame for his class picture. The picture measures 25 in. by $12\frac{1}{2}$ in. If he allows $2\frac{1}{4}$ inches extra for each corner, how many feet of molding will he need?

6. How many feet of baseboard are needed for a room 20 ft. 6 in. long and 16 ft. wide if 5 ft. must be deducted for doorways?

7. At 6¢ per foot, what is the total cost of weatherstripping for 5 window frames, each measuring 32 in. by 66 in.; 3 window frames, each measuring 24 in. by 58 in.; and 2 doorways, each measuring 43 in. by 78 in.?

8. Which lot will take more fencing to enclose it, lot A, 135 ft. long and 93 ft. wide, or lot B, 124 ft. long and 101 ft. wide? How much more fencing?

9. How many times must you walk around the school grounds, 325 ft. long and 203 ft. wide, to walk a mile?

10. How many feet of chrome edging do you need to finish a table top 54 inches long and 30 inches wide?

II. Square

The perimeter of a square is equal to 4 times the length of its side.

Formula: $p = 4\,s$

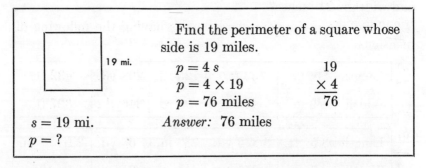

Find the perimeter of a square whose side is 19 miles.

$$p = 4\,s \qquad\qquad 19$$
$$p = 4 \times 19 \qquad\quad \underline{\times 4}$$
$$p = 76 \text{ miles} \qquad\quad 76$$

$s = 19$ mi.   *Answer:* 76 miles
$p = ?$

1. What is the perimeter of a square whose side is 8 inches?

2. Find the perimeters of squares whose sides measure:
(*a*) 25 ft.   (*b*) 11 mi.   (*c*) 880 yd.   (*d*) 76 rd.   (*e*) 5,280 ft.
(*f*) 0.25 in.   (*g*) 17.5 ft.   (*h*) 8¾ ft.   (*i*) 20⅝ in.   (*j*) 2 ft. 9 in.

3. If the distance between bases is 90 feet, how many yards does a batter run when he hits a home run?

4. Find the cost of the wire needed to make a fence of 5 strands around a square lot 132 ft. by 132 ft. if an 80-rod spool of wire costs $7.65.

III. Triangle

The perimeter of a triangle is equal to the sum of its sides.

Formula: $p = a + b + c$

Since the sides of an equilateral triangle are equal, its perimeter is equal to 3 times the length of its side.

Formula: $p = 3\,s$

1. Find the perimeters of triangles with sides measuring:
(a) 18 yd., 9 yd., 15 yd.   (b) 21 in., 17 in., 29 in.   (c) 6.23 ft., 4.7 ft., 3.59 ft. (d) $4\frac{1}{4}$ mi., $7\frac{5}{8}$ mi., $6\frac{1}{2}$ mi. (e) 2 ft. 8 in., 1 ft. 9 in., 1 yd.

2. Find the perimeters of equilateral triangles with sides measuring:
(a) 63 in.   (b) 14 mi.   (c) 4.75 ft.   (d) $16\frac{5}{8}$ in.   (e) 2 ft. 4 in.

3. Find the perimeter of an isosceles triangle if each of the equal sides is 15 inches and the third side is 8 inches.

4. How many feet of hedge are needed to inclose a triangular lot with sides measuring 196 feet, 209 feet, and 187 feet?

5. How many bricks, each 8 inches long, are needed to inclose a triangular vegetable patch with sides measuring 11 ft. 4 in., 8 ft. 11 in., and 7 ft. 9 in.? At $.07 per brick, how much will they cost?

CIRCUMFERENCE OF A CIRCLE

The distance around a circle is called circumference
The parts of the circle are related as follows:
(a) The diameter is twice the radius. Formula: $d = 2\,r$

(b) The radius is one half the diameter. Formula: $r = \dfrac{d}{2}$

(c) The circumference of a circle is equal to pi (π) times the diameter. Formula: $c = \pi d$ where $\pi = 3\frac{1}{7}$ or $\frac{22}{7}$ or 3.14. For greater accuracy 3.1416 is used.

(d) The circumference of a circle is equal to 2 times pi (π) times the radius. Formula: $c = 2\,\pi r$

(e) The diameter of a circle is equal to the circumference divided by pi (π). Formula: $d = \dfrac{c}{\pi}$

Find the circumference of a circle when its diameter is 8 yards.

$c = \pi d$
$c = 3.14 \times 8$
$c = 25.12$ yd.

$$\begin{array}{r} 3.14 \\ \times\, 8 \\ \hline 25.12 \end{array}$$

$d = 8$ yd.
$\pi = 3.14$
$c = ?$

Answer: 25.12 yards

Find the circumference of a circle when its radius is 21 inches.

$c = 2\,\pi r$
$c = 2 \times \frac{22}{7} \times 21$
$c = 132$ in.

$$\frac{2}{1} \times \frac{22}{\underset{1}{7}} \times \frac{\overset{3}{21}}{1} = 132$$

$r = 21$ in.
$\pi = \frac{22}{7}$
$c = ?$

Answer: 132 inches

---

1. How long is the diameter if the radius is: (*a*) 7 yd.? (*b*) 23 ft.? (*c*) 6.5 in.? (*d*) $10\frac{11}{16}$ in.? (*e*) 2 ft. 3 in.?

2. How long is the radius if the diameter is: (*a*) 38 ft.? (*b*) 5 in.? (*c*) 8.9 mi.? (*d*) $10\frac{2}{3}$ ft.? (*e*) 8 yd. 2 ft.?

3. What is the circumference of a circle whose diameter is 60 feet?

4. Find the circumference of a circle having a diameter of: (*a*) 5 in. (*b*) 35 yd. (*c*) 260 ft. (*d*) 49 mi. (*e*) 440 yd. (*f*) 1.8 in. (*g*) 6.3 in. (*h*) $\frac{3}{4}$ in. (*i*) $3\frac{1}{2}$ ft. (*j*) 1 ft. 11 in.

5. What is the circumference of a circle whose radius is 26 feet?

6. Find the circumference of a circle having a radius of: (*a*) 90 ft. (*b*) 7 in. (*c*) 1,000 yd. (*d*) 56 mi. (*e*) 382 ft. (*f*) 0.25 in. (*g*) 8.4 ft. (*h*) $5\frac{1}{2}$ mi. (*i*) $4\frac{3}{8}$ in. (*j*) 2 ft. 4 in.

7. What is the diameter of a circle whose circumference is 286 feet?

8. Find the diameter of a circle when its circumference is: (*a*) 176 ft. (*b*) 198 ft. (*c*) 330 yd. (*d*) 40 in. (*e*) $6\frac{7}{8}$ in.

9. If the diameter of a circular table is 42 inches, what is the circumference of the table?

10. What distance in feet does the tip of a propeller travel in one revolution if its length (*diameter*) is 7 feet?

11. How long a metal bar do you need to make a basketball hoop with a diameter of 18 inches?

12. How much farther do you ride in one turn of a merry-go-round if you sit in the outside lane, 21 ft. from the center, than if you sit in the inside lane, 14 ft. from the center?

13. If the diameter of each wheel is 28 inches, how far does a bicycle go when the wheels revolve once? How many times do the wheels revolve in a distance of 1 mile?

14. Find the circumferences of the earth, moon, and sun if their respective diameters are 7,900 mi., 2,200 mi., and 864,000 mi.

15. The circumference of a tree is 5 ft. 6 in. Find its diameter.

16. What should the diameter of a circular track be if the mile is to be run in 20 laps around the track?

INDIRECT MEASUREMENT

Not all distances or lengths can be measured directly. The distances of ships from the shore, the heights of clouds and mountains, the distances across rivers and lakes, and the distances from the earth to the sun and moon are measured indirectly.

I. Rule of Pythagoras*

An important mathematical principle used in finding distances by indirect means is the hypotenuse rule, sometimes called the rule of Pythagoras. It expresses the relationship of the sides of a right triangle. A right triangle is a triangle having a right angle. The side opposite the right angle is called the hypotenuse. The other two sides or legs are the altitude and base of the triangle.

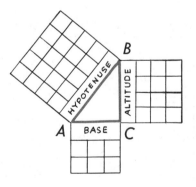

The area of the square drawn on the hypotenuse illustrated in the diagram is 25 square units and is equal to the sum of the

*Pythagoras, a Greek mathematician, lived about 550 B.C.

areas of the squares drawn on the altitude and base (16 square units and 9 square units respectively). This is the rule of Pythagoras. It is usually stated as: *the square of the hypotenuse is equal to the sum of the squares of the other two sides.* As a formula this relationship is expressed:

$$h^2 = a^2 + b^2$$

h representing the hypotenuse, a, the altitude, and b, the base.

If any two sides of a right triangle are known, the third side may be found by the Pythagorean relation expressed in one of the following simplified forms:

$$h = \sqrt{a^2 + b^2} \qquad a = \sqrt{h^2 - b^2} \qquad b = \sqrt{h^2 - a^2}$$

In each case the square root is used because to determine the length of the side of a square when its area is known, the square root of the area must be found.*

Find the hypotenuse of a right triangle if the altitude is 4 inches and the base is 3 inches.	Find the altitude of a right triangle if the hypotenuse is 5 inches and the base is 3 inches.

Find the hypotenuse of a right triangle if the altitude is 4 inches and the base is 3 inches.

$$h = \sqrt{a^2 + b^2}$$
$$h = \sqrt{16 + 9}$$
$$h = \sqrt{25}$$
$$h = 5 \text{ in.}$$

$a = 4$ in.
$b = 3$ in.
$h = ?$

Answer: 5 inches

Find the altitude of a right triangle if the hypotenuse is 5 inches and the base is 3 inches.

$$a = \sqrt{h^2 - b^2}$$
$$a = \sqrt{25 - 9}$$
$$a = \sqrt{16}$$
$$a = 4 \text{ in.}$$

$b = 5$ in.
$h = 3$ in.
$a = ?$

Answer: 4 inches

Find the base of a right triangle if the hypotenuse is 39 feet and the altitude is 15 feet.

$h = 39$ ft. $b = \sqrt{h^2 - a^2}$
$a = 15$ ft. $b = \sqrt{1521 - 225}$
$b = ?$ $b = \sqrt{1296}$
                 $b = 36$ ft..

Answer: 36 feet.

---

*See page 258.

1. Find the hypotenuse of each right triangle with the following dimensions:

Altitude	12 in.	8 ft.	60 yd.	33 ft.	180 ft.	136 yd.
Base	9 in.	15 ft.	25 yd.	56 ft.	112 ft.	255 yd.

2. Find the altitude of each right triangle with the following dimensions:

Hypotenuse	13 in.	35 ft.	89 ft.	53 yd.	219 ft.	325 ft.
Base	5 in.	28 ft.	80 ft.	45 yd.	144 ft.	165 ft.

3. Find the base of each right triangle with the following dimensions:

Hypotenuse	25 in.	87 yd.	73 ft.	91 yd.	153 ft.	477 ft.
Altitude	24 in.	63 yd.	48 ft.	84 yd.	72 ft.	252 ft.

4. By rule of Pythagoras and by actual measurement:

(*a*) Find the diagonal (line segment joining opposite corners) of a rectangle 8 in. long and 6 in. wide.

(*b*) Find the diagonal of a square whose side measures 7 in.

5. What is the shortest distance from first base to third base if the distance between bases is 90 ft.?

6. How high up on a wall does a 25-foot ladder reach if the foot of the ladder is 7 feet from the wall?

7. A boy lets out 150 ft. of string in flying a kite. The distance from a point directly under the kite to where the boy stands is 90 ft. If the boy holds the string 4 ft. from the ground, how high is the kite? Disregard any sag.

8. An airplane, flying 252 miles from town A due west to town B, drifts off its course in a straight line and is 39 miles due south of town B. What distance did the airplane actually fly?

9. Two poles, 34 ft. and 48 ft. high respectively, are 75 ft. apart. What is the distance from the top of one pole to the top of the second pole?

10. A department store escalator is 28 ft. high between floors. It moves a horizontal distance of 25 ft. How many feet is a person carried when he uses the escalator?

II. Similar Triangles

The relationship between the corresponding sides of similar triangles presents another method of measuring lengths and distances indirectly.

Similar triangles have the same shape but differ in size. Their corresponding angles are equal. Also, the ratios of their corresponding sides are equal.

Two triangles are said to be similar when any one of the following conditions are known:

(a) Two angles of one triangle are equal to two angles of the other triangle.

(b) The ratios of all the corresponding sides are equal.

(c) Two sides of one triangle are proportional (equal ratios) to two corresponding sides of the other triangle and the included angles are equal.

Triangles that have the same shape and the same size are called congruent triangles. The corresponding sides are equal in length and the corresponding angles are equal in size. The symbol "≅" means "is congruent to."

To *measure indirectly a distance or length by means of similar triangles,* use the given data to draw two similar triangles. Since the corresponding sides of similar triangles have equal ratios (or are proportional), form and solve a proportion, using three known sides and the required distance as the fourth side. See page 524.

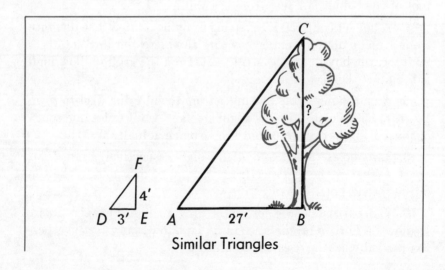

Similar Triangles

A tree casts a shadow (AB) of 27 ft. while a 4-foot post (EF) nearby casts a shadow (DE) of 3 ft. What is the height (BC) of the tree?

Triangles ABC and DEF are similar, therefore the corresponding sides have the same ratio. The side representing the shadow of the tree (AB) corresponds to the side representing the shadow of the post (DE). The side representing the height of the tree (BC) corresponds to the side representing the height of the post (EF).

The ratio of the shadow of the tree to the shadow of the post is 27 to 3 or 9 to 1.

Therefore the height of the tree must be 9 times the height of the post or 9 × 4 ft. = 36 ft. The tree is 36 feet high.

1. In Fig. 1, triangles ABE and CDE are similar. Which side in triangle ABE corresponds to side CE? to side DE? to side AB? Find the length (AB) of the pond.

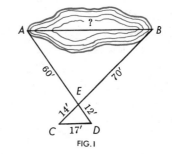

FIG. 1

2. Triangles ABC and CDE are similar in Fig. 2. Which side in triangle ABC corresponds to side CE? to side DE? What is the distance (AB) across the stream?

3. A flagpole casts a shadow 42 ft. long. At the same time a 6-foot pole casts a shadow of 7 ft. How high is the flagpole?

4. Find the height of a building that casts a shadow of 26 ft. at a time when a boy, 5 feet tall, casts a shadow of 2 ft.

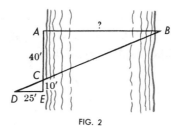

FIG. 2

5. Using Fig. 2, find the distance across the stream if DE is 32 ft., CE is 9 ft., and AC is 45 ft.

6. What is the height of a TV antenna tower that casts a shadow of 12 ft. when the adjacent building, 20 ft. high, casts a shadow of 2½ ft.?

III. Numerical Trigonometry

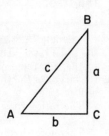

In trigonometry (meaning triangle measure) the relationships between the sides and the angles of the right triangle are used to determine certain parts of the triangle when the other parts are known. The ratios of the sides of the right triangle are related to the acute angles as follows:

The ratio of the side opposite an acute angle to the adjacent side is called the tangent of the angle (abbreviated tan). The expression $\tan A$ means tangent of angle A. In right triangle ABC,

$$\tan A = \frac{a}{b} \text{ and } \tan B = \frac{b}{a}.$$

The ratio of the side opposite an acute angle to the hypotenuse is called the sine of the angle (abbreviated sin). In the right triangle ABC, $\sin A = \frac{a}{c}$ and $\sin B = \frac{b}{c}$.

The ratio of the adjacent side of an acute angle to the hypotenuse is called the cosine of the angle (abbreviated cos). In the right triangle ABC, $\cos A = \frac{b}{c}$ and $\cos B = \frac{a}{c}$.

Angles are measured both vertically and horizontally. An angle measured vertically between the horizontal line and the observer's line of sight to an object is called the angle of elevation when the object is above the observer and the angle of depression when the object is below the observer.

To solve problems using trigonometric ratios, draw a right

In right triangle ABC, find side a when angle $A = 53°$ and side $b = 100$ feet.

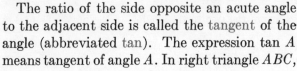

$b = 100$ ft.
$A = 53°$
$a = ?$

$$\tan A = \frac{a}{b}$$

$$\tan 53° = \frac{a}{100}$$

$$1.3270 = \frac{a}{100}$$

$$a = 132.7 \text{ ft.}$$

Answer, 132.7 ft.

triangle if one is not given and place the given dimensions on it. Select the proper formula and substitute the given values, using the table of trigonometric values when necessary. Then solve the resulting equation.

In problems where the complement of an angle (see page 351) is simpler to use for computation than the given angle, it may be determined by either one of the following formulas: $A = 90° - B$ or $B = 90° - A$.

PRACTICE PROBLEMS

The letters in the following problems represent parts of the right triangle ABC with angle C, the right angle; altitude a, the side opposite angle A; and base b, the side opposite angle B. See the drawing on page 326.

1. Find the value of:

   (a) tan 43°;   tan 81°;   tan 63° 30′;   tan 37° 45′
   (b) sin 79°;   sin 7°;   sin 41° 30′;   sin 24° 20′
   (c) cos 18°;   cos 56°;   cos 6° 15′;   cos 71° 40′

2. Find angle A when:

   (a) tan A = .3839;   tan A = 3.0777;   tan A = .2586;
   tan A = 1.6483
   (b) sin A = .9063;   sin A = .3420;   sin A = .7489;
   sin A = .9940
   (c) cos A = .8988;   cos A = .6293;   cos A = .5983;
   cos A = .6626

3. Find angle B when:

   (a) tan B = 19.0811;   tan B = .9004;   tan B = 1.2649;
   tan B = .6129
   (b) sin B = .6561;   sin B = .9986;   sin B = .5075;
   sin B = .9469
   (c) cos B = .1045;   cos B = .9998;   cos B = .4423;
   cos B = .9984

4. Use the tangent ratio to find:

   (a) Side a if angle $A = 30°$ and side $b = 50$ ft.
   (b) Side b if angle $B = 65°$ and side $a = 80$ yd.
   (c) Side b if angle $A = 22°$ and side $a = 101$ ft.
   (d) Side a if angle $B = 70°$ and side $b = 140$ mi.
   (e) Angle A if side $a = 202$ ft. and side $b = 500$ ft.
   (f) Angle B if side $a = 1,000$ ft. and side $b = 1,804$ ft.

5. Use the sine ratio to find:

    (*a*) Side *a* if angle *A* = 60° and side *c* = 75 ft.

    (*b*) Side *b* if angle *B* = 15° and side *c* = 40 in.

    (*c*) Side *b* if angle *A* = 86° and side *c* = 3.49 mi.

    (*d*) Side *a* if angle *B* = 32° and side *c* = 80 yd.

    (*e*) Side *c* if angle *A* = 52° and side *a* = 394 ft.

    (*f*) Side *c* if angle *B* = 20° and side *b* = 855 yd.

    (*g*) Angle *A* if side *a* = 170.5 ft. and side *c* = 250 ft.

    (*h*) Angle *B* if side *b* = 106 yd. and side *c* = 125 yd.

6. Use the cosine ratio to find:

    (*a*) Side *b* if angle *A* = 46° and side *c* = 100 ft.

    (*b*) Side *a* if angle *B* = 62° and side *c* = 250 yd.

    (*c*) Side *c* if angle *A* = 70° and side *b* = 17.1 mi.

    (*d*) Side *c* if angle *B* = 59° and side *a* = 515 yd.

    (*e*) Angle *A* if side *b* = 23 in. and side *c* = 46 in.

    (*f*) Angle *B* if side *a* = 309 mi. and side *c* = 1,000 mi.

7. Find:

    (*a*) Side *a* if angle *A* = 61° and side *b* = 25 in.

    (*b*) Side *a* if angle *A* = 40° and side *c* = 50 yd.

    (*c*) Side *b* if angle *A* = 66° and side *c* = 175 ft.

    (*d*) Side *b* if angle *B* = 49° and side *a* = 1,000 yd.

    (*e*) Side *b* if angle *B* = 13° and side *c* = 80 mi.

    (*f*) Side *a* if angle *B* = 27° and side *c* = 100 yd.

    (*g*) Side *b* if angle *A* = 30° and side *a* = 46 in.

    (*h*) Angle *A* if side *a* = 451 ft. and side *b* = 250 ft.

    (*i*) Angle *B* if side *a* = 511.5 mi. and side *c* = 750 mi.

    (*j*) Angle *A* if side *a* = 53.46 ft. and side *c* = 60 ft.

8. (*a*) The light from a searchlight is seen on a cloud at a horizontal distance of 2,800 feet from the searchlight. What is the height of the cloud if the angle of elevation from the searchlight is 65°?

(*b*) From a cliff 300 feet above the sea, the angle of depression of a boat is 87°. How far is the boat from the foot of the cliff?

(*c*) How high is a kite when 160 feet of string is let out and the string makes an angle of 50° with the ground?

(*d*) The altitude of a right triangle is 220 miles and the angle opposite the base is 77°. How long is the hypotenuse?

(*e*) What is the elevation of a road if the road rises 364 feet in a horizontal distance of 1,000 feet?

Table of Trigonometric Values

Angle	Sine	Cosine	Tangent	Angle	Sine	Cosine	Tangent
0°	.0000	1.0000	.0000	46°	.7193	.6947	1.0355
1°	.0175	.9998	.0175	47°	.7314	.6820	1.0724
2°	.0349	.9994	.0349	48°	.7431	.6691	1.1106
3°	.0523	.9986	.0524	49°	.7547	.6561	1.1504
4°	.0698	.9976	.0699	50°	.7660	.6428	1.1918
5°	.0872	.9962	.0875	51°	.7771	.6293	1.2349
6°	.1045	.9945	.1051	52°	.7880	.6157	1.2799
7°	.1219	.9925	.1228	53°	.7986	.6018	1.3270
8°	.1392	.9903	.1405	54°	.8090	.5878	1.3764
9°	.1564	.9877	.1584	55°	.8192	.5736	1.4281
10°	.1736	.9848	.1763	56°	.8290	.5592	1.4826
11°	.1908	.9816	.1944	57°	.8387	.5446	1.5399
12°	.2079	.9781	.2126	58°	.8480	.5299	1.6003
13°	.2250	.9744	.2309	59°	.8572	.5150	1.6643
14°	.2419	.9703	.2493	60°	.8660	.5000	1.7321
15°	.2588	.9659	.2679	61°	.8746	.4848	1.8040
16°	.2756	.9613	.2867	62°	.8829	.4695	1.8807
17°	.2924	.9563	.3057	63°	.8910	.4540	1.9626
18°	.3090	.9511	.3249	64°	.8988	.4384	2.0503
19°	.3256	.9455	.3443	65°	.9063	.4226	2.1445
20°	.3420	.9397	.3640	66°	.9135	.4067	2.2460
21°	.3584	.9336	.3839	67°	.9205	.3907	2.3559
22°	.3746	.9272	.4040	68°	.9272	.3746	2.4751
23°	.3907	.9205	.4245	69°	.9336	.3584	2.6051
24°	.4067	.9135	.4452	70°	.9397	.3420	2.7475
25°	.4226	.9063	.4663	71°	.9455	.3256	2.9042
26°	.4384	.8988	.4877	72°	.9511	.3090	3.0777
27°	.4540	.8910	.5095	73°	.9563	.2924	3.2709
28°	.4695	.8829	.5317	74°	.9613	.2756	3.4874
29°	.4848	.8746	.5543	75°	.9659	.2588	3.7321
30°	.5000	.8660	.5774	76°	.9703	.2419	4.0108
31°	.5150	.8572	.6009	77°	.9744	.2250	4.3315
32°	.5299	.8480	.6249	78°	.9781	.2079	4.7046
33°	.5446	.8387	.6494	79°	.9816	.1908	5.1446
34°	.5592	.8290	.6745	80°	.9848	.1736	5.6713
35°	.5736	.8192	.7002	81°	.9877	.1564	6.3138
36°	.5878	.8090	.7265	82°	.9903	.1392	7.1154
37°	.6018	.7986	.7536	83°	.9925	.1219	8.1443
38°	.6157	.7880	.7813	84°	.9945	.1045	9.5144
39°	.6293	.7771	.8098	85°	.9962	.0872	11.4301
40°	.6428	.7660	.8391	86°	.9976	.0698	14.3007
41°	.6561	.7547	.8693	87°	.9986	.0523	19.0811
42°	.6691	.7431	.9004	88°	.9994	.0349	28.6363
43°	.6820	.7314	.9325	89°	.9998	.0175	57.2900
44°	.6947	.7193	.9657	90°	1.0000	.0000	
45°	.7071	.7071	1.0000				

REVIEW OF EXERCISE

1. Read, or write in words, each of the following:
$\overleftrightarrow{RT}$; $\overline{OM}$; $\overrightarrow{DG}$.

2. Name each of the following: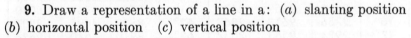

3. Name the endpoints in the above drawings.

4. Name the line segments in the following triangle.

5. $\overline{MN} \cap \overline{LN} = \{?\}$

6. Are points M, L, and N collinear?

7. Are $\overline{LM}$ and $\overline{LN}$ concurrent?

8. Draw a representation of a pair of:
  (*a*) perpendicular lines
  (*b*) parallel lines
  (*c*) intersecting lines

9. Draw a representation of a line in a: (*a*) slanting position (*b*) horizontal position (*c*) vertical position

10. If the scale is 1 inch = 100 miles, what actual distance is represented by the scale distance of $5\frac{3}{4}$ inches?

11. What is the perimeter of a rectangle 135 feet long and 92 feet wide?

12. Find the circumference of a circle whose diameter is 84 yards.

13. What is the perimeter of a square whose side measures $7\frac{5}{8}$ inches?

14. What is the circumference of a circle whose radius is 120 feet?

15. Find the perimeter of a triangle with sides measuring $2\frac{7}{8}$ inches, $4\frac{1}{4}$ inches, and $3\frac{1}{2}$ inches.

16. Find the hypotenuse of a right triangle if the altitude is 76 feet and the base is 57 feet.

17. What is the base of a right triangle if the hypotenuse is 377 yards and the altitude is 145 yards?

18. Find the altitude of a right triangle if the base is 66 feet and the hypotenuse is 130 feet.

19. Find the height of a building that casts a shadow of 40 feet at the time a 7-foot fence casts a shadow of 5 feet.

20. How many yards of linoleum border are needed for a kitchen floor 12 feet by 10 feet 6 inches?

21. Which is longer, the perimeter of a bridge table measuring 30 inches on a side or the circumference of a circular table measuring 35 inches in diameter?

22. Allowing $\frac{1}{2}$ inch for the overlap, how long should a paper label be in order to go around a metal container having a diameter of 7 inches?

23. Show by the rule of Pythagoras that a 30-inch umbrella can be fitted into a suitcase having inside dimensions of 26 inches by 15 inches.

24. How many lines can be drawn through a point? Through two points?

25. (*a*) When two lines intersect, what is their intersection?

(*b*) When two planes intersect, what is their intersection?

26. (*a*) How many points determine a line?

(*b*) How many points determine a plane?

27. The angle of elevation from a ship to the top of a lighthouse, 150 feet high, is 19°. How far from the foot of the lighthouse is the ship?

REFRESH YOUR SKILLS

1. Add:
61,284
9,713
34,882
2,506
1,493

2. Subtract:
290,015
189,025

3. Multiply:
408
603

4. Divide:
$986\overline{)884{,}442}$

5. Add:
$6\frac{5}{8}$
$3\frac{5}{6}$

6. Subtract:
$8\frac{1}{2}$
$5\frac{3}{4}$

7. Multiply:
$4\frac{7}{8} \times 2\frac{2}{3}$

8. Divide:
$\frac{1}{2} \div 1\frac{3}{4}$

9. Add:
$4.96 + .824 + 73.5$

10. Subtract:
$\$40 - \$2.96$

11. Multiply:
$.003 \times 1.15$

12. Divide:
$.8\overline{).1}$

13. Find $3\frac{1}{2}\%$ of $\$4,500$

14. What per cent of $\$40$ is $\$18$?

15. 30% of what number is 12?

16. Round off .0096 to the nearest thousandth.

17. Change $\frac{5}{16}$ to a decimal (4 places).

18. Express 2.1 as a per cent.

19. Square: 82.6

20. Find the square root of 40 to the nearest hundredth.

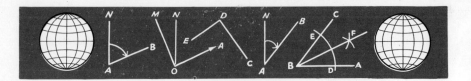

EXERCISE 46

MEASURE OF ANGLES AND ARCS

I. Aim: (A) To change a given number of units of one denomination to units of another denomination and (B) to add, subtract, multiply, and divide measures of angles and arcs.

II. Procedure

Part A

Use either the common method or the method of cancellation of units explained in the procedure of Exercise 44 on page 296.

The following specific rules may also be used:

To change:

(*a*) Degrees to minutes, multiply the number of degrees by 60.

(*b*) Minutes to degrees, divide the number of minutes by 60.

(*c*) Minutes to seconds, multiply the number of minutes by 60.

(*d*) Seconds to minutes, divide the number of seconds by 60.

Part B

Follow the procedure given in Exercise 57 on page 427.

III. Sample Solutions

1. Change 21° to minutes.

$$\begin{array}{r} 21 \\ \times\, 60 \\ \hline 1{,}260 \end{array}$$

Answer: 1,260′

2. Change 389′ to degrees. Write remainder as minutes.

$$\begin{array}{r} 6 \\ 60\overline{)389} \\ 360 \\ \hline 29 \end{array}$$

Answer: 6° 29′

3. Add and simplify:

$$\begin{array}{r} 16°\ 21'\ \ 45'' \\ 37°\ 18'\ \ 21'' \\ 29°\ 36'\ \ 34'' \\ \hline 82°\ 75'\ 100'' = 82°\ 76'\ 40'' \\ = 83°\ 16'\ 40'' \end{array}$$

Answer: 83° 16′ 40″

4. Subtract 72° 38′ from 180°.

$$\begin{array}{r} 180°\ \ \ \ \ = 179°\ 60' \\ 72°\ 38' = \ \ 72°\ 38' \\ \hline 107°\ 22' \end{array}$$

Answer: 107° 22′

5. Multiply 24° 17′ by 4.

    24° 17′

        4

 96° 68′ = 97° 8′

Answer: 97° 8′

6. Divide 18° 43′ 30″ by 3.

     6° 14′ 30″

3)18° 43′ 30″

 18°

    43′

    42′

     1′ 30″ = 90″

         90″

Answer: 6° 14′ 30″

IV. Definitions

1. The unit of measure of angles and arcs is a degree, designated by the symbol °. A degree is $\frac{1}{360}$ part of the entire angular measure about a point in a plane. If a circle is divided into 360 equal parts and line segments are drawn from the center to these points of division, 360 equal central angles are formed, each

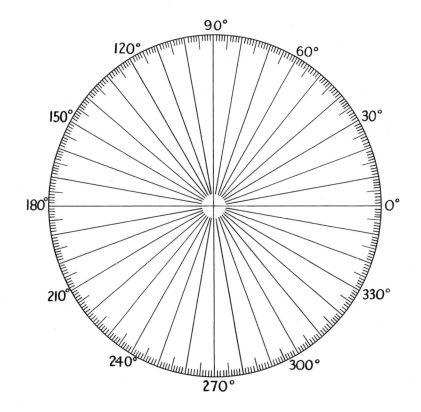

measuring 1 degree. Each of the corresponding 360 equal arcs also measures 1 degree. A circle, therefore, contains 360 degrees of arc.

2. The degree is divided into 60 equal parts called minutes, designated by the symbol ′.

3. The minute is divided into 60 equal parts called seconds, designated by the symbol ″.

4. A radian is an angle subtended by a circular arc whose length is equal to the radius of the circle.

5. A mil is $\frac{1}{1600}$ of a right angle. It is used to express deflection in gunnery.

EQUIVALENTS

1 circle = 360 degrees (°)

1 degree (°) = 60 minutes (′)

1 minute (′) = 60 seconds (″)

1 radian = 57° 17′ 45″

1 mil = $\frac{1}{1600}$ of a right angle

Part A

DIAGNOSTIC TEST A

Change:

1. 15° to minutes	**4.** 23′ 53″ to seconds
2. 36° 18′ to minutes	**5.** 1° 27′ 15″ to seconds
3. 42′ to seconds	**6.** 1,680′ to degrees

    7. 572′ to degrees (Write remainder in minutes.)

    8. 2,040″ to minutes

    9. 435″ to minutes (Write remainder in seconds.)

   10. 4,584″ to degrees (Write remainder in minutes and seconds.)

RELATED PRACTICE EXAMPLES

Change to minutes:	Change to minutes:	Change to seconds:	Change to seconds:
SET 1	SET 2	SET 3	SET 4
1. 8°	**1.** 19° 40′	**1.** 28′	**1.** 14′ 21″
2. 56°	**2.** 5° 38′	**2.** 9′	**2.** 58′ 30″
3. 45°	**3.** 32° 6′	**3.** 50′	**3.** 2′ 45″
4. 13°	**4.** 53° 17′	**4.** 41′	**4.** 37′ 48″
5. 30°	**5.** 47° 24′	**5.** 16′	**5.** 10′ 3″

Change to seconds: Change to degrees: Change to degrees:

In set 7 write the remainder in minutes.

SET 5	SET 6	SET 7
1. 2° 18′ 40″	1. 180′	1. 84′
2. 1° 4′ 38″	2. 480′	2. 105′
3. 5° 21′ 35″	3. 900′	3. 297′
4. 3° 47′ 9″	4. 3,000′	4. 428′
5. 10° 15′ 27″	5. 4,320′	5. 761′

Change to minutes: Change to minutes: Change to degrees:

In set 9 write the remainder in seconds.
In set 10 write the remainder in minutes and seconds.

SET 8	SET 9	SET 10
1. 420″	1. 75″	1. 3,752″
2. 2,940″	2. 116″	2. 7,725″
3. 2,400″	3. 348″	3. 6,138″
4. 1,140″	4. 571″	4. 5,871″
5. 3,180″	5. 256″	5. 12,320″

Part B
PRELIMINARY EXAMPLES

Simplify:

SET 1	SET 2
1. $25° 74′ =$	1. $18° 59′ 60″ =$
2. $96° 60′ =$	2. $133° 83′ 92″ =$
3. $4′ 93″ =$	3. $65° 97′ 103″ =$
4. $31′ 145″ =$	4. $20° 135′ 148″ =$
5. $52° 28′ 169″ =$	5. $117° 154′ 120″ =$

Find the missing numbers:

SET 3	SET 4
1. $15° = 14°$ ——′	1. $64° = 63°$ ——′ 60″
2. $48′ = 47′$ ——″	2. $90° = 89° 59′$ ——″
3. $23° 7′ = 22°$ ——′	3. $8° 26′ = 7°$ ——′ 60″
4. $51′ 38″ = 50′$ ——″	4. $39° 15′ 4″ = 38° 74′$ ——″
5. $84° 19′ 20″ = 84° 18′$ ——″	5. $153° 32′ 29″ = 152°$ ——′ 89″

DIAGNOSTIC TEST B

Add and simplify:

1. 36° 15′
   47° 31′

2. 21° 42′ 13″
   54° 31′ 20″
    9° 24′ 17″

3. 32° 15′ 27″
   45° 8′ 15″
   12° 36′ 18″

Subtract:

4. 107° 48′
    45° 36′

5. 72° 23′ 41″
   57° 39′ 4″

6. 90°
   63° 46′ 12″

Multiply and simplify:

7. 19° 21′
        2

8. 31° 10′ 57″
         3

9. 9° 23′ 30″
          15

Divide:

10. 6)48° 30′

11. 2)15° 26′ 14″

12. 15)32° 9′ 45″

RELATED PRACTICE EXAMPLES

Add and simplify:

SET 1	SET 2	SET 3
1. 14° 26′ 52° 19′	**1.** 32° 54′ 41° 46′	**1.** 86° 48′ 30″ 63° 32′ 45″
2. 67° 34′ 20″ 15° 11′ 34″	**2.** 3° 27′ 40″ 29° 18′ 20″	**2.** 77° 2′ 9″ 12° 57′ 51″
3. 25° 16′ 39° 29′ 6° 14′	**3.** 56° 32′ 97° 50′ 25° 38′	**3.** 44° 21′ 18″ 27° 53′ 25″ 102° 39′ 40″
4. 43° 17′ 3″ 107° 33′ 15″ 18° 4′ 41″	**4.** 126° 13′ 49″ 85° 29′ 36″ 97° 14′ 28″	**4.** 82° 35′ 50″ 55° 49′ 45″ 41° 34′ 25″
5. 37° 24′ 15″ 54° 7′ 25″ 96° 10′ 10″	**5.** 64° 54′ 18″ 55° 16′ 10″ 83° 42′ 31″	**5.** 124° 17′ 36″ 38° 26′ 7″ 17° 48′ 22″

Subtract:

SET 4	SET 5	SET 6
1. 46° 50'	**1.** 53° 21'	**1.** 67° 43' 20''
14° 33'	22° 49'	56° 49' 36''
2. 89° 59' 60''	**2.** 90°	**2.** 84° 5' 14''
62° 24' 45''	48° 15'	35° 5' 51''
3. 75° 31' 48''	**3.** 45° 38' 30''	**3.** 143° 24' 18''
38° 5' 37''	17° 23' 50''	106° 42' 32''
4. 179° 59' 60''	**4.** 131° 52' 29''	**4.** 90°
108° 49' 26''	95° 58' 25''	27° 53' 10''
5. 112° 36' 17''	**5.** 78° 6' 47''	**5.** 180°
57° 18' 4''	26° 15' 30''	131° 26' 47''

Multiply and simplify:

SET 7	SET 8	SET 9
1. 38° 14'	**1.** 42° 57'	**1.** 75° 38' 45''
3	2	2
2. 51° 25'	**2.** 15° 29' 8''	**2.** 46° 24' 53''
2	6	3
3. 23° 12' 10''	**3.** 60° 7' 35''	**3.** 28° 15' 20''
4	3	5
4. 17° 3' 2''	**4.** 12° 32'	**4.** 13° 49' 30''
15	15	15

Divide:

SET 10	SET 11	SET 12
1. 2)56° 18'	**1.** 3)17° 15'	**1.** 4)29° 33' 48''
2. 5)25° 45'	**2.** 2)82° 37' 46''	**2.** 3)53° 25' 36''
3. 3)36° 15' 30''	**3.** 6)74° 48' 54''	**3.** 2)147° 9' 14''
4. 2)114° 8' 24''	**4.** 15)48° 30'	**4.** 15)34° 55' 45''
5. 15)60° 45' 15''	**5.** 15)160° 45' 15''	**5.** 15)128° 41' 30''

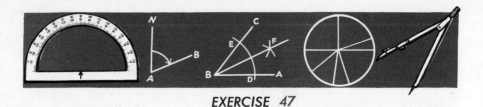

PRACTICAL APPLICATIONS USING ANGLES AND ARCS GEOMETRIC CONSTRUCTIONS

FACTS ABOUT ANGLES

I. Meaning of an Angle

(a) An angle is the figure formed when two different rays are drawn from the same end point. This common point is called the vertex of of the angle and the two rays are called the sides of the angle.

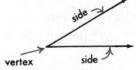

(b) An angle may be considered as the amount of rotation of a ray about its fixed point, the angle being formed when the ray turns from one position to another. As the ray rotates, each of its other points describes an arc of a circle. The angle at the center of the circle corresponding to the arc is called the central angle. Its vertex is at the center and its sides are radii of the circle.

(c) An angle is sometimes used to show direction. See page 342.

(d) The symbol ∠ is used to represent the word "angle."

II. Reading an Angle

Angles are identified or named in the following ways:

(a) By reading the capital letter at the vertex:

(b) By reading the three letters associated with the vertex and one point on each of the sides. The middle letter always indicates the vertex.

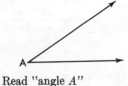

Read "angle A"

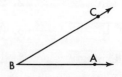

Read "angle ABC" or "angle CBA"

(*c*) By reading the inside letter or numeral:

Read "angle *m*"   Read "angle 4"

III. Kinds of Angles

When a ray turns from one position to another about its fixed endpoint, one complete rotation is equal to 360°.

A right angle is one fourth of a complete rotation; it is an angle whose measure is 90°.

Right

An acute angle is an angle whose measure is greater than 0° but less than 90°.

Acute

An obtuse angle is an angle whose measure is greater than 90° but less than 180°.

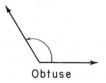

Obtuse

A straight angle is one half of a complete rotation; it is an angle whose measure is 180°. The rays that form a straight angle extend in opposite directions along a straight line that passes through the vertex.

A reflex angle is an angle whose measure is greater than 180° but less than 360°.

Straight

Reflex

IV. Measuring Angles

Measuring an angle means to find how many units of angular measure are contained in it. The protractor is an instrument used to measure and draw angles.

The size of an angle does *not* depend on the length of its sides.

To *measure an angle:*

Place the straight edge of the protractor on one side of the angle with its center mark at the vertex of the angle.

Read the number of degrees at the point where the other side of the angle cuts the protractor, using the scale which has its zero on one side of the angle.

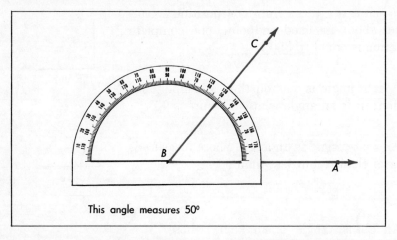

This angle measures 50⁰

The symbol *"m(∠ABC)"* is read "the measure of angle *ABC.*" The measure of the above angle can be written either as $m(\angle ABC) = 50°$ or briefly as $\angle ABC = 50°$.

V. Drawing Angles

To *draw an angle:*

Draw a ray to represent one side of the angle. Sometimes a ray or a line segment is already drawn.

Place the protractor so that its straight edge falls on this ray and its center mark is on the vertex. The vertex usually is the endpoint of the ray but may be any point on a given line.

Counting on the scale which has its zero on the ray, locate the required number of degrees and indicate its position by a dot.

Remove the protractor, then draw a ray from the vertex through this dot.

To draw an angle of 40° using point *E* on ray *DE* as the vertex:

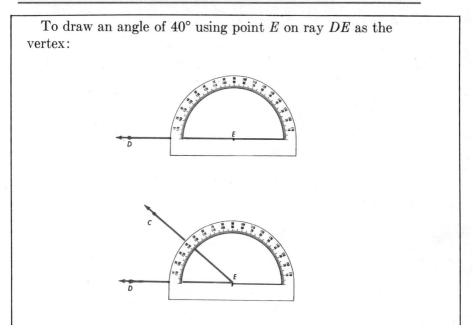

PRACTICE PROBLEMS

1. Name each of the following angles.

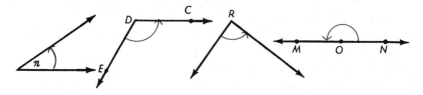

2. Estimate the size of the above angles. Measure each angle with a protractor. Find the amount of your error.

3. Which of the above angles is an acute angle? a right angle? an obtuse angle? a straight angle?

4. How many degrees are in the angle formed by the hands of a clock at 3 o'clock? 4 o'clock? 1 o'clock? 6 o'clock?

5. Through how many degrees does the minute hand of a clock turn in 10 minutes? 25 minutes? 45 minutes? 1 hour?

6. Which of the following angles are acute angles: 65°, 93°, 150°, 7°, 89°? What are the remaining angles called?

7. Which angle is smaller?

Draw the following angles with a protractor:

8. Using a ray with the left endpoint as the vertex:

(*a*) 30° (*b*) 75° (*c*) 83° (*d*) 120° (*e*) 270° (*f*) 145° (*g*) 100° (*h*) 58° (*i*) 225° (*j*) 305°

9. Using a ray with the right endpoint as the vertex:

(*a*) 80° (*b*) 45° (*c*) 9° (*d*) 165° (*e*) 330° (*f*) 25° (*g*) 124° (*h*) 67° (*i*) 96° (*j*) 200°

10. (*a*) A right angle   (*b*) A straight angle   (*c*) An obtuse angle (*d*) An acute angle

ANGLES IN NAVIGATION

An angle is often used to indicate direction. It may show the direction (usually called the course) in which an airplane flies or the direction from which the wind blows or the direction of one object from another (usually called the bearing). Each one of these directions is represented by an angle measured clockwise from the north direction. Sometimes this angle is called an azimuth.

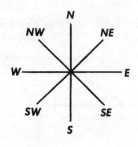

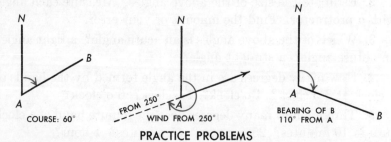

PRACTICE PROBLEMS

1. If you face north, then turn clockwise to face west, how many degrees do you turn?

2. If you face east, then turn clockwise to face southwest, how many degrees do you turn?

In each of the following constructions, first draw a vertical line to indicate the north direction.

3. Draw the following course angles:

(a) 80° (b) 145° (c) 210° (d) 300° (e) 25° (f) 160° (g) 64° (h) 237° (i) 350° (j) 108°.

4. Draw angles indicating the following directions *from* which winds are blowing:

(a) 50° (b) east (90°) (c) west (270°) (d) south (180°) (e) 130° (f) 200° (g) 335° (h) southwest (225°) (i) 95° (j) northwest (315°).

5. Draw angles indicating the following bearings of objects from a given point:

(a) 35° (b) 160° (c) 240° (d) 312° (e) 23° (f) 98° (g) 187° (h) 205° (i) 341° (j) 275°.

Winds decrease or increase the speed developed by an airplane in flight through the air. The speed of the plane in still air is called air speed. The actual speed of the plane measured by land markings is called ground speed. The direction, represented by an angle, in which the plane points is called the heading.

A vector is an arrow which represents a speed or force and at the same time indicates a direction. This vector is drawn to scale usually as one side of the angle which represents the direction measured clockwise from the north.

To find the position of an airplane at the end of 1 hour when flying on a course of 100° with a ground speed of 416 m.p.h.

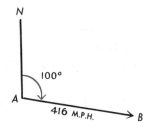

Scale: 1 inch = 320 m.p.h.

Airplane takes off at point *A*. Reaches point *B* at the end of 1 hour.

6. Using appropriate scales, make scale drawings showing the positions of airplanes at the end of one hour flying:

(a) On a course of 130° with a ground speed of 225 m.p.h.

(b) With a heading of 70° and an air speed of 360 m.p.h.

(c) On a course of 48° with a ground speed of 240 m.p.h.

(d) With a heading of 310° and an air speed of 400 m.p.h.

(e) On a course of 263° with a ground speed of 460 m.p.h.

(f) With a heading of 97° and an air speed of 300 m.p.h.

7. Draw vectors representing the following wind velocities:

(a) 50 m.p.h. wind from 45° (b) 40 m.p.h. wind from 200° (c) 25 m.p.h. north wind (0°) (d) 15 m.p.h. wind from 135° (e) 45 m.p.h. wind from 325°.

8. Make a scale drawing showing the position of an airplane at the end of 3 hr. when flying on a course of 60° with a ground speed of 250 m.p.h.

9. An airplane, flying due east (90°) at an air speed of 280 m.p.h., was blown off its course by a 35 m.p.h. south wind (180°). Make a scale drawing showing the position of the airplane at the end of one hour. How far was the airplane from its starting point? What was its ground speed? What course (or track) was it actually flying?

CONSTRUCTIONS

I. Triangles

A triangle contains three sides and three angles. A triangle may be constructed when any of the following combinations of three parts are known:

(a) Two sides and an included angle.

(b) Two angles and an included side.

(c) Three sides.

Two sides and an included angle

1. Draw a line segment 2 inches long. Using the left endpoint as the vertex, draw an angle of 50°. Make the second side of the angle $2\frac{1}{2}$ inches long. Draw a line segment connecting endpoints to form a triangle.

2. Construct triangles having the following sides and included angles:

(a) $1\frac{3}{4}$ in., $1\frac{1}{2}$ in., 85° (b) $2\frac{1}{4}$ in., 3 in., 130° (c) $2\frac{3}{8}$ in., $1\frac{7}{8}$ in., 90°.

3. With the scale of 1 in. = 40 mi., construct a triangle in which two sides measure 30 mi. and 225 mi. and the included angle measures 60°.

4. Draw a right triangle having an altitude of 3 in. and a base of 4 in.

Two angles and an included side

5. Draw a line segment $2\frac{1}{8}$ inches long. Using the left endpoint as the vertex, draw an angle of 40°. Using the right endpoint as the vertex, draw an angle of 70°. Extend the sides until they meet to form a triangle.

6. Construct triangles having the following angles and included sides:

(a) 60°, 90°, $2\frac{1}{2}$ in. (b) 105°, 55°, $3\frac{1}{4}$ in. (c) 45°, 45°, 2 in.

7. With the scale of $\frac{1}{4}$ in. = 1 ft., construct a triangle in which two angles measure 30° and 80° and the included side measures 18 ft.

Three sides

8. To construct a triangle whose sides measure $1\frac{7}{8}$ in., $2\frac{1}{4}$ in., and 2 in., use compasses to lay off a line segment $1\frac{7}{8}$ in. long. With one endpoint as center and setting the compasses so that the radius is $2\frac{1}{4}$ in. long, draw an arc. With the other endpoint as center and a radius of 2 in., draw an arc crossing the first arc. From this point of intersection draw line segments to the endpoints of the base to form the required triangle.

9. Construct triangles having the following sides:

(a) 2 in., $1\frac{1}{2}$ in., $1\frac{5}{8}$ in. (b) $2\frac{3}{4}$ in., $2\frac{1}{4}$ in., 3 in. (c) 1 in., $1\frac{3}{4}$ in., $1\frac{3}{4}$ in. (d) $1\frac{7}{8}$ in., $1\frac{7}{8}$ in., $1\frac{7}{8}$ in.

10. With the scale of $\frac{1}{8}$ in. = 1 ft., construct triangles whose sides are:

(a) 16 ft., 22 ft., 9 ft. (b) 30 ft., 24 ft., 15 ft. (c) 12 ft., 12 ft., 12 ft. (d) 18 ft., 10 ft., 10 ft.

II. Regular Polygons

To *construct a regular polygon:*

First draw a circle.

Divide this circle into the same number of equal arcs as there are sides in the required polygon by drawing a corresponding number of equal central angles.

Draw line segments connecting the points of division to form the polygon.

To construct a regular octagon—8 sides

$$\begin{array}{r} 45° \\ 8\overline{)360°} \end{array}$$

Each central angle equals 45°.

Construct each of the following regular polygons:

1. Pentagon—5 sides   4. Dodecagon—12 sides
2. Hexagon—6 sides   5. Equilateral triangle
3. Decagon—10 sides   6. Square

III. Bisecting a Line Segment

To *bisect a line segment* means to divide it into two equal parts.

(*a*) Using ruler:

Measure the given line segment. Then mark off one half the measurement.

(*b*) Using compasses (see figure):

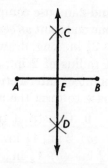

To bisect line segment AB, set compasses so that the radius is more than half the length of $\overline{AB}$. With A and B as centers draw arcs which cross above and below the line segment at C and D.

Draw line CD bisecting $\overline{AB}$ at E.

1. In the above construction (*a*) is E the mid-point of line segment AB? Check it with a ruler.

(*b*) Is each of the 4 angles about point E a right angle? Check them with a protractor.

(*c*) Why is line CD the *perpendicular bisector* of line segment AB?

2. Draw a line segment $2\frac{3}{4}''$ long. Bisect it with compasses. Check with ruler.

3. Draw a line segment $3\frac{5}{8}''$ long. Bisect it with compasses. Check with ruler.

4. With compasses: (*a*) bisect a line segment; (*b*) divide a line segment into 4 equal parts. Check with ruler.

5. Draw any triangle. Bisect its sides. Do the bisectors meet in a point equidistant from the vertices of the triangle?

IV. Bisecting an Angle

To *bisect an angle* means to divide it into two equal angles.

(*a*) Using protractor:
Measure the given angle.
Mark off one half the given angle.
Then draw a ray from the vertex.

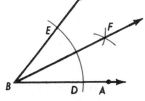

(*b*) Using compasses (see figure):
To bisect angle *ABC*, with *B* as the center and any radius, draw an arc cutting side *AB* at *D* and side *BC* at *E*.

With *D* and *E* as centers and a radius of more than half the distance from *D* to *E*, draw arcs crossing at *F*.

Draw ray *BF* bisecting angle *ABC*.

1. In the above construction does ∠ *ABF* = ∠ *FBC*? Check with protractor.

2. Draw any acute angle. Bisect it with compasses. Check with protractor.

3. Use protractor to draw each of the following angles. Then bisect each angle with compasses and check with protractor:

(*a*) 60°   (*b*) 36°   (*c*) 140°   (*d*) 98°   (*e*) 45°

4. Draw any obtuse angle. Divide it into 4 equal parts. Check with protractor.

5. Draw any triangle. Bisect its angles. Where do the bisectors meet?

V. Constructing a Perpendicular to a Line at a Point on the Line

Two lines that meet to form right angles are called perpendicular lines. The symbol ⊥ means "is perpendicular to."

(*a*) Using protractor:
Using the point on the line as the vertex, draw a 90° angle.

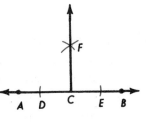

(*b*) Using compasses (see figure):
To draw a ray (or line) perpendicular to line *AB* at *C*, take point *C* as the center and with any radius, draw an arc cutting the line *AB* at *D* and *E*.

With D and E as centers and with a radius greater than CD, draw arcs crossing at F.

Draw ray CF. Ray CF is perpendicular to line AB at point C.

1. Check with protractor whether ray CF is perpendicular to line AB in the construction at the bottom of page 347.

2. Take a point on a line. Construct a perpendicular to the line at this point. Check with protractor.

3. Construct a rectangle 4 in. long and $2\frac{1}{2}$ in. wide.

4. Make a plan of a basketball court 42 ft. by 74 ft., using the scale 1 in. = 16 ft.

5. Construct squares whose sides measure: (a) 2 in. (b) $1\frac{3}{4}$ in.

VI. Constructing a Perpendicular to a Line from a Point outside the Line

Using compasses (see figure):

To draw a ray perpendicular to line AB from point C, take point C as the center and draw an arc cutting line AB at D and E.

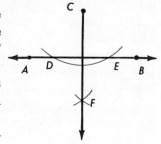

With D and E as centers and a radius of more than one half the distance from D to E, draw arcs crossing at F.

Draw ray CF. Ray CF is perpendicular to line AB from point C.

1. Check with protractor whether ray CF is perpendicular to line AB in the above construction.

2. Take a point outside a line. Construct a perpendicular to the line from this point. Check with protractor.

3. Draw an equilateral triangle. From each vertex draw a perpendicular to the opposite side. Check whether the angles and sides of the triangle are bisected.

VII. Constructing an Angle Equal to a Given Angle

(a) Using protractor:

Measure the given angle. Draw another angle of the same size.

(b) Using compasses (see figure):

To draw an angle at point C on line AB equal to angle MNO, take N as center and draw an arc cutting side MN at P and NO

at Q. With the same radius and C as center, draw an arc cutting line AB at D.

With a radius equal to PQ and D as center, draw an arc crossing the first arc at E.

Draw ray CE. Angle BCE is equal to angle MNO.

1. Check the equality of angles BCE and MNO with a protractor.

2. Draw any angle. Construct an angle equal to it.

3. Draw each of the following angles with a protractor. For each angle construct with compasses an equal angle. Check with protractor:

(a) 70°   (b) 54°   (c) 135°   (d) 81°   (e) 166°

VIII. Constructing a Line Parallel to a Given Line through a Point outside the Given Line

Lines that never meet even when they are extended are called parallel lines The symbol ‖ means "is parallel to."

To draw a line parallel to line AB through point C (see figure), draw any line DE through C, meeting line AB at F.

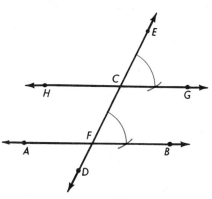

(*a*) Using protractor:

Measure angle BFC.

Draw, at point C on line DE, angle GCE equal to the corresponding angle BFC. Then extend line GC through H. Line HG is parallel to line AB.

(*b*) Using compasses:

Construct, at point C on line DE, angle GCE equal to the corresponding angle BFC. Follow procedure explained in Construction VII. Then extend line GC through H. Line HG is parallel to line AB.

1. Draw a line. Through a point outside this line draw a line parallel to the first line.

2. Construct a parallelogram with a base of $2\frac{3}{4}$ inches long, a side $2\frac{1}{4}$ inches long and an included angle of 60°.

3. Construct a trapezoid with bases of 4 inches and $2\frac{1}{2}$ inches, and a side 3 inches long making an angle of 75° with the longer base.

MORE FACTS ABOUT ANGLES

I. Sums of Angles of Polygons

1. The sum of the angles of a triangle is equal to 180°.

(a) Prove this fact. Draw a triangle. Measure the 3 angles with a protractor. Then find their sum.

(b) How many degrees are in the third angle of a triangle if two of the angles are:

(1) 29° and 87°? (2) 63° and 72°? (3) 106° and 51°? (4) 90° and 45°? (5) 18° and 121°?

(c) How many degrees are in each angle of an equilateral triangle?

(d) If one of the two equal angles of an isoceles triangle is 49°, find the other two angles.

(e) In a right triangle one of the acute angles measures 34°, what does the other acute angle measure?

(f) How many right angles or obtuse angles can a triangle have?

(g) If two triangles have two angles of one equal to two angles of the other, why are the third angles equal?

(h) If one acute angle of a right triangle is 45°, show that the triangle is isosceles.

(i) Draw an equilateral triangle. Show that an equilateral triangle is also equiangular.

2. The sum of the angles of any quadrilateral is 360°.

(a) Prove this fact. Draw any quadrilateral. Measure the 4 angles with a protractor. Then find their sum.

(b) What is the sum of the angles of a rectangle? Of a square? Of a parallelogram? Of a trapezoid?

(c) How many degrees are in the fourth angle if three angles of a quadrilateral measure 76°, 102°, and 161° respectively?

(d) Three angles of a trapezoid measure 90°, 90°, and 52° 47'. What does the fourth angle measure?

(e) The opposite angles of a parallelogram are equal. One angle of a parallelogram measures 65°. Find the other three angles.

II. Pairs of Angles

1. Complementary angles are two angles whose sum is 90°.

(*a*) Find the complements of each of the following angles:

(1) 21°   (2) 87°   (3) 7°   (4) 43° 18′   (5) 68° 51′ 15″

(*b*) Angle *ABC* is a right angle.

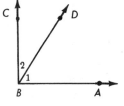

(1) What is the sum of ∠ 1 and ∠ 2?

(2) Find ∠ 1 if ∠ 2 = 58°

(3) Find ∠ 2 if ∠ 1 = 26°.

2. Supplementary angles are two angles whose sum is 180°.

(*a*) Find the supplements of each of the following angles:

(1) 44°   (2) 117°   (3) 39°   (4) 96° 20′   (5) 170° 42′ 59″

(*b*) When one straight line meets another, the adjacent angles, which have the same vertex and a common side, are supplementary. Why? See figure.

(1) Find ∠ *CDF* if ∠ *EDF* = 72°.

(2) Find ∠ *EDF* if ∠ *CDF* = 116°.

3. When two straight lines intersect, the vertical or opposite angles are equal.

(*a*) If ∠ 1 = 35°, find ∠ 2, ∠ 3, and ∠ 4.

(*b*) If ∠ 4 = 142°, find ∠ 1, ∠ 2, and ∠ 3.

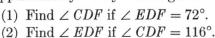

4. An exterior angle of a triangle, which is the angle formed by one side of a triangle and an adjacent side extended, is equal to the sum of the opposite interior angles.

(*a*) Name the exterior angle in the figure.

(*b*) Which angles are the opposite interior angles to this angle?

(*c*) What is the sum of ∠ 1, ∠ 2, and ∠ 3? What is the sum of ∠ 3 and ∠ 4?

(*d*) Show that the exterior angle is equal to the sum of the opposite interior angles.

III. Parallel Lines and Angle Relationships

1. If two *parallel* lines are cut by a third line, the *corresponding angles* are equal and the *alternate-interior angles* are equal.

In the figure, lines AB and CD are parallel and are cut by a third line EF, called a transversal.

$\angle 2$ and $\angle 6$, $\angle 4$ and $\angle 8$, $\angle 1$ and $\angle 5$, $\angle 3$ and $\angle 7$ are pairs of corresponding angles. Each pair of angles is in a corresponding position.

$\angle 3$ and $\angle 6$, $\angle 4$ and $\angle 5$ are pairs of alternate-interior angles. The angles are inside the parallel lines and the related angles fall on alternate sides.

(*a*) What kind of angles are $\angle 1$ and $\angle 4$? Why are they equal?

(*b*) Name other pairs of equal vertical angles.

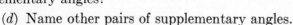

(*c*) What is the sum of $\angle 1$ and $\angle 2$? Why are they supplementary angles?

(*d*) Name other pairs of supplementary angles.

(*e*) Name all the pairs of corresponding angles that are equal.

(*f*) Name the pairs of equal alternate-interior angles.

(*g*) Show that $\angle 1 = \angle 8$.

How many degrees are in

(*h*) $\angle 6$ when $\angle 2 = 130°$?   (*i*) $\angle 5$ when $\angle 4 = 75°$?

(*j*) $\angle 7$ when $\angle 6 = 106°$?   (*k*) $\angle 2$ when $\angle 5 = 63°$?

(*l*)   all the other angles when $\angle 8 = 48°$.

(*m*) all the other angles when $\angle 3 = 125°$.   (*n*) $\overleftrightarrow{CD} \cap \overleftrightarrow{AB} = \{?\}$

2. If two lines are cut by a transversal making a pair of corresponding angles or a pair of alternate-interior angles equal, the lines are parallel.

Are lines AB and CD parallel when:

(*a*) $\angle 1 = 70°$ and $\angle 5 = 70°$?   Explain.

(*b*) $\angle 6 = 120°$ and $\angle 3 = 120°$?   Explain.

(*c*) $\angle 7 = 135°$ and $\angle 4 = 45°$?   Explain.

(*d*) $\angle 8 = 52°$ and $\angle 1 = 52°$?   Explain.

(*e*) $\angle 4 = 81°$ and $\angle 6 = 99°$?   Explain.

LONGITUDE AND LATITUDE

The position of any point on the earth's surface is determined by the intersection of its meridian of longitude and its parallel of latitude. Meridians of longitude are imaginary circles which pass through the North Pole and South Pole. Parallels of latitude are imaginary circles which are parallel to the equator.

The prime meridian from which longitude is calculated is the meridian that passes through Greenwich near London, England. West longitude extends from this prime meridian (0° longitude) westward halfway around the earth to the International Date Line (180° longitude). East longitude extends eastward from the prime meridian to the International Date Line.

The equator is 0° latitude. North latitude is measured north of the equator and south latitude is measured south of the equator. The North Pole is 90° north latitude and the South Pole is 90° south latitude.

North latitude is indicated by the letter N., south latitude by S., east longitude by E., and west longitude by W.

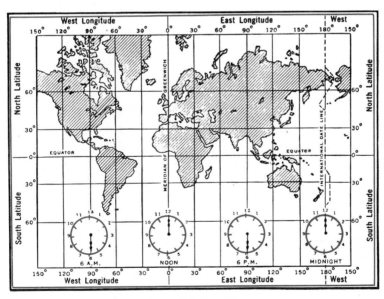

Map of the World

LATITUDE AND NAUTICAL MILE

Since one minute of arc of latitude equals one nautical mile, to *find the distance between two points on the earth's surface located on the same meridian*, find the difference in latitudes, convert to minutes of arc, and then to nautical miles.

Since one minute of arc of longitude measured at the equator only also equals one nautical mile, to *find the distance between two points on the equator*, find the difference in longitude, convert to minutes of arc, and then to nautical miles.

How many nautical miles apart are two ships if one is located 24° N. 36° W. and the other 17° N. 36° W.?

Both ships are located on 36° W. Therefore,

24° N.	7° = 420'
17° N.	420' = 420 nautical miles

7° difference in latitudes

Answer: 420 nautical miles.

Find the difference in latitudes:

	SET 1		SET 2
1.	57° N. and 12° N.	1.	16° 25' N. and 42° 40' N.
2.	29° S. and 63° S.	2.	58° 16' S. and 23° 27' S.
3.	43° N. and 8° S.	3.	27° 32' N. and 10° 51' S.
4.	38° S. and 51° N.	4.	39° 6' S. and 4° 30' N.
5.	0° and 21° S.	5.	42° 18' 25'' N. and 15° 14' 49'' S.

Find the difference in longitudes:

	SET 3		SET 4
1.	36° W. and 93° W.	1.	93° 48' W. and 67° 29' W.
2.	58° E. and 14° E.	2.	6° 17' E. and 31° 14' E.
3.	119° W. and 25° E.	3.	135° 5' W. and 43° 52' E.
4.	45° E. and 0°	4.	28° 40' E. and 104° 36' W.
5.	7° E. and 62° W.	5.	72° 57' 26'' W. and 64° 2' 51'' E.

Set 5

Find how far apart in nautical miles ships A and B are if:

Position of Ship A	*Position of Ship B*
1. 46° N., 140° W.	18° N., 140° W.
2. 62° S., 52° W.	49° S., 52° W.
3. 29° S., 46° W.	7° N., 46° W.
4. 0°, 27° 12′ W.	0°, 42° 54′ W.
5. 26° 43′ N., 176° 39′ E.	18° 26′ S., 176° 39′ E.

Set 6

Find how far apart airports X and Y are if:

Location of Airport X	*Location of Airport Y*
1. 56° N., 94° W.	48° N., 94° W.
2. 37° 43′ N., 83° 25′ W.	33° 29′ N., 83° 25′ W.
3. 46° 32′ N., 118° 43′ W.	48° 6′ N., 118° 43′ W.
4. 28° 17′ N., 105° 39′ W.	35° 58′ N., 105° 39′ W.
5. 54° 27′ 45″ N., 110° 8′ 15″ W.	63° 14′ 30″ N., 110° 8′ 15″ W.

Set 7

1. How many nautical miles away is a ship located 47° 38′ N., 25° 30′ W. from a ship in distress located 49° 28′ N., 25° 30′ W.? How long will it take the ship, steaming at 20 knots, to reach the ship in distress?

2. A ship left a United States port located 33° N., 80° W. and sailed along the 80th meridian to a Cuban port located 23° N., 80° W. How many nautical miles did the ship sail?

3. An airplane flew from a city located 39° N., 93° W. to a city located 45° N., 93° W. How many nautical miles apart are the two cities? How many statute miles apart? If it took the airplane 1 hour 48 minutes to make the flight, what was its ground speed in knots? in statute miles per hour?

4. A ship steamed east along the equator from 168° 20′ W. to 178° 45′ E. before turning south. How many nautical miles did the ship steam along the equator?

LONGITUDE AND TIME

I. Time Zones

The earth rotates from the west to the east about its axis, making one complete revolution each day. It takes the earth 24 hours to pass through 360° of longitude or one hour for 15° of longitude or 4 minutes for one degree of longitude.

The sun or solar time is the same at any given instant for all places located on any one meridian. As the sun crosses each meridian, it becomes noon sun or solar time for all the places

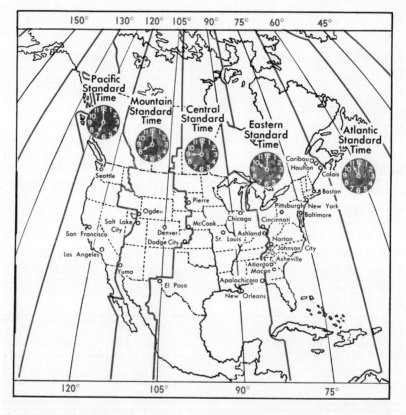

located on this meridian. To avoid the confusion that would arise if towns, just a few miles apart, used their own local solar time, the earth is divided into time zones each about 15° longitude in width. All places within each zone use the sun time of approximately its central meridian. The difference in time of adjacent zones is one hour, earlier to the west, later to the east.

There are four standard time belts in the United States: Eastern (EST), Central (CST), Mountain (MST), and Pacific (PST). Central time is one hour earlier than Eastern time, Mountain time is one hour earlier than Central time, and Pacific time is one hour earlier than Mountain time. The meridians at 75°, 90°, 105°, and 120° west longitude respectively are used to determine the time in these zones. Parts of Canada east of Maine are in another time zone, the Atlantic Standard Time Zone, which is one hour later than Eastern Standard Time.

1. If it is 11 A.M. in the Mountain Zone, what time is it in the
(a) Pacific Zone?   (b) Eastern Zone?   (c) Central Zone?

2. In what time zone is (a) Seattle? (b) Boston? (c) St. Louis?

3. When it is 8 P.M. in Chicago, what time is it in
(a) Baltimore?   (b) San Francisco?   (c) Denver?

4. At what time may a network television program, originating in New York City at 10 P.M., be seen in New Orleans?

5. How long did it take an airplane to fly from Los Angeles to Pittsburgh if it left Los Angeles at 5:30 P.M. (PST) and arrived in Pittsburgh at 2 A.M. (EST) the next day?

II. Longitude Expressed in Units of Time

In navigation the longitude is sometimes expressed in units of time. One hour of time is equivalent to 15° of longitude, one minute of time to 15′ of longitude, one second of time to 15″ of longitude, 1° of longitude to 4 minutes of time, and 1′ of longitude to 4 seconds of time.

Both world time and longitude are calculated from the meridian of Greenwich. Thus, the longitude of any place is equal to the difference between its local sun time and Greenwich time.

To *change units measuring longitude to units of time,* divide the units measuring longitude by 15. Simplify the answer wherever necessary.

Change 44° 15′ of arc of longitude to units of time.

$$\begin{array}{r} 2 \text{ hr. } 57 \text{ min.} \\ 15\overline{)44° \quad 15′} \\ 30° \\ \hline 14° \quad 15′ = 855′ \\ 855′ \end{array}$$

Answer: 2 hr. 57 min.

To *change units of time to units measuring longitude*, multiply the units of time by 15. Simplify the answer wherever necessary.

To *find the time* at point *B* when the lon-

Change 3 hr. 41 min. 18 sec. to units measuring longitude.

3 hr. 41 min. 18 sec.

$$\frac{15}{45° \quad 615' \quad 270''} = 45° \; 619' \; 30''$$
$$= 55° \quad 19' \; 30''$$

Answer: 55° 19′ 30″

---

gitude and time at point *A* and the longitude at point *B* are known, convert the difference in longitude to units of time. If point *B* is east of point *A*, add the difference in time to the time at point *A*. If point *B* is west of point *A*, subtract the difference in time.

If it is 0814 at 63° 45′ W. longitude, what time is it at 46° 30′ W. longitude?

63° 45′
46° 30′
17° 15′ difference in longitude

1 hr. 9 min.
15)17°   15′
   15°
    2°   15′ = 135′
          135′

0814 time at 63° 45′ W.
109
0923 time at 46° 30′ W.

Answer: It is 0923 at 46° 30′ W.

To *find the longitude* at point *B* when the longitude and time at point *A* and the time at point *B* are known, convert the difference in time to units of longitude. Then use the longitude at point *A* and this difference in longitude to obtain the longitude at point *B*.

Express the following arcs of longitude as units of time:

SET 1	SET 2	SET 3	SET 4
1. 45°	**1.** 30′	**1.** 60° 45′	**1.** 20°
2. 75°	**2.** 45′	**2.** 135° 30′	**2.** 175°
3. 180°	**3.** 15″	**3.** 45′ 15″	**3.** 38′
4. 105°	**4.** 30″	**4.** 15° 30′ 45″	**4.** 52′
5. 300°	**5.** 15′	**5.** 120° 15′ 30″	**5.** 84°

SET 5	SET 6	SET 7	SET 8
1. 8°	1. 17° 45′	1. 49° 26′	1. 25° 18′ 30″
2. 14°	2. 31° 15′	2. 28° 20′	2. 106° 37′ 15″
3. 5′	3. 55′ 30″	3. 6° 51′	3. 3° 42′ 45″
4. 11′	4. 7° 15′	4. 1° 43′	4. 9° 20′ 15″
5. 2°	5. 26′ 45″	5. 2° 39′	5. 16° 58′ 30″

Express the following units of time as arcs of longitude:

SET 9	SET 10	SET 11
1. 4 hr.	1. 30 min.	1. 15 sec.
2. 7 hr.	2. 45 min.	2. 40 sec.
3. 2 hr.	3. 20 min.	3. 12 sec.
4. 23 hr.	4. 36 min.	4. 30 sec.
5. 10 hr.	5. 15 min.	5. 49 sec.

SET 12	SET 13
1. 2 hr. 15 min.	1. 3 hr. 45 min. 30 sec.
2. 1 hr. 24 min.	2. 2 hr. 12 min. 48 sec.
3. 4 hr. 50 min.	3. 1 hr. 29 min. 10 sec.
4. 15 hr. 31 min.	4. 8 hr. 3 min. 54 sec.
5. 9 hr. 6 min.	5. 5 hr. 37 min. 25 sec.

SET 14

1. If it is 1200 at Greenwich, what time is it at the following longitudes:

(a) 30° W.   (b) 21° E.   (c) 135° E.
(d) 75° 45′ W.   (e) 64° 15′ E.

2. If it is 1455 at Greenwich, what time is it at the following longitudes:

(a) 45° E.   (b) 120° W.   (c) 60° 30′ W.
(d) 49° 20′ E.   (e) 122° 37′ W.

3. If it is 0732 at 50° W. longitude, what time is it at 72° W. longitude?

4. What time is it at 81° 45′ W. longitude if it is 1826 at 94° 30′ W. longitude?

5. If it is 0907 at 5° 18′ W. longitude, what time is it at 13° 45′ E. longitude?

SET 15

1. If it is 1200 at Greenwich, at what longitude is the time 1100? 1500? 0600? 1720? 0348?

2. If it is 1040 at Greenwich, at what longitude is the time 1120? 0856? 0200? 1812? 0736?

3. If it is 2330 at 150° E. longitude, at what longitude is the time 1445?

4. At what longitude is the time 0050 if it is 1150 at 10° 52′ W. longitude?

5. If it is 1324 at 81° 31′ W. longitude, at what longitude is the time 1248?

SET 16

1. Find the difference between the standard time and the solar time at each of the following cities:

Cleveland, 81° 34′ W.; Boston, 71° 04′ W.; Chicago, 87° 37′ W.; Los Angeles, 118° 14′ W.; Salt Lake City, 111° 53′ W.; Des Moines, 93° 41′ W.; San Francisco, 122° 26′ W.

2. If the sun time at Philadelphia, 75° 10′ W., is 1700, what is the sun time at each of the following cities:

Louisville, 85° 46′ W.; Washington, D.C., 77° 04′ W.; Seattle, 122° 19′ W.; Denver, 104° 57′ W.; El Paso, 106° 29′ W.; New York City, 73° 58′ W.; Kansas City, 94° 35′ W.

THE MAGNETIC COMPASS

When navigating an airplane by chart and compass, called dead reckoning, the navigator frequently determines the compass course from the true course and the true course from the compass course.

The course of an airplane is the direction in which it flies over the earth's surface and is expressed as an angle. It is called the true course when it is measured clockwise from the true north (North Pole). However, since the compass needle points to the magnetic north, the pilot must correct his true course reading. This correction is called magnetic variation or variation and the corrected course reading is called the magnetic course. This variation is designated as west variation when the magnetic north is west of the true north and as east variation when the magnetic north is east of the true north. The variation for any locality may be found on aeronautical maps.

Since the metal parts of the airplane affect the compass, the magnetic course reading must be corrected. This corrected course reading is called the compass course. The correction caused by the magnetism of the plane is called deviation and is designated east or west.

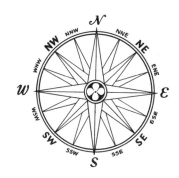

The following angular equivalents in degrees may be used for the given directions:

North (N.) = 0°   South (S.) = 180°
Northeast (N.E.) = 45°   Southwest (S.W.) = 225°
East (E.) = 90°   West (W.) = 270°
Southeast (S.E.) = 135°   Northwest (N.W.) = 315°

To *find the magnetic course* from the true course, add west variation but subtract east variation.

To *find the compass course* from the magnetic course, add west deviation but subtract east deviation.

To *find the compass course* from the true course, first change true course to magnetic course, then to compass course.

To *find the magnetic course* from the compass course, subtract west deviation but add east deviation.

Find the compass course if the true course is 125°; variation, 7° W.; and deviation, 2° W.

125° true course
+ 7° west variation
132° magnetic course
+ 2° west deviation
134° compass course

Answer: Compass course is 134°.

Find the true course if the compass course is 54°; variation 11° W.; and deviation, 50° E.

54° compass course
+ 5° east deviation
59° magnetic course
− 11° west variation
48° true course

Answer: True course is 48°.

To *find the true course* from the magnetic course, subtract west variation but add east variation.

To *find the true course* from the compass course, first change compass course to magnetic course, then to true course.

Find the magnetic course: Find the compass course:

	SET 1			SET 2	
	True Course	*Variation*		*Magnetic Course*	*Deviation*
1.	4°	5° W.	**1.**	157°	1° E.
2.	164°	19° E.	**2.**	65°	2° W.
3.	200°	0°	**3.**	306°	5° E.
4.	E.	3° E.	**4.**	35°	0°
5.	253°	13° W.	**5.**	90°	6° W.

Find the compass course:

	SET 3				SET 4		
	True Course	*Variation*	*Deviation*		*True Course*	*Variation*	*Deviation*
1.	238°	9° W.	5° W.	**1.**	302°	14° E.	1° E.
2.	N.E.	3° E.	6° E.	**2.**	224°	8° E.	6° W.
3.	85°	7° W.	3° E.	**3.**	W.	2° W.	4° E.
4.	130°	4° E.	5° W.	**4.**	113°	0°	0°
5.	69°	0°	4° W.	**5.**	51°	5° W.	3° W.

Find the true course: Find the magnetic course:

	SET 5			SET 6	
	Magnetic Course	*Variation*		*Compass Course*	*Deviation*
1.	51°	2° W.	**1.**	2°	3° E.
2.	252°	13° E.	**2.**	209°	4° W.
3.	195°	0°	**3.**	144°	1° W.
4.	120°	15° W.	**4.**	135°	0°
5.	S.	18° E.	**5.**	97°	5° E.

Find the true course:

	Set 7				Set 8		
	Compass Course	*Deviation*	*Variation*		*Compass Course*	*Deviation*	*Variation*
1.	246°	1° W.	5° W.	**1.**	80°	6° W.	5° E.
2.	327°	2° W.	8° E.	**2.**	349°	2° E.	16° E.
3.	90°	5° E.	12° W.	**3.**	228°	5° W.	19° W.
4.	50°	6° E.	13° W.	**4.**	215°	3° E.	0°
5.	17°	0°	7° E.	**5.**	106°	1° E.	9° W.

Find the missing numbers:

Set 9

	True Course	*Variation*	*Magnetic Course*	*Deviation*	*Compass Course*
1.	60°	7° W.	?	2° E.	?
2.	231°	16° E.	?	5° E.	?
3.	?	10° W.	?	1° W.	148°
4.	?	3° W.	?	6° E.	75°
5.	178°	5° E.	?	4° W.	?

Set 10

	True Course	*Variation*	*Magnetic Course*	*Deviation*	*Compass Course*
1.	?	8° W.	74°	5° W.	?
2.	?	4° W.	193°	6° E.	?
3.	45°	?	51°	?	48°
4.	307°	?	302°	?	296°
5.	?	17° E.	260°	3° W.	?

Set 11

1. The true course from airport A to airport B is 102°. If the variation is 5° W. and the deviation is 2° E., what compass course should be steered?

2. At a certain point during his flight a navigator finds his compass course to be 267°. If the variation is 6° E. and the deviation is 4° E., what is the true course?

3. What compass course should a pilot steer if the true course is 61°, variation 7° E., and deviation 5° W.?

4. A pilot is steering a compass course of 175°. If the variation is 12° W. and deviation is 3° E., what is his true course?

5. A navigator in determining his compass course uses the following data: true course, 340°; variation, 9° W.; deviation, 1° W. What is his compass course?

6. What compass course should be steered if the true course is 233°, variation 10° W., and deviation 2° W.?

7. A plane is steered along a compass course of 198°. If the variation is 11° W. and deviation is 3° E., what is its true course?

8. If the true course is 87°, magnetic course 94°, and compass course 91°, what is the variation and deviation?

9. Compute the compass course if the true course is 126°, variation 6° E., and deviation 2° E.?

10. What is the true course if the compass course is 56°, variation 8° E., and deviation 1° W.?

REVIEW OF EXERCISE

1. Change 8° 29′ to minutes.

2. How many degrees are in 420′?

3. Add: 23° 38′, 61° 20′, and 17° 54′. Simplify if necessary.

4. Subtract 59° 47′ 14″ from 90°.

5. Multiply 6° 28′ 50″ by 15. Simplify if necessary.

6. Divide 14° 35′ 48″ by 4.

7. Which angle is larger: an obtuse angle or a right angle?

8. Name the three angles in the triangle below.

9. Draw with a protractor an angle of 80°. Bisect it using compasses.

10. Construct a triangle that has two sides measuring $3\frac{1}{2}$ inches and $2\frac{5}{8}$ inches and an included angle of 75°.

11. Using compasses, construct a perpendicular to a line at a point on the line.

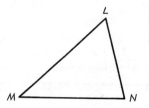

12. Draw with a protractor an angle of 35°. Construct with compasses another angle equal to it.

13. How many degrees does the third angle of a triangle measure if the first two angles are 67° and 59° respectively?

14. What is the complement of an angle measuring 41°?

15. Find the supplement of an angle measuring 16° 30′.

16. How many nautical miles apart are two ships if one ship is located at 18° N. 29° W. and the other ship at 2° S. 29° W.?

17. When it is 3 P.M. in Portland, Oregon, what time is it in Richmond, Virginia?

18. What time is it at 60° W. longitude when it is 1200 at Greenwich?

19. What compass course should a pilot steer if the true course is 86°, variation is 9° W., and deviation is 2° E.?

20. Make a scale drawing, using the scale 1 inch = 160 m.p.h., showing the position of an airplane at the end of one hour when flying on a course of 285° with a ground speed of 340 m.p.h.

REFRESH YOUR SKILLS

1. Add:

638
1,259
17
387
52,495
3,798

2. Subtract:

100,000
96,024

3. Multiply:

6,080
705

4. Divide:

$5,280 \overline{)517,440}$

5. Add:

$6\frac{7}{8}$
$9\frac{1}{4}$
$1\frac{5}{16}$

6. Subtract:

$3\frac{11}{16}$
$\frac{5}{6}$

7. Multiply: $4\frac{1}{2} \times 1\frac{3}{8}$

8. Divide: $\frac{5}{12} \div 3\frac{1}{3}$

9. Add:

$.96 + $4.28 + $19.09 + $6.57 + $.46

10. Subtract:

$9,150 - $79.25

11. Multiply:

48 × $23.94

12. Divide:

$.15 \overline{)$9.}$

13. Find 140% of $37.08

14. $.54 is what per cent of $.72

15. 20% of what number is 9?

EXERCISE 48

MEASURE OF AREA—BASIC UNITS

I. Aim: To change a given number of square units of one denomination to units of another denomination.

II. Procedure

Use either the common method or the method of cancellation of units as explained in the procedure under Exercise 44 on page 296.

The following specific rules may also be used:

To change —

(*a*) Square feet to square inches, multiply the number of square feet by 144.

(*b*) Square inches to square feet, divide the number of square inches by 144.

(*c*) Square yards to square feet, multiply the number of square yards by 9.

(*d*) Square feet to square yards, divide the number of square feet by 9.

(*e*) Square yards to square inches, first change square yards to square feet, then to square inches.

(*f*) Square inches to square yards, first change square inches to square feet, then to square yards.

(*g*) Square rods to square yards, multiply the number of square rods by 30.25 (30$\frac{1}{4}$).

(*h*) Square yards to square rods, divide the number of square yards by 30.25 (30$\frac{1}{4}$).

(*i*) Acres to square rods, multiply the number of acres by 160.

(*j*) Square rods to acres, divide the number of square rods by 160.

(*k*) Square miles to acres, multiply the number of square miles by 640.

(*l*) Acres to square miles, divide the number of acres by 640.

III. Sample Solutions

1. Change 5 sq. ft. to square inches.

Method 1	*Method 2*
144	$5 \text{ sq. ft.} \times \dfrac{144 \text{ sq. in.}}{1 \text{ sq. ft.}} = 720 \text{ sq. in.}$
$\times 5$	
720	

Answer: 720 sq. in.

2. Change 138 sq. ft. to square yards.

Method 1	*Method 2*
$15\frac{1}{3}$	$138 \text{ sq. ft.} \times \dfrac{1 \text{ sq. yd.}}{9 \text{ sq. ft.}} = 15\frac{1}{3} \text{ sq. yd.}$
$9\overline{)138}$	

Answer: $15\frac{1}{3}$ sq. yd.

EQUIVALENTS—MEASURE OF AREA

1 square foot (sq. ft.)   = 144 square inches (sq. in.)
1 square yard (sq. yd.) = 9 square feet (sq. ft.)
1 square rod (sq. rd.)   = 30.25 ($30\frac{1}{4}$) square yards (sq. yd.)
1 acre (acre)   = 160 square rods (sq. rd.)
                  = 4,840 square yards (sq. yd.)
                  = 43,560 square feet (sq. ft.)
1 square mile (sq. mi.) = 640 acres (acre)

DIAGNOSTIC TEST

Change:

1. 8 sq. ft. to square inches
2. 17 sq. yd. to square feet
3. 2 sq. yd. to square inches
4. 12 sq. rd. to square yards
5. 26 acres to square rods
6. 3 sq. mi. to acres
7. 864 sq. in. to square feet
8. 153 sq. ft. to square yards
9. 5,184 sq. in. to square yards
10. 242 sq. yd. to square rods
11. 1,440 sq. rd. to acres
12. 3,200 acres to square miles

RELATED PRACTICE EXAMPLES

Change to square inches:

SET 1

1. 3 sq. ft.
2. 16 sq. ft.
3. 2½ sq. ft.
4. 14.75 sq. ft.
5. 50 sq. ft.

Change to square feet:

SET 2

1. 5 sq. yd.
2. 12 sq. yd.
3. 3⅚ sq. yd.
4. 0.5 sq. yd.
5. 30 sq. yd.

Change to square inches:

SET 3

1. 6 sq. yd.
2. 19 sq. yd.
3. ⅔ sq. yd.
4. 9.25 sq. yd.
5. 24 sq. yd.

Change to square yards:

SET 4

1. 9 sq. rd.
2. 20 sq. rd.
3. 8¼ sq. rd.
4. 31.4 sq. rd.
5. 52 sq. rd.

Change to square rods:

SET 5

1. 8 acres
2. 23 acres
3. 9¾ acres
4. 16.875 acres
5. 45 acres

Change to acres:

SET 6

1. 7 sq. mi.
2. 13 sq. mi.
3. 18⅜ sq. mi.
4. 3.6 sq. mi.
5. 40 sq. mi.

Change to square feet:

SET 7

1. 288 sq. in.
2. 1,584 sq. in.
3. 72 sq. in.
4. 900 sq. in.
5. 2,304 sq. in.

Change to square yards:

SET 8

1. 45 sq. ft.
2. 126 sq. ft.
3. 84 sq. ft.
4. 40.5 sq. ft.
5. 207 sq. ft.

Change to square yards:

SET 9

1. 9,072 sq. in.
2. 15,552 sq. in.
3. 6,804 sq. in.
4. 2,916 sq. in.
5. 38,880 sq. in.

Change to square rods:

SET 10

1. 121 sq. yd.
2. 847 sq. yd.
3. 100 sq. yd.
4. 48.4 sq. yd.
5. 1,452 sq. yd.

Change to acres:

SET 11

1. 800 sq. rd.
2. 2,080 sq. rd.
3. 140 sq. rd.
4. 600 sq. rd.
5. 4,320 sq. rd.

Change to square miles:

SET 12

1. 1,920 acres
2. 8,320 acres
3. 1,600 acres
4. 700 acres
5. 18,560 acres

MISCELLANEOUS EXAMPLES

Change to square feet:

Set 1
1. 6 sq. rd.
2. 3 sq. rd.
3. 15½ sq. rd.
4. 28.2 sq. rd.
5. 40 sq. rd.

Change to square rods:

Set 2
1. 2,178 sq. ft.
2. 3,267 sq. ft.
3. 1,089 sq. ft.
4. 544.5 sq. ft.
5. 1,361.25 sq. ft.

Change to square yards:

Set 3
1. 2 acres
2. 7 acres
3. 4¾ acres
4. 1.6 acres
5. 25 acres

Change to acres:

Set 4
1. 14,520 sq. yd.
2. 24,200 sq. yd.
3. 10,890 sq. yd.
4. 8,470 sq. yd.
5. 4,900 sq. yd.

Change to square yards:

Set 5
1. 3 sq. mi.
2. 4 sq. mi.
3. 1½ sq. mi.
4. 2.75 sq. mi.
5. 20 sq. mi.

Change to square miles:

Set 6
1. 6,195,200 sq. yd.
2. 30,976,000 sq. yd.
3. 1,548,800 sq. yd.
4. 387,200 sq. yd.
5. 4,000,000 sq. yd.

Set 7
1. What part of a square foot is 36 square inches?
2. 48 square inches is what part of a square foot?
3. What part of a square foot is 9 square inches?
4. 72 square inches is what part of a square foot?
5. What part of a square foot is 126 square inches?

Set 8
1. What part of a square yard is 3 square feet?
2. 8 square feet is what part of a square yard?
3. 6 square feet is what part of a square yard?
4. What part of a square yard is 288 square inches?
5. 648 square inches is what part of a square yard?

Set 9
What part of an acre is:
1. 120 sq. rd.?   2. 1,210 sq. yd.?   3. 13,068 sq. ft.
    4. 1,936 sq. yd.?   5. 27,225 sq. ft.?

RELATED PROBLEMS

1. A kitchen has 108 sq. ft. of floor space. How many square yards of linoleum are needed to cover the entire floor?

2. How many children will a playground of 1 acre accommodate if an allowance of 90 sq. ft. of play space is made for each child?

3. In Rhode Island 279,361 acres of its total area of 1,248 sq. mi. are used for farming. How many acres are used for all other purposes?

4. The air pressure at sea level is 14.66 lb. per square inch. Find the pressure on 2 sq. ft. of surface at sea level.

5. The air pressure in a diving bell which had been lowered to a certain depth in sea water is 7,860 lb. per square foot. Find the air pressure in the bell in pounds per square inch.

REFRESH YOUR SKILLS

1. Add: **2.** Subtract: **3.** Multiply: **4.** Divide:

68,404	2,500,000	3,090	5,129)25,316,744
9,825	1,989,043	4,070	
36,218			
84,709			
7,917			

5. Add: **6.** Subtract: **7.** Multiply: **8.** Divide:

$2\frac{1}{4} + 3\frac{1}{3} + 6\frac{1}{5}$ $1\frac{11}{16} - \frac{7}{8}$ $\frac{5}{12} \times 6$ $9\frac{3}{8} \div 15$

9. Add:

$46.25 + $9.09 + $384.29 + $.89 + $692.86

10. Subtract: **11.** Multiply: **12.** Divide:

$1,009.25 − $168.93   .002 × 4.6   .06).0003

13. Find 6% of   **14.** What per cent   **15.** 25% of what
$98.65   of $21 is $.70?   number is 96?

16. Round off 18,999,508,127 to the nearest million.

17. Reduce $\frac{165}{5280}$ to lowest terms.   **18.** Square $3\frac{1}{4}$

19. Find the square root of 6544.81

20. What part of a mile is 440 yards?

PRACTICAL APPLICATIONS—MEASURING AREA

The area of any surface is the number of units of square measure contained in the surface. When computing the area of a geometric figure, *express all linear units in the same denomination.*

I. Rectangle

The area of a rectangle is equal to the length times the width.

Formula: $A = lw$

Or, the area is equal to the altitude times the base.

Formula: $A = ab$

<table>
<tr><td>
23"
16"

$l = 23$ in.
$w = 16$ in.
$A = ?$
</td><td>
Find the area of a rectangle 23 inches long and 16 inches wide.

$A = lw$
$A = 23 \times 16$
$A = 368$ sq. in.

Answer: 368 sq. in.
</td><td>
23
$\times 16$
138
23
368
</td></tr>
</table>

1. What is the area of a rectangle if its length is 14 feet and width is 9 feet?

2. Find the areas of rectangles having the following dimensions:

(a)

Length	23 ft.	125 rd.	6.8 in.	$1\frac{1}{3}$ yd.	2 yd.
Width	17 ft.	95 rd.	1.625 in.	$4\frac{1}{2}$ yd.	20 in.

(b)

Altitude	12 in.	150 yd.	0.4 mi.	$1\frac{7}{8}$ in.	3 ft. 7 in.
Base	8 in.	200 yd.	3.5 mi.	$2\frac{3}{4}$ in.	1 ft. 3 in.

3. Find the cost of each of the following:

(*a*) Cementing a driveway 9 ft. by 16 ft. at $.55 per sq. ft.

(*b*) Covering a floor 11 ft. by 12 ft. with linoleum at $2.85 per sq. yd.

(*c*) Resilvering a mirror 36 in. by 42 in. at $1.25 per sq. ft.

(*d*) Sodding a lawn 13 ft. 6 in. by 8 ft. 9 in. at $.06 per sq. ft.

(*e*) Refinishing a hardwood floor 16 ft. 4 in. by 14 ft. 8 in. at $.12 per sq. ft.

4. A schoolroom is 27 ft. long and 20 ft. wide. It has 6 windows, each measuring 3 ft. by 9 ft. There are also 5 blackboards, each 5 ft. by 3 ft.; 6 blackboards, each $2\frac{1}{2}$ ft. by 5 ft.; and one bulletin board 6 ft. by $3\frac{1}{2}$ ft. What is the ratio of the window area to the floor area? Find the ratio of the total blackboard area to the area of the bulletin board.

5. Find the value of a field 495 by 660 feet at $912 per acre.

6. Find the area of a rectangular wing of an airplane if the span (length) is 47 ft. 6 in. and chord (width) is 8 ft. 3 in.

7. What is the cost per sq. yd. of 54-inch width material costing $3.75 per running yard?

8. How many 2 in. by 3 in. tickets can be cut from 2 ft. by 4 ft. stock?

9. How many acres (nearest tenth) are contained in a football field 120 yd. long and 160 ft. wide?

10. A field measuring 48 rd. by 40 rd. yields 420 bu. of corn. Find the average yield per acre.

II. Square

The area of a square is equal to the length of its side times itself or the side squared. Formula: $A = s^2$

	Find the area of a square whose side is 37 feet.	
37′	$A = s^2$	37
	$A = (37)^2$	$\times 37$
	$A = 37 \times 37$	259
$s = 37$ ft.	$A = 1,369$ sq. ft.	1 11
$A = ?$		1,369
	Answer: 1,369 sq. ft.	

1. What is the area of a square whose side is 23 feet?

2. Find the areas of squares whose sides measure:

(*a*) 10 yd.   (*b*) 42 in.   (*c*) 320 rd.   (*d*) 6,080 ft.   (*e*) 1,760 yd.
(*f*) 0.62 mi.   (*g*) 39.37 in.   (*h*) 18½ ft.   (*i*) 4⅜ in.   (*j*) 3 ft. 8 in.

3. What is the cross sectional area of a square beam 6½ in. on a side?

4. At $8.95 per sq. yd., how much will a broadloom rug 15 ft. by 15 ft. cost?

5. The base of the Great Pyramid is 746 feet square. How many acres (to nearest hundredth) does it cover?

III. Parallelogram

The area of a parallelogram is equal to the altitude times the base.   Formula: $A = ab$

Or, the area is equal to the base times the height.

Formula: $A = bh$

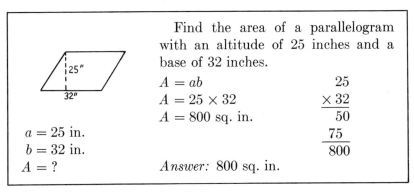

Find the area of a parallelogram with an altitude of 25 inches and a base of 32 inches.

$A = ab$
$A = 25 \times 32$
$A = 800$ sq. in.

$a = 25$ in.
$b = 32$ in.
$A = ?$

$$\begin{array}{r} 25 \\ \times 32 \\ \hline 50 \\ 75 \\ \hline 800 \end{array}$$

Answer: 800 sq. in.

1. What is the area of a parallelogram if its altitude is 6 feet and its base is 8 feet?

2. Find the areas of parallelograms having the following dimensions:

Altitude	26 in.	75 ft.	8.3 mi.	1¼ in.	3 yd. 2 ft.
Base	14 in.	98 ft.	4.7 mi.	½ in.	4 yd. 1 ft.

3. Find the cost of seeding a lawn shaped like a parallelogram with a base of 18 ft. and altitude of 15 ft. One pound of grass seed covers 135 sq. ft. and costs $.59.

IV. Triangle

The area of a triangle is equal to one half the altitude times the base. Formula: $A = \frac{1}{2} ab$ which may be written as $A = \dfrac{ab}{2}$ Or, the area is equal to one half the base times the height.

Formula: $A = \frac{1}{2} bh$

Find the area of a triangle with an altitude of 26 feet and a base of 17 feet.

$A = \frac{1}{2} ab$
$A = \frac{1}{2} \times 26 \times 17$
$A = 221$ sq. ft.

$\dfrac{1}{\cancel{2}} \times \dfrac{\overset{13}{\cancel{26}}}{1} \times \dfrac{17}{1} = 221$

$a = 26$ ft.
$b = 17$ ft.
$A = ?$

Answer: 221 sq. ft.

1. What is the area of a triangle if its altitude is 10 inches and base is 8 inches?

2. Find the areas of triangles having the following dimensions:

(a)

Altitude	18 in.	13 ft.	5 yd.	27 ft.	1 ft. 4 in.
Base	12 in.	10 ft.	7 yd.	$16\frac{1}{2}$ ft.	2 ft.

(b)

Base	8 ft.	4.8 ft.	$1\frac{7}{8}$ in.	$9\frac{1}{3}$ yd.	4 yd. 7 in.
Height	11 ft.	3.4 ft.	$2\frac{1}{4}$ in.	$6\frac{5}{8}$ yd.	1 ft. 11 in.

3. How many square feet of surface does one side of a triangular sail expose if it has a base of 10 ft. and a height of 12 ft. 6 in.?

V. Trapezoid

The area of a trapezoid is equal to the height times the average of the two parallel sides (bases).

Formula: $A = h \times \dfrac{b_1 + b_2}{2}$

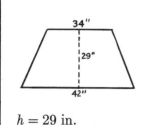

Find the area of a trapezoid with bases of 42 inches and 34 inches and a height of 29 inches.

$h = 29$ in.
$b_1 = 42$ in.
$b_2 = 34$ in.
$A = ?$

$$A = h \times \frac{b_1 + b_2}{2}$$

$$A = 29 \times \frac{42 + 34}{2}$$

$$A = 29 \times 38$$

$$A = 1,102 \text{ sq. in.}$$

Answer: 1,102 sq. in.

$$\begin{array}{r} 42 \\ + 34 \\ \hline 76 \end{array}$$

$$\begin{array}{r} 38 \\ 2\overline{)76} \end{array}$$

$$\begin{array}{r} 29 \\ \times 38 \\ \hline 232 \\ 87 \\ \hline 1,102 \end{array}$$

1. What is the area of a trapezoid if the height is 7 inches and the parallel sides are 8 inches and 14 inches?

2. Find the areas of trapezoids having the following dimensions:

Height	8 in.	5 ft.	18 rd.	6 ft.	10 in.
Upper Base	4 in.	9 ft.	29 rd.	$11\frac{3}{4}$ ft.	1 ft.
Lower Base	10 in.	13 ft.	36 rd.	$14\frac{1}{2}$ ft.	1 ft. 4 in.

3. A section of a tapered airplane wing has the shape of a trapezoid. If the two parallel sides (chords), measuring $3\frac{1}{2}$ ft. and $5\frac{1}{2}$ ft., are 18 ft. apart, find the area of the section.

VI. Circle

The area of a circle is equal to pi (π) times the radius squared.

Formula: $A = \pi r^2$

Any one of the following values of π may be used: $3\frac{1}{7}$ or $\frac{22}{7}$ or 3.14 or, for greater accuracy, 3.1416.

Find the area of a circle having a radius of 5 yards.

$r = 5$ yd.
$\pi = 3.14$
$A = ?$

$$A = \pi r^2$$

$$A = 3.14 \times (5)^2$$

$$A = 3.14 \times 25$$

$$A = 78.5 \text{ sq. yd.}$$

Answer: 78.5 sq. yd.

$$\begin{array}{r} 5 \\ \times 5 \\ \hline 25 \end{array}$$

$$\begin{array}{r} 3.14 \\ \times 25 \\ \hline 15\ 70 \\ 62\ 8 \\ \hline 78.50 \end{array}$$

Or, the area of a circle is equal to one fourth times pi (π) times the diameter squared. Formula: $A = \frac{1}{4}\pi d^2$

Sometimes the formula $A = .7854\, d^2$ is also used.

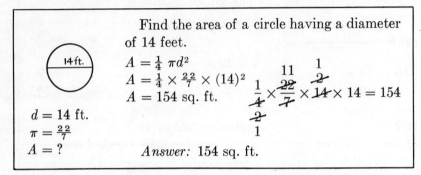

Find the area of a circle having a diameter of 14 feet.

$A = \frac{1}{4}\,\pi d^2$

$A = \frac{1}{4} \times \frac{22}{7} \times (14)^2$

$A = 154$ sq. ft.

$\frac{1}{\cancel{4}} \times \frac{\cancel{22}^{11}}{\cancel{7}} \times \cancel{14} \times 14 = 154$

$d = 14$ ft.

$\pi = \frac{22}{7}$

$A = ?$

Answer: 154 sq. ft.

1. What is the area of a circle whose radius is 6 inches?

2. Find the areas of circles having the following radii:

(*a*) 13 ft.   (*b*) 28 in.   (*c*) 52 rd.   (*d*) 91 yd.   (*e*) 100 ft.
(*f*) 4.5 mi.   (*g*) 1.375 in.   (*h*) $5\frac{2}{3}$ yd.   (*i*) $\frac{1}{2}$ mi.   (*j*) 7 ft. 4 in.

3. What is the area of a circle whose diameter is 24 feet?

4. Find the areas of circles having the following diameters:

(*a*) 2 in.   (*b*) 84 ft.   (*c*) 19 yd.   (*d*) 63 ft.   (*e*) 220 yd.
(*f*) 0.75 in.   (*g*) 16.1 mi.   (*h*) $\frac{5}{8}$ in.   (*i*) $8\frac{1}{6}$ ft.   (*j*) 5 yd. 1 ft.

5. If a forest ranger can see from his tower for a distance of 24 miles in all directions, how many square miles can he watch?

6. The dial of one of the world's largest clocks has a diameter of 50 ft. What is the area of the dial?

7. A revolving sprinkler sprays a lawn for a distance of 21 ft. How many square feet does the sprinkler water in 1 revolution?

8. If a station can televise programs for a distance of 56 miles, over what area may the programs be received?

9. Which is larger: the area of a circle 6 in. in diameter or the area of a square whose side is 6 in.? How much larger?

10. What is the area of one side of a washer if its diameter is $\frac{3}{4}$ in. and the diameter of the hole is $\frac{1}{4}$ in.?

11. Find the area of the head of the piston if the bore (diameter) of the piston is $3\frac{1}{2}$ in.

12. A steel tube has a wall thickness of 0.125 in. and an outside diameter of 2 inches. What is the cross-sectional area of the metal?

13. A circular flower bed 12 ft. in diameter has a circular walk 3 feet wide paved around it. At $.45 per sq. ft., how much did the walk cost?

14. What is the area of one side of a penny? nickel? quarter?

15. Find the minimum number of 2-inch pipes necessary to draw off the water supplied by an 8-inch pipe under full pressure.

VII. Total Area of a Rectangular Solid

The total area of the outside surface of a rectangular solid is equal to the sum of twice the product of the length and width, twice the product of the length and height and twice the product of the width and height. Formula: $A = 2\,lw + 2\,lh + 2\,wh$

Find the total area of a rectangular solid 9 feet long, 6 feet wide, and 7 feet high.

$A = 2\,lw + 2\,lh + 2\,wh$
$A = 2 \times 9 \times 6 \ + \ 2 \times 9 \times 7 \ + \ 2 \times 6 \times 7$
$A = 108 + 126 + 84$
$A = 318$ sq. ft.

$l = 9$ ft.
$w = 6$ ft.
$h = 7$ ft.
$A = ?$ *Answer:* 318 sq. ft.

1. Find the total areas of rectangular solids with the following dimensions:

Length	23 ft.	61 in.	8.1 ft.	$9\frac{1}{2}$ in.	5 ft. 4 in.
Width	14 ft.	37 in.	2.7 ft.	8 in.	4 ft. 3 in.
Height	19 ft.	25 in.	5.9 ft.	$10\frac{3}{8}$ in.	7 ft. 6 in.

2. How many square feet of plywood will be needed to make a packing box with the dimensions 5 ft. by 3 ft. 9 in. by 2 ft. 6 in.?

3. A room is 18 ft. long, 15 ft. wide, and 9 ft. high. Find the total area of the walls and ceiling, allowing a deduction of 64 sq. ft. for the windows and doorway. How many gallons of paint are needed to cover the walls and ceiling with two coats if a gallon will cover 400 sq. ft. one coat? At $5 per gallon, how much will the paint cost?

VIII. Total Area of a Cube

The total area of the outside surface of a cube is equal to 6 times the area of one of its faces.

Formula: $A = 6\,s^2$ or $A = 6\,e^2$

Find the total area of a cube whose sides or edges measure 15 inches.

$s = 15$ in.

$A = ?$

$A = 6\,s^2$
$A = 6 \times (15)^2$
$A = 6 \times 225$
$A = 1{,}350$ sq. in.

Answer: 1,350 sq. in.

15	225
× 15	× 6
75	1,350
15	
225	

- 1. Find the total areas of cubes whose sides measure:
(a) 37 ft.   (b) 20 yd.   (c) 9.2 ft.   (d) $3\frac{7}{8}$ in.   (e) 1 ft. 11 in.

- 2. A carton 18 in. by 18 in. by 18 in. is made of corrugated paper. How many square feet of paper were used to make it if 10% extra was allowed for waste in cutting?

IX. Lateral Area and Total Area of a Right Circular Cylinder

The lateral area or area of the outside curved surface of a cylinder is equal to pi (π) times the diameter times the height.

Formula: $A = \pi dh$

Sometimes the formula $A = 2\,\pi rh$ is used.

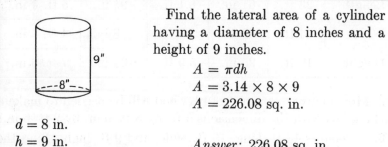

Find the lateral area of a cylinder having a diameter of 8 inches and a height of 9 inches.

$d = 8$ in.
$h = 9$ in.
$\pi = 3.14$
$A = ?$

$A = \pi dh$
$A = 3.14 \times 8 \times 9$
$A = 226.08$ sq. in.

Answer: 226.08 sq. in.

1. Find the lateral areas of cylinders with the following dimensions:

(a)

Diameter	4 in.	60 ft.	28 ft.	$3\frac{1}{2}$ in.	2 ft. 9 in.
Height	10 in.	45 ft.	32 ft.	$5\frac{1}{4}$ in.	4 ft.

(b)

Radius	3 ft.	14 ft.	42 in.	$2\frac{3}{4}$ in.	8 ft. 6 in.
Height	5 ft.	20 ft.	18 in.	8 in.	5 ft. 4 in.

2. How many square inches of paper are needed to make a label on a can 4 inches in diameter and 5 inches high?

The total area of a cylinder equals the lateral area added to the area of the two bases.

$$\text{Formula: } A = 2\ \pi rh + 2\ \pi r^2$$
$$\text{or} \quad A = \pi dh + \tfrac{1}{2}\ \pi d^2$$
$$\text{or} \quad A = 2\ \pi r(h + r)$$

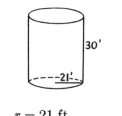

Find the total area of a cylinder when its radius is 21 feet and its height is 30 feet.

$A = 2\ \pi rh + 2\ \pi r^2$
$A = 2 \times \frac{22}{7} \times 21 \times 30\ + 2 \times \frac{22}{7} \times (21)^2$
$A = 3,960 + 2,772$
$A = 6,732$ sq. ft.

$r = 21$ ft.
$h = 30$ ft.
$\pi = \frac{22}{7}$
$A = ?$

Answer: 6,732 sq. ft.

1. Find the total areas of cylinders with the following dimensions:

(a)

Radius	2 in.	7 in.	30 ft.	$4\frac{3}{8}$ in.	1 ft. 6 in.
Height	4 in.	12 in.	25 ft.	20 in.	3 ft.

(b)

Diameter	5 ft.	4 in.	35 ft.	$2\frac{1}{2}$ in.	2 ft. 5 in.
Height	8 ft.	2 in.	40 ft.	7 in.	1 ft. 8 in.

2. How much asbestos paper covering is needed to enclose the curved surface and the two ends of a hot water storage tank 14 inches in diameter and 5 feet high?

X. Sphere

The area of the surface of a sphere is equal to 4 times pi (π) times the radius squared. Formula: $A = 4\pi r^2$

Sometimes the formula $A = \pi d^2$ is used.

1. Find the surface areas of spheres having the following radii:

(a) 10 in. (b) 28 ft. (c) 6.3 yd. (d) $9\frac{5}{8}$ in. (e) 5 ft. 1 in.

2. Find the surface areas of spheres having the following diameters:

(a) 16 ft. (b) 70 in. (c) 14.8 ft. (d) $6\frac{3}{4}$ yd. (e) 4 ft. 6 in.

3. What is the area of the earth's surface if its diameter is 7,900 miles?

REVIEW OF EXERCISE

1. Change 7 square feet to square inches.

2. What part of a square foot is 108 square inches?

3. How many square feet are in 15 square yards?

4. Change 8,960 acres to square miles.

5. How many square rods are in 18 acres?

Find the area of:

6. A rectangle 65 yards long and 43 yards wide.

7. A circle whose radius is 37 feet.

8. A square whose side measures 21 feet.

9. A parallelogram with altitude 159 feet and base 250 feet.

10. A circle whose diameter is $8\frac{3}{4}$ inches.

11. A triangle with an altitude of 82 inches and a base of 60 inches.

12. A trapezoid with bases of 101 feet and 53 feet and a height of 64 feet.

Find the total area of:

13. A cube 19 inches on a side.

14. A rectangular solid 31 yards long, 27 yards wide, and 16 yards high.

15. A right circular cylinder 63 inches in diameter and 75 inches high.

16. A sphere whose radius is 6 inches.

17. How many 9″ by 9″ square tiles are needed for a floor measuring 18 feet long by 12 feet wide?

18. One of the runways at an airport is 237 yd. long and 32 yd. wide. The flight deck of an airplane carrier is 725 ft. by 92 ft. Find the difference in their areas.

19. How many square feet of surface are in the wall of a swimming pool 75 ft. long, 3 ft. deep at one end, and 15 ft. deep at the other?

20. The cooking area of a circular barbecue grill having a diameter of 24 inches is how many times as large as the area of a grill having a diameter of 15 inches?

REFRESH YOUR SKILLS

1. Add:

48,296
38,453
91,027
52,834
69,521

2. Subtract:

1,000,000
842,056

3. Multiply:

1,728
950

4. Divide:

$659)\overline{458,664}$

5. Add:

$4\frac{3}{16} + 2\frac{7}{10}$

6. Subtract:

$9\frac{1}{6} - \frac{2}{3}$

7. Multiply:

$8\frac{2}{5} \times 3\frac{1}{7}$

8. Divide:

$4 \div \frac{1}{3}$

9. Add:

$.6 + .87$

10. Subtract:

$4.5 - .23$

11. Multiply:

$8.02 \times .5$

12. Divide:

$1.2)\overline{.9}$

13. Find $2\frac{1}{2}\%$ of $8,250

14. What per cent of $.75 is $.36?

15. 96% of what number is 24?

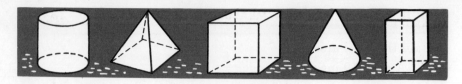

MEASURE OF VOLUME—BASIC UNITS

I. Aim: To change a given number of cubic units of one denomination to units of another denomination.

II. Procedure

Use either the common method or the method of cancellation of units as explained in the procedure under Exercise 44 on page 296.

The following specific rules may also be used:

To change:

(*a*) Cubic feet to cubic inches, multiply the number of cubic feet by 1,728.

(*b*) Cubic inches to cubic feet, divide the number of cubic inches by 1,728.

(*c*) Cubic yards to cubic feet, multiply the number of cubic yards by 27.

(*d*) Cubic feet to cubic yards, divide the number of cubic feet by 27.

(*e*) Cubic yards to cubic inches, first change cubic yards to cubic feet, then to cubic inches.

(*f*) Cubic inches to cubic yards, first change cubic inches to cubic feet, then to cubic yards.

III. Sample Solutions

1. Change $4\frac{1}{3}$ cu. yd. to cubic feet.

$$\textit{Method 1} \qquad\qquad \textit{Method 2}$$

$$
\begin{array}{r}
27 \\
\times\, 4\frac{1}{3} \\
\hline
108 \\
9 \\
\hline
117
\end{array}
\qquad
\frac{1}{\cancel{3}} \times \cancel{27} = 9
\qquad
4\frac{1}{3} \;\cancel{\text{cu. yd.}} \times \frac{27 \text{ cu. ft.}}{1 \;\cancel{\text{cu. yd.}}} = 117 \text{ cu. ft.}
$$

Answer: 117 cu. ft.

2. Change 7,344 cu. in. to cubic feet.

Method 1

```
          4.25
1,728)7,344.00
      6 912
        432 0
        345 6
         86 40
         86 40
```

Method 2

$$7,344 \text{ cu. in.} \times \frac{1 \text{ cu. ft.}}{1,728 \text{ cu. in.}} = 4.25 \text{ cu. ft.}$$

Answer: 4.25 cu. ft.

EQUIVALENTS—MEASURE OF VOLUME

1 cubic foot (cu. ft.)　　= 1,728 cubic inches (cu. in.)
1 cubic yard (cu. yd.)　 = 27 cubic feet (cu. ft.)
1 board foot (ft. b. m.) = 144 cubic inches (cu. in.)
1 cord (cd.)　　　　　　= 128 cubic feet (cu. ft.)

DIAGNOSTIC TEST

Change:

1. 5 cu. ft. to cubic inches
2. 14 cu. yd. to cubic feet
3. 10 cu. yd. to cubic inches
4. 70,848 cu. in. to cubic feet
5. 864 cu. ft. to cubic yards
6. 326,592 cu. in. to cubic yards

RELATED PRACTICE EXAMPLES

Change to cubic inches:	Change to cubic feet:	Change to cubic inches:
SET 1	SET 2	SET 3
1. 9 cu. ft.	**1.** 8 cu. yd.	**1.** 4 cu. yd.
2. 38 cu. ft.	**2.** 25 cu. yd.	**2.** 23 cu. yd.
3. $2\frac{1}{2}$ cu. ft.	**3.** $7\frac{2}{3}$ cu. yd.	**3.** $\frac{3}{4}$ cu. yd.
4. 7.75 cu. ft.	**4.** 6.5 cu. yd.	**4.** 9.375 cu. yd.
5. 92 cu. ft.	**5.** 54 cu. yd.	**5.** 7 cu. yd.

Change to cubic feet:	Change to cubic yards:	Change to cubic yards:
SET 4	SET 5	SET 6
1. 5,184 cu. in.	1. 135 cu. ft.	1. 93,312 cu. in.
2. 29,376 cu. in.	2. 63 cu. ft.	2. 233,280 cu. in.
3. 7,776 cu. in.	3. $6\frac{3}{4}$ cu. ft.	3. 69,984 cu. in.
4. 432 cu. in.	4. 688.5 cu. ft.	4. 11,664 cu. in.
5. 146,880 cu. in.	5. 2,538 cu. ft.	5. 793,152 cu. in.

RELATED PROBLEMS

1. Lead weighs .41 lb. per cu. in. Find the weight of a cubic foot of lead.

2. What is the weight of a cubic inch of wrought iron if a cubic foot of wrought iron weighs 480 lb.?

3. A certain truck can hold 2 cu. yd. of dirt. If a cubic foot of dirt weighs 100 lb., what is the weight of a truck load of dirt?

REFRESH YOUR SKILLS

1. Add:
832,146
799,207
942,579
923,486
268,829

2. Subtract:
904,060
386,058

3. Multiply:
69,857
869

4. Divide:
$5,967\overline{)5,835,726}$

5. Add:
$\frac{3}{4} + \frac{15}{16} + \frac{5}{8}$

6. Subtract:
$4 - \frac{13}{16}$

7. Multiply:
$5\frac{1}{3} \times 3\frac{3}{8}$

8. Divide:
$\frac{5}{8} \div \frac{2}{3}$

9. Add:
.65 + 24 + 9.2

10. Subtract:
8 − .3

11. Multiply:
.05 × .004

12. Divide:
6 ÷ .2

13. Find $4\frac{1}{2}\%$ of $840.

14. 36 is what per cent of 42?

15. 120% of what number is 414?

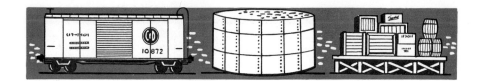

EXERCISE 51

PRACTICAL APPLICATIONS—MEASURING VOLUME

The volume, also called cubical contents or capacity, is the number of units of cubic measure contained in a given space. When computing the volume of a geometric figure, *express all linear units in the same denomination.*

I. Rectangular Solid

The volume of a rectangular solid is equal to the length times the width times the height. Formula: $V = lwh$

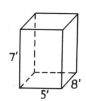

$l = 8$ ft.
$w = 5$ ft.
$h = 7$ ft.
$V = ?$

Find the volume of a rectangular solid 8 feet long, 5 feet wide and 7 feet high.

$$V = lwh$$
$$V = 8 \times 5 \times 7$$
$$V = 280 \text{ cu. ft.}$$

$$\begin{array}{r} 8 \\ \times 5 \\ \hline 40 \end{array} \qquad \begin{array}{r} 40 \\ \times 7 \\ \hline 280 \end{array}$$

Answer: 280 cu. ft.

1. What is the volume of a rectangular solid if it is 7 inches long, 4 inches wide, and 9 inches high?

2. Find the volumes of rectangular solids having the following dimensions:

	Length	8 yd.	12 ft.	17 in.	36 ft.	62 ft.
(a)	Width	3 yd.	9 ft.	18 in.	36 ft.	40 ft.
	Height	6 yd.	10 ft.	14 in.	13 ft.	19 ft.

	Length	3.2 ft.	$5\frac{1}{2}$ in.	$8\frac{1}{4}$ ft.	7 ft. 6 in.	2 ft.
(b)	Width	4.5 ft.	$3\frac{3}{4}$ in.	6 ft.	4 ft. 9 in.	1 ft. 4 in.
	Height	2.75 ft.	$4\frac{5}{8}$ in.	$3\frac{1}{3}$ ft.	5 ft. 7 in.	9 in.

3. A schoolroom is 35 ft. long, 20 ft. wide, and 14 ft. high. How many cu. ft. of air space does the room contain? Allowing 200 cu. ft. of air space per pupil, what is the maximum number of pupils that should be assigned to the room?

4. How many cu. yd. of dirt must be removed when digging for a foundation of a building if the excavation is 94 ft. long, 36 ft. wide, and 25 ft. deep?

5. Find the weight of a steel bar 12 ft. long, 2 in. wide, and $\frac{1}{2}$ in. thick if steel weighs 490 lb. per cu. ft.

6. How many cartons, 2 ft. by 1 ft. 6 in. by 1 ft., can be stored to a height of 9 ft. in a space 10 ft. by 12 ft.?

7. What is the capacity of a freight car in cu. ft. if the inside dimensions are 40 ft. 6 in. by 9 ft. 2 in. by 10 ft.?

II. Cube

The volume of a cube is equal to the length of the edge times itself times itself or the edge or side cubed.

$$\text{Formula:} \quad V = e^3 \quad \text{or} \quad V = s^3$$

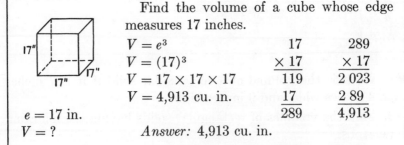

Find the volume of a cube whose edge measures 17 inches.

$V = e^3$ 17   289
$V = (17)^3$ × 17   × 17
$V = 17 \times 17 \times 17$ 119   2 023
$V = 4,913$ cu. in.   17   2 89
              289   4,913

$e = 17$ in.
$V = ?$ *Answer:* 4,913 cu. in.

1. What is the volume of a cube whose edge is 25 feet?

2. Find the volumes of cubes whose edges measure:

(a) 9 ft.   (b) 14 in.   (c) 11 ft. (d) 27 ft.   (e) 1.09 yd.
(f) 0.39 in.   (g) $2\frac{1}{2}$ in. (h) $4\frac{3}{4}$ ft. (i) 5 yd. 2 ft.   (j) 1 ft. 10 in.

3. How many cu. ft. of space are in a bin 6 ft. by 6 ft. by 6 ft.?

4. The volume of an 8-inch cube is how many times as large as the volume of a 2-inch cube?

III. Right Circular Cylinder

The volume of a cylinder is equal to pi (π)* times the square of the radius of the base times the height. Formula: $V = \pi r^2 h$

When the diameter is known, the following formula may be used: $V = \frac{1}{4} \pi d^2 h$

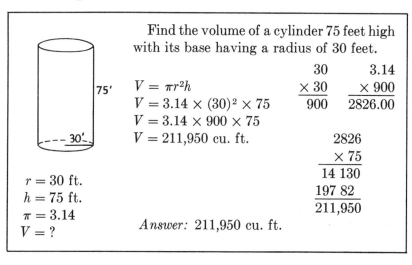

Find the volume of a cylinder 75 feet high with its base having a radius of 30 feet.

75'

$V = \pi r^2 h$
$V = 3.14 \times (30)^2 \times 75$
$V = 3.14 \times 900 \times 75$
$V = 211,950$ cu. ft.

30'

$r = 30$ ft.
$h = 75$ ft.
$\pi = 3.14$
$V = ?$

Answer: 211,950 cu. ft.

```
   30          3.14
 × 30         × 900
  900        2826.00

              2826
             × 75
            14 130
            197 82
            211,950
```

1. What is the volume of a cylinder if the radius of its base is 3 inches and the height is 6 inches?

2. What is the volume of a cylinder if the diameter of its base is 10 feet and the height is 16 feet?

3. Find the volumes of cylinders having the following dimensions:

(a)

Radius	5 in.	14 in.	19 ft.	$2\frac{5}{8}$ in.	1 ft. 6 in.
Height	8 in.	10 in.	25 ft.	$7\frac{1}{2}$ in.	9 ft. 2 in.

(b)

Diameter	4 in.	56 ft.	12 in.	$6\frac{1}{8}$ in.	1 ft. 2 in.
Height	6 in.	20 ft.	28 in.	9 in.	2 ft. 3 in.

$\pi = 3\frac{1}{7}$ or $\frac{22}{7}$ or 3.14. For greater accuracy 3.1416 may be used.

4. Which container holds more, one 3 in. in diameter and 4 in. high or one 4 in. in diameter and 3 in. high? How many cu. in. more?

5. How many cu. yd. of dirt must be dug to make a well 4 ft. 6 in. in diameter and 42 ft. deep?

6. What is the weight of a round steel rod 8 ft. long and $\frac{3}{4}$ in. in diameter? A cu. ft. of steel weighs 490 lb.

7. Find the displacement of a piston (volume of an engine cylinder) whose bore (diameter) is 4 in. and whose stroke (height piston moves) is 5 in.

8. A silo has an inside diameter of 12 ft. 8 in. It is 27 ft. high. How many cu. ft. of silage will it hold?

9. How many cu. ft. of water does a tank hold if its diameter is 18 in. and height is 5 ft.?

10. How many gallons of oil does a tank car hold if it is 10 ft. in diameter and 42 ft. long? 1 cu. ft. = $7\frac{1}{2}$ gal.

IV. Sphere

The volume of a sphere is equal to $\frac{4}{3}$ times pi (π) times the cube of the radius. Formula: $V = \frac{4}{3}\pi r^3$

Sometimes the formula $V = \dfrac{\pi d^3}{6}$ is used.

1. Find the volumes of spheres having the following radii:
(a) 30 in.   (b) 56 ft.   (c) 10.4 yd.   (d) $6\frac{5}{16}$ in.   (e) 2 ft. 8 in.

2. Find the volumes of spheres having the following diameters:
(a) 26 ft.   (b) 84 in.   (c) 11.3 ft.   (d) $12\frac{1}{2}$ in.   (e) 4 ft. 5 in.

3. How many cu. ft. of air does a basketball contain if its diameter is 10 in.?

V. Right Circular Cone

The volume of a right circular cone is equal to $\frac{1}{3}$ times pi (π) times the square of the radius of the base times the height.

Formula: $V = \frac{1}{3}\pi r^2 h$

1. Find the volumes of cones having the following dimensions:

(a)				
Radius	8 in.	14 ft.	$6\frac{1}{2}$ in.	4 ft. 3 in.
Height	23 in.	12 ft.	9 in.	6 ft.

	Diameter	20 ft.	42 in.	7 ft.	1 ft. 5 in.
(b)	Height	15 ft.	58 in.	$4\frac{1}{2}$ ft.	2 ft.

2. A conical pile of sand is 8 ft. in diameter and 3 ft. high. How many cu. yd. of sand are in the pile?

3. How many bushels of grain are in a conical pile 16 ft. in diameter and 5 ft. high?

VI. Pyramid

The volume of a pyramid is equal to $\frac{1}{3}$ times the area of the base times the height. Formula: $V = \frac{1}{3} Bh$

1. Find the volume of a pyramid when the side of its square base is 40 ft. and the height is 27 ft.

2. What is the volume of a pyramid when its rectangular base is 23 ft. long and 18 ft. wide and the height is 35 ft.?

3. How many cu. ft. of space are inside a tent in the shape of a square pyramid 15 ft. on each side of the base and 16 ft. high?

REVIEW OF EXERCISE

1. Change 29,376 cubic inches to cubic feet.

2. How many cubic feet are in 21 cubic yards?

3. Find the number of cubic inches in $1\frac{3}{4}$ cubic feet.

4. How many cubic yards are in 432 cubic feet?

Find the volume of:

5. A cube whose edge measures 38 inches.

6. A cylinder 16 feet high with the radius of its base 10 feet.

7. A rectangular solid 60 feet long, 43 feet wide, and 18 feet high.

8. A sphere whose diameter is 9 inches.

9. A right circular cone 40 feet high with the diameter of its base 28 feet.

10. A square pyramid $12\frac{1}{2}$ feet on each side and 15 feet high.

11. How many cubic feet of food will a freezer hold if its inside dimensions are 48 inches by 28 inches by 21 inches?

12. A circular wading pool is 96 inches in diameter and 14 inches deep. How many cubic feet of water will it hold?

REFRESH YOUR SKILLS

1. Add:

513
79,884
8,935
484,629
9,356
97,803

2. Subtract:

614,904
523,994

3. Multiply:

4,968
759

4. Divide:

$806)\overline{801,164}$

5. Add:

$2\frac{7}{8}$
$1\frac{3}{4}$
$5\frac{13}{16}$

6. Subtract:

$8\frac{1}{6}$
$2\frac{4}{5}$

7. Multiply:

$\frac{3}{8} \times 5\frac{1}{4}$

8. Divide:

$2\frac{11}{12} \div 1\frac{1}{8}$

9. Add:

$.406 + 9.25 + 63.8$

10. Subtract: $\$60 - \$2.75$

11. Multiply:

3.1416
.25

12. Divide:

$\$.25)\overline{\$10}$

13. Find 125% of $43.90

14. What per cent of 360 is 27?

15. 3% of what number is 78?

16. Round off $3.9062 to the nearest cent.

17. Change .75 to a common fraction.

18. Express $\frac{9}{10}$ as a per cent.

19. Square: 1.01

20. Find the square root of 49,843,600.

21. What part of a foot is 6 inches?

22. What part of a square foot is 6 square inches?

23. What part of a cubic foot is 6 cubic inches?

24. Change 1 mile 500 yards to yards.

25. Change 75 square feet to square yards.

EXERCISE 52

CAPACITY—LIQUID MEASURE

I. Aim: To change a given number of units of liquid measure of one denomination to units of another denomination.

II. Procedure

Use either the common method or the method of cancellation of units as explained in the procedure under Exercise 44 on page 296.

The following specific rules may also be used:

To change:

(a) Pints to ounces, multiply the number of pints by 16.
(b) Ounces to pints, divide the number of ounces by 16.
(c) Quarts to pints, multiply the number of quarts by 2.
(d) Pints to quarts, divide the number of pints by 2.
(e) Gallons to quarts, multiply the number of gallons by 4.
(f) Quarts to gallons, divide the number of quarts by 4.

III. Sample Solutions

Change 9 gal. to quarts.

Method 1

$$\begin{array}{r} 9 \\ \times 4 \\ \hline 36 \end{array}$$

Answer: 36 qt.

Method 2

$$9 \text{ gal.} \times \frac{4 \text{ qt.}}{1 \text{ gal.}} = 36 \text{ qt.}$$

Change 64 oz. to pints.

Method 1

$$16\overline{)64}$$
$$\underline{64}$$

Answer: 4 pt.

Method 2

$$64 \text{ oz.} \times \frac{1 \text{ pt.}}{16 \text{ oz.}} = 4 \text{ pt.}$$

EQUIVALENTS—LIQUID MEASURE

1 ounce (oz.)   = 8 drams (dr.)
1 pint (pt.)   = 16 ounces (oz.)
                = 4 gills (gi.)
1 quart (qt.)   = 2 pints (pt.)
1 gallon (gal.) = 4 quarts (qt.)
1 standard barrel (bbl.) = $31\frac{1}{2}$ gallons (gal.)

DIAGNOSTIC TEST

Change:

1. 3 pt. to ounces
2. 5 pt. 6 oz. to ounces
3. 7 qt. to pints
4. 3 qt. 1 pt. to pints
5. 2 qt. to ounces
6. 1 qt. 9 oz. to ounces
7. 8 gal. to quarts
8. 12 gal. 3 qt. to quarts
9. 5 gal. to pints
10. 3 gal. 2 qt. 1 pt. to pints
11. 80 oz. to pints
12. 2 pt. 12 oz. to pints
13. 35 oz. to pints (Write remainder in ounces.)
14. 26 pt. to quarts
15. 6 qt. 1 pt. to quarts
16. 23 pt. to quarts (Write remainder in pints.)

17. 96 oz. to quarts
18. 6 qt. 20 oz. to quarts
19. 52 oz. to quarts (Write remainder in pints and ounces.)
20. 36 qt. to gallons
21. 14 gal. 2 qt. to gallons
22. 9 qt. to gallons (Write remainder in quarts.)
23. 96 pt. to gallons
24. 6 gal. 2 qt. 1 pt. to gallons
25. 37 pt. to gallons (Write remainder in quarts and pints.)
26. What part of a gallon is 2 quarts?

RELATED PRACTICE EXAMPLES

Change to ounces:

Set 1	Set 2
1. 7 pt.	1. 2 pt. 8 oz.
2. 9 pt.	2. 4 pt. 1 oz.
3. $5\frac{1}{2}$ pt.	3. 1 pt. 14 oz.
4. 4.75 pt.	4. 3 pt. 9 oz.
5. 17 pt.	5. 8 pt. 4 oz.

Change to pints:

Set 3	Set 4
1. 3 qt.	1. 5 qt. 1 pt.
2. 12 qt.	2. 2 qt. 1 pt.
3. $\frac{4}{5}$ qt.	3. 8 qt. 3 pt.
4. 1.1 qt.	4. 16 qt. 2 pt.
5. 25 qt.	5. 37 qt. $\frac{1}{2}$ pt.

Change to ounces: Change to quarts:

Set 5	Set 6	Set 7	Set 8
1. 5 qt.	**1.** 3 qt. 4 oz.	**1.** 7 gal.	**1.** 5 gal. 3 qt.
2. 8 qt.	**2.** 1 qt. 18 oz.	**2.** 16 gal.	**2.** 8 gal. 1 qt.
3. $4\frac{1}{4}$ qt.	**3.** 4 qt. $1\frac{1}{2}$ pt.	**3.** $6\frac{3}{4}$ gal.	**3.** 4 gal. 2 qt.
4. 3.5 qt.	**4.** 5 qt. 1 pt. 10 oz.	**4.** .25 gal.	**4.** 1 gal. 3 qt.
5. 26 qt.	**5.** 2 qt. 1 pt. 12 oz.	**5.** 39 gal.	**5.** 17 gal. 2 qt.

Change to pints:

In set 13 write remainder in ounces.

Set 9	Set 10
1. 6 gal.	**1.** 8 gal. 3 pt.
2. 14 gal.	**2.** 5 gal. 1 pt.
3. $7\frac{1}{2}$ gal.	**3.** 6 gal. 2 qt.
4. 16.8 gal.	**4.** 7 gal. 3 qt. 1 pt.
5. 40 gal.	**5.** 4 gal. 1 qt. 1 pt.

Set 11	Set 12	Set 13
1. 48 oz.	**1.** 2 pt. 4 oz.	**1.** 23 oz.
2. 224 oz.	**2.** 1 pt. 9 oz.	**2.** 41 oz.
3. 6 oz.	**3.** 5 pt. 14 oz.	**3.** 56 oz.
4. 28 oz.	**4.** 9 pt. 8 oz.	**4.** 75 oz.
5. 352 oz.	**5.** 17 pt. 13 oz.	**5.** 60 oz.

Change to quarts:

In set 16 write remainder in pints.
In set 19 write remainder in pints and ounces.

Set 14	Set 15	Set 16
1. 10 pt.	**1.** 2 qt. 1 pt.	**1.** 13 pt.
2. 34 pt.	**2.** 8 qt. 1 pt.	**2.** 27 pt.
3. 29 pt.	**3.** 3 qt. $\frac{1}{2}$ pt.	**3.** $4\frac{1}{2}$ pt.
4. 6.5 pt.	**4.** 1 qt. $1\frac{1}{2}$ pt.	**4.** $16\frac{3}{4}$ pt.
5. 42 pt.	**5.** 5 qt. 1 pt.	**5.** $21\frac{1}{2}$ pt.

Set 17	Set 18	Set 19
1. 64 oz.	**1.** 2 qt. 8 oz.	**1.** 35 oz.
2. 288 oz.	**2.** 5 qt. 14 oz.	**2.** 42 oz.
3. 100 oz.	**3.** 4 qt. 15 oz.	**3.** 93 oz.
4. 216 oz.	**4.** 10 qt. 12 oz.	**4.** 145 oz.
5. 700 oz.	**5.** 16 qt. 30 oz.	**5.** 200 oz.

Change to gallons:

In set 22 write remainder in quarts.
In set 25 write remainder in quarts and pints.

SET 20
1. 12 qt.
2. 40 qt.
3. 23 qt.
4. 9 qt.
5. 136 qt.

SET 21
1. 3 gal. 1 qt.
2. 8 gal. 3 qt.
3. 16 gal. 2 qt.
4. 7 gal. 1 qt.
5. 11 gal. 2 qt.

SET 22
1. 7 qt.
2. 18 qt.
3. 85 qt.
4. 50 qt.
5. 123 qt.

SET 23
1. 56 pt.
2. 104 pt.
3. 10 pt.
4. 75 pt.
5. 120 pt.

SET 24
1. 9 gal. 1 pt.
2. 4 gal. 3 pt.
3. 5 gal. 2 qt. 1 pt.
4. 1 gal. 3 qt. 1 pt.
5. 16 gal. 1 qt. 1 pt.

SET 25
1. 9 pt.
2. 15 pt.
3. 34 pt.
4. 26 pt.
5. 47 pt.

SET 26
1. What part of a gallon is 3 quarts?
2. 1 pint is what part of a gallon?
3. 8 ounces is what part of a quart?
4. What part of a gallon is 48 ounces?
5. What part of a quart is 1 pint 2 ounces?

PRACTICAL APPLICATIONS

1. In a certain school 852 bottles of milk were sold in a single day. If each bottle contains 8 oz. of milk, how many gallons of milk were sold?

2. How many ounces of pineapple juice are in a can marked 1 qt. 14 oz.?

3. A salesman changed the oil in his automobile 9 times during the year, using 6 qt. each time. How many gallons were used?

4. If each can contains 14 oz. of tomato juice, how many gallons of tomato juice does a case of 48 cans contain?

5. At a service station 62 quarts of dirty oil were collected from oil changes. How many gallons of dirty oil were collected?

6. A gallon of paint can cover a smooth wood surface at the rate of 600 sq. ft. If the paint is available in 8 oz., 1 pint, 1 quart, and 1 gallon sizes, which size is sufficient to cover 75 sq. ft.?

7. How many quarts of oil are in a drum containing 55 gallons?

8. The capacity of a certain tanker is 56,000 barrels of oil. Find its capacity in gallons if a barrel holds 42 gallons.

9. How many gallons of anti-freeze should be used in a car to make a $33\frac{1}{3}\%$ anti-freeze solution if the water capacity of the radiator is 15 quarts?

10. Oil can be bought at $.45 per quart in individual cans or at $6.85 for 5 gallons in bulk. How much would be saved if 5 gallons of oil were bought in bulk?

11. If a family buys 3 quarts of milk each day, how many gallons of milk does it buy in 1 year (365 days)?

12. A baby's milk formula consists of 11 oz. of condensed milk, 12 oz. of boiled water, and 1 oz. of sweetening. How many pints does the formula contain?

13. Find how much is saved by buying the larger size of the following articles instead of an equivalent quantity in the smaller size:

(a) Vinegar, pint at $.14, quart at $.23.

(b) Paint, quart at $1.75, gallon at $5.98.

(c) Cooking oil, pint at $.35, gallon at $2.09.

14. Find the difference in the price per ounce:

(a) 1 pt. of olive oil at $.80 or 4 oz. at $.28.

(b) 1 pt. 14-oz. bottle of beverage at $.18 or 8-oz. bottle at $.06.

(c) 1 pt. 2-oz. can of fruit juice at $.12 or 1 qt. 14-oz. can at $.23.

15. What is the ratio of: (a) 1 pt. to 1 gal.? (b) 12 oz. to 1 qt.? (c) 1 gal. to 3 qt.? (d) 2 qt. to 2 pt.? (e) 1 pt. to 24 oz.?

16. How many ounces of water should be added to:

(a) 6 oz. of frozen grape juice concentrate to make $1\frac{1}{2}$ pt. of grape juice?

(b) 6 oz. of frozen lemonade concentrate to make 1 qt. lemonade?

(c) 27 oz. of frozen orange juice concentrate to make 1 gal. of orange juice?

EXERCISE 53

CAPACITY—DRY MEASURE

I. Aim: To change a given number of units of dry measure of one denomination to units of another denomination.

II. Procedure

Use either the common method or the method of cancellation of units as explained in the procedure under Exercise 44 on page 296.

The following specific rules may also be used:

To change:

(*a*) Quarts to pints, multiply the number of quarts by 2.

(*b*) Pints to quarts, divide the number of pints by 2.

(*c*) Pecks to quarts, multiply the number of pecks by 8.

(*d*) Quarts to pecks, divide the number of quarts by 8.

(*e*) Bushels to pecks, multiply the number of bushels by 4.

(*f*) Pecks to bushels, divide the number of pecks by 4.

III. Sample Solutions

1. Change 7 bu. to pecks.

Method 1

$$
\begin{array}{r}
7 \\
\times\,4 \\
\hline
28
\end{array}
$$

Answer: 28 pk.

Method 2

$$7\ \cancel{\text{bu.}} \times \frac{4\ \text{pk.}}{1\ \cancel{\text{bu.}}} = 28\ \text{pk.}$$

2. Change 26 qt. to pecks. Write remainder in quarts.

$$
\begin{array}{r}
3 \\
8\overline{)26} \\
24 \\
\hline
2
\end{array}
$$

Answer: 3 pk. 2 qt.

3. Change 5 bu. 2 pk. to bushels.

5 bu. 2 pk. = 5 bu. + 2 pk.*

$\qquad\quad\;\; = 5$ bu. $+\frac{1}{2}$ bu.

$\qquad\quad\;\; = 5\frac{1}{2}$ bu.

Answer: $5\frac{1}{2}$ bu.

*2 pk. $= \frac{2}{4}$ bu. $= \frac{1}{2}$ bu.

EQUIVALENTS—DRY MEASURE

1 quart (qt.) = 2 pints (pt.)
1 peck (pk.) = 8 quarts (qt.)
1 bushel (bu.) = 4 pecks (pk.)
1 barrel (bbl.) = 105 quarts (qt.)

DIAGNOSTIC TEST

Change:

1. 5 qt. to pints
2. 2 qt. 1 pt. to pints
3. 7 pk. to quarts
4. 6 pk. 5 qt. to quarts
5. 4 pk. to pints
6. 1 pk. 6 qt. 1 pt. to pints
7. 9 bu. to pecks
8. 5 bu. 3 pk. to pecks
9. 3 bu. to quarts
10. 2 bu. 9 qt. to quarts
11. 20 pt. to quarts
12. 8 qt. 1 pt. to quarts
13. 15 pt. to quarts (Write remainder in pints.)
14. 48 qt. to pecks
15. 5 pk. 4 qt. to pecks
16. 37 qt. to pecks (Write remainder in quarts.)

17. 64 pt. to pecks
18. 2 pk. 7 qt. 1 pt. to pecks
19. 21 pt. to pecks (Write remainder in quarts and pints.)
20. 40 pk. to bushels
21. 9 bu. 2 pk. to bushels
22. 7 pk. to bushels (Write remainder in pecks.)
23. 96 qt. to bushels
24. 4 bu. 3 pk. 2 qt. to bushels
25. 45 qt. to bushels (Write remainder in pecks and quarts.)
26. What part of a bushel is 3 pecks?

RELATED PRACTICE EXAMPLES

Change to pints:

Set 1	Set 2
1. 4 qt.	1. 3 qt. 1 pt.
2. 13 qt.	2. 9 qt. 1 pt.
3. $3\frac{3}{4}$ qt.	3. 8 qt. 2 pt.
4. 6.5 qt.	4. 14 qt. 3 pt.
5. 30 qt.	5. 5 qt. $1\frac{1}{2}$ pt.

Change to quarts:

Set 3	Set 4
1. 2 pk.	1. 4 pk. 2 qt.
2. 15 pk.	2. 2 pk. 7 qt.
3. $2\frac{1}{4}$ pk.	3. 1 pk. 6 qt.
4. 8.75 pk.	4. 8 pk. 1 qt.
5. 26 pk.	5. 5 pk. 4 qt.

Change to pints: Change to pecks:

Set 5	Set 6	Set 7	Set 8
1. 3 pk.	1. 7 pk. 10 pt.	1. 7 bu.	1. 2 bu. 3 pk.
2. 10 pk.	2. 2 pk. 5 pt.	2. 16 bu.	2. 7 bu. 1 pk.
3. 5$\frac{1}{2}$ pk.	3. 4 pk. 3 qt.	3. $\frac{3}{4}$ bu.	3. 10 bu. 2 pk.
4. 3.25 pk.	4. 9 pk. 5 qt. 1 pt.	4. 5.2 bu.	4. 16 bu. 3 pk.
5. 18 pk.	5. 3 pk. 2 qt. $\frac{1}{2}$ pt.	5. 33 bu.	5. 35 bu. 2$\frac{1}{2}$ pk.

Change to quarts:

In set 13 write remainder in pints.

Set 9	Set 10
1. 6 bu.	1. 2 bu. 2 qt.
2. 17 bu.	2. 10 bu. 7 qt.
3. 3$\frac{5}{8}$ bu.	3. 8 bu. 19 qt.
4. 4.75 bu.	4. 29 bu. 3 pk. 7 qt.
5. 24 bu.	5. 37 bu. 1 pk. 4 qt.

Set 11	Set 12	Set 13
1. 12 pt.	1. 4 qt. 1 pt.	1. 3 pt.
2. 56 pt.	2. 9 qt. 1 pt.	2. 19 pt.
3. 5 pt.	3. 16 qt. 1 pt.	3. 27 pt.
4. 7.25 pt.	4. 20 qt. $\frac{1}{2}$ pt.	4. 51 pt.
5. 100 pt.	5. 48 qt. 1$\frac{1}{2}$ pt.	5. 9$\frac{1}{2}$ pt.

Change to pecks:

In set 16 write remainder in quarts.
In set 19 write remainder in quarts and pints.

Set 14	Set 15	Set 16
1. 40 qt.	1. 1 pk. 6 qt.	1. 9 qt.
2. 112 qt.	2. 4 pk. 4 qt.	2. 18 qt.
3. 35 qt.	3. 9 pk. 5 qt.	3. 25 qt.
4. 22 qt.	4. 3 pk. 2 qt.	4. 54 qt.
5. 136 qt.	5. 8 pk. 3 qt.	5. 76 qt.

Set 17	Set 18	Set 19
1. 96 pt.	1. 2 pk. 4 pt.	1. 17 pt.
2. 144 pt.	2. 5 pk. 11 pt.	2. 25 pt.
3. 18 pt.	3. 8 pk. 3 pt.	3. 30 pt.
4. 27 pt.	4. 3 pk. 6 qt. 1 pt.	4. 43 pt.
5. 240 pt.	5. 7 pk. 5 qt. 1 pt.	5. 74 pt.

Change to bushels:

In set 22 write remainder in pecks.
In set 25 write remainder in pecks and quarts.

SET 20
1. 36 pk.
2. 92 pk.
3. 23 pk.
4. 7 pk.
5. 108 pk.

SET 21
1. 3 bu. 3 pk.
2. 6 bu. 2 pk.
3. 10 bu. 1 pk.
4. 17 bu. 3 pk.
5. 39 bu. 2 pk.

SET 22
1. 6 pk.
2. 13 pk.
3. 21 pk.
4. 30 pk.
5. $17\frac{1}{4}$ pk.

SET 23
1. 64 qt.
2. 160 qt.
3. 53 qt.
4. 108 qt.
5. 352 qt.

SET 24
1. 2 bu. 8 qt.
2. 1 bu. 20 qt.
3. 9 bu. 3 qt.
4. 5 bu. 2 pk. 6 qt.
5. 6 bu. 1 pk. 5 qt.

SET 25
1. 39 qt.
2. 52 qt.
3. 70 qt.
4. 87 qt.
5. 105 qt.

SET 26
1. What part of a bushel is 2 pecks?
2. 1 peck is what part of a bushel?
3. 6 quarts is what part of a peck?
4. What part of a peck is 3 quarts?
5. 4 quarts is what part of a peck?

PRACTICAL APPLICATIONS

1. If a bushel of potatoes weighs 60 lb., how many pecks are in a bag of potatoes weighing 100 lb.?

2. In full bearing under favorable conditions a strawberry plant produces one pint of strawberries while a raspberry plant produces two quarts of raspberries. If there are 8 strawberry plants and 10 raspberry plants in full bearing in a garden, how many quarts of each may be expected?

3. How many more quarts are in a $\frac{5}{8}$ bu. basket than in a $\frac{1}{2}$ bu. basket? If a bushel of apples weighs 50 lb., what is the difference in weight between the $\frac{5}{8}$ bu. and $\frac{1}{2}$ bu. of apples?

4. If it takes one pint of strawberries to make one jar of home-canned strawberry preserves, how many quarts of strawberries should be bought so that 50 jars can be filled?

5. Which is the better value, a peck of potatoes costing $.53 or a 10-lb. bag costing $.40? (A bushel of potatoes weighs 60 lb.)

MEASURE OF WEIGHT

I. Aim: To change a given number of units of weight of one denomination to units of another denomination.

II. Procedure

Use either the common method or the method of cancellation of units as explained in the procedure under Exercise 44 on page 296.

The following specific rules may also be used:

To change:

(*a*) Pounds to ounces, multiply the number of pounds by 16.

(*b*) Ounces to pounds, divide the number of ounces by 16.

(*c*) Short tons to pounds, multiply the number of short tons by 2,000.

(*d*) Pounds to short tons, divide the number of pounds by 2,000.

(*e*) Long tons to pounds, multiply the number of long tons by 2,240.

(*f*) Pounds to long tons, divide the number of pounds by 2,240.

III. Sample Solutions

1. Change $1\frac{3}{4}$ lb. to ounces.

Method 1

$$\begin{array}{r} 16 \\ \times\, 1\frac{3}{4} \\ \hline 16 \\ 12 \\ \hline 28 \end{array}$$

$$\frac{3}{4} \times \overset{4}{\cancel{16}} = 12$$

Answer: 28 oz.

Method 2

$$1\frac{3}{4}\ \cancel{\text{lb.}} \times \frac{16\ \text{oz.}}{1\ \cancel{\text{lb.}}} = 28\ \text{oz.}$$

2. Change 5,600 lb. to long tons.

Method 1

$$\begin{array}{r} 2.5 \\ 2{,}240\overline{)5{,}600.0} \\ 4\,480 \\ \hline 1\,120\,0 \\ 1\,120\,0 \end{array}$$

Answer: 2.5 l.t.

Method 2

$$5{,}600\ \cancel{\text{lb.}} \times \frac{1\ \text{l.t.}}{2{,}240\ \cancel{\text{lb.}}} = 2.5\ \text{l.t.}$$

EQUIVALENTS—MEASURE OF WEIGHT—AVOIRDUPOIS

1 ounce (oz.) = 437.5 grains
= 16 drams (dr.)

1 pound (lb.) = 16 ounces (oz.)
= 7,000 grains

1 short ton (s.t. or T.) = 2,000 pounds (lb.)

1 long ton (l.t.) = 2,240 pounds (lb.)

1 short hundredweight (sh. cwt.) = 100 pounds (lb.)

DIAGNOSTIC TEST

Change:

1. 4 lb. to ounces
2. 8 lb. 6 oz. to ounces
3. 6 s.t. to pounds
4. 5 s.t. 400 lb. to pounds
5. 10 l.t. to pounds

6. 1 l.t. 140 lb. to pounds
7. 48 oz. to pounds
8. 9 lb. 4 oz. to pounds
9. 27 oz. to pounds (Write remainder in ounces.)

10. 6,000 lb. to short tons
11. 2 s.t. 200 lb. to short tons
12. 2,500 lb. to short tons (Write remainder in pounds.)
13. 4,480 lb. to long tons
14. 5 l.t. 280 lb. to long tons
15. 3,000 lb. to long tons (Write remainder in pounds.)
16. What part of a pound is 8 ounces?

RELATED PRACTICE EXAMPLES

Change to ounces:

Set 1(a)	Set 1(b)	Set 2
1. 3 lb.	1. $\frac{1}{4}$ lb.	1. 4 lb. 8 oz.
2. 10 lb.	2. $\frac{3}{4}$ lb.	2. 9 lb. 7 oz.
3. $5\frac{1}{4}$ lb.	3. $\frac{1}{2}$ lb.	3. 1 lb. 2 oz.
4. 2.2 lb.	4. $\frac{7}{8}$ lb.	4. 18 lb. 13 oz.
5. 37 lb.	5. $\frac{11}{16}$ lb.	5. 23 lb. 12 oz.

Change to pounds:

In set 9 write remainder in ounces.

SET 3	SET 4	SET 5
1. 7 s.t.	**1.** 6 s.t. 500 lb.	**1.** 6 l.t.
2. 19 s.t.	**2.** 3 s.t. 1,200 lb.	**2.** 31 l.t.
3. $4\frac{1}{2}$ s.t.	**3.** 10 s.t. 1,000 lb.	**3.** $17\frac{3}{4}$ l.t.
4. 8.75 s.t.	**4.** 29 s.t. 900 lb.	**4.** 9.5 l.t.
5. 148 s.t.	**5.** 18 s.t. 1,750 lb.	**5.** 50 l.t.

SET 6	SET 7	SET 8	SET 9
1. 2 l.t. 560 lb.	**1.** 32 oz.	**1.** 7 lb. 2 oz.	**1.** 21 oz.
2. 9 l.t. 1,540 lb.	**2.** 176 oz.	**2.** 3 lb. 10 oz.	**2.** 39 oz.
3. 15 l.t. 1,120 lb.	**3.** 26 oz.	**3.** 8 lb. 5 oz.	**3.** 86 oz.
4. 46 l.t. 70 lb.	**4.** 55 oz.	**4.** 14 lb. 12 oz.	**4.** 58 oz.
5. 100 l.t. 200 lb.	**5.** 368 oz.	**5.** 20 lb. 9 oz.	**5.** 100 oz.

Change to short tons:

In set 12 write remainder in pounds.

SET 10	SET 11	SET 12
1. 10,000 lb.	**1.** 2 s.t. 500 lb.	**1.** 2,900 lb.
2. 24,000 lb.	**2.** 9 s.t. 1,000 lb.	**2.** 2,240 lb.
3. 800 lb.	**3.** 14 s.t. 750 lb.	**3.** 9,750 lb.
4. 3,500 lb.	**4.** 25 s.t. 1,800 lb.	**4.** 5,868 lb.
5. 32,000 lb.	**5.** 53 s.t. 1,200 lb.	**5.** 11,625 lb.

Change to long tons:

In set 15 write remainder in pounds.

SET 13	SET 14	SET 15
1. 6,720 lb.	**1.** 1 l.t. 1,120 lb.	**1.** 5,000 lb.
2. 17,920 lb.	**2.** 6 l.t. 560 lb.	**2.** 6,500 lb.
3. 4,000 lb.	**3.** 14 l.t. 1,000 lb.	**3.** 9,475 lb.
4. 1,680 lb.	**4.** 31 l.t. 840 lb.	**4.** 15,000 lb.
5. 56,000 lb.	**5.** 46 l.t. 1,960 lb.	**5.** 13,920 lb.

SET 16

1. What part of a pound is 4 ounces?

2. 12 ounces is what part of a pound?

3. What part of a pound is 14 ounces?

4. 3 ounces is what part of a pound?

5. What part of a pound is 11 ounces?

PRACTICAL APPLICATIONS

1. Find the cost of each of the following:

(*a*) 4 oz. of candy at $1.20 per lb.   (*b*) 11 oz. of meat at $.96 per lb.   (*c*) 5 lb. 8 oz. chicken at $.62 per lb.   (*d*) 3,500 lb. of coal at $21.50 per short ton.

2. (*a*) How many 3-oz. boxes of cookies can be made from a 9-lb. box?   (*b*) How many 12-oz. packages of pretzels can be made from a 6-lb. can?   (*c*) How many 50-lb. bags of coal can be made from a short ton of coal?

3. (*a*) At $1.12 per lb., how many oz. of candy should you get for $.35?   (*b*) At $.80 per lb., how many oz. of cake should you get for $.60?   (*c*) At $21 per short ton, how many lb. of coal should you get for $10.50?

4. Find how much is saved by buying the larger size of the following articles instead of an equivalent weight in the smaller size:

(*a*) Spaghetti, 8-oz. package at $.11, 3 lb. at $.55.

(*b*) Cereal, 8-oz. box at $.15, 1 lb. at $.25.

(*c*) Soap flakes, 1 lb. 2 oz. at $.30, 3 lb. 6 oz. at $.75.

5. Find the difference in price per ounce in each of the following:

(*a*) 4 oz. of tea at $.48 or 1 lb. at $1.60

(*b*) 12-oz. jar of jelly at $.33 or 1 lb. at $.40

(*c*) 1 lb. 2-oz. can of fruit at $.24 or 1 lb. 14 oz. at $.35

6. (*a*) If the price of steel increased $5 per ton (2,000 lb.), what was the increase per lb.?

(*b*) Find the discount in the price of a 100-lb. bag of sand at the rate of $1.20 discount for a short ton.

7. (*a*) If milk is sold at $5.60 per hundredweight (100 lb.), what is the price per lb.?

(*b*) Find the increase per lb. if the price of live hogs increased $1.50 per hundredweight.

8. (*a*) A submarine displaces 1,600 tons (1 T. = 2,240 lb.) of water when submerged. Find the number of lb. of water displaced.

(*b*) The centrifugal force on a ship in turning a circle is 1,024,000 pounds. Express this force in tons. (1 ton = 2,000 lb.)

9. (*a*) Dry air weighs .0765 lb. per cu. ft. at 59° F. and standard atmospheric pressure. Express the weight of a cubic foot of dry air in ounces.

(b) Sea water weighs 64 lb. per cu. ft. Express the weight of a cubic inch of sea water in ounces.

10. (a) A cu. in. of copper weighs 5.12 oz. Find its weight in lb.

(b) What is the weight in pounds of a cubic inch of zinc if 3 cu. in. of zinc weigh 12.96 oz.?

REFRESH YOUR SKILLS

1. Add:

69,896
99,635
87,964
69,689
98,899

2. Subtract:

1,000,000
309,208

3. Multiply:

5,280
487

4. Divide:

$144\overline{)1,285,776}$

5. Add:

$3\frac{11}{16} + 1\frac{5}{32} + 2\frac{3}{4}$

6. Subtract:

$8\frac{7}{8} - 2\frac{15}{16}$

7. Multiply:

$6\frac{1}{2} \times 1\frac{1}{4} \times \frac{7}{8}$

8. Divide:

$5\frac{5}{8} \div 2\frac{1}{2}$

9. Add:

$521.39 + $6.87 + $76.55 + $.94 + $369.97

10. Subtract:

$3,250 − $25.75

11. Multiply:

36 × $17.98

12. Divide:

$.10\overline{)$10}$

13. Find 130% of $615.

14. $.16 is what per cent of $.50?

15. 30% of what number is 39?

16. Round off 39,489,615,845 to the nearest billion.

17. Write as a decimal: Six hundred and twenty-five thousandths.

18. Square: $\frac{11}{16}$

19. Find the square root of 5 to the nearest hundredth.

20. What part of a mile is 440 feet?

21. How many ounces are in $1\frac{3}{4}$ pints?

22. What part of a square foot is 48 square inches?

23. Change 56 ounces to pounds.

24. What part of a bushel is 2 pecks?

25. How many cubic feet are in $5\frac{2}{3}$ cubic yards?

EXERCISE 55

MEASURE OF TIME

I. Aim: To change a given number of units of time of one denomination to units of another denomination.

II. Procedure

Use either the common method or the method of cancellation of units as explained in the procedure under Exercise 44 on page 296.

The following specific rules may also be used:

To change:

(a) Years to months, multiply the number of years by 12.

(b) Months to years, divide the number of months by 12.

(c) Years to weeks, multiply the number of years by 52.

(d) Weeks to years, divide the number of weeks by 52.

(e) Years to days, multiply the number of years by 365.

(f) Days to years, divide the number of days by 365.

(g) Weeks to days, multiply the number of weeks by 7.

(h) Days to weeks, divide the number of days by 7.

(i) Days to hours, multiply the number of days by 24.

(j) Hours to days, divide the number of hours by 24.

(k) Hours to minutes, multiply the number of hours by 60.

(l) Minutes to hours, divide the number of minutes by 60.

(m) Minutes to seconds, multiply the number of minutes by 60.

(n) Seconds to minutes, divide the number of seconds by 60.

III. Sample Solutions

1. Change 144 hr. to days.

Method 1

$$24)\overline{144}$$
with quotient 6 and 144 subtracted

Method 2

$$144 \text{ hr.} \times \frac{1 \text{ da.}}{24 \text{ hr.}} = 6 \text{ da.}$$

Answer: 6 da.

2. Change 6.2 min. to seconds.

  Method 1   *Method 2*

   6.2 $6.2 \cancel{\text{min.}} \times \dfrac{60 \text{ sec.}}{1 \cancel{\text{min.}}} = 372 \text{ sec.}$

   <u> 60 </u>

  372.0

Answer: 372 sec.

EQUIVALENTS—MEASURE OF TIME

1 year (yr.)	= 12 months (mo.)
	= 52 weeks (wk.)
	= 365 days (da.)*
1 week (wk.)	= 7 days (da.)
1 day (da.)	= 24 hours (hr.)
1 hour (hr.)	= 60 minutes (min.)
1 minute (min.)	= 60 seconds (sec.)

DIAGNOSTIC TEST A

Change:

1. 4 yr. to months

2. 2 yr. 6 mo. to months

3. 3 yr. to weeks

4. 2 yr. 9 wk. to weeks

5. 3 yr. to days

6. 1 yr. 200 da. to days

7. 6 wk. to days

8. 11 wk. 3 da. to days

9. 5 da. to hours

10. 9 da. 8 hr. to hours

11. 36 mo. to years

12. 3 yr. 8 mo. to years

13. 59 mo. to years (Write remainder in months.)

14. 104 wk. to years

15. 194 wk. to years (Write remainder in weeks.)

16. 730 da. to years

17. 5 yr. 292 da. to years

18. 600 da. to years (Write remainder in days.)

19. 28 da. to weeks

20. 16 wk. 4 da. to weeks

21. 51 da. to weeks (Write remainder in days.)

22. 168 hr. to days

23. 12 da. 18 hr. to days

24. 63 hr. to days (Write remainder in hours.)

---

*Leap year is disregarded in the calculations in this exercise.

RELATED PRACTICE EXAMPLES

Change to months: Change to weeks:

Set 1	Set 2	Set 3	Set 4
1. 3 yr.	**1.** 4 yr. 4 mo.	**1.** 2 yr.	**1.** 3 yr. 16 wk.
2. 8 yr.	**2.** 1 yr. 6 mo.	**2.** 4 yr.	**2.** 5 yr. 23 wk.
3. $\frac{3}{4}$ yr.	**3.** 9 yr. 7 mo.	**3.** $3\frac{1}{2}$ yr.	**3.** 1 yr. 41 wk.
4. $7\frac{5}{12}$ yr.	**4.** 3 yr. 10 mo.	**4.** $1\frac{1}{4}$ yr.	**4.** 2 yr. 37 wk.
5. 20 yr.	**5.** 5 yr. 9 mo.	**5.** $2\frac{3}{4}$ yr.	**5.** 4 yr. 8 wk.

Change to days:

Set 5	Set 6	Set 7	Set 8
1. 6 yr.	**1.** 2 yr. 30 da.	**1.** 8 wk.	**1.** 4 wk. 6 da.
2. 10 yr.	**2.** 7 yr. 58 da.	**2.** 26 wk.	**2.** 9 wk. 2 da.
3. $2\frac{1}{2}$ yr.	**3.** 1 yr. 185 da.	**3.** $5\frac{3}{7}$ wk.	**3.** 17 wk. 1 da.
4. $1\frac{2}{5}$ yr.	**4.** 12 yr. 97 da.	**4.** $6\frac{1}{2}$ wk.	**4.** 30 wk. 5 da.
5. 13 yr.	**5.** 20 yr. 231 da.	**5.** 40 wk.	**5.** 45 wk. 4 da.

Change to hours: Change to years:

Set 9	Set 10	Set 11	Set 12
1. 4 da.	**1.** 2 da. 4 hr.	**1.** 84 mo.	**1.** 2 yr. 4 mo.
2. 7 da.	**2.** 5 da. 13 hr.	**2.** 156 mo.	**2.** 1 yr. 9 mo.
3. $3\frac{5}{8}$ da.	**3.** 8 da. 21 hr.	**3.** 8 mo.	**3.** 7 yr. 1 mo.
4. $8\frac{1}{6}$ da.	**4.** 11 da. 9 hr.	**4.** 35 mo.	**4.** 4 yr. 7 mo.
5. 30 da.	**5.** 14 da. 16 hr.	**5.** 300 mo.	**5.** 8 yr. 10 mo.

Change to years:

In set 13 write remainder in months.
In set 15 write remainder in weeks.

Set 13	Set 14	Set 15
1. 15 mo.	**1.** 260 wk.	**1.** 72 wk.
2. 32 mo.	**2.** 156 wk.	**2.** 89 wk.
3. 46 mo.	**3.** 65 wk.	**3.** 115 wk.
4. 80 mo.	**4.** 39 wk.	**4.** 218 wk.
5. 140 mo.	**5.** 208 wk.	**5.** 100 wk.

Change to years:

In set 18 write remainder in days.

SET 16	SET 17	SET 18
1. 1,095 da.	**1.** 4 yr. 25 da.	**1.** 400 da.
2. 2,555 da.	**2.** 1 yr. 73 da.	**2.** 526 da.
3. 219 da.	**3.** 8 yr. 90 da.	**3.** 843 da.
4. 800 da.	**4.** 3 yr. 146 da.	**4.** 950 da.
5. 4,380 da.	**5.** 6 yr. 200 da.	**5.** 675 da.

Change to weeks:

In set 21 write remainder in days.

SET 19	SET 20	SET 21
1. 35 da.	**1.** 1 wk. 3 da.	**1.** 15 da.
2. 63 da.	**2.** 5 wk. 1 da.	**2.** 11 da.
3. 10 da.	**3.** 4 wk. 6 da.	**3.** 38 da.
4. 54 da.	**4.** 17 wk. 2 da.	**4.** 62 da.
5. 140 da.	**5.** 12 wk. 5 da.	**5.** 90 da.

Change to days:

In set 24 write remainder in hours.

SET 22	SET 23	SET 24
1. 48 hr.	**1.** 2 da. 12 hr.	**1.** 27 hr.
2. 192 hr.	**2.** 5 da. 8 hr.	**2.** 56 hr.
3. 30 hr.	**3.** 10 da. 5 hr.	**3.** 79 hr.
4. 76 hr.	**4.** 15 da. 20 hr.	**4.** 100 hr.
5. 720 hr.	**5.** 3 da. 17 hr.	**5.** 125 hr.

MISCELLANEOUS EXAMPLES

SET 1

1. What part of a year is 10 months?

2. 3 months is what part of a year?

3. What part of a year is 26 weeks?

4. 146 days is what part of a year?

5. What part of a year is 5 months?

SET 2

1. What part of a day is 18 hours?
2. What part of a week is 4 days?
3. 8 hours is what part of a day?
4. What part of a day is 11 hours?
5. 1 day is what part of a week?

DIAGNOSTIC TEST B

Change:

1. 9 hr. to minutes
2. 4 hrs. and 23 min. to minutes
3. 5 min. to seconds
4. 3 min. and 14 sec. to seconds
5. 3 hr. to seconds
6. 2 hr. 49 min. and 52 sec. to seconds
7. 1,080 min. to hours
8. 5 hr. and 45 min. to hours
9. 532 min. to hours (Write remainder in minutes.)
10. 240 sec. to minutes
11. 3 min. and 10 sec. to minutes
12. 918 sec. to minutes (Write remainder in seconds.)
13. 25,200 sec. to hours
14. 8,220 sec. to hours (Write remainder in minutes.)
15. 5,958 sec. to hours (Write remainder in minutes and seconds.)
16. 2 hr. 7 min. 30 sec. to hours

RELATED PRACTICE EXAMPLES

Change to minutes:		Change to seconds:	
SET 1	SET 2	SET 3	SET 4
1. 5 hr.	1. 1 hr. 30 min.	1. 7 min.	1. 5 min. 20 sec.
2. 18 hr.	2. 5 hr. 24 min.	2. 24 min.	2. 32 min. 30 sec.
3. $\frac{3}{4}$ hr.	3. 14 hr. 8 min.	3. $16\frac{1}{4}$ min.	3. 27 min. 48 sec.
4. 3.5 hr.	4. 23 hr. 17 min.	4. 8.3 min.	4. 56 min. 15 sec.
5. 21 hr.	5. 6 hr. 5 min.	5. 52 min.	5. 45 min. 6 sec.

Change to seconds:

Set 5	Set 6(*a*)	Set 6(*b*)
1. 4 hr.	**1.** 2 hr. 15 sec.	**1.** 2 hr. 15 min. 10 sec.
2. 7 hr.	**2.** 4 hr. 28 sec.	**2.** 1 hr. 39 min. 27 sec.
3. 1½ hr.	**3.** 8 hr. 53 sec.	**3.** 3 hr. 5 min. 30 sec.
4. 6.25 hr.	**4.** 5 hr. 45 min.	**4.** 7 hr. 36 min. 43 sec.
5. 20 hr.	**5.** 3 hr. 9 min.	**5.** 4 hr. 51 min. 19 sec.

Change to hours:

In set 9 write remainder in minutes.

Set 7	Set 8	Set 9
1. 480 min.	**1.** 2 hr. 12 min.	**1.** 69 min.
2. 600 min.	**2.** 8 hr. 40 min.	**2.** 125 min.
3. 100 min.	**3.** 3 hr. 36 min.	**3.** 471 min.
4. 84 min.	**4.** 16 hr. 17 min.	**4.** 906 min.
5. 3,180 min.	**5.** 9 hr. 25 min.	**5.** 2,600 min.

Change to minutes:

In set 12 write remainder in seconds.

Set 10	Set 11	Set 12
1. 540 sec.	**1.** 19 min. 30 sec.	**1.** 85 sec.
2. 780 sec.	**2.** 2 min. 15 sec.	**2.** 150 sec.
3. 36 sec.	**3.** 35 min. 49 sec.	**3.** 500 sec.
4. 225 sec.	**4.** 57 min. 24 sec.	**4.** 1,723 sec.
5. 1,800 sec.	**5.** 28 min. 40 sec.	**5.** 2,300 sec.

Change to hours:

In set 14 write remainder in minutes.

Set 13	Set 14
1. 10,800 sec.	**1.** 7,320 sec.
2. 43,200 sec.	**2.** 11,520 sec.
3. 18,000 sec.	**3.** 17,400 sec.
4. 32,400 sec.	**4.** 5,220 sec.
5. 61,200 sec.	**5.** 9,480 sec.

Change to hours:

In set 15 write remainder in minutes and seconds.

SET 15	SET 16
1. 4,157 sec.	**1.** 1 hr. 37 min. 30 sec.
2. 9,650 sec.	**2.** 5 hr. 3 min. 45 sec.
3. 11,743 sec.	**3.** 9 hr. 12 min. 30 sec.
4. 18,456 sec.	**4.** 16 hr. 48 min. 45 sec.
5. 16,449 sec.	**5.** 21 hr. 11 min. 15 sec.

MISCELLANEOUS EXAMPLES

SET 1

1. What part of an hour is 40 minutes?

2. 15 minutes is what part of an hour?

3. What part of an hour is 17 minutes?

4. 30 seconds is what part of an hour?

5. What part of an hour is 54 minutes?

SET 2

1. 45 seconds is what part of a minute?

2. What part of a minute is 18 seconds?

3. What part of a minute is 5 seconds?

4. 31 seconds is what part of a minute?

5. What part of a minute is 24 seconds?

RELATED PROBLEMS

1. Is 6 o'clock in the evening A.M. or P.M. time?

2. Is 4 o'clock in the morning A.M. or P.M. time?

3. Find the length of time:

(*a*) Between 2 A.M. and 6 P.M. the same day.

(*b*) Between 10:45 A.M. and 7:15 P.M. the same day.

(*c*) Between 12:26 P.M. one day and 3:10 A.M. the following day.

4. Look at your calendar. On what date this month does the second Monday fall? the fourth Thursday? the third Saturday?

5. How many days are in the month of May? October? April? November? January? June? August? December?

6. Find the exact number of days from:

(*a*) March 15 to May 15   (*b*) April 3 to October 16   (*c*) July 16 to December 9   (*d*) June 12 of one year to January 8, the following year.

7. How old will Marilyn be on her next birthday if she was born on September 26, 1945?

8. How far can an airplane fly in 4 hr. 48 min. if its average ground speed is 360 m.p.h.?

9. The sun is approximately 93,000,000 miles from the earth. If light travels at a speed of 186,000 miles per second, how many minutes does it take sunlight to reach the earth?

10. Find the number of miles in a light year (the distance that light travels in one year). Use 186,000 miles per second as the speed of light and one year equal to $365\frac{1}{4}$ days.

PRACTICAL APPLICATIONS

Budget—Income

1. Tom's father works 40 hours each week at the rate of $2.75 per hour. How much does he earn each week?

2. If a person works 40 hours per week, what is his weekly salary at each of the following hourly rates:

(*a*) $3.25   (*b*) $1.60   (*c*) $2.95   (*d*) $3.40

3. Find the weekly earnings of a person who works:

(*a*) 28 hours at $1.70 per hour   (*b*) 35 hours at $2.30 per hour
(*c*) 31 hours at $3.05 per hour   (*d*) 39 hours at $1.95 per hour

4. If a person is paid the overtime rate of $1\frac{1}{2}$ times the regular rate for all working time over 40 hours per week, find the weekly earnings of a person who works:

(*a*) 44 hours at $1.80 per hour   (*b*) 41 hours at $2.50 per hour
(*c*) 47 hours at $2.65 per hour   (*d*) $42\frac{1}{2}$ hours at $3.20 per hour

5. Find the annual salary of a person earning:

(*a*) $85 per week   (*b*) $427.50 per month   (*c*) $195.75 semi-monthly   (*d*) $2.25 per hour, 40-hour week.

6. What is your monthly salary and weekly salary if your annual salary is:

(*a*) $4,680?   (*b*) $6,900?   (*c*) $3,750?   (*d*) $5,700?

7. Which is a better wage:

(a) $90 per week or $375 per month?

(b) $5,400 per year or $480 per month?

(c) $3,850 per year or $72.50 per week?

(d) $510 per month or $120 per week?

8. Persons who have a gross income of $600 or more must file an income tax return. What is this minimum per month? per week?

9. Find the total amount of taxes withheld for a year if a person's tax deduction is: (a) $8.10 weekly (b) $26.40 semi-monthly (c) $42.80 monthly.

10. Joan's brother receives $60 per week and 5% commission on sales. If his sales for the year amounted to $23,800, what were his total earnings for the year?

Budget—Expenses

1. Barbara's father plans to spend 28% of his income for food. If he earns $5,800 per year, how much does he plan to spend for food each week?

2. Ted's sister expects to save 15% of her income. How much will she save per year if she earns $60 per week?

3. What is your rent for a year if your monthly rent is:

(a) $60   (b) $105   (c) $92.50   (d) $87.50

4. If a person should not spend more than 25% of his income for the rent of a house, what is the highest monthly rent he can afford to pay if he earns:

(a) $4,500 per year   (b) $6,900 per year
(c) $500 per month   (d) $96 per week

5. If a person should not buy a house costing more than $2\frac{1}{2}$ times his annual income, what is the highest price he can afford to pay if he earns:

(a) $5,300 per year   (b) $6,100 per year
(c) $580 per month   (d) $82.50 per week

6. What are the costs per month of owning a house if the property taxes are $241.80 per year, interest on the mortgage is $125 semi-annually, insurance costs $105 for 5 years, and repairs average $140 per year?

7. A mortgage of $7,000 is to be paid off in 25 years. How much must be paid every 6 months if the mortgage is to be repaid in equal semi-annual payments?

8. If 1,675 gallons of fuel oil costing 12¢ per gallon are consumed during the year for household heating and hot water, what is the average cost per month?

9. What is the total telephone expense for the year if the monthly charges are $6.48?

10. If the monthly charges for electricity used from January to December were $7.10, $6.84, $6.93, $6.25, $5.96, $6.10, $5.80, $5.92, $6.18, $6.75, $7.04, $7.29 respectively, what was the cost per year? What was the average cost per month?

11. Walter's brother arranged to pay off the balance of $864 due on his car in monthly installments over a 2-year period. If a 10% carrying charge is added, what is the amount of each payment?

12. How much did it cost Sally's father to maintain his car for a year if his expenses were: gasoline, 594 gal. at 28¢ per gal.; oil, 51 qt. at 45¢ per qt.; garage rent, $10 per mo.; automobile insurance, $63.50 per yr.; license fees, $11 per yr.; depreciation, $500 per yr.; miscellaneous repairs and supplies, $65? What did the costs average per month? per week?

Simple Interest

Interest is money paid for the use of money. The money borrowed or invested, and on which interest is paid, is called principal. Interest paid on the principal only is called simple interest. The interest charged is generally expressed as a per cent of the principal. This per cent is called the rate of interest. The rate of interest is usually understood as the rate per year unless specified otherwise. The sum of the principal and the interest is called the amount.

(a) To *find the interest*, multiply the principal by the rate of interest per year by the time expressed in years.

Formula: $i = prt$

When using the formula, first write the formula, then substitute the given quantities, and finally compute as required.

The rate may be expressed as a decimal and, when cancellation is possible, as a common fraction.

Find the interest on \$900 for 3 yr. 6 mo. at 4%, using the formula.

$p = \$900$ $i = prt$ $\dfrac{\$900}{1} \times \dfrac{\overset{2}{\cancel{4}}}{\cancel{100}} \times \dfrac{7}{\cancel{2}} = \$126$

$r = 4\% = \tfrac{4}{100}$ $i = \$900 \times \tfrac{4}{100} \times 3\tfrac{1}{2}$

$t = 3\tfrac{1}{2}$ yr. $i = \$126$

$i = ?$

Answer: \$126

(*b*) To *find the amount,* add the interest to the principal.

Find the interest and amount due on \$625 borrowed for 7 yr. at 5%.

\$625 principal	\$625.00 principal
× .05 rate	218.75 interest
\$31.25 interest for 1 year	\$843.75 amount
× 7	
\$218.75 interest for 7 years	

Answer: \$218.75 interest; \$843.75 amount

(*c*) Sixty-day or 6% method: To *find the interest for 60 days at 6%,* write the same figures as in the principal but move the decimal point two places to the left.

Find the interest on \$582 for 60 days at 6%.
Answer: \$5.82

(*d*) To *find the annual rate of interest,* find what per cent the interest for one year is of the principal.

What is the annual rate of interest if the annual interest on a principal of \$250 is \$10?

$$\dfrac{\$10}{\$250} = \$10 \div \$250 = \$250\overline{)\$10.00}\ \ \overset{.04\ =\ 4\%}{}$$

Answer: 4%

(*e*) To *find the principal* when the rate and amount are known, divide the interest by the rate.

1. Find the interest for 1 year on: (*a*) $200 at 6% (*b*) $750 at 2% (*c*) $1,000 at 5½% (*d*) $1,800 at 4½%.

2. Find the interest on: (*a*) $600 for 2 yr. at 3% (*b*) $1,450 for 7 yr. at 5% (*c*) $848 for 3 yr. at 3¼% (*d*) $2,000 for 6 yr. at 2½%.

3. Find the interest on: (*a*) $380 for 3½ yr. at 4% (*b*) $500 for ¾ yr. at 6% (*c*) $1,600 for 2¼ yr. at 4½% (*d*) $1,425 for 1⅔ yr. at 1%.

4. Find the interest on: (*a*) $700 for 3 mo. at 1% (*b*) $4,800 for 11 mo. at 4% (*c*) $400 for 8 mo. at 2½% (*d*) $6,000 for 1 mo. at 3¾%.

5. Find the interest on: (*a*) $50 for 1 yr. 6 mo. at 5% (*b*) $175 for 6 yr. 2 mo. at 3% (*c*) $3,000 for 4 yr. 1 mo. at 3½% (*d*) $2,700 for 2 yr. 10 mo. at 2%.

6. Find the semi-annual (6 mo.) interest on: (*a*) $400 at 5% (*b*) $1,250 at 2% (*c*) $3,500 at 4½% (*d*) $2,100 at 2¼%.

7. Find the quarterly (3 mo.) interest on: (*a*) $900 at 4% (*b*) $1,000 at 6% (*c*) $8,000 at 1¾% (*d*) $1,600 at 5½%.

8. Using 1 year = 360 days and 1 month = 30 days, find the interest on:

(*a*) $800 for 30 da. at 6% (*b*) $675 for 90 da. at 4% (*c*) $2,400 for 60 da. at 5% (*d*) $4,000 for 120 da. at 2% (*e*) $120 for 15 da. at 3% (*f*) $1,000 for 45 da. at 6% (*g*) $500 for 72 da. at 2% (*h*) $800 for 105 da. at 1% (*i*) $600 for 1 mo. 18 da. at 4% (*j*) $960 for 4 mo. 15 da. at 3% (*k*) $1,290 for 2 mo. 24 da. at 1% (*l*) $1,500 for 3 mo. 10 da. at 4½%.

9. Find the exact interest (1 year = 365 days) on:

(*a*) $425 for 73 da. at 4% (*b*) $2,920 for 15 da. at 2% (*c*) $1,000 for 146 da. at 6% (*d*) $2,400 for 30 da. at 3% (*e*) $240 for 6 da. at 5% (*f*) $1,500 for 21 da. at 3% (*g*) $750 for 34 da. at 4% (*h*) $5,000 for 11 da. at 6%.

10. Use the 60-day, 6% method to find the interest on:

(*a*) $4,500 for 60 days at 6% (*b*) $19,375 for 60 days at 6% (*c*) $840 for 30 days at 6% (*d*) $2,000 for 30 days at 3%

11. Find the interest and amount on the following loans:

(*a*) $300 for 1 yr. at 5% (*b*) $1,900 for 4 yr. at 3% (*c*) $18.75 for 10 yr. at 4% (*d*) $8,000 for 6 yr. at 5½% (*e*) $4,500 for 9 mo. at 2% (*f*) $540 for 3 yr. 5 mo. at 4% (*g*) $2,700 for 9 yr. 2 mo. at 2½% (*h*) $12,000 for 1 yr. 11 mo. at 6%.

12. Mr. Thompson bought a house for $14,400. He paid 33⅓% down. If he gave a mortgage bearing 5½% interest for the remainder, how much interest should he pay semi-annually?

13. Find the exact interest Mr. Reynolds owes if he borrowed $730 on his life insurance policy at 6% from September 8 to October 13.

14. Mr. Becker owns a $1,000 bond bearing 3¾% interest. How much interest does he receive every 6 months?

15. What is the amount due on $420 borrowed at 5% and repaid at the end of 2 yr. 8 mo?

16. What is the annual rate of interest if the principal is $3,600 and the annual interest is $108?

17. Find the annual rates of interest when the interest for

(*a*) 1 yr. on $150 is $6   (*b*) 3 yr. on $2,000 is $240
(*c*) 6 yr. on $5,000 is $900   (*d*) 4 yr. on $1,600 is $288

18. Mr. Larson receives $160 interest each year on an investment of $4,000. He also receives $180 semi-annual interest on an investment of $9,000. On which investment does he receive a higher rate of interest?

19. What is the principal if the annual interest is $70 when the annual rate of interest is 5%?

20. What sum, invested at 4%, will earn $6,000 per year?

Compound Interest

Interest paid both on the principal and the previously earned interest is called compound interest.

To *find how much a given principal will amount to* compounded at a given rate for a certain period of time by use of the table:

(*a*) Select from the table how much $1 will amount to based on the given rate and given number of years when the interest is compounded annually; and on half the given rate and twice as many periods as the given number of years when the interest is compounded semi-annually.

(*b*) Multiply this amount by the given principal.

To *find compound interest*, subtract principal from amount.

Find the amount and interest earned on $800 at the end of 6 years invested at 4% compounded annually.

1.2653	$1,012.24
$800	800.00
$1,012.2400 amount	$212.24 interest

Answer: $1,012.24, amount; $212.24, interest

Compound Interest Table

Showing How Much $1 Will Amount to at Various Rates

YEARS OR PERIODS	1%	1½%	2%	3%	4%	5%	6%
1	1.0100	1.0150	1.0200	1.0300	1.0400	1.0500	1.0600
2	1.0201	1.0302	1.0404	1.0609	1.0816	1.1025	1.1236
3	1.0303	1.0457	1.0612	1.0927	1.1249	1.1576	1.1910
4	1.0406	1.0614	1.0824	1.1255	1.1699	1.2155	1.2625
5	1.0510	1.0773	1.1041	1.1593	1.2167	1.2763	1.3382
6	1.0615	1.0934	1.1262	1.1941	1.2653	1.3401	1.4185
7	1.0721	1.1098	1.1487	1.2299	1.3159	1.4071	1.5036
8	1.0829	1.1265	1.1717	1.2668	1.3686	1.4775	1.5939
9	1.0937	1.1434	1.1951	1.3048	1.4233	1.5513	1.6895
10	1.1046	1.1605	1.2190	1.3439	1.4802	1.6289	1.7909
15	1.1610	1.2502	1.3459	1.5580	1.8009	2.0789	2.3966
20	1.2202	1.3469	1.4859	1.8061	2.1911	2.6533	3.2071
25	1.2824	1.4509	1.6406	2.0938	2.6658	3.3864	4.2919

Use the compound interest table in the following examples:

1. Find the amount and interest earned when the interest is:

(*a*) Compounded annually: (*b*) Compounded semi-annually:

Principal	$500	$1,200	$3,250
Time	4 yr.	25 yr.	15 yr.
Rate	3%	6%	5%

Principal	$800	$2,000	$1,650
Time	3 yr.	5 yr.	10 yr.
Rate	4%	3%	6%

2. How much more interest does $1,500 bring when invested for 10 yr. at 4% compounded annually than when invested at 4% simple interest?

24-Hour Clock

To *tell time on a 24-hour clock* a number containing four figures is used. The first two figures indicate the hour and the last two indicate the minutes. 1 P.M. is thought of as the 13th hour, 2 P.M. as the 14th hour, etc. Thus, to express the time from 1 P.M. to 12 midnight, 1200 is added to the given figures. When expressing the time from midnight to 1 A.M. the number 12, representing the hour, is replaced by two zeros. One minute past midnight is indicated as 0001.

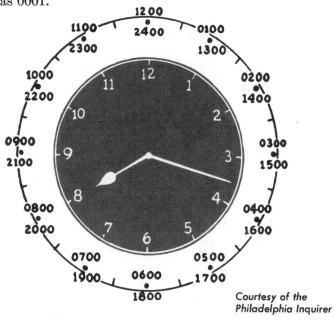

Courtesy of the
Philadelphia Inquirer

1. 6:42 A.M. is represented by 0642.	*5.* 0500 indicates 5:00 A.M.
2. 7:13 P.M. is represented by 1913.	*6.* 1425 indicates 2:25 P.M.
3. 3:00 P.M. is represented by 1500.	*7.* 1018 indicates 10:18 A.M.
4. 12:57 A.M. is represented by 0057.	*8.* 2131 indicates 9:31 P.M.

Using the 24-hour system, express the following:

SET 1	SET 2	SET 3	SET 4
1. 11:26 A.M.	**1.** 9:45 A.M.	**1.** 6:00 A.M.	**1.** 7:00 P.M.
2. 10:30 A.M.	**2.** 2:38 A.M.	**2.** 2:00 A.M.	**2.** 4:00 P.M.
3. 11:47 A.M.	**3.** 5:04 A.M.	**3.** 3:00 A.M.	**3.** 1:00 P.M.
4. 10:09 A.M.	**4.** 4:57 A.M.	**4.** 8:00 A.M.	**4.** 10:00 P.M.
5. 10:53 A.M.	**5.** 1:26 A.M.	**5.** 11:00 A.M.	**5.** 8:00 P.M.

Set 5	Set 6	Set 7	Set 8
1. 3:29 P.M.	1. 10:37 P.M.	1. 12:18 A.M.	1. 12:23 P.M.
2. 7:36 P.M.	2. 11:21 P.M.	2. 12:05 A.M.	2. 12:44 P.M.
3. 9:14 P.M.	3. 10:48 P.M.	3. 12:39 A.M.	3. 12:08 P.M.
4. 2:59 P.M.	4. 11:02 P.M.	4. 12:54 A.M.	4. 12:15 P.M.
5. 9:42 P.M.	5. 10:50 P.M.	5. 12:10 A.M.	5. 12:37 P.M.

Express the following in A.M. and P.M. time:

Set 9	Set 10	Set 11	Set 12
1. 0648	1. 1023	1. 0200	1. 1300
2. 0126	2. 1152	2. 0900	2. 1800
3. 0905	3. 1134	3. 0400	3. 2100
4. 0439	4. 1040	4. 0700	4. 1600
5. 0810	5. 1007	5. 1000	5. 2300

Set 13	Set 14	Set 15	Set 16
1. 1452	1. 2342	1. 0025	1. 1205
2. 1715	2. 2230	2. 0040	2. 1233
3. 1641	3. 2319	3. 0007	3. 1258
4. 2108	4. 2351	4. 0032	4. 1210
5. 1820	5. 2206	5. 0015	5. 1229

Find the difference in time between:

Set 17	Set 18
1. 0415 and 0842	1. 0153 and 0300
2. 0031 and 1058	2. 0641 and 1135
3. 0500 and 1625	3. 1028 and 1902
4. 1307 and 2219	4. 0919 and 2115
5. 0922 and 2050	5. 0058 and 2347

PRACTICAL APPLICATIONS

1. An airplane took off at 0652 and landed at its destination at 1720 the same day. How long did it take the airplane to reach its destination?

2. A train is scheduled to leave at 1836 and arrive at a town, 69 miles away, at 2019. Find the scheduled running time of the train between the two towns.

3. A ship left port at 0503 and arrived at its port of destination at 1310 the next day. Find the time it took the ship to steam from one port to the other.

4. How long was a sentry on guard duty if he reported at 1825 and was relieved at 2255 the same day?

5. The Japanese articles of surrender were signed on September 2, 1945, at 0904 and accepted at 0908. Express in A.M. time.

REVIEW OF EXERCISE

1. How many days are in 6 weeks?

2. What part of a year is 2 months?

3. Change 2 minutes 18 seconds to seconds.

4. What part of an hour is 56 minutes?

5. Which is a better wage: $87.50 per week or $350 per month?

6. What is your rent for a year if your monthly rent is $97.50?

7. What is the amount due on $1,250 borrowed at 4% interest and repaid at the end of 5 years 6 months?

8. What is the difference in the interest when $1,000 is compounded at 6% for 5 years semi-annually instead of annually?

9. How long did it take a ship to reach its destination if it left port at 0148 and arrived at its destination at 2302 the same day?

10. Carol's father borrowed $2,500. At the end of 6 months he paid $68.75 interest. At what rate did he borrow the money?

REFRESH YOUR SKILLS

1. Add:

39,215
4,527
856
28,514
7,228

2. Subtract:

438,501
296,940

3. Multiply:

847
563

4. Divide:

$2,240\overline{)461,440}$

5. Add:

$8\frac{3}{4}$
$1\frac{11}{12}$
$2\frac{5}{6}$

6. Subtract:

$10\frac{1}{2}$
$3\frac{7}{8}$

7. Multiply:

$4\frac{1}{6} \times 2\frac{7}{10}$

8. Divide:

$1\frac{7}{8} \div \frac{15}{16}$

9. Add:

$1.6 + .04$

10. Subtract:

$.982 - .9$

11. Multiply:

$6.50
.86$

12. Divide:

$.04\overline{).3}$

13. Find 6% of 18.

14. 6 is what per cent of 18?

15. 18 is 6% of what number?

RELATIONSHIP OF VOLUME, CAPACITY, AND WEIGHT UNITS OF MEASURE

I. Aim: To change units measuring volume to units of liquid, dry, and weight measures and vice versa.

II. Procedure

1. Find the equivalent relating the two units of measure, that is, the number of units of the one contained in one unit of the other. Then perform the necessary arithmetical operations. See Method 1.

2. Or multiply the given measure by a fraction equal to one, the numerator and denominator of which are the two members of the required equivalent arranged so that the given unit of measure may be canceled. See Method 2.

The following specific directions may be used:

To find:

(*a*) The capacity in gallons equal to a given volume in cubic inches, divide the number of cubic inches by 231.

(*b*) The volume in cubic inches equal to a given capacity in gallons, multiply the number of gallons by 231.

(*c*) The capacity in gallons equal to a given volume in cubic feet, multiply the number of cubic feet by $7\frac{1}{2}$ (7.5).

(*d*) The volume in cubic feet equal to a given capacity in gallons, divide the number of gallons by $7\frac{1}{2}$ (7.5).

(*e*) The weight in pounds of a given volume of water in cubic feet, multiply the number of cubic feet by 64 if sea water or by $62\frac{1}{2}$ (62.5) if fresh water.

(*f*) The volume of water in cubic feet weighing a given number of pounds, divide the number of pounds by 64 if sea water or by $62\frac{1}{2}$ (62.5) if fresh water.

(*g*) The capacity in bushels equal to a given volume in cubic feet, divide the number of cubic feet by $1\frac{1}{4}$ (1.25).

(*h*) The volume in cubic feet equal to a given capacity in bushels, multiply the number of bushels by $1\frac{1}{4}$ (1.25).

III. Sample Solutions

1. Find the capacity in gallons equal to a volume of 1,155 cu. in.

Method 1   Method 2

$$231\overline{)1,155}^{\;5}$$
$$\underline{1\ 155}$$

$$1,155 \ \cancel{\text{cu. in.}} \times \frac{1\ \text{gal.}}{231\ \cancel{\text{cu. in.}}} = 5\ \text{gal.}$$

Answer: 5 gal.

2. Find the weight of 38 cu. ft. of sea water.

Method 1   Method 2

$$\begin{array}{r} 38 \\ \times\ 64 \\ \hline 152 \\ 228 \\ \hline 2432 \end{array}$$

$$38 \ \cancel{\text{cu. ft.}} \times \frac{64\ \text{lb.}}{1\ \cancel{\text{cu. ft.}}} = 2432\ \text{lb.}$$

Answer: 2,432 lb.

EQUIVALENTS—CONVERSIONS OF VOLUME, CAPACITY, AND MASS UNITS

1 gallon (gal.)	= 231 cubic inches (cu. in.)
1 cubic foot (cu. ft.)	= $7\frac{1}{2}$ (7.5) gallons (gal.)
1 bushel (bu.)	= $1\frac{1}{4}$ (1.25) cubic feet (cu. ft.)
	= 2,150.42 cubic inches (cu. in.)

1 cubic foot (cu. ft.) of fresh water = $62\frac{1}{2}$ (62.5) pounds (lb.)
1 cubic foot (cu. ft.) of sea water = 64 pounds (lb.)

DIAGNOSTIC TEST

1. Find the capacity in gallons equal to a volume of 1,617 cu. in.

2. Find the volume in cubic inches equal to a capacity of 6 gal.

3. Find the capacity in gallons equal to a volume of 35 cu. ft.

4. Find the volume in cubic feet equal to a capacity of 90 gal.

5. What is the weight in pounds of 30 cu. ft. of sea water?

6. What volume in cubic feet do 4,480 lb. of sea water occupy?

7. What is the weight in pounds of 27 cu. ft. of fresh water?

8. What volume in cubic feet do 500 lb. of fresh water occupy?

9. Find the capacity in bushels equal to a volume of 15 cu. ft.

10. Find the volume in cubic feet equal to a capacity of 40 bu.

RELATED PRACTICE EXAMPLES

Find the capacity in gallons equal to the following volumes:

Set 1(a)	Set 1(b)
1. 693 cu. in.	1. 154 cu. in.
2. 1,848 cu. in.	2. 539 cu. in.
3. 2,310 cu. in.	3. 121 cu. in.
4. 3,234 cu. in.	4. 1,260 cu. in.
5. 5,775 cu. in.	5. 2,000 cu. in.

Find the volume in cubic inches equal to the following capacities:

Set 2(a)	Set 2(b)
1. 2 gal.	1. $1\frac{1}{2}$ gal.
2. 9 gal.	2. $8\frac{1}{4}$ gal.
3. 4 gal.	3. 3.5 gal.
4. 13 gal.	4. 0.25 gal.
5. 20 gal.	5. $5\frac{3}{4}$ gal.

Find the capacity in gallons equal to the following volumes:

Set 3(a)	Set 3(b)
1. 3 cu. ft.	1. $\frac{3}{4}$ cu. ft.
2. 8 cu. ft.	2. $6\frac{1}{4}$ cu. ft.
3. 28 cu. ft.	3. 4.9 cu. ft.
4. 52 cu. ft.	4. 8.75 cu. ft.
5. 100 cu. ft.	5. $14\frac{2}{3}$ cu. ft.

Find the volume in cubic feet equal to the following capacities:

Set 4(a)	Set 4(b)
1. 30 gal.	1. 100 gal.
2. 105 gal.	2. 275 gal.
3. 195 gal.	3. 51 gal.
4. 240 gal.	4. 61.5 gal.
5. 435 gal.	5. $22\frac{1}{2}$ gal.

Find the weight of sea water in pounds if the volume it occupies is:

Set 5(a)	Set 5(b)
1. 8 cu. ft.	1. $2\frac{1}{4}$ cu. ft.
2. 27 cu. ft.	2. $28\frac{1}{2}$ cu. ft.
3. 50 cu. ft.	3. 16.25 cu. ft.
4. 120 cu. ft.	4. 37.5 cu. ft.
5. 374 cu. ft.	5. $7\frac{3}{4}$ cu. ft.

Find the volume of sea water in cubic feet if its weight is:

SET 6(a)	SET 6(b)
1. 384 lb.	1. 80 lb.
2. 832 lb.	2. 328 lb.
3. 2,560 lb.	3. 824 lb.
4. 4,800 lb.	4. 1,000 lb.
5. 8,320 lb.	5. 2,400 lb.

Find the weight of fresh water in pounds if the volume it occupies is:

SET 7(a)	SET 7(b)
1. 3 cu. ft.	1. $\frac{1}{2}$ cu. ft.
2. 18 cu. ft.	2. $9\frac{3}{4}$ cu. ft.
3. 64 cu. ft.	3. 4.25 cu. ft.
4. 100 cu. ft.	4. 35.125 cu. ft.
5. 225 cu. ft.	5. $87\frac{1}{4}$ cu. ft.

Find the volume of fresh water in cubic feet if its weight is:

SET 8(a)	SET 8(b)
1. 250 lb.	1. 75 lb.
2. 625 lb.	2. 800 lb.
3. 1,000 lb.	3. 312.5 lb.
4. 4,750 lb.	4. 406.25 lb.
5. 6,000 lb.	5. 2,240 lb.

Find the capacity in bushels equal to a volume of:

SET 9(a)	SET 9(b)
1. 25 cu. ft.	1. 12 cu. ft.
2. 10 cu. ft.	2. 78 cu. ft.
3. 55 cu. ft.	3. 11.25 cu. ft.
4. 80 cu. ft.	4. 32.5 cu. ft.
5. 100 cu. ft.	5. $9\frac{3}{4}$ cu. ft.

Find the volume in cubic feet equal to the following capacities:

SET 10(a)	SET 10(b)
1. 4 bu.	1. $27\frac{1}{2}$ bu.
2. 7 bu.	2. $8\frac{3}{4}$ bu.
3. 10 bu.	3. 5.4 bu.
4. 92 bu.	4. 21.75 bu.
5. 145 bu.	5. $14\frac{5}{8}$ bu.

PRACTICAL APPLICATIONS

1. How many gallons of oil can a tank hold if its volume is $36\frac{2}{3}$ cu. ft.?

2. A hold of a certain freighter has a volume of 75,000 cu. ft. How many bushels of wheat can it hold?

3. How many tons of coal can a bin hold if its volume is 405 cu. ft.? (1 ton of coal occupies a volume of 35 cu. ft.)

4. A tanker has a capacity of 1,500,000 gallons. Find its capacity in cubic feet.

5. What is the volume in cubic inches of a 5-gallon can?

6. How many cu. ft. of water does a pump deliver per minute if it delivers $\frac{7}{8}$ cu. ft. of water every stroke and makes 48 strokes per minute? How many gallons does it deliver per minute?

7. A submarine displaces 1,400 tons (1 T. = 2,240 lb.) of water when submerged. How many cu. ft. of sea water does it displace?

8. The normal flow of water over Niagara Falls is 500,000 tons (1 ton = 2,000 lb.) of fresh water a minute. Find its rate of flow in gallons per minute.

9. Find the weight of a column of sea water 1 foot square and 100 feet deep.

10. How many bushels will a storage bin hold if it is 15 ft. long, 7 ft. wide, and 6 ft. deep?

11. A swimming pool 100 ft. long and 25 ft. wide is filled to an average depth of 6 ft. How many gallons of water does it contain? At the rate of 250 gallons per minute, how long will it take to fill the pool? What is the weight of the water?

12. How many gallons of ice cream can a cylindrical container hold if it measures $10\frac{1}{2}$ in. in diameter and 16 in. deep?

13. What is the capacity of a water storage tank in gallons if its diameter is 28 in. and its length is 6 ft.?

14. How many bushels will a silo hold if it has an inside diameter of 20 ft. and a height of 35 ft.?

15. A rectangular wading pool is 66 in. long, 54 in. wide, and 12 in. deep. A circular wading pool has a diameter of 72 in. and is 10 in. deep. Which pool holds more water? How many more gallons of water? Which pool has the greater wading area? How many sq. ft. greater?

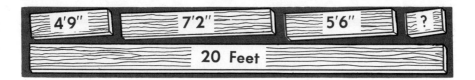

COMPOUND NUMBERS OF TWO OR MORE DENOMI–NATIONS—FUNDAMENTAL OPERATIONS

I. Aim: To add, subtract, multiply, and divide compound numbers of two or more denominations.

II. Procedure

1. In the addition of compound numbers, arrange the units in proper columns, then add each column. If possible, simplify the sum. See sample solutions 1 and 2.

2. In the subtraction of compound numbers, arrange the units in proper columns, then subtract each column, starting from the right. Regrouping may be necessary. See sample solutions 3 and 4.

3. In the multiplication of compound numbers, multiply each unit of the compound number by the multiplier. If possible, simplify the product. See sample solutions 5 and 6.

4. In the division of compound numbers, divide each unit by the divisor. If a unit is not exactly divisible, convert the remainder to the next smaller unit and combine with the given number of smaller units to form the next partial dividend. See sample solutions 7 and 8.

III. Sample Solutions

1. Add 5 ft. 3 in., 2 ft. 1 in., and 4 ft. 5 in.

> 5 ft. 3 in.
> 2 ft. 1 in.
> 4 ft. 5 in.
> 11 ft. 9 in.

Answer: 11 ft. 9 in.

2. Find the sum of 2 hr. 18 min. 41 sec., 5 hr. 36 min. 15 sec., and 1 hr. 8 min. 24 sec.

> 2 hr. 18 min. 41 sec.
> 5 hr. 36 min. 15 sec.
> 1 hr. 8 min. 24 sec.
> 8 hr. 62 min. 80 sec.
> = 8 hr. 63 min. 20 sec.
> = 9 hr. 3 min. 20 sec.

Answer: 9 hr. 3 min. 20 sec.

3. From 7 gal. 2 qt. take 2 gal. 1 qt.

$$\begin{array}{r} 7 \text{ gal. } 2 \text{ qt.} \\ \underline{2 \text{ gal. } 1 \text{ qt.}} \\ 5 \text{ gal. } 1 \text{ qt.} \end{array}$$

Answer: 5 gal. 1 qt.

4. Subtract 1 hr. 23 min. 49 sec. from 3 hr. 18 min.

3 hr. 18 min.   = 3 hr. 17 min. 60 sec. = 2 hr. 77 min. 60 sec.
<u>1 hr. 23 min. 49 sec. = 1 hr. 23 min. 49 sec. = 1 hr. 23 min. 49 sec.</u>
                                           1 hr. 54 min. 11 sec.

Answer: 1 hr. 54 min. 11 sec.

5. Multiply 2 lb. 3 oz. by 4.

$$\begin{array}{r} 2 \text{ lb. } 3 \text{ oz.} \\ \underline{4} \\ 8 \text{ lb. } 12 \text{ oz.} \end{array}$$

Answer: 8 lb. 12 oz.

6. Multiply 3 ft. 8 in. by 7.

$$\begin{array}{r} 3 \text{ ft. } 8 \text{ in.} \\ \underline{7} \\ 21 \text{ ft. } 56 \text{ in.} \end{array}$$
$$= 25 \text{ ft. } 8 \text{ in.}$$

Answer: 25 ft. 8 in.

7. Divide 15 pk. 6 qt. by 3.

$$\begin{array}{r} 5 \text{ pk. } 2 \text{ qt.} \\ \hline 3)15 \text{ pk. } 6 \text{ qt.} \end{array}$$

Answer: 5 pk. 2 qt.

8. Divide 13 ft. 4 in. by 5.

$$\begin{array}{r} 2 \text{ ft. } 8 \text{ in.} \\ \hline 5)13 \text{ ft. } 4 \text{ in.} \\ \underline{10 \text{ ft.}} \\ 3 \text{ ft. } 4 \text{ in. } = 40 \text{ in.} \\ \underline{40 \text{ in.}} \end{array}$$

Answer: 2 ft. 8 in.

PRELIMINARY EXAMPLES

Simplify:

SET 1

1. 4 ft. 28 in. =
2. 7 gal. 9 qt. =
3. 2 bu. 6 pk. =
4. 5 lb. 18 oz. =
5. 3 hr. 80 min. =

SET 2

1. 3 yd. 7 ft. 15 in. =
2. 5 qt. 9 pt. 20 oz. =
3. 8 bu. 10 pk. 12 qt. =
4. 2 T. 3,500 lb. =
5. 11 hr. 59 min. 150 sec. =

Finding the missing numbers:

SET 3

1. 6 ft. = 5 ft. —— in.
2. 3 pt. = 2 pt. —— oz.
3. 8 bu. = 7 bu. —— pk.

4. 4 lb. = 3 lb. —— oz.
5. 32 min. = 31 min. —— sec.

SET 4

1. 5 yd. = 4 yd. —— ft. 12 in.

2. 6 gal. 2 qt. = 5 gal. —— qt. 2 pt.

3. 2 bu. 3 pk. 5 qt. = 1 bu. —— pk. 13 qt.

4. 3 T. 500 lb. = 2 T. —— lb.

5. 4 hr. 18 min. 25 sec. = 3 hr. 77 min. —— sec.

DIAGNOSTIC TEST A

Add and simplify:

Measure of Length

1. 2 ft. 4 in.	**2.** 5 ft. 8 in.	**3.** 4 yd. 2 ft. 5 in.
1 ft. 2 in.	3 ft. 7 in.	2 yd. 1 ft. 6 in.
5 ft. 3 in.		5 yd. 2 ft. 11 in.

Capacity — Liquid Measure

4. 3 pt. 5 oz.	**5.** 1 gal. 3 qt.
2 pt. 9 oz.	3 gal. 2 qt.
6 pt.	5 gal. 3 qt.

Capacity — Dry Measure

6. 4 bu. 1 pk.	**7.** 3 pk. 5 qt.
1 bu. 2 pk.	2 pk. 2 qt.
	1 pk. 7 qt.

Mass — Measure of Weight

8. 5 lb. 3 oz.	**9.** 4 T. 250 lb.
4 lb. 7 oz.	2 T. 1,000 lb.
8 lb. 4 oz.	3 T. 1,500 lb.
	1 T. 1,750 lb.

Measure of Time

10. 4 wk. 2 da.	**11.** 3 hr. 16 min.	**12.** 1 hr. 23 min. 14 sec.
1 wk. 1 da.	5 hr. 38 min.	7 hr. 19 min. 27 sec.
7 wk. 2 da.	4 hr. 53 min.	2 hr. 34 min. 45 sec.

RELATED PRACTICE EXAMPLES

Add and simplify:

Measure of Length

SET 1	SET 2	SET 3
1. 5 ft. 7 in.	**1.** 8 yd. 21 in.	**1.** 3 yd. 2 ft. 9 in.
9 ft. 4 in.	6 yd. 17 in.	5 yd. 1 ft. 5 in.

2. 4 mi. 500 yd.   **2.** 7 yd. 1 ft. 8 in.   **2.** 5 yd. 1 ft. 10 in.
    8 mi. 880 yd.   8 yd. 2 ft.   12 yd. 2 ft. 8 in.
    2 mi. 150 yd.   3 yd. 1 ft. 2 in.   6 yd. 1 ft. 6 in.

3. 4 rd. 1 ft. 2 in.   **3.** 6 ft. 5 in.   **3.** 8 yd. 2 ft. 9 in.
    7 rd. 5 ft.   8 ft. 11 in.   3 yd. 1 ft. 7 in.
    2 ft. 5 in.   4 ft. 7 in.   6 yd. 1 ft.
    2 rd. 4 ft. 3 in.   9 ft. 10 in.   2 ft. 11 in.

Capacity — Liquid Measure

SET 4	SET 5
1. 2 pt. 8 oz.	**1.** 1 gal. 3 qt.
9 pt. 3 oz.	6 gal. 2 qt.

2. 2 gal. 1 qt.   **2.** 2 gal. 3 qt. 1 pt.
    5 gal. 1 qt.   6 gal. 1 qt. $\frac{1}{2}$ pt.
    4 gal. 1 qt.   1 gal. 2 qt. $1\frac{1}{2}$ pt.

3. 3 gal. 3 pt.   **3.** 3 qt. 1 pt. 5 oz.
    8 gal. 1 pt.   4 qt.   10 oz.
    1 gal. 2 pt.   1 pt. 14 oz.
    5 gal.   5 qt. 1 pt. 9 oz.

Capacity — Dry Measure

SET 6	SET 7
1. 4 bu. 2 pk.	**1.** 2 pk. 4 qt.
7 bu. 1 pk.	7 pk. 6 qt.

2. 5 bu. 1 pk. 3 qt.   **2.** 3 bu. 2 pk. 5 qt.
    6 bu. 1 pk. 2 qt.   9 bu. 3 pk. 4 qt.
    2 bu. 1 pk. 1 qt.   4 bu. 1 pk. 7 qt.

3. 8 pk. 2 qt.   **3.** 2 pk. 3 qt. 1 pt.
    2 pk.   5 pk.   1 pt.
    1 pk. 3 qt.   3 pk. 2 qt.
    3 pk. 2 qt.   4 pk. 2 qt. 1 pt.

Mass — Measure of Weight

Set 8	Set 9

1. 3 lb. 6 oz.
<u>1 lb. 8 oz.</u>

1. 6 lb. 4 oz.
<u>4 lb. 12 oz.</u>

2. 7 T. 450 lb.
4 T. 300 lb.
<u>2 T. 900 lb.</u>

2. 5 T. 1,450 lb.
1,000 lb.
<u>12 T. 1,700 lb.</u>

3. 1 lb. 2 oz.
3 lb. 5 oz.
4 lb. 1 oz.
<u>2 lb.</u>

3. 3 lb. 10 oz.
1 lb. 8 oz.
6 lb. 14 oz.
<u>2 lb. 9 oz.</u>

Measure of Time

Set 10 — Set 11

1. 13 min. 29 sec.
<u>32 min. 17 sec.</u>

1. 1 wk. 5 da.
<u>7 wk. 4 da.</u>

2. 8 hr. 12 min. 9 sec.
5 hr. 33 min. 21 sec.
<u>9 hr. 8 min. 15 sec.</u>

2. 5 yr. 6 mo.
4 yr. 9 mo.
<u>9 yr. 8 mo.</u>

3. 3 da. 4 hr. 15 min.
8 da.   26 min.
12 da. 5 hr.
<u>9 da. 8 hr. 3 min.</u>

3. 2 hr. 8 min. 26 sec.
6 hr. 25 min. 18 sec.
1 hr. 10 min. 9 sec.
<u>8 hr. 14 min. 37 sec.</u>

Set 12

1. 6 hr. 39 min. 53 sec.
<u>5 hr. 24 min. 46 sec.</u>

2. 10 hr. 40 min. 32 sec.
8 hr. 27 min. 13 sec.
<u>13 hr. 34 min. 24 sec.</u>

3. 3 hr. 10 min. 5 sec.
16 hr. 27 min. 43 sec.
9 hr. 5 min. 24 sec.
<u>10 hr. 16 min. 48 sec.</u>

DIAGNOSTIC TEST B

Subtract and simplify:

Measure of Length

1. 15 ft. 9 in.   **2.** 5 yd.   **3.** 8 yd. 1 ft. 4 in.
   8 ft. 6 in.   2 yd. 7 in.   3 yd. 2 ft. 5 in.

Capacity — Liquid Measure

4. 8 gal. 3 qt.   **5.** 4 pt. 2 oz.
   4 gal. 1 qt.   2 pt. 13 oz.

Capacity — Dry Measure

6. 8 bu. 2 pk.   **7.** 9 pk. 3 qt.
   3 bu. 1 pk.   5 pk. 7 qt.

Mass — Measure of Weight

8. 9 T. 1,750 lb.   **9.** 15 lb.
   2 T. 1,400 lb.   9 lb. 4 oz.

Measure of Time

10. 6 da. 18 hr.   **11.** 9 hr. 16 min.   **12.** 21 hr. 4 min. 35 sec.
    3 da.   4 hr. 53 min.   15 hr. 32 min. 50 sec.

RELATED PRACTICE EXAMPLES

Subtract and simplify:

Measure of Length

SET 1

1. 9 ft. 11 in.   **2.** 20 mi. 1,400 yd.   **3.** 13 yd. 2 ft. 8 in.
   3 ft. 4 in.   8 mi. 925 yd.   8 yd. 1 ft.

SET 2

1. 8 yd. 13 in.   **2.** 10 ft.   **3.** 4 mi. 1,200 ft.
   2 yd. 20 in.   7 ft. 8 in.   3,700 ft.

SET 3

1. 7 yd. 1 ft. 3 in.   **2.** 3 yd. 2 in.   **3.** 9 yd.
   4 yd. 2 ft. 9 in.   2 yd. 1 ft. 11 in.   2 yd. 1 ft. 10 in.

Capacity — Liquid Measure
SET 4

1. 5 qt. 1 pt.   **2.** 9 gal. 3 qt.   **3.** 6 gal. 7 pt. 14 oz.
   2 qt. 1 pt.   6 gal. 1 qt.   2 gal. 5 pt. 9 oz.

SET 5

1. 1 pt. 8 oz.   **2.** 4 gal.   **3.** 8 gal. 2 qt. 1 pt.
      14 oz.   2 gal. 2 qt.   5 gal. 3 qt. 1 pt.

Capacity — Dry Measure
SET 6

1. 4 bu. 3 pk.   **2.** 12 pk. 7 qt.   **3.** 5 bu. 3 pk. 6 qt.
   3 bu. 1 pk.   8 pk. 2 qt.   3 bu. 1 pk. 5 qt.

SET 7

1. 7 pk. 1 qt.   **2.** 5 bu.   **3.** 10 bu. 3 pk. 1 qt.
   4 pk. 3 qt.   2 bu. 3 pk.   3 bu. 2 pk. 2 qt.

Mass — Measure of Weight
SET 8

1. 8 lb. 12 oz.   **2.** 3 l.t. 800 lb.   **3.** 10 T. 1,600 lb.
   3 lb. 8 oz.   1 l.t. 450 lb.   8 T. 1,125 lb.

SET 9

1. 5 T. 1,000 lb. **2.** 8 lb.   **3.** 6 lb. 3 oz.
   3 T. 1,450 lb.   7 lb. 11 oz.   4 lb. 9 oz.

Measure of Time
SET 10

1. 6 yr. 8 mo.   **2.** 32 min. 47 sec. **3.** 18 hr. 37 min. 50 sec.
   2 yr. 3 mo.   14 min. 21 sec.   10 hr. 9 min. 23 sec.

SET 11

1. 8 hr.   **2.** 8 wk. 3 da.   **3.** 16 hr. 20 min. 15 sec.
   6 hr. 30 min.   5 wk. 6 da.   9 hr. 48 min. 6 sec.

SET 12

1. 13 hr. 42 min. 16 sec.   **2.** 2 hr. 35 min. 10 sec.
    8 hr. 56 min. 29 sec.   1 hr. 52 min. 28 sec.

3. 10 hr.
    8 hr. 49 min. 51 sec.

DIAGNOSTIC TEST C

Multiply and simplify:

Measure of Length

1. 5 ft. 2 in.   **2.** 7 yd. 5 ft.   **3.** 4 yd. 2 ft. 9 in.
    4   8   5

Capacity — Liquid Measure

    4. 1 pt. 4 oz.   **5.** 3 gal. 2 qt.
       3   6

Capacity — Dry Measure

    6. 7 pk. 1 qt.   **7.** 8 bu. 3 pk.
       2   9

Mass — Measure of Weight

    8. 5 T. 160 lb.   **9.** 9 lb. 8 oz.
       4   10

Measure of Time

10. 2 yr. 1 mo.   **11.** 5 da. 6 hr.   **12.** 3 hr. 18 min. 25 sec.
    8   7   6

RELATED PRACTICE EXAMPLES

Multiply and simplify:

Measure of Length

SET 1

1. 2 ft. 3 in.   **2.** 5 mi. 250 ft.   **3.** 4 yd. 1 ft. 5 in.
   3   8   2

SET 2

1. 2 ft. 8 in.   **2.** 4 mi. 300 yd.   **3.** 7 yd. 2 ft. 1 in.
   4   9   3

SET 3

1. 2 yd. 1 ft. 8 in.   **2.** 4 yd. 1 ft. 11 in.   **3.** 10 yd. 2 ft. 3 in.
    2   6   8

Capacity — Liquid Measure
Set 4

1. 5 pt. 3 oz.
   4
____

2. 7 gal. 1 qt.
   3
____

3. 2 gal. 1 pt.
   5
____

Set 5

1. 5 gal. 3 qt.
   6
____

2. 6 qt. 1 pt. 2 oz.
   4
____

3. 8 gal. 3 qt. 1 pt.
   3
____

Capacity — Dry Measure
Set 6

1. 3 bu. 1 pk.
   2
____

2. 5 pk. 2 qt.
   3
____

3. 4 bu. 1 pk. 1 qt.
   3
____

Set 7

1. 2 pk. 3 qt.
   6
____

2. 5 bu. 2 pk.
   8
____

3. 3 bu. 2 pk. 4 qt.
   2
____

Mass — Measure of Weight
Set 8

1. 6 lb. 3 oz.
   5
____

2. 8 T. 150 lb.
   9
____

3. 5 T. 200 lb.
   8
____

Set 9

1. 7 l.t. 1,000 lb.
   3
____

2. 5 T. 800 lb.
   7
____

3. 3 lb. 8 oz.
   4
____

Measure of Time
Set 10

1. 6 min. 8 sec.
   7
____

2. 3 yr. 2 mo.
   4
____

3. 7 hr. 15 min. 9 sec.
   3
____

Set 11

1. 2 yr. 6 mo.
   8
____

2. 3 hr. 8 min. 20 sec.
   5
____

3. 7 wk. 4 da. 6 hr.
   3
____

Set 12

1. 4 hr. 20 min. 16 sec.
   5
____

2. 3 wk. 6 da. 13 hr.
   2
____

3. 2 hr. 18 min. 15 sec.
   4
____

DIAGNOSTIC TEST D

Divide and simplify:

Measure of Length

1. 2)4 ft. 6 in.   **2.** 5)6 mi. 100 ft.   **3.** 3)7 yd. 2 ft. 6 in.

Capacity — Liquid Measure

4. 3)9 gal. 3 qt.   **5.** 5)12 qt. 1 pt.

Capacity — Dry Measure

6. 2)8 bu. 6 pk.   **7.** 6)14 pk. 2 qt.

Mass — Measure of Weight

8. 7)21 T. 1,400 lb.   **9.** 4)9 lb. 8 oz.

Measure of Time

10. 5)10 yr. 45 da.   **11.** 3)7 hr. 12 min.

12. 9)20 hr. 45 min. 18 sec.

RELATED PRACTICE EXAMPLES

Divide and simplify:

Measure of Length

SET 1

1. 5)5 ft. 10 in.   **2.** 10)20 mi. 880 yd.   **3.** 2)6 yd. 2 ft. 8 in.

SET 2

1. 4)5 yd. 1 ft.   **2.** 2)7 mi. 350 ft.   **3.** 5)10 yd. 2 ft. 5 in.

SET 3

1. 6)8 yd. 2 ft. 6 in.   **2.** 3)5 yd. 1 ft. 9 in.   **3.** 2)11 yd. 2 ft. 3 in.

Capacity — Liquid Measure

SET 4

1. 3)6 gal. 3 qt.   **2.** 4)8 pt. 12 oz.   **3.** 2)12 gal. 2 qt. 10 oz.

SET 5

1. 2)3 gal. 2 qt.   **2.** 4)6 qt. 1 pt. 12 oz.   **3.** 3)7 gal. 3 qt. 1 pt.

Capacity — Dry Measure

SET 6

1. 3)9 bu. 3 pk.   **2.** 2)10 pk. 4 qt.   **3.** 3)12 bu. 3 pk. 6 qt.

SET 7

1. 5)8 bu. 3 pk.   **2.** 3)4 qt. 1 pt.   **3.** 6)7 bu. 1 pk. 2 qt.

Mass — Measure of Weight

SET 8

1. 5)10 lb. 15 oz.   **2.** 4)8 T. 100 lb.   **3.** 7)28 lb. 7 oz.

SET 9

1. 6)14 lb. 4 oz.   **2.** 4)5 l.t. 160 lb.   **3.** 8)10 T. 200 lb.

Measure of Time

SET 10   SET 11

1. 6)18 da. 12 hr.   **1.** 5)16 wk. 3 da.

2. 4)20 min. 36 sec.   **2.** 3)9 hr. 14 min. 48 sec.

3. 2)18 hr. 42 min. 30 sec.   **3.** 6)21 hr. 36 min. 54 sec.

SET 12

1. 2)7 hr. 13 min. 20 sec.

2. 4)14 da. 5 hr. 16 min.

3. 5)11 hr. 28 min. 42 sec.

PRACTICAL APPLICATIONS

1. In a series of hops, a plane flew for 2 hr. 18 min., 1 hr. 32 min., and 3 hr. 51 min. Find the total flying time.

2. An aircraft had 6 hr. of fuel at take-off. How many hours of fuel are left after the plane flies for 4 hr. 27 min.?

3. Find the total contents of a dozen cans if each can holds 1 qt. 14 oz.

4. A piece of metal 9 ft. $7\frac{1}{4}$ in. long must be cut into 5 equal parts. Allowing $\frac{1}{4}$ in. for waste, how long will each piece be?

5. Find the total weight of a case of 2 dozen cans of fruit salad if each can weighs 1 lb. 2 oz.

6. The length of a window frame is 5 ft. 8 in. and its width is 2 ft. 7 in. Find the total length of wood needed for the frame of a screen if an extra width must be included for a center bar.

7. The contract time schedule for building a factory was 45 weeks 5 days. If this was reduced by a fourth, how much time was saved?

8. If three pieces of wood measuring 5 ft. 6 in., 4 ft. 9 in., and 7 ft. 2 in. were cut from a 20-ft. length, what was the length of the piece remaining?

9. Find the difference in the capacity of a can containing 1 qt. 14 oz. of fruit juice and the total capacity of 2 smaller cans, each containing 1 pt. 4 oz.

10. What is the difference in the weight of a box of soap flakes weighing 3 lb. 5 oz. and the total weight of 2 smaller boxes, each weighing 1 lb. 3 oz.?

11. A Thunderstreak flew from Los Angeles to New York City in the record time of 3 hr. 44 min. 53.8 sec. A Sabre Jet holds the record from New York City to Los Angeles, 4 hr. 24 min. 26.64 sec. How much longer is the time of the westbound flight?

12. If the unimportant intermediate stops along the railway were eliminated, it would reduce by a third the usual time of 4 days 15 hours required to transport freight between two cities. How long would it then take?

13. If a man works 8 hours each day on Monday, Tuesday, and Friday; 9 hours, 30 minutes on Wednesday; 10 hours, 30 minutes on Thursday; and 4 hours and 30 minutes on Saturday, how much does he earn if he receives $2.20 per hour for the first 40 hours and $3.30 for each additional hour?

14. Would a 10-ft. length of wood be sufficient to make a small storm window measuring 2 ft. 11 in. by 2 ft. 4 in.? Prove your answer.

15. A train leaving Washington at 10:20 A.M. is scheduled to arrive in Philadelphia in 2 hours 58 minutes. After a stop-over of 15 minutes, the train is scheduled to arrive in New York City at 3:25 P.M. How long does it take the train to go from Philadelphia to New York City?

METRIC SYSTEM—MEASURE OF LENGTH, AREA, VOLUME, CAPACITY, AND WEIGHT

I. Aim: To change a given number of metric units of one denomination to units of another denomination.

II. Procedure

Use either the common method or the method of cancellation of units explained in the procedure of Exercise 44 on page 296. Since the conversion factors in the metric system of measurement are 10, 100, 1,000, etc., use short methods. (See Exercises 28 and 29.)

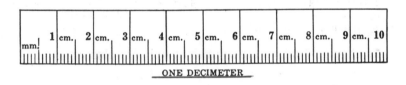

ONE DECIMETER

III. Sample Solutions

1. Change 9 cm. to millimeters.

Method 1

$10 \times 9 = 90$

Answer: 90 mm.

Method 2

$9 \text{ cm.} \times \dfrac{10 \text{ mm.}}{1 \text{ cm.}} = 90 \text{ mm.}$

2. Change 5.2 m. to centimeters.

Method 1

$100 \times 5.2 = 520$

Answer: 520 cm.

Method 2

$5.2 \text{ m.} \times \dfrac{100 \text{ cm.}}{1 \text{ m.}} = 520 \text{ cm.}$

3. Change 24 mm. to centimeters.

Method 1

$24 \div 10 = 2.4$

Answer: 2.4 cm.

Method 2

$24 \text{ mm.} \times \dfrac{1 \text{ cm.}}{10 \text{ mm.}} = 2.4 \text{ cm.}$

4. Change 7.75 liters to milliliters.

Method 1	*Method 2*

$$7.75 \times 1{,}000 = 7{,}750 \qquad 7.75 \text{ liters} \times \frac{1{,}000 \text{ ml.}}{1 \text{ liter}} = 7{,}750 \text{ ml.}$$

Answer: 7,750 ml.

5. Change 5.3 m.^{2} to cm.^{2}

Method 1

$$5.3 \times 10{,}000 = 53{,}000$$

Method 2

$$5.3 \text{ m.}^2 \times \frac{100 \text{ dm.}^2}{1 \text{ m.}^2} \times \frac{100 \text{ cm.}^2}{1 \text{ dm.}^2} = 53{,}000 \text{ cm.}^2$$

Answer: 53,000 cm.^{2}

6. Change 1,700 mm.^{3} to cm.^{3}

Method 1	*Method 2*

$$1{,}700 \div 1{,}000 = 1.7 \qquad 1{,}700 \text{ mm.}^3 \times \frac{1 \text{ cm.}^3}{1{,}000 \text{ mm.}^3} = 1.7 \text{ cm.}^3$$

Answer: 1.7 cm.^{3}

7. Change 7 ml. to an equivalent unit of volume.

$$7 \text{ ml.} = 7 \text{ cm.}^3$$

Answer: 7 cm.^{3}

8. Find the weight in kilograms of 9.2 liters of water.

9.2 liters of water weigh 9.2 kg.

Answer: 9.2 kg.

IV. Definitions

In the metric system the meter is the unit for length, the liter is the unit for capacity, and the gram is the unit for weight. To form the other metric units of measure used in length, capacity, and weight, combine the above three words with the following prefixes:

  milli- meaning one-thousandth (.001)
  centi- meaning one-hundredth (.01)
  deci- meaning one-tenth (.1)
  deka- meaning ten (10)
  hecto- meaning hundred (100)
  kilo- meaning thousand (1,000)

The metric system of measurement, then, is a decimal system with the *meter*, *liter*, and *gram* as its foundation. The measurement of 5 kilometers, 8 hecto-meters, 4 dekameters, 7 meters, 9 decimeters, 1 centimeter, and 6 millimeters can be expressed in meters as the following single number:

5847.916 meters

EQUIVALENTS

Measure of Length

TABLE 1

10 millimeters (mm.) = 1 centimeter (cm.)
10 centimeters (cm.) = 1 decimeter (dm.)
10 decimeters (dm.) = 1 meter (m.)
10 meters (m.) = 1 dekameter (dkm.)
10 dekameters (dkm.) = 1 hectometer (hm.)
10 hectometers (hm.) = 1 kilometer (km.)

TABLE 2

1 centimeter (cm.) = 10 millimeters (mm.)
1 meter (m.) = 100 centimeters (cm.)
= 1,000 millimeters (mm.)
1 kilometer (km.) = 1,000 meters (m.)

Measure of Capacity

10 milliliters (ml.) = 1 centiliter (cl.)
10 centiliters (cl.) = 1 deciliter (dl.)
10 deciliters (dl.) = 1 liter
10 liters = 1 dekaliter (dkl.)
10 dekaliters (dkl.) = 1 hectoliter (hl.)
10 hectoliters (hl.) = 1 kiloliter (kl.)

Measure of Weight

10 milligrams (mg.) = 1 centigram (cg.)
10 centigrams (cg.) = 1 decigram (dg.)
10 decigrams (dg.) = 1 gram (g.)
10 grams (g.) = 1 dekagram (dkg.)
10 dekagrams (dkg.) = 1 hectogram (hg.)
10 hectograms (hg.) = 1 kilogram (kg.)
1,000 kilograms (kg.) = 1 metric ton (t.)

Measure of Area

100 square millimeters (mm.^{2}) = 1 square centimeter (cm.^{2})*
100 square centimeters (cm.^{2}) = 1 square decimeter (dm.^{2})
100 square decimeters (dm.^{2}) = 1 square meter (m.^{2})
1,000,000 square meters (m.^{2}) = 1 square kilometer (km.^{2})

Measure of Volume

1,000 cubic millimeters (mm.^{3}) = 1 cubic centimeter (cm.^{3})†
1,000 cubic centimeters (cm.^{3}) = 1 cubic decimeter (dm.^{3})
1,000 cubic decimeters (dm.^{3}) = 1 cubic meter (m.^{3})

MISCELLANEOUS EQUIVALENTS

1 liter = 1 cubic decimeter (dm.^{3}) = 1,000 cubic centimeters (cm.^{3})
1 milliliter (ml.) = 1 cubic centimeter (cm.^{3})
1 liter of water weighs 1 kilogram (kg.)††
1 milliliter (ml.) or cubic centimeter (cm.^{3}) of water weighs 1 gram (g.)††

Measure of Length

DIAGNOSTIC TEST

Change:

1. 18 cm. to mm.	**11.** 30 mm. to cm.
2. 3.4 dm. to cm.	**12.** 56 cm. to dm.
3. 87 m. to dm.	**13.** 9 dm. to m.
4. 7 m. to cm.	**14.** 704 cm. to m.
5. 2.36 m. to mm.	**15.** 8,200 mm. to m.
6. 6 dkm. to m.	**16.** 4.9 m. to dkm.
7. 4.5 hm. to dkm.	**17.** 34 dkm. to hm.
8. 14 km. to hm.	**18.** 8 hm. to km.
9. 6.8 hm. to m.	**19.** 125 m. to hm.
10. 15 km. to m.	**20.** 4,928.5 m. to km.

---

*In the metric measure of area, the exponent ^{2} is used to represent the word "square."   †In the metric measure of volume, the exponent ^{3} is used to represent the word "cubic."   ††In science where greater accuracy is desired, this is true at 4° C.

RELATED PRACTICE EXAMPLES

Change to millimeters:	Change to centimeters:	Change to decimeters:	Change to centimeters:
Set 1	**Set 2**	**Set 3**	**Set 4**
1. 6 cm.	**1.** 8 dm.	**1.** 5 m.	**1.** 4 m.
2. 10 cm.	**2.** 15 dm.	**2.** 41 m.	**2.** 18 m.
3. 34 cm.	**3.** 50 dm.	**3.** 29 m.	**3.** 63 m.
4. 8.5 cm.	**4.** 4.2 dm.	**4.** .625 m.	**4.** .25 m.
5. .75 cm.	**5.** 9.25 dm.	**5.** 19.48 m.	**5.** 8.9 m.

Change to millimeters:	Change to meters:	Change to dekameters:	Change to hectometers:
Set 5	**Set 6**	**Set 7**	**Set 8**
1. 7 m.	**1.** 2 dkm.	**1.** 9 hm.	**1.** 3 km.
2. 20 m.	**2.** 21 dkm.	**2.** 16 hm.	**2.** 17 km.
3. .6 m.	**3.** 80 dkm.	**3.** 40 hm.	**3.** 58 km.
4. 8.33 m.	**4.** 4.8 dkm.	**4.** 3.5 hm.	**4.** .4 km.
5. 15.125 m.	**5.** 9.54 dkm.	**5.** 10.25 hm.	**5.** 9.67 km.

Change to meters:	Change to meters:	Change to centimeters:	Change to decimeters:
Set 9	**Set 10**	**Set 11**	**Set 12**
1. 8 hm.	**1.** 7 km.	**1.** 50 mm.	**1.** 20 cm.
2. 23 hm.	**2.** 60 km.	**2.** 17 mm.	**2.** 35 cm.
3. 75 hm.	**3.** 132 km.	**3.** 8 mm.	**3.** 6 cm.
4. 14.2 hm.	**4.** .25 km.	**4.** 7.9 mm.	**4.** 18.2 cm.
5. .36 hm.	**5.** 27.8 km.	**5.** 25.4 mm.	**5.** .9 cm.

Change to meters:	Change to meters:	Change to meters:	Change to dekameters:
Set 13	**Set 14**	**Set 15**	**Set 16**
1. 130 dm.	**1.** 500 cm.	**1.** 4,000 mm.	**1.** 80 m.
2. 12 dm.	**2.** 320 cm.	**2.** 2,100 mm.	**2.** 33 m.
3. 7 dm.	**3.** 1,934 cm.	**3.** 15,837 mm.	**3.** 5 m.
4. 9.5 dm.	**4.** 827.5 cm.	**4.** 348.3 mm.	**4.** 192.5 m.
5. 10.25 dm.	**5.** 43 cm.	**5.** 65 mm.	**5.** 7.1 m.

Change to hectometers:	Change to kilometers:	Change to hectometers:	Change to kilometers:
SET 17	SET 18	SET 19	SET 20
1. 190 dkm.	1. 60 hm.	1. 700 m.	1. 3,000 m.
2. 42 dkm.	2. 29 hm.	2. 540 m.	2. 1,780 m.
3. 4 dkm.	3. 7 hm.	3. 2,395 m.	3. 8,596 m.
4. 59.2 dkm.	4. 16.25 hm.	4. 152.8 m.	4. 406.2 m.
5. .8 dkm.	5. 237.5 hm.	5. 63 m.	5. 38 m.

MISCELLANEOUS EXAMPLES

Change to centimeters:

SET 1
1. 4 km.
2. 10 km.
3. .25 km.
4. 5.75 km.
5. 1.875 km.

Change to kilometers:

SET 2
1. 700,000 cm.
2. 1,500,000 cm.
3. 254,900 cm.
4. 198,326 cm.
5. 50,000 cm.

Change to millimeters:

SET 3
1. 3 km.
2. 16 km.
3. .5 km.
4. 1.25 km.
5. 2.625 km.

Change to kilometers:

SET 4
1. 8,000,000 mm.
2. 4,500,000 mm.
3. 2,946,400 mm.
4. 650,000 mm.
5. 20,000 mm.

Find the missing numbers:

SET 5
1. 4 km. 8 m. = —— m.
2. 1 m. 9 cm. = —— cm.
3. 5 cm. 2 mm. = —— mm.
4. 2 m. 3 cm. 6 mm. = —— mm.
5. 6 m. 8 dm. 5 cm. = —— cm.

SET 6
1. 3 cm. 7 mm. = —— cm.
2. 7 m. 62 cm. = —— m.
3. 8 km. 251 m. = —— km.
4. 16 cm. 8 mm. = —— cm.
5. 4 m. 9 cm. 2 mm. = —— m.

Set 7

Express each of the following measurements in meters:

1. 9 km., 4 hm., 2 dkm., 8 m., 5 dm., 7 cm., and 3 mm.
2. 17 km., 6 hm., 3 dkm., and 4 m.
3. 4 m., 8 dm., 6 cm., and 9 mm.
4. 5 dkm. and 2 dm.
5. 3 km., 7 hm., 1 dkm., 4 m., 6 dm., 9 cm., and 8 mm.

Measure of Capacity

PRACTICE EXAMPLES A

Change:

1. 4 cl. to ml.
2. 11 dl. to cl.
3. 16 liters to dl.
4. 52 liters to cl.
5. 4.7 liters to ml.
6. 23 dkl. to liters
7. 30 hl. to dkl.
8. 8.4 kl. to hl.
9. 27 hl. to liters
10. 38 kl. to liters
11. 20 ml. to cl.
12. 45 cl. to dl.
13. 9 dl. to liters
14. 700 cl. to liters
15. 6,925 ml. to liters
16. 113 liters to dkl.
17. 2.625 dkl. to hl.
18. 42 hl. to kl.
19. 340 liters to hl.
20. 93 liters to kl.

PRACTICE EXAMPLES B

Change:

1. 15 cl. to ml.
2. 6 dl. to cl.
3. .25 liter to dl.
4. 10 liters to cl.
5. 24 liters to ml.
6. 8 dkl. to liters
7. 6.9 hl. to dkl.
8. 35 kl. to hl.
9. 17.25 hl. to liters
10. 60 kl. to liters
11. 7 ml. to cl.
12. 80 cl. to dl.
13. 23.1 dl. to liters
14. 89 cl. to liters
15. 5,000 ml. to liters
16. 5 liters to dkl.
17. 64 dkl. to hl.
18. 26.7 hl. to kl.
19. 48 liters to hl.
20. 3,860 liters to kl.

Measure of Weight

PRACTICE EXAMPLES A

Change:

1. 7 cg. to mg.
2. 28 dg. to cg.
3. 10 g. to dg.
4. 65 g. to cg.
5. .875 g. to mg.
6. 3 dkg. to g.
7. 9.64 hg. to dkg.
8. 41 kg. to hg.
9. 19 hg. to g.
10. 2.2 kg. to g.
11. 5 t. to kg.

12. 50 mg. to cg.
13. 18 cg. to dg.
14. 9 dg. to g.
15. 200 cg. to g.
16. 1,283 mg. to g.
17. 67.4 g. to dkg.
18. 136 dkg. to hg.
19. 16.25 hg. to kg.
20. 4,000 g. to hg.
21. 3,800 g. to kg.
22. 15,968 kg. to t.

PRACTICE EXAMPLES B

Change:

1. 4.75 cg. to mg.
2. 35 dg. to cg.
3. 9 g. to dg.
4. 21 g. to cg.
5. 7.8 g. to mg.
6. 56 dkg. to g.
7. 40 hg. to dkg.
8. 17 kg. to hg.
9. 10.25 hg. to g.
10. 8 kg. to g.
11. 30 t. to kg.

12. 6 mg. to cg.
13. 40 cg. to dg.
14. 8.7 dg. to g.
15. 1,612 cg. to g.
16. 95 mg. to g.
17. 4 g. to dkg.
18. 56.125 dkg. to hg.
19. 29 hg. to kg.
20. 714 g. to hg.
21. 4,236 g. to kg.
22. 8,520 kg. to t.

Measure of Area

PRACTICE EXAMPLES A

Change:

1. 6 cm.^{2} to mm.^{2}
2. 75 dm.^{2} to cm.^{2}
3. 30 m.^{2} to dm.^{2}
4. 5.6 m.^{2} to cm.^{2}
5. 19 m.^{2} to mm.^{2}
6. .25 km.^{2} to m.^{2}

7. 200 mm.^{2} to cm.^{2}
8. 778 cm.^{2} to dm.^{2}
9. 8 dm.^{2} to m.^{2}
10. 70,000 cm.^{2} to m.^{2}
11. 1,325,000 mm.^{2} to m.^{2}
12. 600,000 m.^{2} to km.^{2}

PRACTICE EXAMPLES B
Change:

1. 13 cm.^{2} to mm.^{2}

2. 2.54 dm.^{2} to cm.^{2}

3. 49 m.^{2} to dm.^{2}

4. 10 m.^{2} to cm.^{2}

5. .5 m.^{2} to mm.^{2}

6. 6.375 km.^{2} to m.^{2}

7. 427 mm.^{2} to cm.^{2}

8. 98 cm.^{2} to dm.^{2}

9. 167.82 dm.^{2} to m.^{2}

10. 9,600 cm.^{2} to m.^{2}

11. 500,000 mm.^{2} to m.^{2}

12. 3,750,000 m.^{2} to km.^{2}

Measure of Volume
PRACTICE EXAMPLES A
Change:

1. 5 cm.^{3} to mm.^{3}

2. 20 dm.^{3} to cm.^{3}

3. 13.2 m.^{3} to dm.^{3}

4. 16 m.^{3} to cm.^{3}

5. 9 m.^{3} to mm.^{3}

6. 3,000 mm.^{3} to cm.^{3}

7. 850 cm.^{3} to dm.^{3}

8. 4,720 dm.^{3} to m.^{3}

9. 8,000,000 cm.^{3} to m.^{3}

10. 9,400,000 mm.^{3} to m.^{3}

PRACTICE EXAMPLES B
Change:

1. 23 cm.^{3} to mm.^{3}

2. .8 dm.^{3} to cm.^{3}

3. 50 m.^{3} to dm.^{3}

4. 7.1 m.^{3} to cm.^{3}

5. 3.125 m.^{3} to mm.^{3}

6. 2,756 mm.^{3} to cm.^{3}

7. 62.5 cm.^{3} to dm.^{3}

8. 9,000 dm.^{3} to m.^{3}

9. 46,000 cm.^{3} to m.^{3}

10. 10,000,000 mm.^{3} to m.^{3}

Conversions of Volume, Capacity, and Weight Units
PRACTICE EXAMPLES
Change to equivalent units of volume:

SET 1	SET 2	SET 3	SET 4
1. 8 ml.	1. 5 cl.	1. 7 dl.	1. 3 liters
2. 19 ml.	2. 6 cl.	2. 24 dl.	2. 85 liters
3. 40 ml.	3. 13 cl.	3. 100 dl.	3. 70 liters
4. 9.4 ml.	4. .8 cl.	4. 5.3 dl.	4. 4.9 liters
5. 6.25 ml.	5. 2.39 cl.	5. 46.84 dl.	5. 14.75 liters

Change to equivalent units of capacity:

SET 5	SET 6	SET 7	SET 8
1. 9 cm.³	**1.** 40 mm.³	**1.** 2 dm.³	**1.** 4 m.³
2. 23 cm.³	**2.** 75 mm.³	**2.** 30 dm.³	**2.** 9 m.³
3. 50 cm.³	**3.** 6 mm.³	**3.** 56 dm.³	**3.** 22 m.³
4. 8.5 cm.³	**4.** 3.2 mm.³	**4.** 7.1 dm.³	**4.** .83 m.³
5. 32.46 cm.³	**5.** 9.8 mm.³	**5.** 24.625 dm.³	**5.** 15.6 m.³

Find the weight of the following volumes or capacities of water:

Find in kilograms:	Find in grams:	Find in kilograms:	Find in grams:
SET 9	SET 10	SET 11	SET 12
1. 7 dm.³	**1.** 9 cm.³	**1.** 4 liters	**1.** 5 ml.
2. 26 dm.³	**2.** 14 cm.³	**2.** 90 liters	**2.** 67 ml.
3. 9.42 dm.³	**3.** 4.7 cm.³	**3.** 32 liters	**3.** 17.3 ml.
4. 18 dm.³	**4.** 20 cm.³	**4.** 8.5 liters	**4.** 6 cl.
5. 5.6 dm.³	**5.** 78 cm.³	**5.** 12.25 liters	**5.** 3.5 cl.

Find the volume or capacity occupied by the following weights of water:

Find in cubic decimeters:	Find in cubic centimeters:	Find in liters:	Find in milliliters:
SET 13	SET 14	SET 15	SET 16
1. 8 kg.	**1.** 7 g.	**1.** 3 kg.	**1.** 8 g.
2. 25 kg.	**2.** 30 g.	**2.** 14 kg.	**2.** 36 g.
3. 40 kg.	**3.** 85 g.	**3.** 100 kg.	**3.** 50 g.
4. 5.8 kg.	**4.** .4 g.	**4.** 1.3 kg.	**4.** 4.5 g.
5. .125 kg.	**5.** 36.75 g.	**5.** 29.67 kg.	**5.** 68.32 g.

PRACTICAL APPLICATIONS

1. If an airplane flies at a speed of 125 meters per second, how many kilometers can it fly in one minute?

2. How many kilograms will 300 coins weigh if each coin weighs 5 grams?

3. At an annual international track meet the winning discus throw was 53 meters 38 centimeters. If the record is 56.84 meters, how many meters short of the record was the winning throw?

4. The winner of the high jump leaped 1 meter 97 centimeters. Express the height of his jump in meters.

5. The volume of an aquarium is 24 cubic decimeters. How many liters of water will it hold? If it is two thirds filled, how many kilograms will the water weigh?

6. The density of air at 0° C. and a pressure of 76 cm. of mercury is 0.00129 gram per cubic centimeter. Express the density of air in terms of milligrams per cubic centimeter.

7. If the pressure exerted is 1.3 kilograms per square centimeter, what is the pressure in grams per square centimeter?

8. A certain airplane climbed 1 kilometer in 50 seconds. What was its rate of climb in meters per second?

9. How many grams does a mixture of 1.25 liters of water at 3° C. and 1.25 liters of water at 5° C. weigh?

10. If the acceleration of gravity on the earth is 9.8 meters per second per second, what is it in terms of centimeters per second per second?

11. Find the perimeter of a rectangle 27 cm. long and 15 cm. wide.

12. Find the circumference of a circle if its diameter is 9 mm.

13. What is the perimeter of a square when its side measures 16 km.?

14. Find the area of a rectangle 18 meters long and 13 meters wide.

15. What is the area of a circle whose diameter is 42 meters?

16. What is the area of a parallelogram when its altitude is 25 cm. and its base is 46 cm.?

17. Find the area of a square whose side is 6 mm.

18. What is the area of a triangle when its altitude is 23 cm. and its base is 18 cm.?

19. Find the volume in cubic meters of a room 6 meters long, 5 meters wide, and 3 meters high.

20. How many cu. cm. of water will a can hold if it is 10 cm. in diameter and 14 cm. high? Find its capacity in liters. What is the weight of the water?

EXERCISE 59

RELATIONSHIP OF ENGLISH AND METRIC SYSTEMS

I. Aim: To change measures of the Metric System to equivalent measures of the English System and vice versa.

II. Procedure

1. Find the equivalent relating the two units of measure, then perform the necessary arithmetical operations. Use the conversion factor given in the parentheses wherever greater accuracy is required. See Method 1.

2. Or multiply the given measure by a fraction equal to one, the numerator and denominator of which are the two members of the required equivalent arranged so that the given unit of measure may be canceled. See Method 2.

The following specific directions may be used to convert some of the more common measures:

To change:

(*a*) Meters to yards, multiply the number of meters by 1.09 (1.0936).

(*b*) Yards to meters, multiply the number of yards by .91 (.9144).

(*c*) Meters to inches, multiply the number of meters by 39.37.

(*d*) Inches to meters, multiply the number of inches by .0254.

(*e*) Millimeters to inches, multiply the number of millimeters by .04 (.03937).

(*f*) Inches to millimeters, multiply the number of inches by 25.4.

(*g*) Kilometers to miles, multiply the number of kilometers by .62 (.6214).

(*h*) Miles to kilometers, multiply the number of miles by 1.61 (1.6093).

(*i*) Liters to liquid quarts, multiply the number of liters by 1.06 (1.0567).

(*j*) Liquid quarts to liters, multiply the number of liquid quarts by .95 (.9463).

(*k*) Liters to dry quarts, multiply the number of liters by .91 (.9081).

(*l*) Dry quarts to liters, multiply the number of dry quarts by 1.1 (1.1012).

(*m*) Kilograms to pounds, multiply the number of kilograms by 2.2 (2.2046).

(*n*) Pounds to kilograms, multiply the number of pounds by .45 (.4536).

(*o*) Centimeters to inches, multiply the number of centimeters by .39 or .4 (.3937).

(*p*) Inches to centimeters, multiply the number of inches by 2.54.

III. Sample Solutions

1. Change 145 meters to yards.

Method 1

$$
\begin{array}{r}
145 \\
\times\,1.09 \\
\hline
13\ 05 \\
145\ 0 \\
\hline
158.05
\end{array}
$$

Method 2

$$145 \text{ m.} \times \frac{1.09 \text{ yd.}}{1 \text{ m.}} = 158.05 \text{ yd.}$$

Answer: 158.05 yd.

2. Change 3 inches to centimeters.

Method 1

$$
\begin{array}{r}
3 \\
\times\,2.54 \\
\hline
7.62
\end{array}
$$

Method 2

$$3 \text{ in.} \times \frac{2.54 \text{ cm.}}{1 \text{ in.}} = 7.62 \text{ cm.}$$

Answer: 7.62 cm.

3. Change 17 kilometers to miles.

Method 1   *Method 2*

$$\begin{array}{r} 17 \\ \times\ .62 \\ \hline 34 \\ 10\ 2 \\ \hline 10.54 \end{array}$$

$$17\ \cancel{km} \times \frac{.62\ mi.}{1\ \cancel{km.}} = 10.54\ mi.$$

Answer: 10.54 mi.

4. Change 5 liters to liquid quarts.

Method 1   *Method 2*

$$\begin{array}{r} 5 \\ \times\ 1.06 \\ \hline 5.30 \end{array}$$

$$5\ \cancel{liters} \times \frac{1.06\ qt.}{1\ \cancel{liter}} = 5.30\ qt.$$

Answer: 5.3 qt.

5. Change 10.5 kilograms to pounds.

Method 1   *Method 2*

$$\begin{array}{r} 10.5 \\ \times\ 2.2 \\ \hline 2\ 10 \\ 21\ 0 \\ \hline 23.10 \end{array}$$

$$10.5\ \cancel{kg.} \times \frac{2.2\ lb.}{1\ \cancel{kg.}} = 23.10\ lb.$$

Answer: 23.1 lb.

6. Change 18 square centimeters to square inches.

Method 1   *Method 2*

$$\begin{array}{r} 18 \\ \times\ .16 \\ \hline 1\ 08 \\ 1\ 8 \\ \hline 2.88 \end{array}$$

$$18\ \cancel{cm.^2} \times \frac{.16\ sq.\ in.}{1\ \cancel{cm.^2}} = 2.88\ sq.\ in.$$

Answer: 2.88 sq. in.

7. Change 126 cubic centimeters to cubic inches.

Method 1   *Method 2*

$$\begin{array}{r} 126 \\ \times\ .06 \\ \hline 7.56 \end{array}$$

$$126\ \cancel{cm.^3} \times \frac{.06\ cu.\ in.}{1\ \cancel{cm.^3}} = 7.56\ cu.\ in.$$

Answer: 7.56 cu. in.

EQUIVALENTS

Measure of Length

Metric to English Units

1 meter = 39.37 inches
        = 3.28 feet (3.2808)
        = 1.09 yards (1.0936)
1 centimeter = .39 or .4 inch (.3937)
1 millimeter = .04 inch (.03937)
1 kilometer = .62 mile (.6214)

English to Metric Units

1 inch = 25.4 millimeters
       = 2.54 centimeters
       = .0254 meter
1 foot = .3 meter (.3048)
1 yard = .91 meter (.9144)
1 mile = 1.61 kilometers (1.6093)

Capacity — Liquid Measure

Metric to English Units

1 liter = 1.06 liquid quarts (1.0567)

English to Metric Units

1 liquid quart = .95 liter (.9463)

Capacity — Dry Measure

Metric to English Units

1 liter = .91 dry quart (.9081)

English to Metric Units

1 dry quart = 1.1 liters (1.1012)

Measure of Weight

Metric to English Units

1 gram	= .04 ounce (.0353)
1 kilogram	= 2.2 pounds (2.2046)
1 metric ton	= 2204.62 pounds

English to Metric Units

1 ounce	= 28.35 grams (28.3495)
1 pound	= .45 kilogram (.4536)
1 short ton	= .91 metric ton (.9072)

Measure of Area

Metric to English Units

1 square centimeter	= .16 square inch (.1550)
1 square meter	= 10.76 square feet (10.7639)
	= 1.2 square yards (1.1960)
1 square kilometer	= .39 square mile (.3861)

English to Metric Units

1 square inch	= 6.45 square centimeters (6.4516)
1 square foot	= .09 square meter (.0929)
1 square yard	= .84 square meter (.8361)
1 square mile	= 2.59 square kilometers

Measure of Volume

Metric to English Units

1 cubic centimeter	= .06 cubic inch (.0610)
1 cubic meter	= 35.31 cubic feet (35.3145)
1 cubic meter	= 1.31 cubic yards (1.3079)
1 liter	= .04 cubic foot (.0353)

English to Metric Units

1 cubic inch	= 16.39 cubic centimeters (16.3872)
1 cubic foot	= .03 cubic meter (.0283)
1 cubic yard	= .76 cubic meter (.7646)
1 cubic foot	= 28.32 liters (28.316)

Measures of Length, Capacity, and Weight

DIAGNOSTIC TEST

Use the approximate equivalents. Wherever necessary, find answer correct to the nearest hundredth.

Change:

1. 8 meters to inches
2. 120 meters to yards
3. 65 meters to feet
4. 42 kilometers to miles
5. 88 millimeters to inches
6. 27 centimeters to inches
7. 56 inches to meters
8. 100 yards to meters
9. 18 feet to meters

10. 35 miles to kilometers
11. 4 inches to millimeters
12. 7 inches to centimeters
13. 6 liters to liquid quarts
14. 9 liquid quarts to liters
15. 13 liters to dry quarts
16. 10 dry quarts to liters
17. 27 kilograms to pounds
18. 50 pounds to kilograms

RELATED PRACTICE EXAMPLES

Use the approximate equivalents. Wherever necessary, find answer correct to the nearest hundredth.

Change to inches:	Change to yards:	Change to feet:	Change to miles:
SET 1	SET 2	SET 3	SET 4
1. 3 m.	1. 7 m.	1. 5 m.	1. 6 km.
2. 14 m.	2. 50 m.	2. 47 m.	2. 31 km.
3. 25 m.	3. 382 m.	3. 200 m.	3. 100 km.
4. .6 m.	4. 1,800 m.	4. 1,350 m.	4. 283 km.
5. 9.75 m.	5. 23.5 m.	5. 81.4 m.	5. 4.8 km.

Change to inches:	Change to inches:	Change to meters:	Change to meters:
SET 5	SET 6	SET 7	SET 8
1. 8 mm.	1. 4 cm.	1. 90 in.	1. 16 yd.
2. 75 mm.	2. 30 cm.	2. 42 in.	2. 880 yd.
3. 39 mm.	3. 17 cm.	3. $58\frac{1}{4}$ in.	3. $7\frac{3}{4}$ yd.
4. 90 mm.	4. 5.9 cm.	4. 64.5 in.	4. 49.5 yd.
5. 6.35 mm.	5. 38.2 cm.	5. 107.3 in.	5. 2,000 yd.

Change to meters:	Change to kilometers:	Change to millimeters:	Change to centimeters:
SET 9	SET 10	SET 11	SET 12
1. 7 ft.	1. 4 mi.	1. 3 in.	1. 5 in.
2. 25 ft.	2. 11 mi.	2. 19 in.	2. 21 in.
3. $6\frac{1}{2}$ ft.	3. $5\frac{3}{4}$ mi.	3. $\frac{3}{4}$ in.	3. $\frac{5}{8}$ in.
4. 11.7 ft.	4. 21.4 mi.	4. $1\frac{7}{8}$ in.	4. $3\frac{1}{2}$ in.
5. 108 ft.	5. 50 mi.	5. 8.25 in.	5. 6.9 in.

Change to liquid quarts:	Change to liters:	Change to dry quarts:
SET 13	SET 14	SET 15
1. 3 liters	1. 5 liq. qt.	1. 6 liters
2. 8 liters	2. 13 liq. qt.	2. 17 liters
3. 19 liters	3. $27\frac{1}{2}$ liq. qt.	3. 30 liters
4. 6.2 liters	4. 7.4 liq. qt.	4. 2.8 liters
5. 9.5 liters	5. 40 liq. qt.	5. 3.25 liters

Change to liters:	Change to pounds:	Change to kilograms:
SET 16	SET 17	SET 18
1. 8 dry qt.	1. 7 kg.	1. 9 lb.
2. 15 dry qt.	2. 18 kg.	2. 23 lb.
3. $4\frac{1}{2}$ dry qt.	3. 60 kg.	3. $6\frac{3}{4}$ lb.
4. 7.2 dry qt.	4. 8.6 kg.	4. 4.4 lb.
5. 21 dry qt.	5. 14.52 kg.	5. 100 lb.

MISCELLANEOUS EXAMPLES

Measure of Length

PRACTICE EXAMPLES

Change to rods:	Change to meters:	Change to nautical miles:*	Change to kilometers:†
SET 1	SET 2	SET 3	SET 4
1. 7 m.	1. 8 rd.	1. 4 km.	1. 9 naut. mi.
2. 12 m.	2. 5 rd.	2. 27 km.	2. 35 naut. mi.
3. 25 m.	3. 10 rd.	3. 60 km.	3. 83 naut. mi.
4. 40 m.	4. 24 rd.	4. 7.3 km.	4. 100 naut. mi.
5. 8.4 m.	5. 46 rd.	5. 16.9 km.	5. 21.6 naut. mi.

* 1 kilometer = .54 nautical mile (.5396)　　　† 1 nautical mile = 1.85 km. (1.8532)

Capacity — Liquid Measure

PRACTICE EXAMPLES A

Change:

1. 3 liters to pints.

2. 25 pints to liters.

3. 4.6 liters to gallons.

4. $5\frac{3}{4}$ gallons to liters.

5. 39 milliliters to ounces.

6. 12 ounces to milliliters.

PRACTICE EXAMPLES B

Change:

1. 12.75 liters to pints.

2. 7 pints to liters.

3. 20 liters to gallons.

4. 9 gallons to liters.

5. 6.2 milliliters to ounces.

6. $4\frac{1}{2}$ ounces to milliliters.

Capacity — Dry Measure

PRACTICE EXAMPLES A

Change:

1. 14 liters to pecks.

2. 2 pecks to liters.

3. 6.9 hectoliters to bushels.

4. 5 bushels to hectoliters.

PRACTICE EXAMPLES B

Change:

1. 5.8 liters to pecks.

2. $3\frac{1}{4}$ pecks to liters.

3. 45 hectoliters to bushels.

4. 26 bushels to hectoliters.

Measure of Weight

PRACTICE EXAMPLES A

Change:

1. 34 grams to ounces.

2. 15 ounces to grams.

3. 8 metric tons to pounds.

4. 5,000 pounds to metric tons.

5. 20 metric tons to short tons.

6. 7 short tons to metric tons.

7. 4.1 metric tons to long tons.

8. 18 long tons to metric tons.

9. 13 grams to grains.

10. 100 grains to grams.

PRACTICE EXAMPLES B

Change:

1. 160 grams to ounces.

2. $11\frac{1}{2}$ ounces to grams.

3. 17 metric tons to pounds.

4. 220,462 pounds to metric tons.

5. 9.2 metric tons to short tons.

6. 13 short tons to metric tons.

7. 29 metric tons to long tons.

8. $7\frac{3}{4}$ long tons to metric tons.

9. 2.6 grams to grains.

10. 85 grains to grams.

Measure of Area

PRACTICE EXAMPLES

Change to square inches:

SET 1

1. 7 cm.^{2}
2. 22 cm.^{2}
3. 50 cm.^{2}
4. 4.3 cm.^{2}
5. 23.98 cm.^{2}

Change to square centimeters:

SET 2

1. 4 sq. in.
2. 25 sq. in.
3. $19\frac{1}{2}$ sq. in.
4. 7.8 sq. in.
5. 11 sq. in.

Change to square feet:

SET 3

1. 3 m.^{2}
2. 8 m.^{2}
3. 20 m.^{2}
4. 13.4 m.^{2}
5. 84.25 m.^{2}

Change to square meters:

SET 4

1. 39 sq. ft.
2. 16 sq. ft.
3. $159\frac{1}{4}$ sq. ft.
4. 21.52 sq. ft.
5. 7 sq. ft.

Change to square yards:

SET 5

1. 6 m.^{2}
2. 79 m.^{2}
3. 45 m.^{2}
4. 9.1 m.^{2}
5. 15.72 m.^{2}

Change to square meters:

SET 6

1. 2 sq. yd.
2. 15 sq. yd.
3. $39\frac{1}{3}$ sq. yd.
4. 4.98 sq. yd.
5. 24 sq. yd.

Change to square miles:

SET 7

1. 8 km.^{2}
2. 37 km.^{2}
3. 70 km.^{2}
4. 2.6 km.^{2}
5. 41.23 km.^{2}

Change to square kilometers:

SET 8

1. 5 sq. mi.
2. 48 sq. mi.
3. $33\frac{7}{8}$ sq. mi.
4. 8.64 sq. mi.
5. 100 sq. mi.

Measure of Volume

PRACTICE EXAMPLES

Change to cubic inches:

SET 1
1. 9 cm.³
2. 17 cm.³
3. 62 cm.³
4. 10.5 cm.³
5. 83.91 cm.³

Change to cubic centimeters:

SET 2
1. 5 cu. in.
2. 48 cu. in.
3. 29¾ cu. in.
4. 58.26 cu. in.
5. 190 cu. in.

Change to cubic feet:

SET 3
1. 7 m.³
2. 36 m.³
3. 80 m.³
4. 12.2 m.³
5. 9.34 m.³

Change to cubic meters:

SET 4
1. 8 cu. ft.
2. 55 cu. ft.
3. 76¼ cu. ft.
4. 23.9 cu. ft.
5. 172 cu. ft.

Change to cubic yards:

SET 5
1. 3 m.³
2. 14 m.³
3. 46 m.³
4. 7.8 m.³
5. 18.25 m.³

Change to cubic meters:

SET 6
1. 4 cu. yd.
2. 27 cu. yd.
3. 12¾ cu. yd.
4. 8.5 cu. yd.
5. 50 cu. yd.

Change to cubic feet:

SET 7
1. 26 dm.³ (liter)
2. 9 dm.³ (liter)
3. 68 dm.³ (liter)
4. 11.3 dm.³ (liter)
5. 35.86 dm.³ (liter)

Change to cubic decimeters (liters):

SET 8
1. 5 cu. ft.
2. 13 cu. ft.
3. 62½ cu. ft.
4. 21.7 cu. ft.
5. 40 cu. ft.

PRACTICAL APPLICATIONS

Use approximate equivalents. Whenever necessary, find answer correct to nearest hundredth.

1. A certain motion-picture camera uses 8-mm. film. Express the film size in inches.

2. Which holds more tomato juice, a can containing 591 cm.³ or one containing 1 pt. 2 oz.?

3. The motion-picture projector used in a certain school can only show 16-mm. film. What does this film measure in inches?

4. Express the net weight of a can of peaches in ounces if it is marked 250 grams.

5. Size 120 film exposures are 6 × 9 cm. What are their dimensions in inches?

6. (*a*) In an international track meet the winner of the 2-kilometer run was 25 meters ahead of the runner who came in second. How many yards ahead was the winner?

(*b*) Which is shorter, the 1,000-meter or the half-mile run?

7. The weight of a certain volume of fresh water is 11 pounds. Find its weight in kilograms and its volume in liters.

8. Find the weight in ounces of 400 cm.³ of water.

9. If a cubic foot of oil weighs 56 lb., find the weight in kilograms of a liter of oil.

10. A green light ray that measures exactly to one-billionth of an inch is made with 5 mg. of gold. Express this weight in ounces.

11. One formation of aircraft flew at an altitude of 10,000 feet, while another flew at an altitude of 4,000 meters. Which formation flew at the higher altitude?

12. Express the bore diameter of a 75-mm. gun in inches.

13. Records of the Olympic Games show that the best mark in the running hop, step, and jump is 16.23 meters; in the high jump, 2.12 meters; in the broad jump, 8.13 meters; in the discus, 59.28 meters; and in the javelin, 80.41 meters. Express each record in feet and inches.

14. The tolerance specified in a contract is .01 mm. Express this tolerance in inches.

15. The wing area of a model plane is 54 square centimeters. Express this area in square inches.

16. The world aviation altitude record is 22,066 meters. Express this altitude record in feet.

17. One truck averages 8 km. per liter of gasoline, while another truck averages 15 mi. per gallon. Which truck will go the greater distance on a full tank of gasoline if both tanks hold the same amount of gasoline?

18. (*a*) Which area is larger: France with 550,926 square kilometers or Texas with 265,896 square miles? (*b*) Which is taller: Eiffel Tower, 300 meters high, or Rockefeller Center, 850 ft. high?

19. A column of mercury 76 cm. high is used to determine the standard atmospheric pressure at sea level. Find the height of this column in inches.

20. The temperature of a parcel of air decreases 1° Centigrade per 100 meters, following the dry adiabatic lapse rate. Express this rate in Centigrade degrees per 1,000 feet.

REFRESH YOUR SKILLS

1. Add:
639,845
217,937
556,616
835,929
469,708
986,819

2. Subtract:
1,426,847
987,899

3. Multiply:
1,760
800

4. Divide:
$231\overline{)202,356}$

5. Add:
$16\frac{9}{10} + 4\frac{3}{5}$

6. Subtract:
$9\frac{1}{3} - 2\frac{1}{12}$

7. Multiply:
$3\frac{1}{7} \times 5\frac{1}{2}$

8. Divide:
$32 \div \frac{3}{4}$

9. Add:
$6.38 + $17.06 + $.87 + $4.79 + 129.96

10. Subtract:
$2,059.60 - 85

11. Multiply:
$948.25
.125

12. Divide:
$.075\overline{)3}$

13. Find $66\frac{2}{3}\%$ of 438

14. What per cent of 24 is 30?

15. $4\frac{1}{2}\%$ of what number is 270?

16. Square: $1\frac{5}{8}$

17. Find the square root of 4.9 to nearest hundredth.

EXERCISE 60

MEASURE OF SPEED

I. Aim: To change a given speed to an equivalent speed measured in other units.

II. Procedure

1. Change the given units to the required units, then perform the necessary arithmetical operations. See Method 1.

2. The alternate method of cancellation of units may also be used. See Method 2.

III. Sample Solutions

1. Change 60 stat. m.p.h. to feet per second.

Method 1

(*a*) $60 \text{ m.p.h.} = \dfrac{60 \times 5{,}280}{3{,}600} = 88 \text{ ft. per sec.}$

> *1.* Miles per hour is changed to feet per hour (mi. × 5,280).
> *2.* Feet per hour is changed to feet per second (ft. ÷ 3,600).

(*b*) Or multiply the number of miles per hour by either $\frac{22}{15}$ or 1.47. ($\frac{5280}{3600} = \frac{22}{15} = 1.47$).

$$\tfrac{22}{15} \times 60 \text{ m.p.h.} = 88 \text{ ft. per sec.}$$

Method 2

$$\frac{60 \text{ mi.}}{1 \text{ hr.}} \times \frac{5{,}280 \text{ ft.}}{1 \text{ mi.}} \times \frac{1 \text{ hr.}}{3{,}600 \text{ sec.}} = 88 \text{ ft. per sec.}$$

Answer: 88 ft. per sec.

2. Change 132 ft. per sec. to statute miles per hour.

Method 1

(*a*) $132 \text{ ft. per sec.} = \dfrac{132 \times 3{,}600}{5{,}280} = 90 \text{ m.p.h.}$

> *1.* Feet per second is changed to feet per hour (ft. × 3,600).
> *2.* Feet per hour is changed to miles per hour (ft. ÷ 5,280).

(*b*) Or multiply the number of feet per second by either $\frac{15}{22}$ or .68. ($\frac{3600}{5280} = \frac{15}{22} = .68$).

$$\frac{15}{22} \times 132 \text{ ft. per sec.} = 90 \text{ m.p.h.}$$

Method 2

$$\frac{132 \,\cancel{\text{ft.}}}{1 \,\cancel{\text{sec.}}} \times \frac{3,600 \,\cancel{\text{sec.}}}{1 \text{ hr.}} \times \frac{1 \text{ mi.}}{5,280 \,\cancel{\text{ft.}}} = 90 \text{ m.p.h.}$$

Answer: 90 m.p.h.

3. Change 26 knots to nautical miles per hour. (See definition.)

Answer: 26 naut. m.p.h.

4. Change 110 knots to statute miles per hour.

Method 1	*Method 2*

Method 1

$$\begin{array}{r} 110 \\ \times\, 1.15 \\ \hline 5\,50 \\ 11\,0 \\ 110 \\ \hline 126.50 \end{array}$$

Method 2

$$\frac{110 \,\cancel{\text{naut. mi.}}}{1 \text{ hr.}} \times \frac{1.15 \text{ stat. mi.}}{1 \,\cancel{\text{naut. mi.}}}$$
$$= 126.5 \text{ stat. m.p.h.}$$

Answer: 126.5 stat. m.p.h.

5. Change 185 stat. m.p.h. to nautical miles per hour (knots).

Method 1

$$\begin{array}{r} 185 \\ \times\, .87 \\ \hline 12\,95 \\ 148\,0 \\ \hline 160.95 \end{array}$$

Method 2

$$\frac{185 \,\cancel{\text{stat. mi.}}}{1 \text{ hr.}} \times \frac{.87 \text{ naut. mi.}}{1 \,\cancel{\text{stat. mi.}}}$$
$$= 160.95 \text{ naut. m.p.h.}$$

Answer: 160.95 naut. m.p.h.

IV. Definition

A knot is the unit of speed at sea. It is equal to one nautical mile per hour.

DIAGNOSTIC TEST

Wherever necessary, find answer correct to the nearest hundredth.

Change:

    1. 105 stat. m.p.h. to feet per second
    2. 198 ft. per second to statute miles per hour
    3. 18 knots to nautical miles per hour
    4. 31.5 naut. m.p.h. to knots
    5. 90 knots to statute miles per hour
    6. 246 stat. m.p.h. to knots

RELATED PRACTICE EXAMPLES

Wherever necessary, find answer correct to the nearest hundredth:

Change to feet per second:

SET 1(a)	SET 1(b)	SET 1(c)
1. 45 stat. m.p.h.	**1.** 48 stat. m.p.h.	**1.** 13 stat. m.p.h.
2. 225 stat. m.p.h.	**2.** 9 stat. m.p.h.	**2.** 22 stat. m.p.h.
3. 300 stat. m.p.h.	**3.** 100 stat. m.p.h.	**3.** 61 stat. m.p.h.
4. 120 stat. m.p.h.	**4.** 186 stat. m.p.h.	**4.** 254 stat. m.p.h.
5. 195 stat. m.p.h.	**5.** 265 stat. m.p.h.	**5.** 178 stat. m.p.h.

SET 1(d)	SET 1(e)
1. 6.5 stat. m.p.h.	**1.** $12\frac{1}{2}$ stat. m.p.h.
2. 14.2 stat. m.p.h.	**2.** $46\frac{1}{4}$ stat. m.p.h.
3. 57.1 stat. m.p.h.	**3.** $93\frac{3}{4}$ stat. m.p.h.
4. 109.75 stat. m.p.h.	**4.** $177\frac{2}{5}$ stat. m.p.h.
5. 282.3 stat. m.p.h.	**5.** $128\frac{2}{3}$ stat. m.p.h.

Change to statute miles per hour:

SET 2(a)	SET 2(b)	SET 2(c)
1. 44 ft. per second	**1.** 50 ft. per second	**1.** 27 ft. per second
2. 110 ft. per second	**2.** 77 ft. per second	**2.** 65 ft. per second
3. 462 ft. per second	**3.** 170 ft. per second	**3.** 103 ft. per second
4. 264 ft. per second	**4.** 208 ft. per second	**4.** 189 ft. per second
5. 352 ft. per second	**5.** 429 ft. per second	**5.** 334 ft. per second

SET 2(d)

1. 32.2 ft. per second
2. 89.3 ft. per second
3. 121.75 ft. per second
4. 245.25 ft. per second
5. 406.54 ft. per second

SET 2(e)

1. $18\frac{1}{2}$ ft. per second
2. $35\frac{1}{3}$ ft. per second
3. $96\frac{1}{4}$ ft. per second
4. $172\frac{3}{4}$ ft. per second
5. $263\frac{5}{6}$ ft. per second

Change to nautical miles per hour:

SET 3

1. 9 knots
2. 32 knots
3. $29\frac{3}{4}$ knots
4. 16.4 knots
5. 125 knots

Change to knots:

SET 4

1. 7 naut. m.p.h.
2. 89 naut. m.p.h.
3. $14\frac{1}{2}$ naut. m.p.h.
4. 158.1 naut. m.p.h.
5. 233 naut. m.p.h.

Change to statute miles per hour:

SET 5

1. 8 knots
2. 50 knots
3. $176\frac{1}{4}$ knots
4. 39.5 knots
5. 127 knots

Change to knots:

SET 6

1. 15 stat. m.p.h.
2. 86 stat. m.p.h.
3. $118\frac{1}{2}$ stat. m.p.h.
4. 61.3 stat. m.p.h.
5. 200 stat. m.p.h.

MISCELLANEOUS EXAMPLES

Change to statute miles per hour:

SET 1

1. 21 naut. m.p.h.
2. 76 naut. m.p.h.
3. $37\frac{1}{2}$ naut. m.p.h.
4. 11.8 naut. m.p.h.
5. 150 naut. m.p.h.

Change to nautical miles per hour:

SET 2

1. 16 stat. m.p.h.
2. 53 stat. m.p.h.
3. $308\frac{3}{4}$ stat. m.p.h.
4. 21.7 stat. m.p.h.
5. 178 stat. m.p.h.

Change to knots:*

SET 3
1. 24 km.p.h.
2. 70 km.p.h.
3. 127 km.p.h.
4. 48.5 km.p.h.
5. 293.82 km.p.h.

Change to statute miles per hour:

SET 5
1. 18 km.p.h.
2. 42 km.p.h.
3. 163 km.p.h.
4. 82.1 km.p.h.
5. 112.65 km.p.h.

Change to feet per second:

SET 7
1. 13 knots
2. 29 knots
3. 90 knots
4. 172 knots
5. 141.7 knots

Change to feet per minute:

SET 9
1. 88 ft. per second
2. 300 yd. per second
3. 60 stat. m.p.h.
4. 145 naut. m.p.h.
5. 23 knots

Change to kilometers per hour:†

SET 4
1. 9 knots
2. 37 knots
3. 60 knots
4. 115 knots
5. 249.6 knots

Change to kilometers per hour:

SET 6
1. 30 stat. m.p.h.
2. 56 stat. m.p.h.
3. 145 stat. m.p.h.
4. 237 stat. m.p.h.
5. 41.2 stat. m.p.h.

Change to knots:

SET 8
1. 45 ft. per second
2. 100 ft. per second
3. 225 ft. per second
4. 369 ft. per second
5. 183.5 ft. per second

Change to statute miles per hour:

SET 10
1. 1,320 ft. per minute
2. 1,800 ft. per minute
3. 3,000 ft. per minute
4. 2,000 yd. per minute
5. 40 yd. per second

*1 km. = .54 nautical mile (.5396)

†1 nautical mile = 1.85 km. (1.8532)

Change to feet per second: Change to centimeters per second:

SET 11

1. 50 cm. per second
2. 187 cm. per second
3. 843 cm. per second
4. 68 km.p.h.
5. 279 km.p.h.

SET 12

1. 35 km.p.h.
2. 192 km.p.h.
3. 7 ft. per second
4. 32 ft. per second
5. 47.3 ft. per second

PRACTICAL APPLICATIONS

Find answers correct to nearest hundredth:

1. A ship steams at 18 naut. m.p.h. Find its speed in knots.

2. The top air speed of a certain airplane is 420 knots. Express this air speed in statute miles per hour.

3. How many nautical miles will a ship go in 5 hr. if it steams at an average of 26.5 knots?

4. A plane flies at an air speed of 360 stat. m.p.h. What is its air speed in knots?

5. If an aircraft flies at a ground speed of 245 stat. m.p.h., how many feet will it go in 20 sec.?

6. Arrange in order of speed (highest speed first) 1 ft. per second, 1 stat. m.p.h., 1 cm. per second, 1 knot, 1 km. per hour, and 1 naut. m.p.h.

7. In evaluating the formula for lift, the air speed must be expressed in terms of feet per second.

(a) In finding the lift of a plane flying at an air speed of 390 stat. m.p.h., what air speed in feet per second must be used in the formula?

(b) In finding the lift of a plane flying at an air speed of 450 knots, what air speed in feet per second must be used in the formula?

8. Which is going at the fastest speed, a submarine doing 14 knots, a freighter going in the same direction at a speed of 12.6 naut. m.p.h., or a navy blimp going at 15 stat. m.p.h.? Find the difference in their speeds in feet per second.

9. The top air speed of a certain type of foreign plane is 620 km. per hour, while the top air speed of a similar American plane is 400 stat. m.p.h. Which plane has the greater top air speed?

10. A destroyer steaming at 40 knots is overtaking a cruiser steaming at 28 knots. How many yards is the destroyer gaining on the cruiser each minute?

11. Find the average ground speed, in miles per hour, of a plane when it travels a distance of:

(a) 1,000 miles in 4 hours.

(b) 90 miles in 12 minutes.

(c) 45 miles in 5 minutes and 24 seconds.

(d) 660 miles in 2 hours and 45 minutes.

(e) 370 miles in 1 hour and 14 minutes.

12. How far can an aircraft go in 3 hours 40 minutes if its average ground speed is 396 m.p.h.?

13. A certain plane has fuel for 6 hours. What is its radius of action (how far can it fly and still return to its base) at an average ground speed of 325 m.p.h.?

14. Find the number of fuel hours of gasoline required to fly a distance of 1,155 miles at an average ground speed of 210 m.p.h.

15. How long will it take a ship to steam a distance of 76 nautical miles at a speed of 30 knots?

16. The *United States*, a passenger ship, crossed the Atlantic Ocean in the record time of 3 days 10 hours 40 minutes. What speed in knots did it average in going the distance of 2,942 nautical miles?

17. An airplane flew non-stop from Long Beach, California, to Washington, D.C., a distance of 2,295 statute miles, in 5 hr. 17 min. 34 sec. What was its average speed in knots?

18. Find the closing speed in miles per minute if one plane is flying at 180 m.p.h. head-on toward a plane flying at 220 m.p.h.

19. (a) If a car travels at 40 m.p.h., how many revolutions per minute will its wheels turn? The diameter of the wheels is 35 in.

(b) At a speed of 45 m.p.h., how many minutes will it take to go a distance of 12 miles?

20. If the driver's reaction time before applying his brakes is 1 second, how many feet will the car go in 1 second at the following speeds: (a) 20 m.p.h.? (b) 35 m.p.h.? (c) 45 m.p.h.? (d) 60 m.p.h.? (e) 50 m.p.h.?

Tip Speed and Rim Speed

1. The tip speed of a propeller is the number of feet the tip of the propeller travels in 1 second.

(*a*) Find the tip speed of a propeller 7 ft. in diameter and turning at 1,650 revolutions per minute.

(*b*) Find the tip speed of an 8-foot propeller turning at 1,400 revolutions per minute.

2. The rim speed of a revolving object (sometimes called surface speed or cutting speed) is the number of feet traveled in 1 minute by a point on the circumference of the revolving object.

(*a*) A grinding wheel has a diameter of 14 inches. What is its rim speed when it revolves at 1,200 revolutions per minute (r.p.m.)?

(*b*) What is the rim speed of a pulley with a diameter of 18 inches turning at 200 r.p.m.?

(*c*) A circular saw blade has a 28-inch diameter and revolves at 800 r.p.m. Find its cutting speed.

REFRESH YOUR SKILLS

1. Add: **2.** Subtract: **3.** Multiply: **4.** Divide:

84,289	475,261	8,297	$625\overline{)1,000,000}$
67,176	384,198	5,869	
9,258			
187			
49,075			

5. Add: **6.** Subtract: **7.** Multiply:

$8\frac{2}{3} + 4\frac{7}{12} + 2\frac{3}{8}$ $4\frac{1}{6} - \frac{7}{8}$ $19 \times 9\frac{5}{6}$

       8. Divide: **9.** Add:

         $6\frac{3}{4} \div 7\frac{1}{2}$ $6.48 + .088 + 42.6$

10. Subtract: **11.** Multiply: **12.** Divide:

   $10.6 - .69$ 87.5×400 $.008\overline{).002}$

13. Find $6\frac{1}{4}\%$ **14.** \$4.50 is what   **15.** 9% of what number is 19.8?
of \$84.36   per cent of \$5.40?   ber is 19.8?

16. Square: 709   **17.** Find the square root of 65,076,489.

18. Change 15.9 miles to feet.

ADDITIONAL TOPICS

PRECISION AND ACCURACY

Measurement is never exact. Precision is the closeness to the true measurement. It is determined by the smallest unit of measure used to make the measurement.

If we use a ruler with eighths of an inch as the smallest subdivision (or unit of measure), then a measurement of $2\frac{3}{8}$ is precise to the nearest $\frac{1}{8}$ inch.

If we use a ruler with sixteenths of an inch as the smallest subdivision (or unit of measure), then a measurement of $2\frac{5}{16}$ inches is precise to the nearest $\frac{1}{16}$ inch.

The smaller the unit of measure, the more precise is the measurement.

The precision of a measurement named by a numeral for a whole number ending in zeros is indicated by an underlined zero as shown in the illustrations. Also see page 472.

16,00̲0 miles is precise to the nearest mile.
16,0̲00 miles is precise to the nearest 100 miles.
16,̲000 miles is precise to the nearest 1,000 miles.
16,000.0 miles is precise to the nearest tenth of a mile.

Suppose we find the length of a given segment to be $2\frac{3}{8}$ inches when the unit of measure is $\frac{1}{8}$ inch. Since this measurement is not exact, the true measurement is between $2\frac{5}{16}$ inches and $2\frac{7}{16}$ inches. The greatest possible error between the measurement $2\frac{3}{8}$ inches and the true measurement can only be $\frac{1}{16}$ inch.

The greatest possible error is one-half of the unit used to measure.

The relative error is the ratio of the greatest possible error to the measurement. The accuracy of the measurement is determined by the relative error. The relative error is sometimes expressed as a per cent.

The smaller the relative error, the more accurate is the measurement.

The measurement $2\frac{3}{8}''$ has the greatest possible error of $\frac{1}{16}''$. The ratio of $\frac{1}{16}''$ to $2\frac{3}{8}''$ is $\frac{1}{38}$. The relative error is $\frac{1}{38}$.

The allowance for error in measurement is called tolerance. A required measurement of 7.3 inches with a tolerance of .05 inch in both directions is indicated as $7.3'' \pm .05''$ and would represent any measurement from 7.25 inches to 7.35 inches. See page 174.

PRACTICE PROBLEMS

1. To what unit of measure are these measurements precise?

(a) $2\frac{13}{16}$ in.   (e) $8\frac{3}{4}$ lb.   (i) .030 in.

(b) $4\frac{21}{64}$ in.   (f) 460 tons   (j) 9.75 lb.

(c) $9\frac{3}{5}$ hr.   (g) .00007 in.   (k) 846 mi.

(d) $7\frac{1}{2}$ pt.   (h) 35.6 mi.   (l) 25,000 ft.

(m) 10 hr. 14 min.   (o) 11 ft. $8\frac{1}{4}$ in.

(n) 9 lb. 5 oz.   (p) 3 min. 54.8 sec.

2. Which measurement in each of the following is more precise?

(a) .03 in. or .019 in.?   (d) $8\frac{3}{4}$ mi. or $5\frac{2}{3}$ yd.?

(b) $7\frac{1}{16}$ in. or $3\frac{17}{32}$ in.?   (e) $2\frac{2}{3}$ hr. or 10 hr. 8 min.?

(c) 9.6 in. or 18.0 in.?   (f) $5\frac{1}{2}$ ft. or 3 ft. 7 in.?

3. Find the greatest possible error in each of the following measurements:

(a) $8\frac{1}{4}$ in.   (d) 4.03 ft.   (g) 160,000 ft.

(b) $5\frac{7}{8}$ lb.   (e) .0098 in.   (h) 2 ft. 11 in.

(c) $1\frac{25}{32}$ in.   (f) 59 lb.   (i) 1 lb. 4 oz.

4. Find the greatest possible error in each of the measurements given in problem 1.

5. Find the relative error in each of the measurements given in problems 1 and 3.

6. Find the relative error as a per cent for each of the following measurements:

(a) 0.9 in.   (b) 50 ft.   (c) $2\frac{2}{3}$ yd.   (d) $9\frac{3}{8}$ in.   (e) 12 mi.

7. Which measurement in each of the following is more accurate?

(a) $3\frac{1}{2}$ in. or $5\frac{1}{8}$ in.   (d) 20,000 mi. or 1 ft.

(b) 28.3 in. or 3.52 in.   (e) .06 in. or 250 mi.

(c) 58 ft. or 5.8 ft.   (f) 30 in. or .003 in.

8. Which is more precise: 65,000 ft. or .004 in.? Which is more accurate?

9. Arrange the measurements .07″, .7″, .007″, 70″ in order of precision, most precise first; and in order of accuracy, most accurate first.

10. What range of measurements does each of the following represent?

(a) $8.4'' \pm .05''$ (c) $3.07'' \pm .075''$ (e) $2'' \pm .001''$

(b) $2\frac{3}{4}'' \pm \frac{1}{8}''$ (d) $4\frac{5}{8}'' \pm \frac{7}{16}''$ (f) $9\frac{1}{2}'' \pm \frac{3}{32}''$

Significant Digits

Digits are significant in an approximate number when they indicate the precision which is determined by the value of the place of the last significant digit on the right.

In 64.75, the significant digit 5 indicates precision to the nearest hundredth.

In 83,000, the underlined 0 indicates precision to the nearest ten.

The digits described below in items (1) to (4) inclusive are significant, those described in items (5) and (6) are not significant except as noted in (5).

1. All non-zero digits are significant.

> (1) 684 has 3 significant digits (6,8,4).

2. Zeros located between non-zero digits are significant.

> (2) 5,006 has 4 significant digits (5,0,0,6).

3. When a decimal or mixed decimal ends in zeros, these zeros are significant.

> (3) 86.190 has 5 significant digits (8,6,1,9,0).

4. When numbers are expressed in scientific notation, all the digits in the first factor are significant.

> (4) In 7.32×10^9, digits 7, 3, and 2 are significant.

5. When a number ends in zeros, these zeros are not significant unless they are specified as being significant or indicated as significant by a line drawn under them.

(5) 51,000 has 2 significant digits (5,1).

51,0̲00 has 3 significant digits (5,1,0).

51,00̲0̲ has 5 significant digits (5,1,0,0,0).

4,030 has 3 significant digits (4,0,3).

6. In a decimal fraction (when the number is between 0 and 1) the zeros immediately following the decimal point are not significant.

(6) .00296 has 3 significant digits (2,9,6) but 2.0096 has 5 significant digits (2,0,0,9,6). .0070 has 2 significant digits (7,0).

PRACTICE PROBLEMS

Determine the number of significant digits in each of the following. What are they in each case?

1. 28	11. 23.05	21. 3.1416
2. 600	12. .0001000	22. 7,060
3. 4,271	13. 87,0̲00	23. 95,280
4. 37,000	14. 350̲,000	24. 16,003
5. 9	15. 6.3 × 10⁵	25. 40,0̲00
6. .08	16. 8.49 × 10⁷	26. .000000015
7. .0095	17. 2,500	27. 9.00000027
8. .013	18. .0007	28. 8,259,078
9. .0130	19. 6,810	29. 4.0060
10. 9,050,000	20. 51.0	30. 203,00̲0̲

APPROXIMATE NUMBERS

Numbers used to count are exact. Numbers used to measure are approximate. An **approximate number** is a number that is almost equal to the true number.

Since measurement is approximate, we may be required to compute with approximate numbers arising through measurement. The result of a computation with approximate numbers cannot be more accurate than the least accurate approximate number involved in the computation. There are several methods of computing approximate numbers, one of which is given on p. 474.

Addition

To add approximate numbers, add as you usually do, then round the sum using the unit of the least precise addend.

Subtraction

To subtract approximate numbers, subtract as you usually do, then round the difference using the unit of the less precise of the given numbers.

Multiplication

To multiply approximate numbers, multiply as you usually do, then round the product so that it contains the same number of significant digits as the factor having the smaller number of significant digits.

Division

To divide approximate numbers, divide as you usually do, then round the quotient so that it contains the same number of significant digits as there are in either the dividend or divisor, whichever is less.

Add:
```
   1.7
   2.564
   1.42
   5.684 = 5.7
```
Answer: 5.7

Subtract:
```
   8.543
   3.82
   4.723 = 4.72
```
Answer: 4.72

Multiply:
```
    3.49
     2.5
    1745
    698
   8.725 = 8.7
```
Answer: 8.7

Divide:
```
              4.08 = 4.1
   1.6∧)6.5∧34
         6 4
         1 34
         1 28
            6
```
Answer: 4.1

PRACTICE PROBLEMS

Compute the following approximate numbers as indicated:

1. Add:
   - (a) $6.8 + 3.44$
   - (b) $8.14 + 7.275 + 3.6$
   - (c) $19 + .84 + 9.3$

2. Subtract:
   - (a) $93.174 - 8.32$
   - (b) $27.6 - .039$
   - (c) $58 - 1.8$

3. Multiply:
   - (a) 5.9×6.7
   - (b) $48 \times .903$
   - (c) 6.1504×13.85

4. Divide:
   - (a) $12\overline{)8.29}$
   - (b) $9\overline{).022}$
   - (c) $3.8\overline{)954.15}$

PART IV

ALGEBRA

RATIO AND PROPORTION

STATISTICS

INTRODUCTION

The algebra in this section of the book contains (1) the study of positive and negative numbers, thus extending the number system; (2) the reading, writing, and evaluation of algebraic expressions and sentences including formulas, thus developing the basic language and using the symbolism of algebra; and (3) the solution and graphing of open sentences in one variable including both equations and inequalities, thus developing a very essential tool for solving problems. The use of the ratio and proportion concepts for solving problems is also stressed.

The section on statistics includes the interpretation and construction of bar, line, and circle graphs, and the study of averages (mean, median, and mode) and of probability.

This test is keyed by page number. Explanatory material may be found on the page indicated by the numeral at the end of each problem.

1. Draw a number line and indicate the points corresponding to $\{-4, -2, 0, +1, +3\}$. **480**

2. If -5 pounds means 5 pounds underweight, what does $+3$ pounds mean? **480**

3. (*a*) What is the opposite of -18? **483**
(*b*) What is the additive inverse of $+23$?

4. Write symbolically: The negative of negative five is positive five. **484**

5. Which of the following are true? **480**
(*a*) $-3 > -1$ (*b*) $+2 \nless -2$ (*c*) $0 < -4$ (*d*) $+4 \ngtr +6$

6. Find the absolute value: **482**
(*a*) $|-3| = ?$ (*b*) $|+10| = ?$

7. Add: **485**

-5	$+6$	-12	-9	-3
$+9$	$+7$	$+8$	-7	$+3$

$$(-7) + (+4) + (-9) + (+11)$$

8. Subtract: **487**

$+6$	$+9$	-5	-14	0
-8	$+11$	-4	$+5$	-4

$$(+5) - (-5)$$

9. Multiply: **489**

$+9$	-4	-10	$+7$	0
-7	$+8$	-10	$+3$	-5

$$(-1)(-5)(-2)(+7)$$

10. Divide: **491**

-40	-72	$+24$	$+60$	-16
-8	$+9$	-1	$+15$	$+16$

$$(-56) \div (-7)$$

11. Write as an algebraic expression: **494**
(*a*) The sum of l and w.
(*b*) The difference between ten and four.
(*c*) The quotient of six divided by r.
(*d*) The product of a and nine.
(*e*) Six times the square of the side(s).

12. Write each of the following as a sentence symbolically: **496**

(*a*) Some number *y* decreased by five is equal to twelve.

(*b*) Each number *x* increased by two is greater than eight.

(*c*) Six times each number *n* is less than or equal to fourteen.

(*d*) Each number *s* is greater than negative two and less than positive nine.

13. Express as a formula: **496**

Centripetal force (*F*) equals the product of the weight of the body (*w*) and the square of the velocity (*v*) divided by the product of the acceleration of gravity (*g*) and the radius of the circle (*r*).

14. Find the value of: **499**

(*a*) $m + 9\,n$ when $m = 8$ and $n = 3$.

(*b*) $a + b(a - b)$ when $a = 6$ and $b = 2$.

(*c*) $2\,x^2 - 3\,xy - y^2$ when $x = 4$ and $y = -3$.

(*d*) $\dfrac{r^2 - s^2}{(r - s)^2}$ when $r = 7$ and $s = 5$.

(*e*) E in $E = Ir + IR$ when $I = 5$, $r = 16$, and $R = 20$.

15. Solve and check, using the set of real numbers: **504**

(*a*) $x + 6 = 13$ (*d*) $b - 7 = 4$ (*f*) $6\,n + 17 = 35$

(*b*) $-7\,y = 63$ (*e*) $\dfrac{a}{9} = 18$ (*g*) $5\,x - x = 10$

(*c*) $0 = 8\,r - 24$ (*h*) $\frac{4}{7}\,m = 76$

16. Read, or write in words, the following: **509**

$$\{x \mid 5\,x - 2 = 13\}$$

17. Find the solution set of: **509**

(*a*) $n - 5 = 7$ when the replacement set is the set of all natural numbers.

(*b*) $3\,x + 11 = 2$ when the replacement set is the set of all integers.

(*c*) $4\,b - 3 = 21$ when the replacement set is the set of all prime numbers.

18. Find the solution set of $|\,y\,| + 6 = 15$, using the **511**
set of real numbers.

19. Find the value of *t* when $v = 217$, $V = 25$, and **502**
$g = 32$. Formula: $v = V + gt$

20. Find the solution set of each of the following in- **511**
equalities when the replacement set is the set of all real
numbers:

(a) $8x > 136$ (d) $4a + 13 \geqq 1$ (g) $-7y \nless -21$
(b) $n + 3 < 11$ (e) $6a - 7a < 0$ (h) $2n - 5n > -15$
(c) $t - 5 \ngtr -7$ (i) $\frac{3}{5}x \leqq 42$
                  (f) $\frac{d}{3} \neq -1$

21. Find the solution set of: **514**

(a) $3d + 6 > 21$ when the replacement set is the set of
all integers.

(b) $-5y \leqq -60$ when the replacement set is the set
of all multiples of 3.

(c) $2x - 4 < -12$ when the replacement set is
$$\{-4, -3, -2, -1, 0, 1, 2, 3, 4\}.$$

22. On a number line draw the graph of each of the **517**
following equations when the replacement set is the set of
all real numbers:

(a) $x + 4 = 9$ (b) $-7c = 28$ (c) $5y - 3 = 7$

23. On a number line draw the graph of each of the **519**
following inequalities when the replacement set is the set
of all real numbers:

(a) $n < 5$ (c) $s - 3 \geqq 1$ (e) $2y - 8y \ngtr 18$
(b) $8a > -16$ (d) $5b + 2 \neq 7$ (f) $-1 < x < 2$

24. Find the ratio of 96 to 16. Of 30 to 75. Of 8 inches **522**
to 2 feet.

25. Solve and check: $\dfrac{n}{54} = \dfrac{13}{18}$ **524**

26. Construct a bar graph showing the areas of the con- **529**
tinents: Africa, 11,600,000 sq. mi.; Antarctica, 5,100,000
sq. mi.; Asia, 16,235,000 sq. mi.; Australia, 2,974,581
sq. mi.; Europe, 3,781,407 sq. mi.; North America,
9,375,000 sq. mi.; South America, 6,846,000 sq. mi.

27. Construct a line graph showing the changes in the **530**
market price of an industrial stock. On Monday it sold
at $19 per share, on Tuesday at $22.50, on Wednesday
at $24, on Thursday at $23.25, and on Friday at $21.75.

28. Construct a circle graph showing that a certain com- **531**
pany distributes its advertising costs as follows: television,

25%; radio, 10%; newspapers, 30%; magazines, 20%; contests, 10%; all other, 5%.

29. Find the mean, median, mode, and range for the following scores: 12, 17, 11, 14, 19, 20, 11, 15, 18, 15, 16, 11, 13, 12, 11, 13, 10   **532**

30. A bag contains 9 blue marbles and 6 green marbles. What is the probability of selecting on the first draw: (a) a blue marble? (b) a green marble? What are the odds of selecting a blue marble? A green marble?   **533**

POSITIVE AND NEGATIVE NUMBERS

Extension of the Number System—Integers, Rational Numbers, Real Numbers—Number Line, Absolute Value

The number system used in the preceding parts of this book contains only the numbers of arithmetic, namely the whole numbers and the fractions. With this limited number system we could not subtract 7 from 5, or $\frac{3}{4}$ from $\frac{1}{2}$, or .58 from .09. By enlarging our number system to include negative numbers so that the operation of subtraction is closed (see page 487), we shall be able to do all kinds of subtractions.

On page 18 we found that numerals may be arranged in a definite order on the number line so that they correspond one-to-one with points on the line. Thus far the number line has been restricted to points which are associated with whole numbers and fractions and are located to the right of the point labeled 0.

Let us extend the number line to the left of the point labeled 0. Again using the interval between 0 and 1 as the unit of measure, we locate equally spaced points to the left of the 0. The first new point is labeled − 1 (read "negative one"), the second point − 2 (read "negative two"), the third point − 3 (read "negative three"), etc. There are fractional subdivisions to the left of zero matching those to the right of zero.

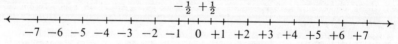

$$-\tfrac{1}{2} \quad +\tfrac{1}{2}$$

$$-7 \quad -6 \quad -5 \quad -4 \quad -3 \quad -2 \quad -1 \quad 0 \quad +1 \quad +2 \quad +3 \quad +4 \quad +5 \quad +6 \quad +7$$

The numbers corresponding to the points to the left of the point marked 0 are negative numbers and their numerals are identified by the minus signs that precede the digits, either centered or to the upper left.

> − 4 or ⁻4 names the number negative four.

The numbers corresponding to the points to the right of the point marked 0 are positive numbers and their numerals are identified by the plus signs that precede the digits.

> + 5 or ⁺5 names the number positive five.

A numeral without a sign for a number greater than zero is considered to represent a positive number. Zero is neither positive nor negative.

In arithmetic plus and minus signs are used to indicate the operations of addition and subtraction. However in algebra they are used not only to indicate these operations but also to indicate positive and negative numbers (sometimes called signed or directed numbers).

Positive and negative numbers are used in science, statistics, sports, and weather and stock reports among many other things. They are used to express opposites: opposite meanings or opposite directions.

The set consisting of all the positive whole numbers, all the negative whole numbers, and zero is usually called the set of integers.

The set consisting of all the positive and negative fractions and all the integers (since each may be expressed in fraction form) is usually called the set of rational numbers.

Real numbers are all the rational and irrational numbers. They include zero, the positive and negative whole numbers, fractions and irrational numbers.

The real number line is the complete set of points which corresponds to the set of all real numbers. The real number line is endless in both directions and only a part of it is shown at any one time.

The number line may be drawn horizontally or vertically. On the horizontal number line, of two numbers the number corresponding to the point on the line farther to the right is the greater number. On the vertical number line, the numbers corresponding to points above the point marked 0 are positive and those below are negative. Any number corresponding to a point is greater than any number corresponding to a point located below it.

The absolute value of any number is the value of the corresponding arithmetic number which has no sign. The absolute value of − 4 is 4 and the absolute value of + 4 is 4. The absolute value of 0 is 0.

A pair of vertical bars | | is the symbol used to designate absolute value. | − 4 | is read "the absolute value of negative four."

PRACTICE PROBLEMS

1. Read, or write in words, each of the following:

− 6;   + 11;   − 8;   + $\frac{7}{8}$;   − .09; $^{+}$50;   − $\frac{15}{4}$;   + $6\frac{1}{3}$

2. Write symbolically:

(*a*) Negative twelve

(*b*) Positive forty

(*c*) Positive one-third

(*d*) Negative six thousandths

(*e*) Negative fifteen

(*f*) Positive eight fifths

3.

On the number line:

(*a*) Which number corresponds to point *M*? *I*? *R*? *K*? *S*? *H*? *D*?

(*b*) Which letter labels the point corresponding to each of the following numbers? − 3; + 1; − 6; − 9; + 4; − 7; + 8; − 2

(*c*) Is the point corresponding to − 5 to the left or to the right of the point corresponding to − 8? Which number is greater, − 5 or − 8?

(*d*) Which letter corresponds to the greater number:

(**1**) Point *N* or Point *Q*?   (**3**) Point *R* or point *G*?

(**2**) Point *S* or Point *D*?   (**4**) Point *A* or Point *J*?

4. For each of the following sets of numbers draw a number line and indicate the points corresponding to the numbers:

(*a*) {0, + 3, + 5, + 8}

(*b*) {− 3, − 2, − 1, 0, + 1, + 2, + 3}

(*c*) {− 6, + 7, − 3, + 4, − 1, 0}

(*d*) {+ 3, − 5, + 2, − 4, − 1, + 6, − 2}

5. Which of the following are true?

(a) $+3 > -4$ (f) $-7 < -7$ (k) $+3 \not< +2$
(b) $0 < -5$ (g) $+6 > +1$ (l) $-1 \not> +1$
(c) $+2 < +8$ (h) $+3 < -4$ (m) $-6 < +6$
(d) $-12 > +10$ (i) $0 > +4$ (n) $-2 > -1$
(e) $-6 < -3$ (j) $-5 > -2$ (o) $+15 \not< -21$

6. (a) If an increase of 4% in the cost of living is indicated by $+4\%$, how can a 2% decrease in the cost of living be represented?

(b) If a loss of $1\frac{1}{2}$ points in a stock is indicated by $-1\frac{1}{2}$ points, how can a gain of $\frac{3}{4}$ point be indicated?

(c) If -30 pounds represents a downward force of 30 pounds, what does $+75$ pounds represent?

(d) If $+18$ m.p.h. indicates a tail wind of 18 m.p.h., what does -23 m.p.h. represent?

(e) If $+250$ feet represents 250 feet above sea level, what does -60 feet represent?

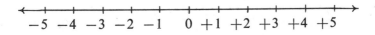 (f) If 85 degrees west longitude is indicated by $-85°$, how can 54° east longitude be indicated?

7. Find the absolute value of each of the following:

(a) $|-9|$ (c) $|-12|$ (e) $|+25|$ (g) $|+1\frac{1}{2}|$ (i) $|-8.6|$
(b) $|+7|$ (d) $|0|$ (f) $|-\frac{3}{8}|$ (h) $|-.3|$ (j) $|+100|$

8. (a) Is $+9$ an integer? A rational number? A real number?

(b) Is -7 an integer? A rational number? A real number?

(c) Is $-\frac{5}{8}$ an integer? A rational number? A real number?

Opposites; Negative of a Number; Additive Inverse

Examination of the number line will show that for every point on one side of the point labeled 0 there is a corresponding point on the opposite side exactly the same distance from this point labeled 0.

$$-5 \quad -4 \quad -3 \quad -2 \quad -1 \quad 0 \quad +1 \quad +2 \quad +3 \quad +4 \quad +5$$

A pair of numbers (like coordinates $+4$ and -4) which corresponds to such a pair of points are called opposites. Each is the opposite of the other. The opposite of zero is zero. Sometimes the opposite of a number is called the negative of a number.

If the sum of two numbers is zero, each addend is said to be the additive inverse of the other addend. Since the sum of a number and its opposite is zero, then the additive inverse, the opposite, and the negative of a number all describe the same number.

Thus, -6 is the *opposite* of or the *negative* of or the *additive inverse* of $+6$

and $+6$ is the *opposite* of or the *negative* of or the *additive inverse* of -6.

A negative sign is used to indicate the opposite or the negative of a number. Not all negatives of numbers are negative numbers. The negative of -6 is $+6$ or just 6.

The sentence $-(-6) = +6$ is usually read as:
The opposite of negative six is positive six.

or   The negative of negative six is positive six.

PRACTICE PROBLEMS

1. Read, or write in words, each of the following:

(a) $-(+5)$ (c) $-(-3) = +3$ (e) $-(+.9) = -.9$

(b) $-(-8)$ (d) $-(+4) = -4$ (f) $-(-\frac{3}{4}) = +\frac{3}{4}$

2. Write symbolically:

(a) The opposite of negative eleven.

(b) The negative of negative seven.

(c) The additive inverse of positive twenty.

(d) The negative of negative twelve is positive twelve.

(e) The opposite of positive forty is negative forty.

3. Write the opposite of:

(a) -2 (b) $+16$ (c) $-.35$ (d) $+\frac{14}{5}$ (e) $+150$ (f) $-9\frac{1}{2}$

4. Write the negative of:

(a) $+17$ (b) -9 (c) $-\frac{11}{16}$ (d) $+1.603$ (e) $+6\frac{7}{8}$ (f) -72

5. Write the additive inverse of:

(a) -15 (b) $+.1$ (c) $-\frac{31}{8}$ (d) $+4\frac{1}{3}$ (e) -2.3 (f) $+805$

6. Find the:

(a) Opposite of the opposite of: -14; $+29$; $-.4$; $+\frac{4}{5}$

(b) Negative of the negative of: $+23$; $-\frac{2}{3}$; -700; $+8.1$

7. Are all negatives of numbers negative numbers? If not, illustrate.

Computation

Arrows or vectors may be used to add or subtract positive and negative numbers on the number line. The absolute value of a signed number indicates the length of the vector and the sign of the given number indicates the direction of the vector. On the horizontal number line moving to the right is the positive direction and to the left is the negative direction.

Addition

To add on a number line, draw a vector for the first addend, starting at the point labeled 0; then draw the vector representing the second addend, starting from the point reached by the first vector. If there are more than two addends, continue in this way for each addend. The coordinate of the final point reached is the sum.

When two addends are both positive numbers, the final direction is positive. When two addends are both negative numbers, the final direction is negative. When one addend is a positive number and the other is a negative number, the number containing the greater absolute value determines the final direction.

Thus algebraically,

To add two positive numbers, find the sum of their absolute values and prefix the numeral with a positive sign.

To add two negative numbers, find the sum of their absolute values and prefix the numeral with a negative sign.

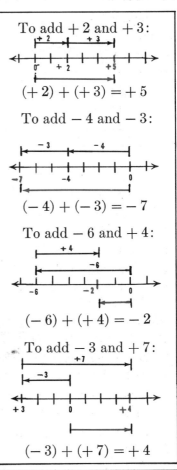

To add $+2$ and $+3$:

$$(+2) + (+3) = +5$$

To add -4 and -3:

$$(-4) + (-3) = -7$$

To add -6 and $+4$:

$$(-6) + (+4) = -2$$

To add -3 and $+7$:

$$(-3) + (+7) = +4$$

Add: $\begin{array}{r} +2 \\ +3 \\ \hline +5 \end{array}$ Add: $\begin{array}{r} -4 \\ -3 \\ \hline -7 \end{array}$

(Continued)

To add a positive number and a negative number, subtract the smaller absolute value from the greater absolute value and prefix the difference with the sign of the number having the greater absolute value.

The sum of any number and its opposite is zero.

To add three or more signed numbers, add algebraically first the positive numbers, then the negative numbers, and finally the two answers.

$$
\begin{array}{ccc}
\text{Add:} & -6 & -3 & +9 \\
& \underline{+4} & \underline{+7} & \underline{-6} \\
& -2 & +4 & +3
\end{array}
$$

$$
\begin{array}{cc}
\text{Add:} & +7 & -5 \\
& \underline{-7} & \underline{+5} \\
& 0 & 0
\end{array}
$$

$$(+2) + (-9) + (+6) + (-3)$$
$$= (+8) + (-12)$$
$$= -4$$

To simplify an algebraic expression such as $6 - 9 + 4 - 3$, think of it as $(+6) + (-9) + (+4) + (-3)$ where the given signs are part of the numerals for the signed numbers but the operation is considered to be addition. See page 487.

$$6 - 9 + 4 - 3 = (+6) + (-9) + (+4) + (-3) = -2$$

PRACTICE PROBLEMS

1. Add on the number line, using vectors:

$$
\begin{array}{cccccccc}
+5 & -4 & +7 & +2 & -8 & -1 & +4 & 0 \\
\underline{+3} & \underline{-1} & \underline{-3} & \underline{-6} & \underline{+2} & \underline{+5} & \underline{-4} & \underline{-9}
\end{array}
$$

2. Add:

(a)
$$
\begin{array}{cccccccc}
+3 & +9 & +24 & +8 & -5 & -9 & -27 & -83 \\
\underline{+6} & \underline{+7} & \underline{+19} & \underline{+15} & \underline{-4} & \underline{-14} & \underline{-35} & \underline{-49}
\end{array}
$$

(b)
$$
\begin{array}{cccccccc}
+5 & +11 & +25 & +91 & -9 & -8 & -23 & -54 \\
\underline{-2} & \underline{-3} & \underline{-14} & \underline{-37} & \underline{+1} & \underline{+6} & \underline{+12} & \underline{+39}
\end{array}
$$

(c)
$$
\begin{array}{cccccccc}
+1 & +3 & +12 & +20 & -6 & -2 & -18 & -45 \\
\underline{-8} & \underline{-10} & \underline{-36} & \underline{-41} & \underline{+8} & \underline{+15} & \underline{+27} & \underline{+68}
\end{array}
$$

(d)
$$
\begin{array}{cccccccc}
+6 & -12 & 0 & -5 & +\frac{3}{4} & -\frac{7}{8} & -.4 & -5.28 \\
\underline{-6} & \underline{+12} & \underline{+7} & \underline{0} & \underline{-\frac{1}{4}} & \underline{-\frac{2}{3}} & \underline{+1.5} & \underline{-2.64}
\end{array}
$$

(e)
$$
\begin{array}{cccccccc}
+8 & -3 & -3 & +9 & +2 & -3 & -4 & -6 \\
+5 & -8 & +6 & -15 & +1 & -1 & +7 & -9 \\
\underline{+7} & \underline{-9} & \underline{-5} & \underline{+3} & +4 & -5 & -8 & +7 \\
& & & & \underline{+6} & \underline{-2} & \underline{+5} & \underline{-2}
\end{array}
$$

3. Add as indicated:

(a) $(-3) + (-4)$

(b) $(+8) + (-15)$

(c) $(-1) + (+11)$

(d) $(+5) + (-14) + (+7)$

(e) $(-3) + (-9) + (-5)$

(f) $[(+8) + (-11)] + (-4)$

(g) $(-10) + [(-8) + (-2)]$

(h) $(+7) + (-5) + (-10) + (+9)$

(i) $(-7) + (+4) + (-1) + (+6)$

(j) $(-12) + (+9) + (-6) + (+9)$

4. Simplify:

(a) $2 + 6$

(b) $4 - 8$

(c) $-6 + 7$

(d) $-5 - 3$

(e) $18 - 9 + 5$

(f) $9 - 7 + 2$

(g) $5 - 6 - 8$

(h) $-3 + 8 - 7$

(i) $14 - 5 + 3 - 11$

(j) $-9 - 6 + 7 - 2$

(k) $6 - 8 + 2 - 4 + 5$

(l) $-2 - 3 + 9 - 1 + 3$

5. Simplify by performing the indicated operations and finding the absolute values:

(a) $|7 + 4|$

(b) $|9 - 11|$

(c) $|-4 - 5|$

(d) $|-8 + 2|$

(e) $|-10| + |+7|$

(f) $|(-6) + (-2)|$

(g) $-|14 - 5|$

(h) $-|16 - 24|$

(i) $-9 + |-8|$

(j) $-|-(-4) + (-6)|$

Subtraction

Used as the inverse operation of addition, the operation of subtraction requires that we find the addend which when added to the given addend (subtrahend) will equal the given sum (minuend).

$(+3) - (-2) = ?$ is thought of as $(-2) + ? = (+3)$

Thus, to subtract on the number line, draw the vectors for the given addend and the sum. Find the missing addend by calculating the distance and determining the direction (or representing them by a vector) from the point associated with the given addend (subtrahend) to the point associated with the sum (minuend).

$(+3) - (-2) = ?$

$? = +5$

-2

$-2 \quad 0 \quad +3$

$+3$

The distance from -2 to $+3$ is 5 units. The direction is to the right or the positive direction.

$(+3) - (-2) = +5$

This distance in units is the absolute value of the missing addend and the direction indicates the sign of the addend. Counting to the right is the positive direction and to the left is the negative direction.

In addition we learned that $(+3) + (+2) = +5$
On page 487 we find that $\qquad (+3) - (-2) = +5$
A comparison of $(+3) - (-2) = +5$
$\qquad\qquad$ and $(+3) + (+2) = +5$
shows that *subtracting* -2 from $+3$ gives the same answer as *adding* $+2$ to $+3$. That is, *subtracting a number gives the same answer as adding its opposite.*

Thus algebraically,

To subtract a number (positive, negative, or zero) from another number (positive, negative, or zero), add to the minuend the additive inverse (or opposite) of the number to be subtracted.

Subtract:	Add:	Subtract:	Add:	Subtract:	Add:	Subtract:	Add:	Subtract:	Add:
$+2$	$+2$	$+2$	$+2$	-2	-2	-2	-2	0	0
$+8 \rightarrow$	-8	$-8 \rightarrow$	$+8$	$+8 \rightarrow$	-8	$-8 \rightarrow$	$+8$	$+8 \rightarrow$	-8
	-6		$+10$		-10		$+6$		-8
Answer: -6		*Answer:* $+10$		*Answer:* -10		*Answer:* $+6$		*Answer:* -8	

We may also subtract by changing the sign of the given subtrahend mentally and adding this number to the minuend. This method, generally used in traditional mathematics, is another way of finding the additive inverse and adding it to the minuend.

PRACTICE PROBLEMS

1. Subtract on the number line, using vectors:

$+6$	$+2$	-5	-3	$+4$	-2	0	-4
$+3$	$+9$	-1	-7	-6	$+5$	-8	-4

2. Subtract:

(a)

9	$+11$	$+15$	$+17$	5	6	$+2$	$+28$
3	$+6$	$+9$	$+8$	7	15	$+14$	$+45$

(b)

-6	-10	-8	-12	-5	-7	-6	-51
-4	-5	-3	-7	-8	-9	-13	-70

(c)

$+7$	$+9$	$+6$	$+18$	-12	-6	-5	-16
-2	-11	-5	-27	$+3$	$+19$	$+1$	$+25$

(d)	$+6$	-5	0	$+8$	$+11$	$-.6$	$-\frac{7}{8}$	$-2\frac{1}{2}$
	$+6$	-5	-1	0	-11	$-.7$	$+\frac{3}{4}$	$-1\frac{2}{3}$
(e)	$+5$	-6	-13	$+20$	-3	-14	$+.9$	0
	$+9$	-2	$+7$	-15	0	$+14$	-1.5	-17

3. Subtract as indicated:

(a) $(-8) - (+3)$
(b) $(+6) - (-11)$
(c) $(2) - (-2)$
(d) $(4 - 3) - (6 - 10)$
(e) $(2 - 6) - (7 - 8)$

(f) $(8 + 7) - (6 - 13)$
(g) $[(-2) + (-7)] - (-9)$
(h) $(+4) - [(-5) - (+6)]$
(i) $[(-5) - (+8)] - (-12)$
(j) $(-6) - [(-10) + (+3)]$

4. (a) From -5 subtract 5.
(b) Take 4 from 1.
(c) From -3 take -7.

(d) Subtract 10 from 3.
(e) Take -9 from $+9$.
(f) From 0 subtract -8.

5. Simplify by performing the indicated operations and finding the absolute values:

(a) $|-4| - |-9|$
(b) $|6 - 2| - |-5|$
(c) $|1 - 3| - |4 - 7|$

(d) $|-3 - 8| - 6$
(e) $8 - |5 + 9|$
(f) $|(0 - 2) - (4 - 2)|$

Multiplication

The expression three times four may be written as 3×4, $3 \cdot 4$, $(3) \times (4)$, $3(4)$, $(3)\, 4$, or $(3)(4)$. Observe that the $\times$ symbol or raised dot is used or the factors may be written next to each other within parentheses without any multiplication symbol.

Since a numeral without a sign represents a positive number and multiplication may be thought of as repeated addition, then

$$3 \times 4 \text{ or } (+3)(+4) = (+4) + (+4) + (+4) = +12$$

The product of two positive numbers is a positive number.
Similarly, $(+3)(-4) = (-4) + (-4) + (-4) = -12$
and since $(+4)(-3) = -12$ and $(-3)(+4) = (+4)(-3)$ by the commutative property of multiplication,

then $$(-3)(+4) = -12$$

The product of a positive number and a negative number is a negative number.

To determine what $(-3)(-4)$ equals, examine the following step-by-step development:

1. $(-3) \cdot 0 = 0$ The product of any number and zero is zero.

2. But $[(+4) + (-4)] = 0$ The sum of a number and its additive inverse is zero.

3. Then
   $(-3) \cdot [(+4) + (-4)] = 0$ By substituting $[(+4) + (-4)]$ for 0 in step (1).

4. $(-3)(+4) + (-3)(-4) = 0$ Multiplication is distributive over addition.

5. $-12 + (-3)(-4) = 0$ Since $(-3)(+4) = -12$

6. Therefore $(-3)(-4) = +12$ In order for the sentence $-12 + (-3)(-4) = 0$ to be true, the product of $(-3)(-4)$ must be the additive inverse of -12, which is $+12$.

The product of two negative numbers is a positive number.

Summarizing

To multiply two positive numbers or two negative numbers, find the product of their absolute values and prefix the numeral for this product with a positive sign.

To multiply a positive number by a negative number or a negative number by a positive number, find the product of their absolute values and prefix the numeral for this product with a negative sign.

Multiply:

$$\begin{array}{r} +5 \\ +6 \\ \hline +30 \end{array} \qquad \begin{array}{r} -5 \\ -6 \\ \hline +30 \end{array}$$

Multiply:

$$\begin{array}{r} +5 \\ -6 \\ \hline -30 \end{array} \qquad \begin{array}{r} -5 \\ +6 \\ \hline -30 \end{array}$$

Observe that an odd number of negative factors produces a negative number as a product while an even number of negative factors produces a positive number as a product provided zero is not a factor.

$$(-2)(+1)(-4)(-2) = -16 \qquad (-1)(-5)(-2)(-1) = +10$$

PRACTICE PROBLEMS

1. Multiply:

(a) $\begin{array}{r} +5 \\ +9 \end{array}$ $\begin{array}{r} +8 \\ +6 \end{array}$ $\begin{array}{r} +7 \\ +7 \end{array}$ $\begin{array}{r} +6 \\ +4 \end{array}$ $\begin{array}{r} -2 \\ -3 \end{array}$ $\begin{array}{r} -9 \\ -4 \end{array}$ $\begin{array}{r} -6 \\ -7 \end{array}$ $\begin{array}{r} -8 \\ -5 \end{array}$

(b) $\begin{array}{r} -7 \\ +8 \end{array}$ $\begin{array}{r} -2 \\ +9 \end{array}$ $\begin{array}{r} -4 \\ +12 \end{array}$ $\begin{array}{r} -13 \\ +5 \end{array}$ $\begin{array}{r} +6 \\ -6 \end{array}$ $\begin{array}{r} +12 \\ -8 \end{array}$ $\begin{array}{r} +4 \\ -5 \end{array}$ $\begin{array}{r} +6 \\ -9 \end{array}$

(c) $\begin{array}{r} 0 \\ +3 \end{array}$ $\begin{array}{r} -5 \\ 0 \end{array}$ $\begin{array}{r} 0 \\ -8 \end{array}$ $\begin{array}{r} +4 \\ 0 \end{array}$ $\begin{array}{r} -.4 \\ -.2 \end{array}$ $\begin{array}{r} +2.5 \\ -1.4 \end{array}$ $\begin{array}{r} -3\frac{1}{2} \\ +2\frac{1}{4} \end{array}$ $\begin{array}{r} -12 \\ -1\frac{2}{3} \end{array}$

2. Multiply as indicated:

(a) $(-3)(-9)$

(b) $(+4)(-7)$

(c) $11(3-14)$

(d) $-8(-7-5)$

(e) $(+6)(-2)(-4)$

(f) $(-2)\times[(-6)(-7)]$

(g) $-5(3-8)-(1-4)$

(h) $[(+10)(-4)]\times(-3)$

(i) $(-2)(+3)(-1)(-4)$

(j) $(-6)(-3)(-2)(-5)$

3. Find the value of each of the following:

(a) $(-3)^2$ (c) $(-5)^3$ (e) $(-4)^5$ (g) $(-3)^4$

(b) $(+6)^2$ (d) $(+2)^4$ (f) $(-1)^6$ (h) $(-1)^5 \cdot (-3)^3$

4. Simplify by performing the indicated operations and then finding the absolute values:

(a) $|(-1)(-5)|$

(b) $|-4|\times|-7|$

(c) $-10\times|-6|$

(d) $|12-3|\times|6-8|$

(e) $(-6)\times|(-2)(-9)(-1)|$

(f) $|-5|^2\times|(-4)(-11)|$

Division

Since $(+3)\times(+4)=+12$,

then $(+12)\div(+3)=+4$ or $\dfrac{+12}{+3}=+4$

Since $(-3)\times(+4)=-12$,

then $(-12)\div(-3)=+4$ or $\dfrac{-12}{-3}=+4$

When the dividend and the divisor are both positive numbers or both negative numbers, the quotient is a positive number.

Since $(+3)\times(-4)=-12$,

then $(-12)\div(+3)=-4$ or $\dfrac{-12}{+3}=-4$

Since $(-3)\times(-4)=+12$,

then $(+12)\div(-3)=-4$ or $\dfrac{+12}{-3}=-4$

When the dividend is a positive number and the divisor is a negative number or vice-versa, the quotient is a negative number.

Summarizing

To divide a positive number by a positive number or a negative number by a negative number, divide their absolute values and prefix the numeral for this quotient with a positive sign.

To divide a positive number by a negative number or a negative number by a positive number, divide their absolute values and prefix the numeral for this quotient with a negative sign.

PRACTICE PROBLEMS

1. Divide:

(a) $\dfrac{+30}{+5}$ $\dfrac{+16}{+4}$ $\dfrac{+54}{+9}$ $\dfrac{+60}{+10}$ $\dfrac{-8}{-2}$ $\dfrac{-15}{-5}$ $\dfrac{-90}{-18}$ $\dfrac{-72}{-12}$

(b) $\dfrac{+56}{-7}$ $\dfrac{+18}{-3}$ $\dfrac{+45}{-5}$ $\dfrac{+36}{-6}$ $\dfrac{-48}{+8}$ $\dfrac{-63}{+7}$ $\dfrac{-80}{+10}$ $\dfrac{-144}{+16}$

(c) $\dfrac{-9}{-9}$ $\dfrac{+7}{-7}$ $\dfrac{-15}{-1}$ $\dfrac{-40}{+1}$ $\dfrac{0}{+6}$ $\dfrac{0}{-3}$ $\dfrac{0}{+15}$ $\dfrac{0}{-20}$

2. Divide as indicated:

(a) $(+36) \div (-9)$ (f) $(-8\frac{1}{2}) \div (-\frac{3}{4})$

(b) $(-20) \div (-4)$ (g) $(+.24) \div (-.3)$

(c) $(-42) \div (+7)$ (h) $(-40) \div (-40)$

(d) $(+75) \div (+5)$ (i) $(+19) \div (-1)$

(e) $(0) \div (-7)$ (j) $(-100) \div (+25)$

3. Divide as indicated:

(a) $+2\overline{)-14}$ (c) $-3\overline{)-27}$ (e) $.4\overline{)-3.2}$

(b) $-8\overline{)-64}$ (d) $-5\overline{)+50}$ (f) $-7\overline{)+21}$

4. Simplify by performing the indicated operations:

(a) $\dfrac{8-17}{3}$ (c) $\dfrac{12-3(4)}{-2}$ (e) $\dfrac{(-4)^3 - (-2)^4}{(-10)^2}$

(b) $\dfrac{-10-4}{-7}$ (d) $\dfrac{8(-1)+7(-6)}{-5(5)}$ (f) $\dfrac{6(4-3)-5(6-12)}{-3(1-5)}$

5. Simplify by performing the indicated operations and finding the absolute values:

(a) $\dfrac{|-16|}{8}$ (c) $\left|\dfrac{-30}{-5}\right|$ (e) $\dfrac{|(-12)(+7)|}{|8-9|-|1-5|}$

(b) $\dfrac{|-24|}{|-2|}$ (d) $\dfrac{|-8| \times |-6|}{|-9|-|-5|}$ (f) $\dfrac{|-3|^3 - |1|^4}{|(-6)+(-7)|}$

LANGUAGE OF ALGEBRA

Symbols

The symbolism previously used in arithmetic is also used in algebra. This includes the operational symbols of addition (+ sign), of subtraction (− sign), of multiplication (× sign or raised dot ·), of division (÷ or $\overline{)}$ symbols), exponents, parentheses, the square root symbol $\sqrt{}$, verbs of mathematical sentences such as =, ≠, >, ≯, <, ≮, ≧, ≩, ≦, ≨, and symbols of sets such as { }, ϕ, ∈, ∉, ∪, ∩, ⊂, ⊃. The fraction bar, as in $\frac{c}{d}$, generally indicates division. $\frac{c}{d}$ is sometimes read "c over d."

A numeral consisting of one or more digits represents an arithmetic number which is definite in value. A numeral is sometimes called a *constant.*

A *variable* is a letter (small letter, capital letter, letter with a subscript such as "b_1," read "b sub one" or letter with prime marks such as S' read "S prime") or a frame (such as □, ▭, ○, and △) or a blank which holds a place open for a number. Sometimes the first letter of a key word is used as the variable. A variable may represent any number but, under certain conditions, it represents a specific number or numbers.

Mathematical Expressions or Phrases

A *numerical expression* or *numerical phrase* consists of a single numeral with or without operational symbols like 18 or 3^4 or two or more numerals with operational symbols like $7 + 5$; $28 - 14$; 5×43; $63 \div 7$; $8 \times (3 + 11)$; etc.

An *algebraic expression* or *algebraic phrase* may be a numerical expression as described above or an expression containing one or more variables joined by operational symbols like b; $a - 5x$; $3y^2 - 7x + 9$; etc.

Both numerical expressions and algebraic expressions are *mathematical expressions.*

In an algebraic expression no multiplication symbol is necessary when the factors are two letters (variables) or a numeral and a letter. In the latter case the numeral always precedes the letter or the variable. This numeral is called the *numeral coefficient* of the variable. In $5x^3$, the 5 is the numerical coefficient of x^3.

---

b times d may be expressed as bxd, $b \cdot d$, bd (preferred), $(b)(d)$, $b(d)$, or $(b)d$.

To write algebraic expressions, write numerals, variables, and operational symbols as required in the proper order.

Write each of the following as an algebraic expression:

(1) The sum of five and seven.   *Answer:* $5 + 7$

(2) The difference between x and eight.   *Answer:* $x - 8$

(3) The product of the force (F) and the distance (d).

Answer: Fd

(4) The area (A) divided by the length (l).   *Answer:* $\dfrac{A}{l}$

(5) The square of the velocity (v).   *Answer:* v^2

(6) The square root of the radius (r).   *Answer:* $\sqrt{r}$

PRACTICE PROBLEMS

1. Write each of the following as an algebraic expression:

(a) Six added to four.

(b) Twelve times nineteen.

(c) From ten subtract two.

(d) Fifteen divided by three.

(e) The square of nine.

(f) The square root of twenty.

(g) The sum of eight and three.

(h) The difference between six and two.

(i) The product of nine and five.

(j) The quotient of twelve divided by four.

(k) The sum of b and x.

(l) a times y.

(m) The product of g and eight.

(n) The difference between c and g.

(o) The quotient of d divided by r.

(p) Two times the sum of l and w.

(q) The cube of r.

(r) The square root of s.

(s) The product of b and h.

(t) Three times the difference between t and y.

2. Read, or write in words, each of the following:

(a) $5 n$ (c) $y + 25$ (e) $cd^2 x^3$ (g) $(m + 2 n)(3 m - n)$

(b) $19 - 7$ (d) $\dfrac{m}{x}$ (f) $6 a - 9 b$ (h) $3 x^2 - 4 xy + 7 y^2$

3. Write each of the following as an algebraic expression:

(a) Twice the radius (r).

(b) Three times the side (s).

(c) The principal (p) plus the interest (i).

(d) 90° decreased by angle B.

(e) The sum of angles A, B, and C.

(f) The circumference (c) divided by pi (π).

(g) The length (l) times the width (w) times the height (h).

(h) The profit (p) added to the cost (c).

(i) One half the product of the altitude (a) and base (b).

(j) Angle B subtracted from 180°.

(k) The square of the side (s).

(l) The base (b) multiplied by the height (h) divided by two.

(m) The sum of twice the length (l) and twice the width (w).

(n) The cube of the edge (e).

(o) The quotient of the interest (i) for one year divided by the principal (p).

(p) The sum of bases b_1 and b_2 divided by two.

(q) Four thirds the product of pi (π) and the cube of the radius (r).

(r) The square of the altitude (a) added to the square of the base (b).

(s) Twice pi (π) times the radius (r) times the sum of the height (h) and radius.

(t) The square root of the difference between the square of the hypotenuse (h) and the square of the base (b).

4. Write an algebraic expression for each of the following:

(a) Marilyn has n cents. She spends 65 cents for lunch. How many cents does she have left?

(b) Scott is x years old. How old will he be in fifteen years?

(c) Steve has d dollars in the bank. If he deposits y dollars, how many dollars will he then have in the bank?

(d) How many hours did it take a train to travel m miles if it averaged r m.p.h.?

(e) How many notebooks can be bought for x cents if one notebook costs y cents?

Mathematical Sentences—Open Sentences; Equations; Inequalities; Formulas; Compound Sentences

Sentences such as:

$7 + 9 = 16$	read as "Seven plus nine is equal to sixteen"
or $x - 4 = 9$	read as "Some number x decreased by four is equal to nine"
or $8\,a > 20$	read as "Eight times each number a is greater than twenty"
or $n + 10 < 14$	read as "Each number n increased by ten is less than fourteen"

are *mathematical sentences*.

An *open sentence* is a mathematical sentence that contains a variable. $x - 4 = 9$, $8\,a > 20$, and $n + 10 < 14$ are open sentences.

An *equation* is an open sentence that has the equality sign "$=$" as its verb. The sentence $x - 4 = 9$ is an equation.

If a sentence uses $\neq$, $>$, $<$, $\not>$, $\not<$, $\geqq$, $\leqq$, $\not\geqq$, or $\not\leqq$ as its verb, it is called an *inequation* or *inequality*. The sentences $8\,a > 20$ and $n + 10 < 14$ are inequalities.

An open sentence is neither true nor false. It is only after a number is substituted for the variable that the open sentence becomes a statement and the sentence can be determined to be true or false.

A *formula* is a special kind of equation. It is a mathematical rule expressing the relationship of two or more quantities by means of numerals, variables, and operating symbols. The formula consists of algebraic expressions.

Sentences like $6\,n \leqq 30$, $8 < x < 12$, and $20 \geqq b \geqq 15$ are compound sentences with connectives "or" or "and."

The sentence "$6\,n \leqq 30$" is the shortened form of "$6\,n < 30$ or $6\,n = 30$", a *disjunction*, and is read "Six times each number n is less than or equal to thirty".

The sentence $8 < x < 12$ is the shortened form of "$8 < x$ and $x < 12$", a *conjunction*, and is read "Eight is less than each number x and each number x is less than twelve" or "Each number x is greater than eight and less than twelve."

The sentence $20 \geqq b \geqq 15$ is read "Twenty is greater than or equal to each number b which is greater than or equal to fifteen" or "Each number b is less than or equal to twenty and greater than or equal to fifteen."

To express mathematical and scientific principles as formulas, write numerals, operating symbols, and letters (variables) representing the given quantities in the required order to indicate the relationship between quantities. A quantity may be represented by the first letter of a key word.

> Write as a formula:
>
> The circumference of a circle is equal to pi (π) times the diameter (d).
>
> *Answer:* $c = \pi d$

To translate a formula to a word statement, write a word rule stating the relationship expressed by the formula.

Translate:

$a = \dfrac{360°}{n}$ where a = central angle of a regular polygon and

n = the number of sides.

Answer: A central angle of a regular polygon equals 360° divided by the number of sides.

PRACTICE PROBLEMS

1. Read, or write in words, each of the following:

(a) $n < 16$

(b) $x > 29$

(c) $3y \neq 17$

(d) $b + 6 > 25$

(e) $a - 5 < 53$

(f) $7t \nless -14$

(g) $9m + 4 = 15$

(h) $8c - 9 \ngtr c + 7$

(i) $2n + 6 < 3n - 8$

(j) $\dfrac{b}{5} > 20$

(k) $15x - 4 \ngtr 18 - 7x$

(l) $h \geqq -6$

(m) $19w \leqq 38$

(n) $5d + 7 \nleqq 12$

(o) $n - 16 \ngeqq 4n + 9$

(p) $-3 < n < 8$

(q) $18 > x > 0$

(r) $4 \leqq b \leqq 27$

(s) $12 \geqq 7r \geqq -6$

(t) $2 < a \leqq 45$

2. Write each of the following as an open sentence symbolically:

(a) Some number x increased by ten is equal to forty-one.

(b) Each number n decreased by four is less than eighteen.

(c) Four times each number t is greater than twelve.

(d) Nine times each number y plus two is not equal to fifty.

(e) Each number *a* increased by five is not less than nine.

(f) Each number *m* divided by seven is not greater than fourteen.

(g) Seven times each number *x* is greater than or equal to thirty.

(h) Each number *c* plus nine is less than or equal to ten.

(i) Each number *t* is less than negative one and greater than negative five.

(j) Twelve times each number *y* is greater than or equal to four and less than or equal to fifteen.

3. Express each of the following as a formula:

(a) The perimeter of a square (*p*) is equal to four times the length of the side (*s*).

(b) The area of a rectangle (*A*) is equal to the length (*l*) multiplied by the width (*w*).

(c) The circumference of a circle (*c*) is equal to twice pi (*π*) times the radius (*r*).

(d) The interest (*i*) is equal to the principal (*p*) times the rate of interest per year (*r*) times the time in years (*t*).

(e) The radius of a circle (*r*) is equal to the diameter (*d*) divided by two.

(f) The total amount (*A*) is equal to the sum of the principal (*p*) and the interest (*i*).

(g) The area of a parallelogram (*A*) is equal to the product of the base (*b*) and height (*h*).

(h) The volume of a cube (*V*) is equal to the cube of the edge (*e*).

(i) The area of a circle (*A*) is equal to pi (*π*) times the square of the radius (*r*).

(j) The area of a triangle (*A*) is equal to one half the product of the altitude (*a*) and base (*b*).

(k) The sum of two complementary angles (*A* and *B*) equals 90°.

(l) The net price (*n*) is equal to the list price (*l*) less the discount (*d*).

(m) The volume of a cylinder (*V*) is equal to one fourth pi (*π*) times the square of the diameter (*d*) times the height (*h*).

(n) The perimeter of an isosceles triangle (*p*) is equal to the base (*b*) added to twice the length of the equal side (*e*).

(o) The rate of commission (*r*) is equal to the commission (*c*) divided by the sales (*s*).

(p) The perimeter of a rectangle (p) is equal to twice the sum of the length (l) and width (w).

(q) The area of a trapezoid (A) is equal to the height (h) times the sum of the two parallel bases, b_1 and b_2, divided by two.

(r) The area of the surface of a rectangular solid (A) is equal to the sum of twice the product of the length (l) and width (w), twice the product of the length and height (h), and twice the product of the width and height.

(s) The hypotenuse of a right triangle (h) is equal to the square root of the sum of the square of the altitude (a) and the square of the base (b).

(t) The total area of a cylinder (A) is equal to twice pi (π) times the radius (r) times the sum of the height (h) and the radius.

4. Express each of the following formulas as a word statement:

(a) $p = 3\,s$ where $p =$ perimeter of an equilateral triangle and $s =$ length of triangle side.

(b) $E = IR$ where $E =$ electromotive force in volts, $I =$ current in amperes, and $R =$ resistance in ohms.

(c) $t = \dfrac{d}{r}$ where $t =$ time of travel, $d =$ distance traveled, and $r =$ average rate of speed.

(d) $F = 1.8\,C + 32°$ where $F =$ Fahrenheit temperature reading and $C =$ Centigrade temperature reading.

(e) $d = \frac{1}{2}\,gt^2$ where $d =$ distance a freely falling body drops, $g =$ acceleration due to gravity, and $t =$ time of falling.

EVALUATION

Algebraic Expressions

The value of an algebraic expression is dependent on the numerical values assigned to each variable of the expression. If these values change, the value of the expression usually changes.

To evaluate an algebraic expression, copy the expression and substitute the given numerical value for each variable. Perform the necessary operations as indicated in the expression.

Observe in the following models how a fractional expression, an expression containing parentheses, and an expression containing exponents are evaluated.

(1) Find the value of $2d + x$ when $d = 7$ and $x = 9$.

$$2d + x$$
$$= (2 \cdot 7) + 9$$
$$= 14 + 9$$
$$= 23$$

Answer: 23

(2) Find the value of $\dfrac{A}{b}$ when $A = 28$ and $b = 4$.

$$\frac{A}{b}$$
$$= \frac{28}{4}$$
$$= 7$$

Answer: 7

(3) Find the value of $2(l + w)$ when $l = 17$ and $w = 14$.

$$2(l + w)$$
$$= 2(17 + 14)$$
$$= 2(31)$$
$$= 62$$

Answer: 62

(4) Find the value of $c^2 + d^2$ when $c = 8$ and $d = 3$.

$$c^2 + d^2$$
$$= (8)^2 + (3)^2$$
$$= 64 + 9$$
$$= 73$$

Answer: 73

PRACTICE PROBLEMS

Find the value of each of the following algebraic expressions:

1. When $a = 12$ and $b = 6$:

(a) $a + b$
(b) $a - b$
(c) ab
(d) $\dfrac{a}{b}$
(e) a^2
(f) $7a$
(g) $4(a - b)$
(h) $a^2 - b^2$

2. When $x = 4$ and $y = 3$:

(a) $x + 6y$
(b) $5xy$
(c) $4x - 8y$
(d) $x(x - y)$
(e) $9x^2y$
(f) $x^2 - y^2$
(g) $(x + y)^2$
(h) $\dfrac{x + y}{2x - y}$

3. When $m = -8$, $n = -2$, and $x = 4$:

(a) $3mnx$
(b) $10mn - 7nx$
(c) $(m + n)(m - n)$
(d) $\dfrac{(n - x)^2}{n^2 - x^2}$
(e) $m - n(m + n)$
(f) $5m^2 + 2mx - 3x^2$

4. (a) $4s$ when $s = 6$
(b) $2r$ when $r = 12$
(c) bh when $b = 10$ and $h = 7$
(d) πd when $\pi = 3.14$ and $d = 26$
(e) ab when $a = 45$ and $b = 51$
(f) lwh when $l = 11$, $w = 7$, and $h = 15$

(g) $2\pi r$ when $\pi = \frac{22}{7}$ and $r = 21$

(h) prt when $p = 400$, $r = .06$, and $t = 8$

(i) πdh when $\pi = \frac{22}{7}$, $d = 63$, and $h = 20$

(j) $2\pi rh$ when $\pi = 3.14$, $r = 48$, and $h = 85$

5. (a) $p + i$ when $p = 500$ and $i = 120$

(b) $b + 2e$ when $b = 32$ and $e = 29$

(c) $b_1 + b_2$ when $b_1 = 47$ and $b_2 = 35$

(d) $2l + 2w$ when $l = 63$ and $w = 54$

(e) $2lw + 2lh + 2wh$ when $l = 18$, $w = 14$, and $h = 17$

6. (a) $90 - B$ when $B = 72$

(b) $A - p$ when $A = 214$ and $p = 185$

(c) $l - d$ when $l = 67$ and $d = 29$

(d) $180 - A$ when $A = 104$

(e) $A - i$ when $A = 843$ and $i = 196$

7. (a) $\dfrac{d}{2}$ when $d = 46$

(b) $\dfrac{ab}{2}$ when $a = 25$ and $b = 30$

(c) $\dfrac{c}{\pi}$ when $c = 12.56$ and $\pi = 3.14$

(d) $\dfrac{Bh}{3}$ when $B = 216$ and $h = 17$

(e) $\dfrac{b_1 + b_2}{2}$ when $b_1 = 52$ and $b_2 = 38$

8. (a) a^2 when $a = 6$

(b) s^2 when $s = 27$

(c) b^2 when $b = 105$

(d) h^2 when $h = 300$

(e) πr^2 when $\pi = \frac{22}{7}$ and $r = 28$

(f) $.7854\,d^2$ when $d = 50$

(g) $6s^2$ when $s = 41$

(h) e^3 when $e = 19$

(i) $\frac{4}{3}\pi r^3$ when $\pi = 3.14$ and $r = 20$

(j) $\pi r^2 h$ when $\pi = \frac{22}{7}$, $r = 70$, and $h = 45$

9. (a) $\frac{1}{2}ab$ when $a = 72$ and $b = 66$

(b) $\frac{1}{3}Bh$ when $B = 135$ and $h = 20$

(c) $\frac{1}{4}\pi d^2$ when $\pi = 3.14$ and $d = 55$

(d) $\frac{4}{3}\pi r^3$ when $\pi = \frac{22}{7}$ and $r = 42$

(e) $\frac{1}{3}\pi r^2 h$ when $\pi = 3.14$, $r = 69$, and $h = 80$

10. (a) $a^2 + b^2$ when $a = 11$ and $b = 9$

(b) $h^2 - a^2$ when $h = 36$ and $a = 27$

(c) $V + gt$ when $V = 150$, $g = 32$, and $t = 7$

(d) $p + prt$ when $p = 300$, $r = .06$, and $t = 8$

(e) $2\,\pi rh + 2\,\pi r^2$ when $\pi = 3.14$, $r = 20$, and $h = 75$

(f) $\pi dh + \frac{1}{2}\,\pi d^2$ when $\pi = \frac{22}{7}$, $d = 14$, and $h = 39$

11. (a) $2(l + w)$ when $l = 37$ and $w = 28$

(b) $2\,\pi r(h + r)$ when $\pi = \frac{22}{7}$, $r = 7$, and $h = 13$

(c) $I(r + R)$ when $I = 8$, $r = 3$, and $R = 10$

(d) $(n - 1)d$ when $n = 10$ and $d = 6$

(e) $h\left(\dfrac{b_1 + b_2}{2}\right)$ when $h = 34$, $b_1 = 27$, and $b_2 = 19$

(f) $\frac{5}{9}(F - 32)$ when $F = -13$

12. (a) $\sqrt{A}$ when $A = 49$

(b) $\sqrt{\dfrac{V}{\pi h}}$ when $V = 1{,}100$, $\pi = \frac{22}{7}$, and $h = 14$

(c) $\sqrt{a^2 + b^2}$ when $a = 18$ and $b = 24$

(d) $\sqrt{h^2 - a^2}$ when $h = 78$ and $a = 72$

(e) $\sqrt{h^2 - b^2}$ when $h = 145$ and $b = 116$

Formulas

To determine the value of any variable in a formula when the values of the other variables are known, copy the formula, substitute the given values for the variables, and perform the necessary operations. Solve the resulting equation (see page 504) for the value of the required variable.

Find the value of p when $s = 16$, using the formula $p = 4s$.	Find the value of w when $A = 54$ and $l = 9$, using the formula $A = lw$.
$p = 4s$	$A = lw$
$p = 4 \cdot 16$	$54 = 9w$
$p = 64$	$\dfrac{54}{9} = \dfrac{9w}{9}$
	$6 = w$
Answer: $p = 64$	$w = 6$
	Answer: $w = 6$

PRACTICE PROBLEMS

1. Find the value of:

(a) d when $r = 85$.   Formula: $d = 2r$

(b) p when $s = 26$.   Formula: $p = 4s$

(c) A when $b = 32$ and $h = 49$.   Formula: $A = bh$

(d) c when $\pi = \frac{22}{7}$ and $d = 84$.   Formula: $c = \pi d$

(e) A when $p = 620$ and $i = 53$.   Formula: $A = p + i$

(f) p when $l = 73$ and $w = 28$.   Formula: $p = 2l + 2w$

(g) A when $B = 47$.   Formula: $A = 90 - B$

(h) i when $p = 650$, $r = .04$, and $t = 9$.   Formula: $i = prt$

(i) V when $l = 41$, $w = 27$, and $h = 30$.   Formula: $V = lwh$

(j) A when $\pi = 3.14$, $r = 48$, and $h = 75$.   Formula: $A = 2\pi rh$

(k) A when $s = 50$.   Formula: $A = s^2$

(l) V when $e = 8$.   Formula: $V = e^3$

(m) V when $\pi = 3.14$, $r = 40$, and $h = 65$.   Formula: $V = \pi r^2 h$

(n) A when $\pi = \frac{22}{7}$, $d = 56$, and $h = 100$.

           Formula: $A = \frac{1}{4}\pi d^2 h$

(o) d when $c = 282.6$ and $\pi = 3.14$.   Formula: $d = \dfrac{c}{\pi}$

(p) p when $l = 427$ and $w = 393$.   Formula: $p = 2l + 2w$

(q) B when $A = 75$ and $C = 48$.   Formula: $B = 180 - (A + C)$

(r) l when $a = 6$, $n = 12$, and $d = 5$.   Formula: $l = a + (n - 1)d$

(s) I when $E = 220$ and $R = 11$.   Formula: $I = \dfrac{E}{R}$

(t) P when $F = 90$, $d = 10$, and $t = 3$.   Formula: $P = \dfrac{Fd}{t}$

(u) C when $F = -22$.   Formula: $C = \frac{5}{9}(F - 32)$

2. Find the value of:

(a) s when $p = 18$.   Formula: $p = 3s$

(b) r when $d = 56$.   Formula: $d = 2r$

(c) w when $A = 96$ and $l = 6$.   Formula: $A = lw$

(d) d when $c = 15.7$ and $\pi = 3.14$.   Formula: $c = \pi d$

(e) t when $i = 140$, $p = 400$, and $r = 5\%$.   Formula: $i = prt$

(f) h when $V = 6{,}280$, $\pi = 3.14$, and $r = 10$.

           Formula: $V = \pi r^2 h$

(g) b when $A = 72$ and $h = 18$.   Formula: $A = bh$

(h) l when $A = 777$ and $w = 21$.   Formula: $A = lw$

(i) p when $i = 108$, $r = 4\%$, and $t = 9$.   Formula: $i = prt$

(j) w when $V = 1{,}536$, $l = 16$, and $h = 12$.   Formula: $V = lwh$

(k) r when $A = 660$, $\pi = \frac{22}{7}$, and $h = 21$. Formula: $A = 2\,\pi r h$
(l) p when $A = 428$ and $i = 43$. Formula: $A = p + i$
(m) b when $p = 91$ and $e = 29$. Formula: $p = b + 2\,e$
(n) A when $C = 42$. Formula: $C = A - 273$
(o) A when $L = 3{,}500$ and $C = 9{,}300$. Formula: $L = A - C$
(p) l when $p = 162$ and $w = 34$. Formula: $p = 2\,l + 2\,w$
(q) w when $p = 266$ and $l = 81$. Formula: $p = 2\,l + 2\,w$
(r) V when $v = 323$, $g = 32$, and $t = 9$. Formula: $v = V + gt$
(s) h when $A = 572$, $\pi = \frac{22}{7}$ and $d = 14$.

$$\text{Formula: } A = \pi d h + \tfrac{1}{2}\,\pi d^2$$

(t) r when $A = 640$, $p = 500$, $t = 7$. Formula: $A = p + prt$
(u) V when $P = 75$, $V' = 38$, $P' = 25$. Formula: $PV = P'V'$

(v) d when $r = 17$. Formula: $r = \dfrac{d}{2}$

(w) c when $d = 15$ and $\pi = 3.14$. Formula: $d = \dfrac{c}{\pi}$

(x) h when $V = 56$ and $B = 24$. Formula: $V = \dfrac{Bh}{3}$

(y) a when $A = 144$ and $b = 18$. Formula: $A = \dfrac{ab}{2}$

OPEN SENTENCES

Solving Equations In One Variable

To solve an equation in one variable (for example $n + 3 = 15$ which indicates that some number plus three equals fifteen) means to find the number represented by the variable (n) which when substituted for the variable will make the sentence true.

Any number that makes the sentence true is said to satisfy the equation and to be the **root** or the **solution** of the open sentence. 12 is the root of the equation $n + 3 = 15$ because the sentence $12 + 3 = 15$ is true.

The set of all numbers which satisfy the sentence is called the **solution set** or the **truth set** of the sentence. Checking an equation is testing whether some number belongs to its solution set by substituting the number for the variable. If the resulting sentence is true, the number belongs to the solution set, if not, the number does not belong to the solution set.

Equations which have exactly the same root or roots or solution sets are **equivalent equations**. The expressions at the left and at the right of the equality sign are called **members** of the equation.

To solve an equation, transform the given equation to a simpler equivalent equation which has only the variable by itself as one member and a constant or numeral as the other member.

These transformations are based on the principles called axioms which state that when equals are increased or decreased or multiplied or divided by equals, the results are equal. Of course, divide only by non-zero numbers since division by zero is excluded. The additive and multiplicative inverses are also used for these transformations.

An equation may be compared to balanced scales. To keep the equation in balance, any change on one side of the equality sign must be balanced by an equal change on the other side of the equality sign.

Observe in the solutions by axioms of the following four basic types of equations $\left(n + 3 = 15; \; n - 3 = 15; \; 3\,n = 15; \; \frac{n}{3} = 15 \right)$ that the operation indicated in each case by the variable and the connected number is undone by using the inverse operation.

Basic Type I

Solve and check $n + 3 = 15$.

Solution by subtraction axiom:
The indicated operation of $n + 3$ is addition. To find the root, subtract 3 from each member.

$$n + 3 = 15$$
$$n + 3 - 3 = 15 - 3$$
$$n = 12$$

Answer: $n = 12$

Solution by additive inverse:
The additive inverse of $+ 3$ is $- 3$. Add the additive inverse to both members, using addition axiom.

$$n + 3 = 15$$
$$n + 3 + (- 3) = 15 + (- 3)$$
$$n = 12$$

Answer: $n = 12$

Check:
$$n + 3 = 15$$
$$12 + 3 = 15$$
$$15 = 15 \checkmark$$

PRACTICE PROBLEMS

Solve and check:

1. $c + 6 = 14$
2. $b + 18 = 31$
3. $i + 37 = 63$
4. $48 + w = 75$
5. $29 + p = 106$
6. $54 + n = 162$

7. $67 = a + 28$
8. $50 = m + 33$
9. $105 = y + 79$
10. $87 = 40 + x$
11. $36 = 19 + d$
12. $210 = 96 + r$

13. $n + 80 = 80$
14. $c + \$.09 = \$.23$
15. $\$50 = i + \$42.50$
16. $t + \frac{3}{4} = 4$
17. $1\frac{1}{2} + x = 3\frac{5}{8}$
18. $6.5 = .48 + n$

19. $a + \$9 = \$10.50$ **23.** $a + 5 = -3$ **27.** $n + 7 = 3.8$

20. $8\frac{1}{3} = 4\frac{1}{4} + d$ **24.** $-9 = r + 10$ **28.** $25 + a = 97$

21. $b + 9 = 4$ **25.** $g + 15 = 0$ **29.** $7 = s + .4$

22. $3 + y = 1$ **26.** $62 = 62 + x$ **30.** $\frac{3}{8} = \frac{1}{4} + x$

Basic Type II

Solve and check $n - 3 = 15$.

Solution by addition axiom: The indicated operation of $n - 3$ is subtraction. To find the root, add 3 to both members.

$$n - 3 = 15$$
$$n - 3 + 3 = 15 + 3$$
$$n = 18$$

Answer: $n = 18$

Solution by additive inverse: The additive inverse of -3 is $+3$. Add the additive inverse to both members, using the addition axiom.

$$n - 3 = 15$$
$$n - 3 + (+3) = 15 + (+3)$$
$$n = 18$$

Answer: $n = 18$

Check:

$$n - 3 = 15$$
$$18 - 3 = 15$$
$$15 = 15 \checkmark$$

PRACTICE PROBLEMS

Solve and check:

1. $c - 7 = 21$ **11.** $s - \$51 = \$120$ **21.** $x - 2\frac{1}{2} = 2\frac{1}{2}$

2. $l - 18 = 5$ **12.** $9 = b - 2\frac{1}{2}$ **22.** $18 = n - 1.3$

3. $A - 42 = 124$ **13.** $y - \$4.75 = \$3.25$ **23.** $0 = x - 75$

4. $35 = n - 19$ **14.** $d - \frac{7}{8} = 1\frac{1}{4}$ **24.** $-5 = r - 5$

5. $16 = b - 47$ **15.** $9.6 = n - 7$ **25.** $51 = t - 51$

6. $28 = y - 16$ **16.** $a - \$.08 = \$.75$ **26.** $w - 34 = -2$

7. $t - 9 = 0$ **17.** $c - 4 = -9$ **27.** $a - 29 = 76$

8. $0 = y - 26$ **18.** $r - 23 = -45$ **28.** $\frac{1}{2} = d - 1\frac{3}{4}$

9. $c - 40 = 40$ **19.** $x - 18 = -10$ **29.** $x - \$.75 = \$.35$

10. $52 = m - 52$ **20.** $b - 6 = -6$ **30.** $y - 1 = -9$

Basic Type III

Solve and check $3n = 15$.

Solution by division axiom: The indicated operation of $3n$ is multiplication. To find the root, divide both members by 3.

$$3n = 15$$
$$\frac{3n}{3} = \frac{15}{3}$$
$$n = 5$$

Answer: $n = 5$

Solution by multiplicative inverse: The multiplicative inverse of 3 is $\frac{1}{3}$. Multiply both members by $\frac{1}{3}$, using the multiplication axiom.	$3n = 15$ $\frac{1}{3} \cdot 3n = \frac{1}{3} \cdot 15$ $n = 5$ Answer: $n = 5$	Check: $3n = 15$ $3 \cdot 5 = 15$ $15 = 15 \checkmark$

PRACTICE PROBLEMS

Solve and check:

1. $5a = 45$
2. $9c = 54$
3. $14n = 42$
4. $91 = 7y$
5. $60 = 12x$
6. $105 = 15b$
7. $2r = 18$
8. $48 = 4s$
9. $10w = 10$
10. $19 = 19h$
11. $8y = 0$
12. $0 = 16x$
13. $5c = 8$
14. $18w = 27$
15. $4y = 1$

16. $12d = 10$
17. $23 = 9n$
18. $4 = 5b$
19. $54 = 8r$
20. $12 = 16x$
21. $7t = 2.8$
22. $.4n = 36$
23. $10c = \$.90$
24. $\$.05a = \$1.45$
25. $\frac{1}{4}c = 20$
26. $\frac{7}{8}n = 42$
27. $24 = \frac{2}{3}n$
28. $3\frac{1}{2}t = 14$
29. $.06p = \$240$
30. $\frac{9}{16}r = 72$

31. $8x = -32$
32. $-5m = 40$
33. $-7y = -56$
34. $-x = -10$
35. $-64 = -4c$
36. $-y = 19$
37. $44 = -18b$
38. $-20s = -5$
39. $10c = -50$
40. $10 = -50c$
41. $12m = 300$
42. $140 = 15y$
43. $3.14d = 12.56$
44. $2\frac{1}{4}n = 13\frac{1}{2}$
45. $15 = \frac{3}{8}h$

Basic Type IV

Solve and check $\frac{n}{3} = 15$.

Solution by multiplication axiom:

The indicated operation of $\frac{n}{3}$ is division. To find the root, multiply both members by 3.

$$\frac{n}{3} = 15$$
$$3 \cdot \frac{n}{3} = 3 \cdot 15$$
$$n = 45$$

Answer: $n = 45$

Solution by multiplicative inverse:

Since $\frac{n}{3} = \frac{1}{3}n$, use the multiplicative inverse of $\frac{1}{3}$, which is 3. Multiply both members by 3.

$$\frac{n}{3} = 15$$
$$3 \cdot \frac{n}{3} = 3 \cdot 15$$
$$n = 45$$

Answer: $n = 45$

Check:

$\frac{n}{3} = 15$
$\frac{45}{3} = 15$
$15 = 15 \checkmark$

Solve and check:

1. $\dfrac{d}{2} = 19$ 9. $\dfrac{x}{3} = 9$ 17. $\dfrac{n}{4} = -5$

2. $\dfrac{s}{4} = 24$ 10. $\dfrac{c}{3.14} = 100$ 18. $\dfrac{r}{9} = -7$

3. $\dfrac{b}{7} = 3$ 11. $\dfrac{b}{5} = 1.4$ 19. $\dfrac{y}{-3} = 12$

4. $\dfrac{n}{5} = 0$ 12. $\tfrac{1}{2} a = 17$ 20. $\dfrac{a}{-6} = -18$

5. $\dfrac{t}{8} = 8$ 13. $\tfrac{3}{4} c = \$.36$ 21. $-8 = \dfrac{d}{-11}$

6. $12 = \dfrac{b}{3}$ 14. $0 = \dfrac{g}{8}$ 22. $\dfrac{x}{6} = 1$

7. $45 = \dfrac{m}{5}$ 15. $\dfrac{w}{5} = 30$ 23. $-5 = \dfrac{z}{7}$

8. $1 = \dfrac{s}{9}$ 16. $\dfrac{k}{12} = 3$ 24. $\dfrac{b}{16} = 16$

Solution By More Than One Axiom

The solution of more difficult equations may involve the use of more than one axiom or the combining of terms as shown below.

Solve and check: $7x + 2 = 72$	Solve and check: $7x + 2x = 72$
$7x + 2 = 72$ Check:	$7x + 2x = 72$ Check:
$7x + 2 - 2 = 72 - 2$ $7x + 2 = 72$	$9x = 72$ $7x + 2x = 72$
$7x = 70$ $(7 \cdot 10) + 2 = 72$	$\dfrac{9x}{9} = \dfrac{72}{9}$ $(7 \cdot 8) + (2 \cdot 8) = 72$
$\dfrac{7x}{7} = \dfrac{70}{7}$ $70 + 2 = 72$	$x = 8$ $56 + 16 = 72$
$x = 10$ $72 = 72 \checkmark$	$72 = 72 \checkmark$
Answer: $x = 10$	*Answer:* $x = 8$

Solve and check:

1. $2b + 18 = 46$ 5. $22h + 154 = 374$ 9. $6a - 7 = 29$

2. $3 + 5n = 62$ 6. $1.8c + 32 = 113$ 10. $37 = 14b - 19$

3. $51 = 9y + 6$ 7. $7t - 11 = 38$ 11. $n + n = 50$

4. $120 = 76 + 2w$ 8. $0 = 10n - 30$ 12. $9x + 3x = 84$

13. $p + .06\,p = 689$ **19.** $l - .35\,l = 195$ **25.** $8\,a + 43 = 11$

14. $7\,y - y = 18$ **20.** $\frac{3}{5}\,b = 21$ **26.** $6\,y - 4\,y = -28$

15. $a - .05\,a = 760$ **21.** $\frac{5}{8}\,d = \$.75$ **27.** $2 - 3\,b = 8$

16. $6\,b = 91 - 15$ **22.** $t + \frac{1}{4}\,t = 6\frac{1}{2}$ **28.** $5\,n - 9\,n = -56$

17. $82 = 5\,a + 9\,a$ **23.** $\frac{7}{8}\,n + 18 = 46$ **29.** $\$2.76 = \frac{3}{4}\,a$

18. $1.8\,c + 32 = 50$ **24.** $\frac{5}{9}\,b - 13 = 27$ **30.** $c + .25\,c = \$15.50$

Solution Set Notation; Replacement Sets

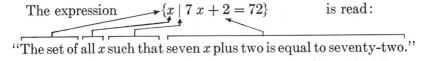

The expression $\{x \mid 7\,x + 2 = 72\}$ is read:

"The set of all x such that seven x plus two is equal to seventy-two."

The notation $\{x \mid 7\,x + 2 = 72\}$ represents the set of numbers which are selected by the condition that $7\,x + 2 = 72$ and which makes this sentence true when they replace the variable. The solution set for $7\,x + 2 = 72$ (see page 504) consists of only one member which may be expressed as $\{10\}$.

Thus $\{x \mid 7\,x + 2 = 72\} = \{10\}$.

A replacement set is a defined set of numbers which may replace the variable. The description of the replacement set is sometimes called the domain of the variable. This may be a listing of possible replacements such as $\{0, 2, 4, 6, 8\}$ or a description like "the set of all natural numbers."

The solution set of an equation not only depends on the equation but also on its replacement set. The same equation with different replacement sets may have different solution sets.

The solution set of $3\,n = 15$ is:

$\{5\}$ when the replacement is the set of all natural numbers;

$\{5\}$ when the replacement set is the set of all prime numbers; and

ϕ or $\{\,\}$ when the replacement set is the set of all even numbers.

The equation $3\,n = 2$, whose solution set in the system of real numbers is $\{\frac{2}{3}\}$, would have no solution or a solution with no members (the empty or null set, ϕ) when the replacement set is the set of whole numbers since the replacement set contains no fractions.

PRACTICE PROBLEMS

1. Read, or write in words, each of the following:

(a) $\{x \mid 4\,x = 28\}$

(b) $\{y \mid y - 7 = 4\}$

(c) $\{a \mid a + 9 = 15\}$

(d) $\left\{n \mid \dfrac{n}{5} = 2\right\}$

(e) $\{s \mid 3\,s - 4 = 15\}$

(f) $\{b \mid 4\,b + 6\,b = 42\}$

2. Write each of the following symbolically using set notation:

(a) The set of all y such that y minus nine is equal to forty.

(b) The set of all n such that 4 times n is equal to eight.

(c) The set of all d such that d divided by nine equals five.

(d) The set of all t such that eight times t plus two equals nineteen.

3. Find the solution set of each of the following equations:

(a) When the replacement set is $\{0, 1, 2, 3, 4, 5, 6, 7, 8, 9, 10\}$:

(1) $n + 5 = 11$ (2) $b - 2 = 9$ (3) $7\,x = 24$ (4) $\dfrac{b}{2} = 5$

(b) When the replacement set is the set of all natural numbers:

(1) $8\,c = 56$ (2) $\dfrac{n}{3} = 1$ (3) $8 + y = 5$ (4) $0 = t - 7$

(c) When the replacement set is $\{-4, -3, -2, -1, 0, 1, 2, 3, 4\}$:

(1) $r - 1 = 1$ (2) $-5\,y = 15$ (3) $3\,n + 6 = -3$ (4) $\dfrac{t}{2} = 2$

(d) When the replacement set is the set of all integers:

(1) $6\,b = 9$ (2) $\dfrac{c}{4} = -7$ (3) $2\,n - n = 8$ (4) $4\,a + 9 = 1$

(e) When the replacement set is the set of all prime numbers:

(1) $m + 1 = 6$ (2) $5\,a + 3\,a = 48$ (3) $5\,t - 1 = 9$ (4) $\dfrac{b}{7} = 5$

(f) When the replacement set is the set of all integers greater than -5 and less than 6:

(1) $-10 = 20\,a$ (2) $s - 3 = 3$ (3) $\dfrac{n}{2} = -3$ (4) $8\,d + 18 = 2$

(g) When the replacement set is the set of all one-digit odd whole numbers:

(1) $r + 1 = 7$ (2) $9\,b + 3\,b = 60$ (3) $-7\,x = -28$ (4) $\dfrac{c}{3} = 3$

(h) When the replacement set is the set of all multiples of 3 which are greater than 9 and less than 27:

(1) $t - 8 = 4$　(2) $\dfrac{b}{2} = 12$　(3) $6c + 5 = 59$　(4) $8y + 2y = 270$

(i) When the replacement set is $\{0, 1, 2, 3, 4, \cdots\}$:

(1) $\dfrac{n}{16} = 8$　(2) $12a - 5 = 67$　(3) $-9b = -36$　(4) $3z + 4z = 84$

(j) When the replacement set is the set of all odd prime numbers less than 20:

(1) $b + 7 = 16$　(2) $4w = 68$　(3) $8t - 3t = 65$　(4) $3 + 5x = 78$

Equations Involving Absolute Values

Since $|+4| = 4$ and $|-4| = 4$, replacement of the variable in the equation $|x| = 4$ by either $+4$ or -4 will make the sentence true. Therefore the roots of $|x| = 4$ are $+4$ and -4 or its solution set is $\{+4, -4\}$.

The equality axioms are used to solve equations as shown in the model.

$$|x| + 5 = 9$$
$$|x| + 5 - 5 = 9 - 5$$
$$|x| = 4$$
$$x = +4 \text{ or } -4$$

Answer, $+4$ or -4

PRACTICE PROBLEMS

Find the solution set of each of the following equations when the replacement set is the set of all real numbers:

1. $|r| = 7$
2. $|n| = 15$
3. $|x| - 2 = 9$
4. $|y| + 1 = 6$

5. $9 \times |t| = 108$
6. $|d| - 15 = 7$
7. $6 \times |a| = 84$
8. $|s| + 11 = 29$

9. $\dfrac{|b|}{4} = 5$

10. $\dfrac{|y|}{8} = 6$

Solving Inequalities In One Variable

To solve an inequality means to find the set of all numbers which make the inequality true. This solution set may consist of an unlimited number of elements, a finite number of one or more elements, or no elements.

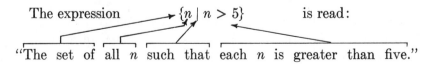

The expression 　　　　→ $\{n \mid n > 5\}$ 　　　　 is read:

"The set of all n such that each n is greater than five."

The notation $\{n \mid n > 5\}$ represents the set of numbers which are selected by the condition $n > 5$ and which makes the inequality $n > 5$ true when they replace the variable.

Inequalities, like equations, are solved by using transformations based on the axioms and on the additive and multiplicative inverses to get an equivalent inequality in each case which has the same solution set as the given inequality. The equivalent inequality is expressed with only the variable itself as one member of the inequality and a numeral for the other member.

The following axioms are used to solve inequalities:

I. When the same number is added to or subtracted from both members of an inequality, another inequality of the *same order* results.

Solve $n + 2 < 6$ when the replacement set is the set of all whole numbers.	Solve $x - 2 > 3$ when the replacement set is the set of all real numbers.

$$n + 2 < 6$$
$$n + 2 - 2 < 6 - 2$$
$$n < 4$$
$$n = 0, 1, 2, \text{ or } 3$$
or $\{n \mid n + 2 < 6\} = \{n \mid n < 4\}$
$$= \{0, 1, 2, 3\}$$

$$x - 2 > 3$$
$$x - 2 + 2 > 3 + 2$$
$$x > 5$$
$x = $ all real numbers greater than 5
or $\{x \mid x - 2 > 3\} = \{x \mid x > 5\}$
$= \{$all real numbers greater than 5$\}$

II. When both members of an inequality are either multiplied or divided by the same positive non-zero number, another inequality of the *same order* results.

Solve $3 c > 27$ when the replacement set is the set of all natural numbers.	Solve $4 y + 7 \leqq 7$ when the replacement set is $\{-2, -1, 0, 1, 2\}$.

$$3 c > 27$$
$$\frac{3 c}{3} > \frac{27}{3}$$
$$c > 9$$
$$c = 10, 11, 12, \cdots$$
or $\{c \mid 3 c > 27\} = \{c \mid c > 9\}$
$$= \{10, 11, 12, \cdots\}$$

$$4 y + 7 \leqq 7$$
$$4 y + 7 - 7 \leqq 7 - 7$$
$$4 y \leqq 0$$
$$y \leqq 0$$
$$y = -2, -1, \text{ or } 0$$
or $\{y \mid 4 y + 7 \leqq 7\} = \{y \mid y \leqq 0\}$
$$= \{-2, -1, 0\}$$

III. When both members of an inequality are either multiplied or divided by the same negative non-zero number, an inequality of the *reverse order* results.

Solve $-5x > 30$ when the replacement set is the set of all integers.

$$-5x > 30$$
$$\frac{-5x}{-5} < \frac{30}{-5}$$
$$x < -6$$
$$x = \cdots, -9, -8, -7$$

or $\{x \mid -5x > 30\} = \{x \mid x < -6\}$
$$= \{\cdots, -9, -8, -7\}$$

Solve $-2b < -6$ when the replacement set is the set of all integers.

$$-2b < -6$$
$$\frac{-2b}{-2} > \frac{-6}{-2}$$
$$b > 3$$
$$b = 4, 5, 6, \cdots$$

or $\{b \mid -2b < -6\} = \{b \mid b > 3\}$
$$= \{4, 5, 6, \cdots\}$$

PRACTICE PROBLEMS

1. Read, or write in words, each of the following:

(a) $\{t \mid t > 8\}$

(b) $\{x \mid 5x < 10\}$

(c) $\{y \mid y + 3 \geqq -7\}$

(d) $\{n \mid 4n - 2 \neq 8\}$

(e) $\{s \mid 8s - 3s > 0\}$

(f) $\left\{a \mid \dfrac{a}{6} \leqq -3\right\}$

2. Write each of the following symbolically using set notation:

(a) The set of all x such that each x is less than four.

(b) The set of all y such that each y is not equal to negative one.

(c) The set of all a such that each a is greater than zero.

(d) The set of all n such that each n is less than or equal to eleven.

(e) The set of all b such that each b is greater than or equal to negative two.

3. Match each of the following sets with its description:

(a) $\{-1, 0, 1, 2, 3, \cdots\}$

(b) $\{1, 2, 3\}$

(c) $\{4,$ all real numbers greater than $4\}$

(d) $\{\cdots, -3, -2, 0, 1, 2, 3, \cdots\}$

(e) $\{\cdots, -4, -3, -2\}$

(f) $\{0, 1, 2, 3, 5, 6, \cdots\}$

(g) $\{\cdots, -1, 0, 1, 2, 3\}$

(h) $\{5, 6, 7, 8, \cdots\}$

(1) All integers less than negative one

(2) All integers except negative one

(3) All whole numbers less than four

(4) All integers less than four

(5) All natural numbers less than four

(6) All integers greater than four

(7) All natural numbers less than or equal to four

(8) All integers greater than or equal to negative one

(Continued)

(i) {0, 1, 2, 3}

(j) {1, 2, 3, 4}

(9) All real numbers greater than or equal to four

(10) All whole numbers except four

4. Using the set of all: (a) natural numbers (b) whole numbers (c) integers (d) real numbers, write the solution set of each of the following inequalities:

(1) $x < 5$ (3) $y \neq 2$ (5) $d \leqq -2$ (7) $d \ngtr 1$

(2) $b > 6$ (4) $n \geqq -3$ (6) $m \nless 0$ (8) $n < -1$

Type I

Find the solution set of each of the following inequalities when the replacement set is the set of all real numbers:

1. (a) $n + 7 > 10$ (b) $a + 6 > 6$ (c) $23 + d > 12$

2. (a) $c - 5 > 18$ (b) $x - 3 > -4$ (c) $r - \frac{1}{2} > 3\frac{1}{2}$

3. (a) $b + 1 < 7$ (b) $g + 9 < 2$ (c) $m + .5 < 2.4$

4. (a) $d - 9 < 6$ (b) $t - 10 < 18$ (c) $h - 3 < -5$

5. (a) $m + 8 \geqq 12$ (b) $f + 17 \geqq 0$ (c) $w + 8 \nless -8$

6. (a) $x - 11 \geqq 4$ (b) $k - 3.5 \geqq 8.7$ (c) $a - 7 \nless -4$

7. (a) $y + 2 \leqq 9$ (b) $e + \frac{1}{4} \ngtr \frac{3}{4}$ (c) $v + 16 \leqq 13$

8. (a) $r - 4 \leqq 10$ (b) $c - 6 \ngtr -8$ (c) $x - 9 \leqq 9$

9. (a) $s + 9 \neq 17$ (b) $n + .3 \neq 1.6$ (c) $b + 12 \neq 1$

10. (a) $w - 11 \neq 6$ (b) $y - \frac{7}{8} \neq 1\frac{1}{2}$ (c) $r - 2 \neq -2$

11. (a) $x - 5 > 4$ (d) $a - 9 \leqq 11$ (g) $r + 4 > 0$

(b) $y + 8 < 3$ (e) $t + 3 \neq 3$ (h) $z - 12 \nless 7$

(c) $n + 7 \geqq 1$ (f) $b - 5 < -9$ (i) $w + 6 \leqq -4$

Type II

Find the solution set of each of the following inequalities when the replacement set is the set of all real numbers:

1. (a) $7x > 14$ (b) $9y > -72$ (c) $8a > 2$

2. (a) $\dfrac{m}{4} > 2$ (b) $\dfrac{c}{10} > 7$ (c) $\dfrac{r}{9} > -6$

3. (a) $6z < 30$ (b) $12s < -96$ (c) $16b < 24$

4. (a) $\dfrac{h}{8} < 3$ (b) $\dfrac{p}{15} < -1$ (c) $\dfrac{w}{7} < 5$

5. (a) $10n \geqq 50$ (b) $18a \geqq 12$ (c) $\frac{3}{4}x \nless 24$

6. (a) $\dfrac{b}{30} \geqq 0$ (b) $\dfrac{r}{4} \geqq -6$ (c) $\dfrac{z}{5} \nless 3$

7. (a) $8\,s \leqq 72$ (b) $48\,h \ngtr 96$ (c) $.05\,n \leqq 20$

8. (a) $\dfrac{y}{6} \leqq 7$ (b) $\dfrac{t}{14} \ngtr 2$ (c) $\dfrac{b}{3} \leqq -10$

9. (a) $9\,c \neq 144$ (b) $\frac{5}{8}\,x \neq 80$ (c) $24\,f \neq 0$

10. (a) $\dfrac{n}{12} \neq 5$ (b) $\dfrac{d}{6} \neq -2$ (c) $\dfrac{y}{10} \neq 9$

11. (a) $15\,b < 60$ (d) $9\,y \leqq 39$ (g) $\dfrac{n}{12} > 0$

     (b) $\dfrac{a}{8} > -2$ (e) $6\,m \neq -48$

     (c) $20\,x \geqq -15$ (f) $\dfrac{t}{7} < 7$ (h) $\dfrac{z}{5} \nless 15$

                                                     (i) $\frac{7}{16}\,x \ngtr 56$

Type III

Find the solution set of each of the following inequalities when the replacement set is the set of all real numbers:

1. (a) $-5\,d > 30$ (b) $-7\,c > 98$ (c) $-.4\,h > 1.2$

2. (a) $-4\,b > -28$ (b) $-3\,m > -40$ (c) $-\frac{3}{8}\,z > -15$

3. (a) $-9\,x < 81$ (b) $-16\,r < 96$ (c) $-8\,a < 36$

4. (a) $-2\,t < -16$ (b) $-17\,y < -51$ (c) $-1.5\,m < -9$

5. (a) $-3\,y \geqq 21$ (b) $-10\,r \geqq 0$ (c) $-x \nless 2$

6. (a) $-7\,n \geqq -63$ (b) $-\frac{4}{9}\,g \geqq -72$ (c) $-4\,t \nless -17$

7. (a) $-9\,s \leqq 180$ (b) $-3\,y \ngtr 0$ (c) $-18\,x \leqq 90$

8. (a) $-6\,z \leqq -216$ (b) $-7\,n \ngtr 63$ (c) $-\frac{2}{3}\,y \leqq -60$

9. (a) $\dfrac{n}{-3} < 12$ (d) $\dfrac{c}{-10} \geqq 9$ (g) $\dfrac{s}{-12} \nless -5$

     (b) $\dfrac{b}{-6} > -2$ (e) $\dfrac{a}{-3} < -7$ (h) $\dfrac{m}{-9} > 4$

     (c) $\dfrac{y}{-8} \leqq 6$ (f) $\dfrac{x}{-5} > 8$ (i) $\dfrac{d}{-4} \ngtr -1$

10. (a) $-7\,m < 56$ (d) $-10\,a \geqq 45$ (g) $-15\,y > 105$

     (b) $-12\,z > -132$ (e) $-3\,r < 0$ (h) $-2\,n \nless -1$

     (c) $-4\,x \leqq 92$ (f) $\dfrac{b}{-7} > -8$ (i) $-13\,g \ngtr -91$

Miscellaneous

Find the solution set of each of the following inequalities when the replacement set is the set of all real numbers:

1. (a) $2x + 7 < 15$ (e) $8n + 3 \neq -61$ (i) $9t + 6 < -57$
   (b) $5a - 3 > -28$ (f) $3y - 7 < 20$ (j) $14z - 8 \not> 69$
   (c) $6m + 1 \leq 13$ (g) $10b + 5 > 0$ (k) $7w + 15 > 113$
   (d) $7s - 5 \cong 9$ (h) $17r - 9 \not< 42$ (l) $4x - 11 \neq -9$

2. (a) $3x + 2x > 15$ (g) $12b + 13b < -100$
   (b) $9c - 3c < -72$ (h) $4x - 8x \not< 36$
   (c) $5d - 7d \cong 14$ (i) $n - 2n \not> -5$
   (d) $y + y \neq -30$ (j) $10r + 3r \neq 65$
   (e) $8m - 3m \leq 0$ (k) $12w - 5w > -84$
   (f) $6t - 11t > -85$ (l) $7a - 15a < 144$

Restricted Replacement Sets

Find the solution set of each of the following inequalities:

1. When the replacement set is $\{0, 1, 2, 3, 4, 5, 6, 7, 8, 9\}$:

$x + 5 > 8$ $n - 6 < 1$ $2b \leq 6$ $-3t \not< -12$

2. When the replacement set is $\{-3, -2, -1, 0, 1, 2, 3\}$:

$b - 2 \neq 0$ $5n + 3 < 13$ $\dfrac{d}{6} > -1$ $2a - 5 \leq -1$

3. When the replacement set is the set of all natural numbers:

$9a \cong 63$ $7w + 6w < -26$ $4x - 13 \not> -4$ $\dfrac{b}{-5} > -1$

4. When the replacement set is the set of all prime numbers:

$-2n > -8$ $m - 7 \not> 16$ $6c - c \neq 55$ $12d - 4d < 56$

5. When the replacement set is the set of all integers:

$d + 5 < -2$ $-7s \cong 35$ $\dfrac{y}{-4} \not> -5$ $4a - 7 \neq -15$

6. When the replacement set is the set of all even whole numbers:

$6b < 45$ $2a - 5 > 9$ $8a - 2a \not> 18$ $\dfrac{d}{9} \not< 4$

7. When the replacement set is the set of all non-positive integers:

$m - 1 > -6$ $-5x < -20$ $4t - 9 \not> -13$ $11y - y \cong -10$

8. When the replacement set is the set of integers greater than -3 and less than 4:

$-7r < -21$ $b - 8 > -4$ $6x - 12 \leq 0$ $9m - 4m \neq 10$

9. When the replacement set is the set of one-digit prime

numbers:

$$b - 2 > 1 \qquad 10\,c < 20 \qquad \frac{b}{5} \neq 1 \qquad 12\,x + 7 \cong 79$$

10. When the replacement set is the set of all multiples of 4 which are greater than 8 and less than 30:

$$-5\,g < -60 \qquad 2\,t - 13 > 15 \qquad 4\,a - 16\,a \not< 144 \qquad \frac{n}{8} \not> 3$$

Graphing Equations On The Number Line

There are an infinite number of real numbers in our number system and an infinite number of points on the real number line. However, there is one and only one real number that corresponds to each point on the number line and one and only one point on the number line that corresponds to each real number of our number system.

Each point on the number line is called the *graph* of the real number to which it corresponds

$$\begin{array}{ccccccc} A & B & C & D & E & F & G \end{array}$$
$$\begin{array}{ccccccc} -3 & -2 & -1 & 0 & 1 & 2 & 3 \end{array}$$

and each real number is called the *coordinate* of the related point on the line. Point C on the number line above is the graph of the number -1 and -1 is the coordinate of point C.

Thus, *the graph of a number is a point on the number line whose coordinate is the number.*

The graph of a set of numbers is the set of points on the number line whose coordinates are the numbers. The set of points $\{B, D, E, G\}$ is the graph of the set of numbers $\{-2, 0, 1, 3\}$.

The graph on a number line of an equation in one variable is the set of all points on the number line whose coordinates are the numbers belonging to the solution set of the equation. *The graph of the equation is the graph of its solution set.*

To draw the graph of an equation in one variable on the number line, locate the point or points whose coordinate or coordinates are numbers belonging to the solution set of the equation. Indicate these points by heavy or colored dots.

(1) The solution set of the equation $n + 2 = 8$ is $\{6\}$. The graph of $n + 2 = 8$ is the point whose coordinate is 6.	(2) The solution set of the equation $7\,n + 6 = 41$ is $\{5\}$. The graph of $7\,n + 6 = 41$ is the point whose coordinate is 5. *(Continued)*

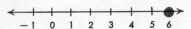

(3) The solution set of the equation $x = x + 3$ is ϕ.

We have no points to draw the graph.

(4) The solution set of $|x| = 2$ is $\{-2, +2\}$. The graph of $|x| = 2$ is the set of points whose coordinates are -2 and $+2$.

(5) The solution set of $3x + 12 = 3(x + 4)$ is an infinite set since the equation (identity) is satisfied by every real number. The graph of $3x + 12 = 3(x + 4)$ is the entire number line indicated by a heavy or colored line with an arrowhead in each direction to show that it is endless.

(6) The graph 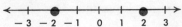 is a picture of the equation $x = 3$ or any equivalent equation such as $4x = 12$, $x + 2 = 5$, $x - 1 = 2$, etc.

PRACTICE PROBLEMS

1. For each of the following equations draw an appropriate number line, then graph its solution set. The replacement set is the set of all real numbers.

(a) $x = 5$ (e) $8a = 32$ (i) $5b - 6 = 29$

(b) $b = -3$ (f) $3y + 8 = 5$ (j) $|x| = 3$

(c) $x + 4 = 7$ (g) $6n - n = 15$ (k) $z = z + 2$

(d) $a - 5 = 2$ (h) $\dfrac{b}{3} = 2$ (l) $5(x + 2) = 5x + 10$

2. Write a corresponding equation which is pictured by each of the following graphs:

(a)

(b)

(c)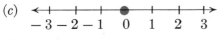

(d)

Graphing Inequalities On The Number Line

The graph on the number line of an inequality in one variable is the set of all points on the number line whose coordinates are the numbers belonging to the solution set of the inequality.

To draw the graph of an inequality in one variable on the number line, first find its solution set, then draw the graph of the solution set.

Basic graphs of solution sets, typical of those generally used in graphing inequalities, are described below. A solid dot indicates the inclusion and an open dot indicates the exclusion of the endpoint.

The graph of a set of all real numbers greater than a given number is a half-line extending to the right along the number line.

Graph of $x > 3$

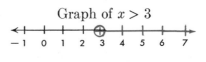

(A line is a set of points. A point on the line separates the line into two half-lines. The half-line extends indefinitely in one direction only and does not include the endpoint separating it from the other half-line. An open dot indicates the exclusion of this endpoint and the arrowhead indicates the half-line is endless.)

The graph of a set of all real numbers less than a given number is a half-line extending to the left along the number line.

Graph of $x < 3$

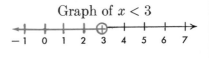

The graph of a set of all real numbers greater than or equal to a given number is a ray extending to the right along the number line. A *ray* is a half-line

Graph of $x \geqq 3$

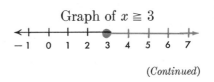

(Continued)

which includes one end-point. A solid dot indicates the inclusion of this endpoint.

The graph of a set of all real numbers less than or equal to a given number is a ray extending to the left along the number line.

Graph of $x \leqq 3$

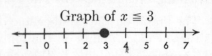

The graph of a set of all real numbers with the exception of one number is the entire real number line excluding the point corresponding to the excluded number—or two half-lines.

Graph of $x \neq 2$

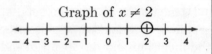

The graph of a set of numbers between two given numbers and including the two given numbers is a line segment which is a definite part of a line including the two endpoints.

Graph of $-2 \leqq x \leqq 3$

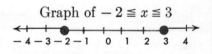

The graph of a set of numbers between the two given numbers but not including the two given numbers is an interval which is a definite part of a line excluding the two endpoints.

Graph of $-2 < x < 3$

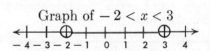

The graph of $5x - 6 > 4$, when the replacement set is the set of all real numbers, is the graph of its solution, $x > 2$, or the graph of its solution set:

Graph of $5x - 6 > 4$ is graph of: $x > 2$

$\{x \mid 5x - 6 > 4\} = \{x \mid x > 2\} = \{\text{all real numbers greater than 2}\}$.

PRACTICE PROBLEMS

1. For each of the following inequalities draw an appropriate number line, then graph its solution set. The replacement set is the set of all real numbers.

(a) $x > 1$

(b) $y < -3$

(c) $a \geqq -2$

(d) $4c > 20$

(e) $a + 5 < 7$

(f) $d - 3 \geqq 1$

(g) $\dfrac{x}{2} \leqq 2$

(h) $2x - 1 \neq 1$

(i) $-9x > 18$

(j) $n + 2n \not> -12$

(k) $-7y \not< -7$

(l) $10d - 6 < 24$

(m) $2b - 5b > -12$

(n) $4r + 9 < -7$

(o) $\dfrac{m}{3} \not< -1$

2. Write a corresponding inequality which is pictured by each of the following graphs:

(a)
$$-3 \quad -2 \quad -1 \quad 0 \quad 1 \quad 2 \quad 3$$

(b)
$$-5 \quad -4 \quad -3 \quad -2 \quad -1 \quad 0 \quad 1$$

(c)
$$-2 \quad -1 \quad 0 \quad 1 \quad 2 \quad 3 \quad 4$$

(d)
$$1 \quad 2 \quad 3 \quad 4 \quad 5 \quad 6 \quad 7$$

(e)
$$-5 \quad -4 \quad -3 \quad -2 \quad -1 \quad 0 \quad 1$$

(f)
$$-4 \quad -3 \quad -2 \quad -1 \quad 0 \quad 1 \quad 2$$

3. Draw the graph for each of the following on an appropriate number line:

(a) $-3 < x < 4$

(b) $0 \leqq x \leqq 5$

(c) $-1 \leqq x < 3$

(d) $6 > x > 2$

(e) $2 \geqq x \geqq -5$

(f) $-1 > x \geqq -4$

REVIEW

1. Simplify:

(a) $\dfrac{(+7)(-8)}{(-9) - (+5)}$

(b) $\dfrac{|2 - 12| \times |-2|^2}{|(-4)(3)| - \left|\dfrac{-6}{3}\right|}$

2. Find the solution set of each of the following sentences when the replacement set is the set of all real numbers:

(a) $c + 25 = 43$

(b) $15 = m - 18$

(c) $-9n = -72$

(d) $6x - x = 65$

(e) $12y - 3 = 0$

(f) $4a > 36$

RATIO AND PROPORTION

Ratio

Two numbers may be compared by subtraction or by division. When we compare 12 with 4, we find by subtraction that 12 is eight more than 4 and by division that 12 is three times as large as 4. When we compare 4 with 12, we find by subtraction that 4 is eight less than 12 and by division that 4 is one-third as large as 12.

The answer we obtain when we compare two quantities by division is called the ratio of the two quantities.

When 12 is compared to 4, 12 is divided by 4 as $\frac{12}{4}$ which equals $\frac{3}{1}$. The ratio is $\frac{3}{1}$ or 3 to 1.

When 4 is compared to 12, 4 is divided by 12 as $\frac{4}{12}$ which equals $\frac{1}{3}$. The ratio is $\frac{1}{3}$ or 1 to 3.

The ratio of 3 inches to 5 inches is $\frac{3}{5}$. The fraction $\frac{3}{5}$ is an indicated division and means 3 divided by 5 ($3 \div 5$). Usually the ratio is expressed as a common fraction but it may also be expressed as a decimal fraction or a per cent.

The ratio $\frac{3}{5}$ is sometimes written as $3 : 5$. The colon may be used instead of the fraction bar. This ratio in either form is read "3 to 5."

If the quantities compared are denominate numbers, they must first be expressed in the same units. The ratio is an abstract number; it contains no unit of measurement.

A ratio has two terms. In the common fraction form the first term is found in the numerator and is the number that is being compared. The second term is found in the denominator and is the number to which the first number is being compared. The ratio in fraction form is usually expressed in lowest terms.

Although ratio is generally used to make comparisons showing the relationship between two quantities, it may be used to express a rate. The average rate of speed of a vehicle when it travels 90 miles in 2 hours may be expressed by the ratio $\frac{90}{2}$ which is $\frac{45}{1}$ or 45 miles per hour. If oranges sell at the rate of 6 for 25¢, the ratio expressing this rate is $\frac{6}{25}$ and is read "6 for 25." If shirts sell at the rate of $10 for 3, the ratio $\frac{10}{3}$ describes it. When a ratio is used to express a rate, the two quantities have different names like miles and hours, oranges and cents, dollars and shirts, and so forth.

Ratios like $\frac{2}{4}$, $\frac{8}{16}$, $\frac{10}{20}$, although written with different number pairs, express the same comparison or rate. These ratios are equal to each other because they are all equal to the ratio $\frac{1}{2}$.

1. Find the ratio of:

(a) 12 to 3	(f) 72 to 56	(k) 7 to 4	(p) 1,000 to 25
(b) 9 to 6	(g) 27 to 81	(l) 25 to 85	(q) 49 to 63
(c) 6 to 8	(h) 54 to 18	(m) 100 to 30	(r) 14 to 91
(d) 14 to 21	(i) 16 to 20	(n) 8 to 15	(s) 84 to 28
(e) 4 to 24	(j) 6 to 11	(o) 2 to 9	(t) 39 to 65

2. Find the ratio of:

(a) 6 in. to 10 in.	(i) 2 ft. to 5 yd.
(b) 8 in. to 2 ft.	(j) 3 quarters to 4 nickels
(c) 1 gal. to 1 pt.	(k) 12 sq. in. to 1 sq. ft.
(d) 45 min. to 1 hr.	(l) 1 qt. to 20 oz.
(e) 3 things to 1 doz.	(m) 195 sec. to 3 min.
(f) 1 lb. to 12 oz.	(n) 45 cu. ft. to 2 cu. yd.
(g) 1 dime to 1 quarter	(o) 1 km. to 1 cm.
(h) 2 bu. to 6 pk.	(p) 4 ounces to 2 lb.

3. Express each of the following rates as a ratio:

(a) 645 mi. per hr.	(i) 7,000 rev. in 14 min.
(b) 86 gal. per min.	(j) 96¢ per 24 kw. hr.
(c) 32 ft. per sec.	(k) $105 for 7 cu. yd.
(d) $5 per dozen	(l) 10 tablets for 50¢
(e) 60¢ per sq. yd.	(m) 384 mi. in 8 hr.
(f) 3 for $7	(n) $8 for 6 ties
(g) $50 for 2 tons.	(o) 1,200 gal. in 15 min.
(h) 100 miles on 5 gal.	(p) 81¢ for 3 qt.

Proportion

A proportion is a statement that one ratio is equal to another.

Using the equal ratios $\frac{2}{4}$ and $\frac{6}{12}$ we may write the proportion $\frac{2}{4} = \frac{6}{12}$. This proportion may also be expressed as $2 : 4 = 6 : 12$. The proportion in both forms is read "2 is to 4 as 6 is to 12."

There are four terms in a proportion as shown:

$$\text{first} \rightarrow \frac{2}{4} = \frac{6}{12} \leftarrow \text{third} \atop \leftarrow \text{fourth}$$
$$\text{second} \rightarrow$$

$$\begin{array}{cccc} \text{1st} & \text{2nd} & \text{3rd} & \text{4th} \\ \downarrow & \downarrow & \downarrow & \downarrow \\ 2 & : 4 & = 6 & : 12 \end{array}$$

In the proportion $2 : 4 = 6 : 12$, the first term (2) and the fourth term (12) are in the extreme positions. They are sometimes called the extremes. The second term (4) and the third term (6) are called the means. Notice that the product of the means (4×6) is equal to the product of the extremes (2×12). In the form $\frac{2}{4} = \frac{6}{12}$ notice that the cross products are equal. $4 \times 6 = 2 \times 12$. These products are equal only when the ratios are equal. We can check whether two ratios are equal by either reducing each ratio in fractional form to lowest terms or by determining whether the cross products are equal.

Since ratios are generally written in fractional form, a proportion may be treated as a fractional equation, If any three of the four terms of the proportion are known quantities, the fourth may be determined as follows:

(*a*) Clear the equation of all fractions by multiplying both sides of the equation by the lowest common denominator of the given fractions. Then solve the resulting equation.

$$\frac{n}{20} = \frac{7}{10}$$

$$\frac{n}{20} \cdot 20 = \frac{7}{10} \cdot \overset{2}{20}$$

$$n = 14$$

$$\frac{36}{100} = \frac{9}{n}$$

$$\frac{36}{100} \cdot 100\,n = \frac{9}{n} \cdot 100\,n$$

$$36\,n = 900$$

$$n = 25$$

(*b*) Or use the idea of the product of the means being equal to the product of the extremes to transform the given proportion to a simpler equation. Here find the cross products by multiplying the denominator of the

$\dfrac{n}{20} = \dfrac{7}{10}$	$\dfrac{36}{100} = \dfrac{9}{n}$
$10 \cdot n = 20 \cdot 7$	$36 \cdot n = 9 \cdot 100$
$10\,n = 140$	$36\,n = 900$
$n = 14$	$n = 25$

first fraction by the numerator of the second fraction and the denominator of the second fraction by the numerator of the first fraction. Write one product equal to the other; then solve the resulting equation.

Often in the solution of problems there are four possible ways of writing the proportion. Corresponding terms must be matched. For example, in the problem, "Traveling at the rate of 200 miles in 5 hours, how far can you go in 8 hours?" the proportion may be written as follows:

1. $\dfrac{n \text{ mi.}}{8 \text{ hr.}} = \dfrac{200 \text{ mi.}}{5 \text{ hr.}}$ Traveling n mi. in 8 hr. is the same rate as traveling 200 mi. in 5 hr.

$$\frac{n}{8} = \frac{200}{5}$$

2. $\dfrac{8 \text{ hr.}}{n \text{ mi.}} = \dfrac{5 \text{ hr.}}{200 \text{ mi.}}$ It takes 8 hr. to travel n mi. at the rate it will take 5 hr. to travel 200 mi.

$$\frac{8}{n} = \frac{5}{200}$$

3. $\dfrac{n \text{ mi.}}{200 \text{ mi.}} = \dfrac{8 \text{ hr.}}{5 \text{ hr.}}$ The distance of n mi. compared to the distance of 200 mi. is the same as 8 hr.

$$\frac{n}{200} = \frac{8}{5}$$
(time it takes to travel n mi.) compared to 5 hr. (time it takes to travel 200 mi.)

4. $\dfrac{200 \text{ mi.}}{n \text{ mi.}} = \dfrac{5 \text{ hr.}}{8 \text{ hr.}}$ The distance of 200 mi. compared to the distance of n mi. is the same as 5 hr.

$$\frac{200}{n} = \frac{5}{8}$$
(time it takes to travel 200 mi.) compared to 8 hr. (time it takes to travel n mi.)

Note that the cross products in each proportion will be the same ($5\,n = 1600$).

PRACTICE PROBLEMS

1. Write each of the following as a proportion:

(a) 26 compared to 13 is the same as 2 compared to 1.

(b) 4 compared to 12 is the same as 5 compared to 15.

(c) 18 compared to 32 is the same as 45 compared to 80.

(d) 56 compared to 14 is the same as 76 compared to 19.

(e) 150 compared to 100 is the same as 54 compared to 36.

2. Find the missing value in each of the following proportions:

(a)

$\dfrac{n}{15} = \dfrac{4}{5}$	$\dfrac{t}{32} = \dfrac{3}{4}$	$\dfrac{a}{96} = \dfrac{7}{12}$	$\dfrac{c}{5} = \dfrac{54}{30}$	$\dfrac{m}{7} = \dfrac{25}{28}$
$\dfrac{b}{56} = \dfrac{5}{14}$	$\dfrac{n}{21} = \dfrac{5}{6}$	$\dfrac{y}{72} = \dfrac{3}{8}$	$\dfrac{d}{3} = \dfrac{26}{39}$	$\dfrac{x}{9} = \dfrac{49}{63}$
$\dfrac{n}{9} = \dfrac{7}{8}$	$\dfrac{b}{5} = \dfrac{2}{3}$	$\dfrac{d}{6} = \dfrac{8}{11}$	$\dfrac{t}{12} = \dfrac{52}{25}$	$\dfrac{a}{19} = \dfrac{107}{40}$

(b) $\dfrac{90}{54}=\dfrac{a}{3}$ $\dfrac{75}{120}=\dfrac{x}{8}$ $\dfrac{56}{105}=\dfrac{n}{15}$ $\dfrac{108}{243}=\dfrac{b}{27}$ $\dfrac{12}{21}=\dfrac{y}{14}$

      $\dfrac{5}{8}=\dfrac{n}{72}$ $\dfrac{93}{200}=\dfrac{s}{800}$ $\dfrac{5}{6}=\dfrac{c}{78}$ $\dfrac{13}{16}=\dfrac{n}{32}$ $\dfrac{18}{63}=\dfrac{r}{84}$

      $\dfrac{3}{4}=\dfrac{r}{3}$ $\dfrac{1}{6}=\dfrac{t}{5}$ $\dfrac{9}{10}=\dfrac{x}{9}$ $\dfrac{2}{7}=\dfrac{a}{15}$ $\dfrac{17}{30}=\dfrac{g}{21}$

(c) $\dfrac{16}{x}=\dfrac{2}{7}$ $\dfrac{6}{n}=\dfrac{15}{25}$ $\dfrac{4}{b}=\dfrac{36}{117}$ $\dfrac{8}{y}=\dfrac{6}{48}$ $\dfrac{24}{n}=\dfrac{108}{18}$

      $\dfrac{7}{h}=\dfrac{1}{15}$ $\dfrac{9}{m}=\dfrac{3}{38}$ $\dfrac{5}{n}=\dfrac{50}{75}$ $\dfrac{4}{a}=\dfrac{10}{25}$ $\dfrac{27}{t}=\dfrac{147}{49}$

      $\dfrac{8}{y}=\dfrac{7}{8}$ $\dfrac{3}{b}=\dfrac{13}{6}$ $\dfrac{2}{r}=\dfrac{19}{7}$ $\dfrac{11}{s}=\dfrac{3}{4}$ $\dfrac{17}{e}=\dfrac{16}{9}$

(d) $\dfrac{5}{8}=\dfrac{15}{a}$ $\dfrac{16}{9}=\dfrac{96}{d}$ $\dfrac{24}{150}=\dfrac{8}{n}$ $\dfrac{21}{19}=\dfrac{42}{x}$ $\dfrac{6}{7}=\dfrac{54}{s}$

      $\dfrac{12}{40}=\dfrac{3}{b}$ $\dfrac{105}{35}=\dfrac{27}{n}$ $\dfrac{54}{72}=\dfrac{36}{y}$ $\dfrac{84}{210}=\dfrac{4}{m}$ $\dfrac{81}{180}=\dfrac{9}{g}$

      $\dfrac{3}{5}=\dfrac{4}{x}$ $\dfrac{7}{3}=\dfrac{2}{s}$ $\dfrac{8}{15}=\dfrac{9}{d}$ $\dfrac{100}{17}=\dfrac{52}{y}$ $\dfrac{11}{16}=\dfrac{25}{n}$

(e) $\dfrac{x}{8}=\dfrac{7}{8}$ $\dfrac{5}{b}=\dfrac{5}{12}$ $\dfrac{9}{10}=\dfrac{y}{10}$ $\dfrac{17}{24}=\dfrac{17}{a}$ $\dfrac{n}{100}=\dfrac{59}{100}$

(f) $\dfrac{1.5}{.3}=\dfrac{a}{8}$ $\dfrac{.04}{.12}=\dfrac{.6}{n}$ $\dfrac{x}{.01}=\dfrac{.2}{.16}$ $\dfrac{.005}{c}=\dfrac{1.4}{.28}$ $\dfrac{d}{.02}=\dfrac{2}{.2}$

(g) $\dfrac{\frac{1}{2}}{10}=\dfrac{2\frac{1}{2}}{x}$ $\dfrac{y}{3\frac{1}{2}}=\dfrac{8}{7}$ $\dfrac{9}{1\frac{1}{4}}=\dfrac{a}{10}$ $\dfrac{24}{b}=\dfrac{2\frac{1}{3}}{5\frac{5}{6}}$ $\dfrac{n}{2\frac{1}{4}}=\dfrac{15}{\frac{3}{4}}$

(h) $\dfrac{\frac{1}{3}}{\frac{1}{5}}=\dfrac{x}{\frac{2}{3}}$ $\dfrac{b}{40}=\dfrac{\frac{3}{4}}{\frac{5}{6}}$ $\dfrac{\frac{7}{3}}{\frac{1}{2}}=\dfrac{\frac{3}{4}}{c}$ $\dfrac{21}{x}=\dfrac{\frac{7}{10}}{\frac{3}{5}}$ $\dfrac{y}{\frac{2}{3}}=\dfrac{\frac{9}{2}}{\frac{11}{12}}$

3. In the proportion $\dfrac{8}{2}=\dfrac{16}{4}$

(a) What is the ratio of 8 to 2? Of 16 to 4? Are the ratios equal?

(b) What is the ratio of 2 to 8? Of 4 to 16? Are the ratios equal?

(c) What is the ratio of 8 to 16? Of 2 to 4? Are the ratios equal?

(d) What is the ratio of 16 to 8? Of 4 to 2? Are the ratios equal?

(e) Does one cross product equal the other cross product?

4. Which of the following are true proportions?

$$\frac{12}{10} = \frac{5}{6} \qquad \frac{17}{19} = \frac{51}{57} \qquad \frac{42}{35} = \frac{14}{12} \qquad \frac{2}{3} = \frac{3}{2} \qquad \frac{15}{90} = \frac{2}{12}$$

Using proportions, solve each of the following:

5. (a) What number compared to 10 is the same as 3 compared to 5?

(b) 5 compared to 20 is the same as what number compared to 40?

(c) 52 compared to what number is the same as 4 compared to 14?

(d) 16 compared to 80 is the same as 47 compared to what number?

(e) What number compared to 100 is the same as 19 compared to 25?

6. (a) At the rate of 3 items for 10¢, how many items can you buy for 50¢?

(b) At the rate of $3.50 per sq. yd., how much will 8 sq. yd. of broadloom cost?

(c) At the rate of 5 items for $9, how much will 7 items cost?

(d) At the rate of 8 items for 75¢, how many items can you get for $4.50?

(e) At the rate of 4 items for 30¢, how much will 24 items cost?

7. (a) An automobile travels 240 mi. on 15 gal. of gasoline. At the same rate of gasoline consumption, how far can the automobile travel on a full tank of 20 gal. of gasoline?

(b) If 3 gallons of paint cover a surface containing 825 square feet, how many gallons at the same rate will be needed to paint a surface containing 1,925 square feet?

(c) A basketball player scored 128 points in 5 games. If he continues to score at this rate, how many points will he have at the end of 30 games?

(d) A recipe calls for 4 cups of flour to 6 tablespoons of shortening. How many tablespoons of shortening are needed when 6 cups of flour are used?

(e) John earned $47 in 4 days. At that rate how many working days will it take him to earn $117.50?

(f) A picture $2\frac{1}{4}$ in. wide and $3\frac{1}{4}$ in. high is to be enlarged. If the height of the enlargement will be $9\frac{3}{4}$ in., how wide will it be?

(*g*) The ratios of the corresponding sides of similar triangles are equal. Find the missing sides indicated in the following pair of similar triangles:

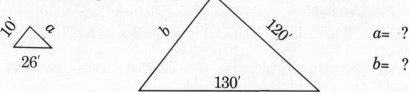

a= ?

b= ?

(*h*) A tree casts a shadow of 39 feet when a 4-foot post nearby casts a shadow of 6 feet. Find the height of the tree.

(*i*) A building casts a shadow of 28 feet when a boy, 5 feet tall, casts a shadow of 2 feet. Find the height of the building.

(*j*) If a scale distance of 3 inches on a map represents an actual distance of 288 miles, what actual distance does a scale distance of $5\frac{3}{4}$ inches represent?

(*k*) If the actual distance of 29 feet is represented by the scale distance of $3\frac{5}{8}$ inches on a floor plan, what scale distance will represent the actual distance of 34 feet?

(*l*) A motorist traveled 190 miles on the turnpike in $3\frac{1}{3}$ hours. How long will it take him at that rate to travel 285 miles?

(*m*) How many square feet of lawn will 20 pounds of grass seed cover if 5 pounds of seed are required for 1,125 square feet?

(*n*) Tom saved $32 in 7 weeks. At that rate how long will it take him to save $160?

(*o*) If it takes 14 yards of satin to make 3 pairs of window drapes, how many yards are required to make 5 pairs of drapes?

(*p*) The leading batter on the school baseball team hit safely 7 times in 3 games. If he maintains that rate, how many hits will he have at the end of the season consisting of 15 games?

(*q*) If 100 pounds of lawn food feeds an area of 4,800 square feet, how many pounds of lawn food will be required to feed an area of 3,600 square feet?

(*r*) A motorist uses 8 gallons of gasoline in traveling 116 miles. How many gallons of gasoline will the car use at that rate of consumption in going 522 miles?

(*s*) Jack's father pays $274.05 taxes on his house which is assessed for $8,700. Jack's friend, Tom, lives next door in a house assessed for $8,900. If the tax rate is the same, what is the amount of property tax on Tom's house?

STATISTICS

Bar Graph

The bar graph is used to compare the size of quantities, generally statistical information, by means of lengths of lines or bars.

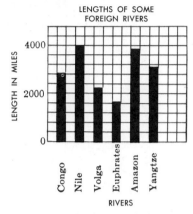

LENGTHS OF SOME
FOREIGN RIVERS

1. How many miles does the side of a small square represent in the vertical scale of the bar graph? $\frac{1}{4}$ of the side of a square?

2. Which river is the longest? shortest?

3. Find the length of each river.

To *construct a bar graph:*

(*a*) Draw a horizontal guide line on the bottom of the squared paper and a vertical guide line on the left.

(*b*) Select a convenient scale for the numbers that are being compared, first rounding off large numbers. For a vertical bar graph, write the number scale along the vertical guide line; for a horizontal bar graph, use the horizontal guide line. Label the scale.

(*c*) Print names of the items opposite alternate squares along the other guide line. Label the items. Mark off for each item the height corresponding to the given number. Draw lines to complete the bars. All bars should have the same width. Select and print an appropriate title.

PRACTICE PROBLEMS

Draw bar graphs showing the following data:

1. Marilyn's final grades for the year: English, 92; Mathematics, 87; Social Studies, 85; Science, 90; Art, 86; Music, 82; Physical and Health Education, 78.

2. The lengths of the channel spans of some famous suspension bridges in the United States:

> Golden Gate, 4,200 ft.
> Bear Mountain, 1,632 ft.
> George Washington, 3,500 ft.
> Delaware River, 1,750 ft.
> Brooklyn, 1,595 ft.

Line Graph

The line graph is used to show changes and the relationship between quantities.

1. How many pupils late does the side of a small square indicate in the vertical scale of the line graph? $\frac{1}{2}$ of the side of a square?

2. During what month was the punctuality poorest? best?

3. How many pupils were late each month?

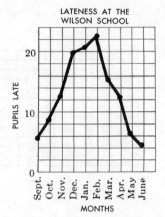

LATENESS AT THE WILSON SCHOOL

To *construct a line graph:*

(*a*) Draw a horizontal guide line on the bottom of the squared paper and a vertical guide on the left.

(*b*) Select a convenient scale for the related numbers, first rounding off large numbers. Write the number scale along one of the guide lines. Label the scale.

(*c*) Print names of the items below the other guide line, using a separate line for each item. Label the items. On each of these lines mark with a dot the location of the value corresponding to the given number. Draw straight lines to connect successive dots. Select and print an appropriate title.

PRACTICE PROBLEMS

Draw line graphs showing the following data:

1. In twelve arithmetic progress tests, each containing 20 examples, George solved 8, 10, 13, 15, 12, 11, 14, 17, 16, 19, 18, and 20 examples correctly.

2. The monthly normal temperature (Fahrenheit) in some United States cities:

	Jan.	Feb.	Mar.	Apr.	May	June	July	Aug.	Sept.	Oct.	Nov.	Dec.
Atlanta	43	45	52	61	70	76	78	77	72	63	52	45
Chicago	24	26	35	47	58	67	72	72	65	54	40	29
Cincinnati	30	33	41	52	63	71	75	74	67	56	42	33
Los Angeles	55	56	58	59	62	66	70	71	69	65	61	57
New Orleans	54	57	63	69	75	81	82	82	79	71	62	56
New York	31	31	38	49	61	69	74	73	67	56	44	35
Philadelphia	33	34	41	52	63	71	76	75	68	58	46	36
St. Paul	13	16	29	46	58	67	72	69	61	49	32	19
Seattle	41	43	46	51	57	61	66	65	60	54	47	43

Circle Graph

The circle graph is used to show the relation of the parts to the whole and to each other.

1. What fractional part of its entire income does the Harris family plan to spend for food? for shelter?

2. Compare the per cent to be spent for shelter to the per cent of savings.

3. If the family income is $6,200 per year, what are the amounts to be spent for each item per year? per month? per week?

The Harris Family Budget

To *construct a circle graph:*

(*a*) Make a table showing: (1) given facts; (2) fractional part or per cent each quantity is of the whole; (3) the number of degrees representing each fractional part or per cent, obtained by multiplying the fraction or per cent by 360°.

(*b*) Draw a convenient circle. With a protractor construct successive central angles, using the number of degrees representing each part.

(*c*) Label each sector (part of circle bounded by 2 radii). Select and print an appropriate title.

PRACTICE PROBLEMS

Construct circle graphs showing the following data:

1. A certain large city planned to spend its income as follows: schools, 30%; interest on debt, 25%; safety, 15%; health and welfare, 12%; public works, 10%; other services, 8%.

2. Charles spends his time as follows: 9 hr. for sleep, 6 hr. for school, 2 hr. for study, 3 hr. for recreation, and 4 hr. for miscellaneous activities.

3. A mathematics test showed the following distribution of marks: A, 6 pupils; B, 8 pupils; C, 12 pupils; D, 10 pupils.

4. A family spends its monthly income of $450 as follows: food, $135; housing, $90; clothing, $58.50; transportation, $40.50; savings, $45; miscellaneous expenses, $81.

Averages

The arithmetic mean, the median, and the mode are three commonly used averages or measures of central tendency of data.

The arithmetic mean (or simply the mean) of a set of numbers is determined by dividing the sum of numbers by the number of members in the set.

The median of a set of numbers is the middle number when the numbers are arranged in order of size. If the number of members is even, the median is determined

Find the arithmetic mean of the following set of scores: 78, 83, 91, 82, and 86

$$\frac{78 + 83 + 91 + 82 + 86}{5}$$

$$= \tfrac{420}{5}$$

$$= 84$$

Answer: 84

by dividing the sum of the two middle numbers by 2.

The mode of a set of numbers is the number that occurs most frequently in the set. There may be more than one mode.

The range is the difference between the highest and the lowest numbers in the set of numbers.

Arrange the following set of scores in a frequency table, then find the mean, median, mode, and range: 5, 7, 9, 8, 5, 8, 6, 5, 9, 8, 7, 8, 7, 5, 9, 5, 8, 5, 9

Frequency Table		Arithmetic Mean:	Median or Middle Score
Score	Number	$9 \times 4 = 36$	10th score from top or
9	4	$8 \times 5 = 40$	bottom $= 7$
8	5	$7 \times 3 = 21$ $\tfrac{133}{19} = 7$	Mode or most frequent
7	3	$6 \times 1 = 6$	score $= 5$
6	1	$5 \times 6 = 30$	Range: $9 - 5 = 4$
5	6	Sum $= 133$	
Total	19	Arithmetic mean $= 7$	

PRACTICE PROBLEMS

1. Find the mean for each of the following sets of scores:

(*a*) 83, 89, 80, 81, 84, 85, 86

(*b*) 9, 5, 8, 4, 10, 3, 7, 8, 6, 7, 9, 9, 7, 3, 8, 9

2. Find the median for each of the following sets of scores:

(*a*) 8, 6, 7, 5, 9, 10, 3, 0, 5

(*b*) 4.2, 5.6, 3.8, 4.7, 6.1, 4.5

3. Find the mode and range for each of the following sets of scores:

(a) 11, 15, 10, 19, 15, 12, 11, 17, 14, 15, 13, 12

(b) 57, 49, 64, 53, 58, 55, 53, 60, 58, 52

4. Find the mean, median, mode, and range for each of the following sets of scores:

(a) 17, 21, 16, 18, 24, 15, 18, 23, 16, 19, 23, 18, 20, 19, 25

(b) 85, 95, 65, 70, 95, 80, 100, 75, 90, 75, 95, 65, 85

5. Arrange each of the following sets of scores in a frequency table, then find the mean, median, mode, and range:

(a) 6, 4, 8, 3, 7, 8, 6, 9, 2, 5, 7, 9, 8, 4, 9, 6, 7, 8, 9, 5, 3, 4, 8, 6

(b) 43, 47, 50, 48, 42, 47, 49, 43, 45, 47, 48, 46, 47, 44, 40, 44, 47, 49, 42

Probability

Probability or chance is the ratio of favorable outcomes to the total possibilities. If there are no favorable outcomes, the probability is 0. If all are favorable outcomes, the probability is 1.

In a bag containing 12 marbles of which 3 are blue, the probability of selecting a blue marble is three out of twelve, written as the ratio $\frac{3}{12}$ or its equivalent $\frac{1}{4}$. There are twelve possibilities; and only three favorable outcomes, the 3 blue marbles. Three out of twelve is equivalent to one out of four.

The odds for an event to happen against its failure to happen is the ratio of its favorable outcomes to unfavorable outcomes.

When there are 3 blue marbles and 9 marbles of other colors in a bag, the odds of selecting a blue marble are 3 to 9 or 1 to 3.

PRACTICE PROBLEMS

1. There are 8 black and 12 red checkers in a box. What is the probability of selecting on the first draw: (a) a black checker? (b) a red checker? What are the odds of selecting a black checker? A red checker?

2. A bag contains 12 red, 6 yellow, 3 black, 9 green gum drops.

What is the probability of selecting on the first draw:

(a) a red gum drop?   (d) a red or a yellow gum drop?

(b) a green gum drop?   (e) a black or a red gum drop?

(c) a black gum drop?   (f) a red or a green gum drop?

What are the odds of selecting:

(g) a green gum drop?   (i) a red or a yellɔw gum drop?

(h) a red gum drop?   (j) a red, a yellow, or a green gum drop?

REVIEW OF PART IV

1. Compute as indicated:

(a) $(-6) + (+11) + (-7)$

(b) $(-9) - (-12)$

(c) $(-3)(+4)(-2)$

(d) $\dfrac{-90}{-15}$

2. Simplify:

(a) $\dfrac{6(-7+5) - 4(-1-1)}{-2(9-13)}$

(b) $\dfrac{|-2| + |+4|}{|-3|^2 - |(-5)(-3)|}$

3. Find the solution set of each of the following sentences when the replacement set is the set of all real numbers:

(a) $x - 6 = 11$ (e) $8b - 19 = 13$ (i) $t + 2 \not< -3$

(b) $n + 9 = 7$ (f) $7x + 8x = 75$ (j) $3x - 5 \leq -10$

(c) $-12y = 84$ (g) $5n < 60$ (k) $\frac{7}{12}y \neq 56$

(d) $\dfrac{c}{14} = 10$ (h) $b - 4 > 9$ (l) $\dfrac{n}{6} \geq -5$

4. Find the value of d when $l = 61$, $a = 7$, and $n = 9$. Formula: $l = a + (n - 1)d$

5. Find the solution set of each of the following sentences when the replacement set is the set of all prime numbers:

(a) $11y + 6 = 83$ (b) $4n - 15 < 61$ (c) $3b - 10b > -42$

6. Using the set of all real numbers, draw on a number line the graph of:

(a) $4x - 7 = 13$ (b) $2n - 5 > -3$ (c) $-5b \leq -15$

7. What is the ratio of 27 to 36?

8. Solve and check:

$$\frac{x}{100} = \frac{18}{75}$$

9. Find the mean, median, mode, and range for the following scores: 53, 58, 54, 51, 57, 55, 56, 58, 59, 56, 59

PART V

EVERYDAY PROBLEMS

INTRODUCTION

This section contains a variety of practical applications including the mathematical activities dealing with the earner, consumer, business, industry, school, sports, and aviation, arranged according to specific topics. Other applications may be found in the Exercises of Part I and II of this book, selected according to the concept developed in each Exercise.

The problems in Part V comprise a compact but comprehensive unit covering the basic mathematical practical applications of everyday life.

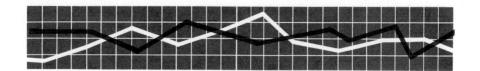

INCOME

1. Mary's father is a skilled carpenter. His hourly wage rate is $5.40. What are his earnings for a week when he works 46 hours? 40 hours per week is his standard work week. He is paid time and a half for overtime.

2. Paul's sister is a secretary. Her annual salary is $3,600 a year. If she is paid semi-monthly, what is her gross income each pay period before any deductions are made?

3. Helen works 5 days per week in a factory where she is paid at the piece-work rate of $.30 per unit. If she averages 32 units a day, what are her earnings per week?

4. Mr. Evans is a salesman in a department store. He earns a fixed salary of $50 per week and 1% commission on sales. During a week-long clearance sale he sold $6,348 of merchandise. What were his total earnings that week?

5. Find the annual salary of a person earning: (*a*) $62.50 per week (*b*) $425 per month (*c*) $292.50 semi-monthly (*d*) $1.60 per hour for 48 hour week, time and a half rate over 40 hours.

TAKE–HOME PAY

Take-home pay is the gross income less both the Federal income tax withheld and the social security deduction. The social security deduction rate on earnings up to $4,800 is $3\frac{5}{8}\%$ for the employee. The Federal withholding tax on weekly earnings is equal to 14% of the difference between the total wage payment and the number of exemptions times $13. For a semi-monthly payroll period it is 14% of the difference between the total wage payment and the number of exemptions times $28.

1. Find the Federal income tax withheld from a person's

(*a*) Weekly wage of $65 when 1 exemption is claimed.

(*b*) Weekly wage of $138 when 3 exemptions are claimed.

(*c*) Semi-monthly wage of $210 when 2 exemptions are claimed.

(*d*) Semi-monthly wage of $192 when 1 exemption is claimed.

(*e*) Weekly wage of $87.50 when 4 exemptions are claimed.

2. What is the amount deducted for social security if an employee earns:

(a) $60 weekly?   (d) $168 semi-monthly?
(b) $74.90 weekly?   (e) $104.75 semi-monthly?
(c) $57.50 weekly?   (f) $330 monthly?

3. Find the amount of take-home pay for each of the following earnings:

(a) Weekly wage of $75 with 2 exemptions claimed.
(b) Weekly wage of $79.75 with 4 exemptions claimed.
(c) Weekly wage of $63.50 with 1 exemption claimed.
(d) Semi-monthly wage of $160 with 3 exemptions claimed.
(e) Semi-monthly wage of $172.25 with 5 exemptions claimed.

4. Mr. Smith earns $80 a week. He has 4 tax exemptions: his wife, 2 young children, and himself. How much of his pay is deducted for Federal income tax? for social security? What is his weekly take-home pay?

5. The Benson family consists of a husband, a wife, and one young daughter. How many tax exemptions may Mr. Benson claim? If he earns $240 semi-monthly, how much Federal income tax is withheld from his pay each payroll period? How much Federal income tax is withheld from his pay in the course of the entire year?

THRIFT

1. Marilyn buys a 25¢ saving stamp every week at school. How many weeks will it take her to save enough to buy a $25 bond at the issue cost price of $18.75?

2. Charlotte's father uses the bus going to and from work five days a week. How much does he save each week by buying a ten-trip ticket for $1.95 instead of paying the regular one-way fare of $.25 each time?

3. At a sale Bob's sister bought a coat for $69.95, which regularly sells for $98.50. How much did she save?

4. Find how much you save on each can when you buy the greater quantity:

(a) 2 cans of beans for $.33 or $.17 each.
(b) 6 cans of tomato paste for $.49 or $.09 each.
(c) 3 cans of peaches for $1 or $.37 each.

5. Find how much you save by buying the larger size of the following articles instead of an equivalent quantity in the smaller size:

    (*a*) A 3 lb. can of shortening costs $.89; 1 lb. cans cost $.32

    (*b*) A 1 gallon can of paint costs $4.98; 1 quart cans cost $1.49

    (*c*) A 2 lb. 13 oz. box of detergent costs $.75; 15 oz. boxes cost $.29

HOUSEHOLD AND FAMILY–CAR EXPENSES

1. Draw a circle graph showing how Arnold's family spends their monthly income: food, 30%; housing, 20%; clothing, 10%; transportation, 12%; savings, 10%; and miscellaneous expenses, 18%. How much is appropriated for each item if the monthly income is $480?

2. Find the yearly cost of each service and the total cost of all the services for the year:

	Jan.	Feb.	Mar.	Apr.	May	June	July	Aug.	Sept.	Oct.	Nov.	Dec.
Electric	$8.65	$7.99	$7.56	$7.42	$7.31	$7.19	$6.95	$6.91	$7.53	$7.75	$8.19	$8.92
Gas	4.22	4.16	4.29	4.12	4.05	3.96	3.25	3.64	3.90	4.08	4.27	4.53
Telephone	7.14	6.83	8.50	7.25	8.93	6.78	6.90	7.45	8.12	9.65	8.72	8.60
Heating	23.60	22.80	17.90	4.10					9.15	15.05	18.45	30.20

3. How much did it cost Mr. Williams to run his car for a year if his expenses were: license fees, $11; automobile insurance, $64.50; depreciation, $425; repairs, $36.80; gasoline, 620 gallons at 29¢ per gallon; oil, 36 quarts at 45¢ per quart? What was the average cost per week?

4. How many miles was a car driven during the year if on January 1 the speedometer read 18989 and on January 1 the following year it read 31463? If 996 gallons of gasoline were purchased during the year at 28¢ per gallon, how many miles per gallon did the car average and what did gasoline cost per mile?

5. Find how much cash should be on hand at the end of the week if the household account shows:

Receipts: cash from the previous week, $41.80; salary, $104.25

Expenditures: food, $36.84; bank deposit, $15.00; gasoline, $5.50; telephone service, $4.28; dress, $11.95; laundry, $2.09; allowances, $12.25; miscellaneous, $5.67

6. (*a*) What is the reading of the gas meter on April 1? On May 1?

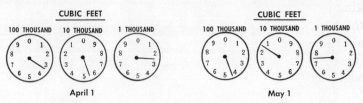

(*b*) How many cubic feet of gas were consumed during the month of April?

(*c*) Find the cost of the gas consumed if the rates were:

First   200 cu. ft. or less $1.00
Next 1,800 cu. ft. $1.30 per 1,000 cu. ft.
Next 8,000 cu. ft. $.80 per 1,000 cu. ft.
Over 10,000 cu. ft. $.65 per 1,000 cu. ft.

7. (*a*) What is the reading of the electric meter on November 1? on December 1?

(*b*) How many kilowatt hours of electricity were used during the month of November?

(*c*) Find the cost of the electricity used if the rates were:

First 12 kw-hr. or less $1.00
Next   44 kw-hr. @ $.05
Next   44 kw-hr. @ $.03
Over 100 kw-hr. @ $.02

HOMEMAKING

1. How long will it take to roast $5\frac{3}{4}$ pounds of beef if it takes 32 minutes per pound?

2. 3 teaspoons = 1 tablespoon   16 tablespoons = 1 cup
2 tablespoons = 1 ounce   2 cups = 1 pint

A recipe calls for:

(*a*) 6 teaspoons of baking powder. How many tablespoons of baking powder could be used?

(*b*) ½ cup of shortening. How many tablespoons of shortening could be used?

(*c*) ¼ cup of sugar. How many tablespoons of sugar could be used?

(*d*) ¾ cup of milk. How many ounces of milk could be used?

(*e*) 12 tablespoons of butter. What part of a cup of butter could be used?

3. The following recipe will make 14 biscuits:

2 cups flour   5 tablespoons shortening
2½ teaspoons baking powder   ¾ cup milk
¾ teaspoon salt

How much of each ingredient is needed to make 7 biscuits? 35 biscuits?

4. How many yards of material, 48 inches wide, are needed to make 6 pairs of drapes if each panel is 8 feet long and 72 inches wide?

5. Anne wants to make a bedspread 96 inches by 108 inches. How many yards of material, 54 inches wide, does she need?

INTEREST *

1. Bert has $180 in a savings bank. The bank pays $3\frac{1}{2}\%$ interest. How much interest will Bert receive at the end of the year?

2. Joan's brother borrowed $2,000 at $5\frac{1}{4}\%$ interest. Find the interest and the amount due at the end of 6 years.

3. Mr. Wilson receives $81 interest semi-annually on an investment of $3,600. What annual rate of interest is being paid?

4. How much money must Mr. Carter invest at 5% interest to earn $4,000 per year?

5. What amount was due on December 11 if $7,300 was borrowed on September 26 at 6% interest? Find the exact interest.

INSTALLMENT BUYING

Installment buying is a purchase plan by which a customer pays a certain amount of cash at the time of purchase and then

*See page 414.

pays the balance in equal installments at regular intervals. Interest or carrying charges are calculated on the entire balance for the full time of payment even though the actual balance owed decreases each time a payment is made.

1. A piano can be purchased for $975 cash or $100 down and $32.15 a month for 30 months. How much more does the piano cost on the installment plan?

2. What are the carrying charges on a freezer which sells for $298 cash or 20% down and $14.50 each month for 18 months?

3. A clothes dryer is advertised to sell for $235 cash or $25 down with 6% interest charged on the balance. If this amount is to be paid in 12 equal monthly installments, what is the amount of each monthly payment?

4. Jane's father bought a television set, paying $50 down and $26.25 per month for 12 months. If the set sells for $350 cash, what rate of interest was Jane's father charged?

5. A cabinet sink sells for $142 cash or $10 down and $11.66 a month for 12 months. How much does Ethel's mother save by buying it for cash? What rate of interest is being charged?

FIRE INSURANCE

Fire insurance is a plan by which persons share risks so that each person is protected against financial loss. The insured person is charged a sum of money called a premium.

The premium rate for fire insurance for 3 years is $2\frac{1}{2}$ times the yearly rate and for 5 years it is 4 times the yearly rate.

1. Mr. Morgan lives in a brick house with an approved roof. He insured his house against loss by fire for $11,000 for one year at the rate of $.12 per $100. What is his annual premium?

2. Fred lives in a frame house with an approved roof. What is the premium that his father pays if the house is insured for $9,800 for one year at the rate of $.32 per $100?

3. Mr. Collins insured his house for $12,500. How much was his premium if he took a 3-year policy at the yearly rate of $.24 per $100? How much did he save by buying a 3-year policy instead of three 1-year policies?

4. A house is insured for $15,600. What is the premium for a five-year policy if the yearly rate is $.30 per $100?

5. Betty's house cost $14,500 and the household contents cost $9,200. Her father purchased 5-year policies, insuring the house for 80% of its value and the contents for 75% of their value. What was the total premium if the yearly rate on the building was $.22 per $100 and on the contents was $.18 per $100?

LIFE INSURANCE

Life insurance offers financial protection to the dependents of an insured person in event of his death. The person who receives the face of the policy (*amount of insurance*) when the insured person dies is called the beneficiary.

(*a*) *Term insurance*—Insured for a specified time, premiums paid only during that time.

(*b*) *Ordinary life insurance*—Insured until death, premiums paid until death.

(*c*) *Limited-payment life insurance*—Insured until death, premiums paid for a specified time.

(*d*) *Endowment insurance*—Insured for a specified time, premiums paid only during that time. Insured person receives face of policy if alive at the end of the specified time.

Annual Premiums Per $1,000

Age	10-Year Term	Ordinary Life	20-Payment Life	20-Year Endowment
15	$9.01	$18.08	$30.42	$51.05
20	9.52	20.02	32.69	51.44
25	9.87	22.28	35.01	51.70
30	10.40	25.09	37.71	52.15
35	11.78	28.75	41.04	53.11
40	14.51	33.57	45.25	54.91

1. Find the annual premium on each of the following policies:

(*a*) 20-payment life for $1,000 issued at age 30.

(*b*) 10-year term for $20,000 issued at age 40.

(*c*) 20-year endowment for $5,000 issued at age 25.

(*d*) Ordinary life for $6,000 issued at age 20.

2. Mr. Myers bought a 20-payment life insurance policy for $8,000 when he was 35 years old. What is the total amount of premium he must pay before the policy is fully paid up?

3. At the age of 25 Mr. Ryan bought an ordinary life policy for $10,000. What annual premium does he pay? How much will his beneficiary receive when he dies?

4. Mr. Miller purchased a 20-year endowment policy for $4,000 when he was 30 years old. He is now 50 years old. How much will he receive? What was the total premium he paid?

5. When Mr. Walker was 40 years old he purchased a 10-year term policy for $25,000. He died after paying 3 annual premiums. How much more did the beneficiary receive than Mr. Walker paid?

PROPERTY TAX

The tax on property may be expressed as cents per $1, mills per $1, dollars and cents per $100, dollars and cents per $1,000, and per cent. A tax rate of $.03 per $1 is the same as 30 mills per $1, $3 per $100, $30 per $1,000, and 3%. 1 mill equals $\frac{1}{10}$ of a cent or $.001.

The assessed value of a property is the value that the tax officials place on the property for tax purposes.

1. A community requires $100,000 in tax money for a year. The assessed valuation of the property in the community is $5,000,000. What per cent of the assessed valuation is the tax needed? Express this tax rate in dollars per $100; in cents per $1; in mills per $1.

2. How much does Mr. Hamilton pay for taxes on his property which is assessed for $11,800 if the tax rate is $3.15 per $100?

3. Mr. Moore's house is assessed for 75% of its cost. The tax rate is $2.45 per $100. How much property tax does he pay if the house cost $12,400?

4. The assessed valuation of Mr. Bell's house is $9,700. The tax rate is $3.40 per $100. What is the yearly property tax? A 3% discount is allowed if the tax is paid within the first quarter of the year. How much will Mr. Bell save and how much tax will he pay if he takes advantage of the discount?

5. Which will produce a greater increase in taxes, an increase in the assessment of a property from $14,200 to $16,700 or an increase in the tax rate from $2.80 per $100 to $3.05 per $100? How much greater?

OWNING A HOUSE

When a person borrows money to buy a house, he gives the lender a written claim, called a mortgage, to the property in case he fails to repay the loan or pay the interest on it when due.

1. Tom's father earns $450 a month. He wishes to buy a new house. If he should not spend more than $2\frac{1}{2}$ times his annual salary, what is the top price he can afford to pay for a house?

2. If Mr. Smith paid $3,500 down on a house costing $15,490, how much does he need to borrow on a mortgage?

3. Mr. Johnson bought a house for $13,500. He paid $33\frac{1}{3}\%$ down and gave a mortgage bearing $5\frac{1}{2}\%$ interest for the balance. How much interest does he pay semi-annually?

4. Barbara's father bought a house for $17,500, paying $7,500 down. He is charged 5% interest on the balance. The house is assessed for $10,600 and the tax rate is $3.20 per $100. The house is insured for 80% of its cost at $.28 per $100. The mortgage is to be paid off in 20 equal annual installments. The down payment of $7,500 was formerly invested at 4% interest.

(*a*) How much interest is due on the mortgage for the first year?

(*b*) What is the property tax?

(*c*) What does the insurance cost?

(*d*) How much interest does Barbara's father lose on the money used as the down payment?

(*e*) How much does home ownership cost Barbara's father for the first year?

(*f*) How much is an annual installment due on the mortgage?

5. Compare the costs of renting and buying a house when the house can be rented for $95 per month or can be purchased for $12,900 with a down payment of $5,000. It is assessed for $7,500 with a tax rate of $2.85 per $100. Insurance costs $45 for a year. The principal used as a down payment could be invested at 3% interest. The interest on the mortgage is 6%. Repairs average $200 per year.

STOCKS AND BONDS

A person who buys a share of stock becomes a part-owner of the company that issues it and receives dividends from the profits that are earned during the year. A person who buys a bond is lending money to the company or branch of government that issues it and receives interest on the face value of the bond.

A bond is a written guarantee by the company or government to repay the face value of the bond at a specified time (date of maturity) and to pay a given rate of interest at stated times. The original value of a stock or bond is called par value or face value. The value at which it sells at any given time is market value. Brokers are paid a fee for buying and selling stocks and bonds.

Stock market prices are quoted in dollars.

$47\frac{1}{4}$ means \$47.25

Bond market prices are quoted in per cents.

$101\frac{1}{2}$ means $101\frac{1}{2}\%$ of face value

In the bond quotation: Am T & T $2\frac{3}{4}$s   '80 $91\frac{3}{4}$

$2\frac{3}{4}$s represents a $2\frac{3}{4}\%$ rate of interest

'80 is the date of maturity, 1980

$91\frac{3}{4}$ is the market price, $91\frac{3}{4}\%$ of face value

---

1. Mr. Bailey bought 25 shares of stock at $32\frac{1}{2}$. What is the total cost of the stock if the brokerage fee is 1% of cost plus \$5?

2. How much profit does Jane's father make on 100 shares of stock which he purchased at $27\frac{3}{4}$ and sold at $36\frac{1}{4}$? His broker charged him a fee of $\frac{1}{2}\%$ of cost plus \$19 each time.

3. In the bond quotation: Chi Gt West   4s   '88 $96\frac{1}{4}$

(*a*) What is the date of maturity?

(*b*) What is the rate of interest?

(*c*) What is the cost of a bond, face value \$1,000? Use the quoted market price.

4. In the bond quotation: Gen Mtr Cp $3\frac{1}{4}$s   '79 $100\frac{1}{2}$

(*a*) What is the date of maturity?

(*b*) What rate of interest is specified?

(*c*) Find the market price of one bond, face value \$1,000. Find the price of eight bonds.

(*d*) How much annual interest will the owner receive on each bond? What is the total semi-annual interest on eight bonds?

5. Mr. Roberts bought a 5% $1,000 bond at 95. How much interest does he receive each year? What rate of interest is he actually receiving on what he paid for the bond?

COMMISSION*

1. If an insurance broker receives 18% of the premium as his commission, how much money is due him when the premium on a fire insurance policy is $83.50?

2. A used car salesman earned $62.65 commission for selling a car for $895. What rate of commission did he receive?

3. A lawyer charged Ann's father 25% commission for settling a claim in the amount of $2,250. How much money did Ann's father receive?

4. Ted's brother receives a fixed salary of $45 and a commission of 6% on all sales above $500. What were his total earnings during a week when his sales amounted to $1,647.50?

5. What amount of sales in dollars must a salesman reach each week at the rate of 8% commission to earn $120 weekly?

6. If an agent charges $4\frac{1}{2}$% commission for purchasing goods, how much will he receive for buying 890 boxes of honeydew melons at $2.40 a box?

7. A salesman receives 3% commission on sales. How much did he earn during a week when he sold 4 refrigerators at $399.50 each, 3 television sets at $249.75 each, 7 electric irons at $12.95 each, 2 clothes dryers at $197.50 each, and 3 dishwashers at $267.50 each?

8. What rate of commission did a real estate agent charge if he sold a house for $13,200 and received $660 commission?

9. A grower shipped 495 boxes of oranges and 308 boxes of grapefruit to his agent who charges 6% commission. If the agent sold the oranges at $5.20 a box and the grapefruit at $3.85 a box, what was his commission? What net proceeds did the grower receive?

10. A commission merchant sold for a farmer 250 bags of potatoes at $3.40 a bag, 175 bushels of apples at $5.60 a bushel, and 90 bushels of peaches at $6.85 a bushel, charging $9\frac{1}{2}$% for his services. What net proceeds were due the farmer?

*See page 237.

DISCOUNT*

1. A typewriter marked $98 was sold at a discount of 25%. What is the discount and the net price?

2. Jane's brother bought a coat that regularly sells for $87.50 at a reduction of 30%. How much did he pay for it?

3. What is the sale price of a refrigerator that is listed at $450 but is reduced $12\frac{1}{2}\%$?

4. What rate of discount was given if a lamp that usually sells for $30 is sold for $25?

5. What is the regular price of a lawn mower if its net price is $79.80 when a 16% discount is allowed?

6. Tom paid $6 for a pair of skates that sell regularly for $7.50. What rate of discount was he allowed?

7. The catalog list price of an electric drill set is $42.50. Find the net price if the trade discount is 18%.

8. An appliance dealer purchased 6 radios at $23.40 each, 3 television sets at $182.90 each, and 12 electric heaters at $8.29 each. If he receives a 2% discount for paying cash, what is the net amount of his bill?

9. A furniture dealer purchased 4 lamps at $18.75 each, 2 tables at $36.50 each, 6 chairs at $69.95 each, and 2 sofas at $176.25 each. The terms of payment were 4/10, n/30, meaning 4% discount is allowed if the bill is paid within 10 days but the full amount is to be paid by the 30th day. If the bill was paid on the sixth day, what was the net amount paid?

10. A manufacturer lists a bicycle to sell at $49.50. If he allows a trade discount of 20% and an additional 3% cash discount, what is the net cash price of the bicycle?

PROFIT AND LOSS†

The difference between the *selling price* and the *cost* is called the gross profit or margin or markup. The net profit is the actual profit earned and is equal to the selling price of the goods less both the cost of the goods and the operating expenses.

1. Sales for the entire year at the Miller Department Store amounted to $946,104.61. The cost of goods was $597,686.48 and the operating expenses were $158,574.75. Find the net profit.

2. What is the gross profit if a table costs $36.75 and sells for $59.95?

3. Find the selling price of a clock-radio if it costs $21.60 and the rate of markup on the cost is $33\frac{1}{3}\%$.

4. An air conditioner was sold for $273. If a 30% markup on the selling price was used, how much did it cost?

5. Find the rate of gross profit on the selling price of a sofa if it cost $240 and sold for $320.

6. A dishwasher was purchased by a dealer for $161 and marked to sell for $230. Find the gross profit if it was sold at a discount of 10%.

7. A merchant bought a gas range at $105. His markup is $33\frac{1}{3}\%$ of the selling price. What is the selling price of the gas range?

8. A piano that cost $800 was sold for $680. What was the rate of loss on the cost?

9. A clothes dryer that cost $190 was sold for $250. If the overhead expenses of the merchant were 8% of the selling price, what was the net profit? What was the rate of net profit on the selling price?

10. A merchant purchased baseball bats at $18 a dozen. At what price each must he sell them to realize a gross profit of 40% on the selling price?

GENERAL BUSINESS

1. The *net worth* of a business is equal to the assets minus the liabilities. Find the net worth of a business with the following assets: cash, $5,890.50; accounts receivable, $3,743.75; merchandise, $10,481.33; other assets, $4,619.00; and the following liabilities: accounts payable, $2,487.94; notes payable, $1,900.00; other liabilities, $862.64.

2. What is the annual amount of depreciation on a typewriter that originally cost $130 if a 20% depreciation is allowed each year?

3. When a person borrows money at a bank and gives a promissory note, the bank deducts the interest in advance (*bank discount*) from the amount borrowed (*face of note*) and credits the balance (*proceeds*) to the borrower's account.

Mr. Evans borrowed $1,200 from a bank for 90 days. He gave a note which was discounted at 6%. What were the proceeds credited to his account?

4. (*a*) The *cost of goods sold* is equal to the inventory at the beginning of the period plus the purchases less inventory at the end of the period. What is the cost of goods sold by the Walker Company when the inventory at the beginning of the year was valued at $9,674.25, purchases made during the year were $93,906.80 and the inventory at the end of the year was valued at $10,807.16?

(*b*) Find the *total operating expenses* of the Walker Company when the salaries amounted to $18,540; rent, $2,550; delivery expense, $1,975.90; insurance, $235.30; and miscellaneous expenses, $384.25.

(*c*) If the net sales for the year amounted to $131,280, find the gross profit and net profit earned by the Walker Company.

5. Parcel Post

Weight in lbs.	Zones							
	Local	1 & 2	3	4	5	6	7	8
Over 1 up to 2 lbs.	$0.24	$0.33	$0.35	$0.39	$0.45	$0.51	$0.58	$0.64
3	.26	.38	.41	.47	.55	.64	.74	.83
4	.28	.43	.47	.55	.65	.77	.90	1.02
5	.30	.48	.53	.63	.75	.90	1.06	1.21
6	.32	.53	.59	.70	.85	1.03	1.22	1.40
7	.34	.58	.65	.77	.95	1.16	1.38	1.59

Fractions of pounds are computed as full pounds.

Find the cost of sending by parcel post a package weighing:

(*a*) 4 lb. to zone 5   (*b*) 5 lb. to zone 3

(*c*) 6 lb. 8 oz. local   (*d*) 1 lb. 14 oz. to zone 7

(*e*) 2 lb. 13 oz. to zone 6   (*f*) 5 lb. 7 oz. to zone 4

COMMON BUSINESS FORMS

I. Deposit Slip

A form supplied by the bank on which the amounts of cash, checks, and total deposit are entered. Checks are listed separately. Checks to be deposited must be endorsed by the depositor, his signature written across the back of the check.

Make out deposit slips in your name for each of the following deposits:

1. On November 30, you deposit three $20 bills, four $10 bills, seven $5 bills, sixteen $1 bills, five half-dollars, eleven quarters, twenty dimes, thirty nickels, a check drawn on the State Bank for $51.86, a check drawn on the Sixth National Bank for $109.42, and a check drawn on the Township Trust Co. for $9.69.

2. On February 28, you deposit nineteen $10 bills, thirteen $5 bills, twenty-nine $1 bills, ten half-dollars, forty dimes, sixty nickels, a check drawn on the Bankers Trust Co. for $83.35, and a check drawn on the State Bank for $69.46.

LOCAL TRUST COMPANY		
Your city _Knoxville_ 19 _6 8_		
By _John Nelson_		
Bills, 5's and upward		
Bills, 1's and 2's		
Silver		
Checks		
1		
2		
3		
4		
5		
6		
7		
8		
TOTAL		

II. Check

A form supplied by the bank for the purpose of withdrawing money.

The stub should be filled in before the corresponding check is written.

Write a check for each of the following, using today's date:

1. Paying Sears and Co. $286.37 for furniture purchased.

No._____19___		
To_____		
For_____		
	Dollars	Cents
Bal. Bro't For'd		
Am't Deposited		
Total		
Am't This Check		
Bal. Car'd For'd		

Your City *Knox.* 19 **69** No. **69**

LOCAL TRUST COMPANY

Pay to the
order of *Miller's* $*800*

Eight Hundred no/100 Dollars

Robert E. Jones

Stub   Check

Assume that you had $521.82 as your bank balance before writing the check. Fill in the stub.

2. Paying Local Electric Co. $9.28 for electric service. Assume that you had $1,904.17 as your bank balance before writing the check. Fill in stub.

III. Invoice

A bill that the seller sends to the purchaser listing the terms of the purchase, the quantity, description, unit price and extensions (*total cost*) for each item purchased, and the total amount of the

---

GROCER SUPPLY COMPANY

129 Walnut Street
Los Angeles, California   19 __

SOLD TO: R. Clark
73 Fourth Ave.
Los Angeles, Cal.

Terms: 3/10, n/30

2 cases	Tuna fish	@ $7.20			
5 cases	Soap powder	@ $5.52			
3 cases	Corn	@ $3.78			

bill. A copy of the invoice is usually sent with the order. When the bill is paid, it should be marked paid, dated, and signed by the person receiving the money.

1. Find the extensions for each item in the invoice on page 552 and determine the total amount of the bill. What is the net amount due if the bill is paid within 10 days?

2. Prepare an invoice for the following:

Sport Equipment Company, 65 Main St., New York, N.Y., sold to J. Allen, 120 W. Third St., Trenton, N.J., 6 doz. baseballs @ $15.30, 3 doz. bats @ $13.20, 2 doz. fielder's gloves @ $60.00, and ½ doz. catcher's mitts @ $92.50. Terms were n/30.

IV. Promissory Note

A written promise by the borrower to repay the loan. The amount of money borrowed that is written on the note is the *face of the note* and the date when the money is due is the *date of maturity*.

$800 00/100   *April 5,* 19*57*

_____*Sixty days*_____ after date _*I*_ promise to pay

to the order of _____*Harris Supply Company*_____

_____*Eight Hundred and   no/100*_____ Dollars

Value received

No. *62*   Due *June 4*   *Robert E. Jones*

---

1. What is the date of maturity in the above note? How much is the face of the note?

2. Prepare a promissory note showing the following:

The Modern Manufacturing Company received a note for $2,500 from Mr. James Ryan, dated September 8, 1957, and due in 90 days.

INDUSTRIAL APPLICATIONS

I. Lumber

The measure of a piece of lumber one foot long, one foot wide, and one inch thick is a unit called a board foot.

1. Find the number of board feet in each of the following:

(1) 1 piece of spruce 3 in. by 12 in. and 20 ft. long.

(2) 5 pieces of pine 1 in. by 6 in. and 14 ft. long.

(3) 12 pieces of hemlock 2 in. by 10 in. and 16 ft. long.

(4) 8 pieces of fir 1 in. by 8 in. and 18 ft. long.

(5) 23 pieces of cedar 1 in. by 4 in. and 12 ft. long.

2. At \$.16 per board foot what is the total cost of 20 pieces of knotty pine each 1 in. by 6 in. and 16 ft. long?

3. What is the cost of 50 pieces of hemlock each 2 in. by 8 in. and 18 ft. long at \$110 per thousand (M.) board feet?

II. Construction

1. How many cubic yards of dirt must be removed to make an excavation 63 feet long, 48 feet wide, and 14 feet deep?

2. At \$1.75 per square foot how much will it cost to build a stone wall 72 feet long and 5 feet high?

3. How much will it cost to make a concrete patio 18 feet long and 15 feet wide at \$.50 per square foot? How many cubic yards of concrete are needed if the patio will be 4 inches thick?

4. If a bundle of cedar closet lining covers 40 square feet and costs \$6.40, how much will the lining cost to make a closet 8 feet long, 6 feet wide, and $7\frac{1}{2}$ feet high? The floor, ceiling, four walls, and door are to be covered with the lining.

5. How many bundles of shingles are needed to cover two sections of a roof, each section measuring 35 feet by 10 feet, if one bundle of shingles covers $33\frac{1}{3}$ square feet? At \$2.65 per bundle, what is the total cost of the shingles?

III. Miscellaneous

1. How many pieces, each $1\frac{3}{4}$ in. long, can be cut from a 7-foot metal rod, disregarding waste?

2. Two $\frac{7}{16}$ inch holes are drilled in a strip of steel, one at each end with the outside of each hole $2\frac{1}{2}$ inches from the edge. If the strip is 8 inches long, how long is the metal between the two holes?

3. The outside diameter of certain tubing is 2.125 in. and its wall thickness is 0.375 in. Find the inside diameter.

4. What is the cross-sectional area of a wire $\frac{1}{8}$ inch in diameter?

5. Find the weight of a steel bar 1 in. by 3 in. by 6 ft. Steel weighs 490 lb. per cu. ft.

6. A gallon of a certain varnish covers 225 sq. ft. of surface with two coats. How many gallons of this varnish are needed to cover a floor 18 ft. by 25 ft. with two coats?

7. What is the efficiency (per cent) of a motor if its output is 1,260 watts when its input is 1,400 watts?

8. Find the cutting speed of a bandsaw having a diameter of 21 inches and rotating at 900 revolutions per minute.

9. If the largest exposed number on the barrel of a micrometer indicates 0.7 inch, the uncovered subdivisions on the barrel indicate .05 inch, and the divisions on the thimble indicate .016 inch, what is the complete reading?

10. What is the displacement of a piston whose bore is 5 in. and whose stroke is $5\frac{1}{2}$ in.?

11. Find which of the following lengths may be accepted if a tolerance of $\pm$ .003 in. is permitted on a part designed to be 2 inches long: (*a*) 1.99 in. (*b*) 2.03 in. (*c*) 1.998 in. (*d*) 2.0015 in. (*e*) 1.989 in.

SCHOOL

1. In the election for school treasurer the seventh-, eighth-, and ninth-year classes voted 152, 125, and 107 respectively for Laura and 127, 139, and 123 respectively for Arthur. Who won the election? By how many votes?

2. The athletic association at the Township High School sold 927 memberships at $.50 each. The cost of athletic equipment and maintenance of teams for the school year amounted to $359.85. How much money was left over?

3. Draw a bar graph showing the enrollment at the Hamilton Junior-Senior High School:

Grade	7	8	9	10	11	12
Number of pupils	215	192	206	185	170	167

4. How many examples did Ted have right if he received a mark of 88% in a test of 25 examples?

5. The total attendance at the Holmes School for the 18 school days in February was 11,322. What was the average daily attendance?

6. How many questions out of 60 may a pupil miss and still get a grade of 85%?

7. How much more than the quota of $200 did the students of the Roosevelt High School contribute to the March of Dimes if the freshmen gave $72.50; sophomores, $56.75; juniors, $61.30; and seniors, $58.45?

8. What per cent (nearest tenth) of a class with 42 pupils on roll attended school on a day when 3 pupils were absent?

9. The school auditorium measures 40 ft. by 80 ft. by 27 ft. It seats 360 pupils. How many cu. ft. of air does it allow each pupil?

10. The school playground is 310 ft. long and 190 ft. wide. What is its area? How much fencing is needed to enclose it? Make a scale drawing of the playground, using the scale $\frac{1}{8}$ in. = 10 ft.

SPORTS

1. Find the final scores of the following games:

Football					Basketball				
Hilldale	13	0	20	0 =	Hilldale	17	15	13	12 =
Newton	6	12	6	7 =	Newton	12	19	16	11 =

2. The leading scorer in the high school football league scored 18 touchdowns, 4 field goals, and converted 12 points after touchdown. How many points did he score?

3. In 30 times at bat Harry hit safely 12 times. What is his batting average (to nearest thousandth)?

4. Make a scale drawing of a basketball court 50 ft. by 84 ft. with the scale $\frac{1}{8}$ in. = 4 ft.

5. The results of a track meet showed the Wilson School scored $19\frac{1}{2}$ points; Taft School, 15 points; and McKinley School, $13\frac{1}{2}$ points. How many more points did the Wilson School score than either of the other two schools?

6. What is the average weight of the players in the backfield of the Thomas High School football team if their weights are 198 lb., 161 lb., 175 lb., and 184 lb.?

7. The official world record time for running 100 yd. is 9.3 seconds and for the 100-meter race is 10.2 seconds. Find the difference in the distances and in the recorded times.

8. Out of 20 attempts a basketball player scored 8 times. What per cent of his chances did he score?

9. At the end of the baseball season the league records showed Central won 4 games and lost 4 games, East won 6 and lost 2, South won 1 and lost 7, and North won 5 and lost 3. Express as a decimal correct to the nearest thousandth the part of the games each team won. Arrange this information in tabular form, placing the team with the highest standing first.

10. If the distance from the pitcher's box to home plate is 60 ft. 6 in. and the distances between bases are 90 ft., what is the distance from the pitcher's box to second base?

AVIATION

1. What is the radius of action of an airplane (how far can it fly and still return to its base) at an average ground speed of 210 m.p.h. if it has fuel for 10 hours?

2. The regional aeronautical maps of the United States are made at a scale of 1 to 1,000,000. What distance in miles is represented by 2 inches on a regional map?

3. Using the dry adiabatic lapse rate of $5\frac{1}{2}°$ F. per 1,000 ft., find the temperature at an altitude of 7,000 ft. if the temperature at the surface is 69° F.

4. For a certain altitude and temperature the true air speed is 6% greater than the indicated air speed. What is the true air speed if the indicated air speed is 270 m.p.h.?

5. If it is 1200 at Greenwich, at what longitude is the time 1000? 1600? 1830?

6. Find the tip speed of a 7-foot propeller turning at 1,500 revolutions per minute.

7. A *Mach number* is the ratio of the speed of an object through a gas to the speed of sound through the gas. The air speed of the airplane is Mach 1 if it is equal to the speed of sound, Mach 2 if it is twice the speed of sound, Mach 0.5 if it is half the speed of sound. Speeds faster than the speed of sound are *supersonic* speeds.

If the speed of sound is 740 miles per hour:

(*a*) What speed in miles per hour is expressed by:
Mach 1?   Mach 4?   Mach 2.3?   Mach 0.85?

(*b*) Express each of the following speeds by a Mach number:
2,220 m.p.h.,   518 m.p.h.,   1,406 m.p.h.,   3,108 m.p.h.

8. (*a*) Find the Lift-Drag Ratio if the lift of an airplane is 1,680 lb. and the drag is 120 lb.

(*b*) What is the Aspect Ratio of an airplane having a span of 39 ft. and a wing area of 234 sq. ft.?   Aspect Ratio is ratio of length of wing (span) to width of wing (chord).

9. How many nautical miles apart are Washington, D.C., 39° N., 77° W., and Lima, Peru, 12° S., 77° W.?   How many statute miles apart?   If it takes an airplane 12 hr. 45 min. to fly between the two cities, what is the average ground speed of the airplane in knots?   in statute miles per hour?

10. What compass course should be steered if the true course is 78°, variation 9° W., and deviation 3° E.?

REFRESH YOUR SKILLS

1. Add: **2.** Subtract: **3.** Multiply: **4.** Divide:

948,269	451,032	3,869	$1{,}728\overline{)17{,}015{,}616}$
328,475	394,956	6,587	
867,869			
594,598			
217,386			

5. Add: **6.** Subtract: **7.** Multiply: **8.** Divide:

$2\frac{1}{2} + 4\frac{11}{16} + \frac{7}{8}$ $4\frac{1}{6} - \frac{3}{4}$ $3\frac{1}{7} \times 1\frac{5}{8}$ $16 \div \frac{1}{4}$

9. Add: **10.** Subtract: **11.** Multiply: **12.** Divide:

$8.46 + 93.8 + .687$ $9.45 - .8$ $.015 \times .2$ $.06\overline{)9.6}$

13. Find $5\frac{3}{4}\%$ of   **14.** What per cent of   **15.** $33\frac{1}{3}\%$ of what
$6,000.   52 is 8?   number is 9?

16. Square 9.05.

17. Find the square root of 50 to the nearest hundredth.

18. What part of a yard is 30 inches?

TABLE OF SQUARES AND SQUARE ROOTS

No.	Square	Square Root	No.	Square	Square Root	No.	Square	Square Root
1	1	1.000	34	1,156	5.831	67	4,489	8.185
2	4	1.414	35	1,225	5.916	68	4,624	8.246
3	9	1.732	36	1,296	6.000	69	4,761	8.307
4	16	2.000	37	1,369	6.083	70	4,900	8.367
5	25	2.236	38	1,444	6.164	71	5,041	8.426
6	36	2.449	39	1,521	6.245	72	5,184	8.485
7	49	2.646	40	1,600	6.325	73	5,329	8.544
8	64	2.828	41	1,681	6.403	74	5,476	8.602
9	81	3.000	42	1,764	6.481	75	5,625	8.660
10	100	3.162	43	1,849	6.557	76	5,776	8.718
11	121	3.317	44	1,936	6.633	77	5,929	8.775
12	144	3.464	45	2,025	6.708	78	6,084	8.832
13	169	3.606	46	2,116	6.782	79	6,241	8.888
14	196	3.742	47	2,209	6.856	80	6,400	8.944
15	225	3.873	48	2,304	6.928	81	6,561	9.000
16	256	4.000	49	2,401	7.000	82	6,724	9.055
17	289	4.123	50	2,500	7.071	83	6,889	9.110
18	324	4.243	51	2,601	7.141	84	7,056	9.165
19	361	4.359	52	2,704	7.211	85	7,225	9.220
20	400	4.472	53	2,809	7.280	86	7,396	9.274
21	441	4.583	54	2,916	7.348	87	7,569	9.327
22	484	4.690	55	3,025	7.416	88	7,744	9.381
23	529	4.796	56	3,136	7.483	89	7,921	9.434
24	576	4.899	57	3,249	7.550	90	8,100	9.487
25	625	5.000	58	3,364	7.616	91	8,281	9.539
26	676	5.099	59	3,481	7.681	92	8,464	9.592
27	729	5.196	60	3,600	7.746	93	8,649	9.644
28	784	5.292	61	3,721	7.810	94	8,836	9.695
29	841	5.385	62	3,844	7.874	95	9,025	9.747
30	900	5.477	63	3,969	7.937	96	9,216	9.798
31	961	5.568	64	4,096	8.000	97	9,409	9.849
32	1,024	5.657	65	4,225	8.062	98	9,604	9.899
33	1,089	5.745	66	4,356	8.124	99	9,801	9.950

INDEX

67 68 69 CP 9 8 7 6